Plant Anatomy

Plant Anatomy

KATHERINE ESAU

Professor of Botany
University of California
Davis, California

JOHN WILEY & SONS, INC.

New York   *London*

Preface

The writing of this volume was prompted by a wish to bring together, in a comprehensive form, the substance of a course in the anatomy of seed plants. The book has been planned primarily for advanced students in various branches of plant science and for teachers of plant anatomy. At the same time, an effort has been made to attract the less advanced student by presenting the subject in a straightforward style and by explaining and analyzing the basic terms and concepts.

My botanical interests, directed toward research in developmental anatomy, unavoidably color the presentation of the material. Developmental aspects are utilized to enhance the understanding of plant structure and its variability. Phylogenetic data and information on the relation between structure and function are reviewed for the same purpose, but less extensively. Consideration of historical aspects plays a minor role, despite the recognized pedagogic value of such an approach.

A large number of selected references are listed to support descriptions and interpretations, and to direct the interested person toward wider reading. Many references that seemed of less immediate import than those listed were omitted, and some pertinent ones were, no doubt, overlooked. If an author has a review paper adequately covering his own research, such a review is sometimes listed in the place of the individual publications by the same author. Among the references listed, those that were deemed strongest in supporting interpretations and conclusions have been placed in the foreground. Frequently, the descriptive matter has been substantiated by an examination of original preparations of pertinent plant material.

The organization of the subject matter in plant anatomy and the order of its presentation are challenging problems which are related to classification of cells and tissues and to matters of emphasis and attitudes in teaching. In this book, the problems of classification are not resolved and the subject matter is presented in an orthodox sequence, considering first the cell and tissue types, then the arrangement of the structural elements within the plant organs. In general, the topics are delimited and arranged in accordance with the organization developed by A. S. Foster in his *Practical Plant Anatomy* (D. Van Nostrand Company, New York, 1949). This organization is simple and coherent and permits the development of each chapter as an organic whole.

Admittedly, some students may find the topics on meristems too complex to master at the beginning of the course. However, an early acquaintance with the structure and growth of the meristems and with phenomena of tissue differentiation should increase appreciation of the developmental interpretation which is emphasized throughout the book.

The chapters on flower, fruit, and seed were approached with a feeling of adventure. The boundary between morphology, in the sense of study of external form, and anatomy, in the sense of study of internal form, seems to be especially vague in investigations dealing with the flower and its derivatives. The study of the flower also merges with the vast field of investigations of phenomena of reproduction. It is, therefore, difficult to recognize the proper limits in a discussion of these plant parts. The chapters on the flower, the fruit, and the seed are here offered as an experiment in treatment of these topics.

Despite its length, this book does not cover the subject exhaustively. Instead of depicting numerous examples, it treats a few in detail. However, the student is made aware of the endless variability in form and structure and of the vagueness of boundaries between different types of structures. This attitude should prepare him to interpret an unfamiliar structure and to relate it to those that are known.

This book is not a generous source of new concepts and terms. Existing ones, however, are scrutinized for accuracy and usefulness. Some terms and concepts appeared to have lost their accuracy and had to be revised. There are also those that have been relegated to the domain of history because they seemed to have outlived their usefulness. The guiding principle in this evaluation was the realization that, unless terms and concepts are flexible, they fail to account for the inherent variability in the phenomena to which they refer. Readers may disagree with the treatment of some of the established notions. It is hoped, however, that the usage in this book is clear in every instance and consistent throughout.

Illustrations form an important part of a book in plant anatomy. Although a combination of quality, adequacy, and balance of illustrative material was the goal in the present undertaking, shortcomings were unavoidable. Illustrations whose source is not indicated in the legends are original. The others were copied from various research papers and occasionally from books. With few exceptions, the original drawings and the copies were made by the writer. The original photomicrographs were prepared from research material, original and borrowed, and from slides used in teaching. The slides were either purchased from various commercial concerns or prepared locally. For the sake of economy in printing the halftones had to be assembled at the end of the book in the form of plates.

In the tracing of the origin of technical terms to their Greek or Latin roots, B. D. Jackson's *A Glossary of Botanic Terms* (Duckworth, London, 1928) was the principal reference.

In conclusion I wish to express my appreciation to those who so generously gave of their time to review the manuscript or parts of it. In particular, Dr. A. S. Foster and Dr. V. I. Cheadle extended competent counsel regarding matters of organization and presentation; Dr. A. S. Crafts has advised on physiological aspects; Dr. I. W. Bailey was generous with information from research still unpublished. Valuable suggestions were offered by Dr. E. M. Gifford, Jr. and Dr. R. H. Wetmore. Thanks are also due to Dr. R. B. Wylie for reading the chapter on the leaf; to Dr. Charlotte G. Nast and to Dr. R. M. Brooks for reviewing the chapters on the flower, the fruit, and the seed; to Dr. G. M. Smith for the loan of his lecture notes on morphology of the angiosperm flower. Mrs. Fay V. Williams was the trusted assistant with the preparation of the manuscript. Persons who extended the courtesy of lending microscope slides, negatives, or finished illustrations are mentioned in the appropriate legends.

K. E.

Davis, California
January, 1953

Contents

General References

Andrews, H. N. *Ancient plants and the world they lived in.* Ithaca, N. Y., Comstock Publishing Company. 1947.

Biebl, R., and H. Germ. *Praktikum der Pflanzenanatomie.* Wien, Springer-Verlag. 1950.

Bower, F. O. *Size and form in plants.* London, Macmillan and Company. 1930.

Chamberlain, C. J. *Gymnosperms, structure and evolution.* Chicago, University of Chicago Press. 1935.

De Bary, A. *Comparative anatomy of the vegetative organs of the phanerogams and ferns.* (English translation by F. O. Bower and D. H. Scott.) Oxford, Clarendon Press. 1884.

Eames, A. J. *Morphology of vascular plants. Lower groups.* New York, McGraw-Hill Book Company. 1936.

Eames, A. J., and L. H. MacDaniels. *An introduction to plant anatomy.* 2nd ed. New York, McGraw-Hill Book Company. 1947.

Fitting, H., W. Schumacher, R. Harder, and F. Firbas. *Lehrbuch der Botanik für Hochschulen.* (Founded by E. Strasburger, F. Noll, H. Schenk, and A. F. W. Schimper.) 25th ed. Stuttgart, Piscator-Verlag. 1951.

Foster, A. S. *Practical plant anatomy.* 2nd ed. New York, D. Van Nostrand Company. 1949.

Goebel, K. *Organographie der Pflanzen, insbesondere der Archegoniaten und Samenpflanzen.* 3rd ed. Jena, Gustav Fischer. 1928–33.

Goebel, K. *Organography of plants, especially of the Archegoniatae and Spermatophyta. Part 1. General organography. Part 2. Special organography.* Oxford, Clarendon Press. 1900–05.

Haberlandt, G. *Physiological plant anatomy.* London, Macmillan and Company. 1914.

Hayward, H. E. *The structure of economic plants.* New York, The Macmillan Company. 1938.

Hector, J. M. *Introduction to the botany of field crops.* 2 vols. Johannesburg, South Africa, Central News Agency Ltd. 1938.

Hofmann, E. *Paläohistologie der Pflanze.* Wien, Julius Springer. 1934.

Jackson, B. D. *A glossary of botanic terms.* 4th ed. London, Duckworth. 1928.

Jeffrey, E. C. *The anatomy of woody plants.* Chicago, University of Chicago Press. 1917.

Jepson, G. L. Editor. *Genetics, paleontology, and evolution.* Princeton, Princeton University Press. 1949.

Johansen, D. A. *Plant microtechnique.* New York, McGraw-Hill Book Company. 1940.

Küster, E. *Pathologische Pflanzenanatomie.* 3rd ed. Jena, Gustav Fischer. 1925.

Linsbauer, K. Editor. *C. K. Schneiders illustriertes Handwörterbuch der Botanik.* 2nd ed. Leipzig, Wilhelm Engelmann. 1917.

Linsbauer, K. *Handbuch der Pflanzenanatomie.* Band 1 et seq. Berlin, Gebrüder Borntraeger. 1922–43.

Mansfield, W. *Histology of medicinal plants.* New York, John Wiley & Sons. 1916.

Metcalfe, C. R., and L. Chalk. *Anatomy of the dicotyledons.* 2 vols. Oxford, Clarendon Press. 1950.

Molisch, H. *Anatomie der Pflanze.* 5th ed. Jena, Gustav Fischer. 1947.

Priestley, J. H., and L. I. Scott. *An introduction to botany.* London, Longmans, Green & Company. 1938.

Rauh, W. *Morphologie der Nutzpflanzen.* Heidelberg, Quelle und Meyer. 1950.

Rawlins, T. E. *Phytopathological and botanical research methods.* New York, John Wiley & Sons. 1933.

Record, S. J. *Identification of the timbers of temperate North America.* New York, John Wiley & Sons. 1947.

Sachs, J. *Textbook of botany.* Oxford, Clarendon Press. 1875.

Sass, J. E. *Botanical microtechnique.* 2nd ed. Ames, Iowa State College Press. 1951.

Sharp, L. W. *Introduction to cytology.* 3rd ed. New York, McGraw-Hill Book Company. 1934.

Sharp, L. W. *Fundamentals of cytology.* New York, McGraw-Hill Book Company. 1943.

Smith, G. M. *Cryptogamic botany.* Vol. 2. *Bryophytes and Pteridophytes.* New York, McGraw-Hill Book Company. 1938.

Solereder, H. *Systematic anatomy of the dicotyledons.* Oxford, Clarendon Press. 1908.

Solereder, H., and F. J. Meyer. *Systematische Anatomie der Monokotyledonen.* Berlin, Gebrüder Borntraeger. Heft 1, 1933; Heft 3, 1928; Heft 4, 1929; Heft 6, 1930.

Stebbins, G. L., Jr. *Variation and evolution in plants.* New York, Columbia University Press. 1950.

Stover, E. L. *An introduction to the anatomy of seed plants.* Boston, D. C. Heath and Company. 1951.

Strasburger, E. *Über den Bau und die Verrichtungen der Leitungsbahnen in den Pflanzen. Histologische Beiträge.* Band 3. Jena, Gustav Fischer. 1891.

Troll, W. *Vergleichende Morphologie der höheren Pflanzen.* Band 1. *Vegetationsorgane.* Berlin, Gebrüder Borntraeger. Heft 1, 1937; Heft 2, 1939; Heft 3, 1941–42.

Tschirch, A. *Angewandte Pflanzenanatomie. Ein Handbuch zum Studium des anatomischen Baues der in der Pharmacie, den Gewerben, der Landwirtschaft und dem Haushalte benutzten pflanzlichen Rohstoffe.* Wien und Leipzig, Urban und Schwarzenberg. 1889.

Tschirch, A., and O. Oesterle. *Anatomischer Atlas der Pharmakognosie und Nahrungsmittelkunde.* Leipzig, H. Tauschnitz. 1900.

The Plant Body

THE PLANT ORGANS

The subject of the present book is the structure and development of seed plants, with emphasis on the angiosperms. The complex multicellular body of a seed plant is a result of evolutionary specialization of long duration. This specialization has led to the establishment of morphologic and physiologic differences between the various parts of the plant body and caused the development of the concept of *plant organs* (cf. Arber, 1950; Troll, 1937, p. 176). At first many organs were recognized; later their number was reduced to three: *stem, leaf,* and *root* (Eames, 1936, p. 380).

The relationship of leaf, stem, and root to each other and to the plant as a whole has long been, and still is, one of the fundamental problems of plant morphology. Early in botanical research the question was raised whether plant organs differ essentially from one another or whether they are modifications of one basic type of structure (cf. Arber, 1950, and Troll, 1937). The organization of the plant body of the oldest known land plants, the Psilophytales, suggests that the differentiation of the vegetative plant into leaf, stem, and root is a result of evolutionary development from an originally simple axial structure (Arnold, 1947; Eames, 1936). Plant organs are also interrelated on the basis of ontogeny (development of an individual) and of mature structure. The root and the stem have many similarities in form, structure, and method of growth, and in higher plants stem and root are initiated as one continuous structure. The association between the leaves and the stem is also close. The two kinds of plant parts form a unit, the *shoot,* in which the limits between the stem and the leaf are vague, both externally and internally.

The morphologic nature of the angiospermous flower is another subject of much research and speculation. One of the most widely used interpretations is that the flower is homologous with a shoot and the floral parts with leaves.

Despite the lack of absolute distinction among the various parts of the plant, the division of the plant body into morphological categories of stem, leaf, root, and flower (where present) is commonly resorted to for convenience in treating the material descriptively. Such division is also necessary for the proper understanding of the many distinct functions of the various plant parts.

DEVELOPMENT OF THE PLANT BODY

A vascular plant begins its existence as a morphologically simple unicellular zygote. The zygote develops into the embryo and eventu-

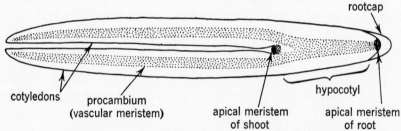

rootcap

cotyledons   procambium   apical meristem   hypocotyl   apical meristem
(vascular meristem)   of shoot   of root

Fig. 1.1.   Diagram of mature embryo of *Lactuca sativa* (lettuce).   (×34.)

ally into the mature sporophyte. This development involves division and differentiation of cells, and an organization of cells into more or less specialized complexes, the *tissues* and *systems of tissues*. The embryo of a seed plant (fig. 1.1) has a relatively simple structure as compared with the adult plant. It has a limited number of parts—frequently only an axis bearing one or more cotyledons—and its cells and tissues are mostly at a low level of differentiation. However, the embryo has a potentiality for further growth, because of the presence, at two opposite ends of the axis, of meristems (the *apical meristems*) of future shoot and root. During the development of shoot and root, subsequent to seed germination, the appearance of new apical meristems may cause a repetitive branching of these organs. After a certain period of vegetative growth, the plant enters the reproductive stage with the development of spore-bearing structures.

The increments of plant organs originating from apical meristems usually undergo a period of expansion, particularly in length. The

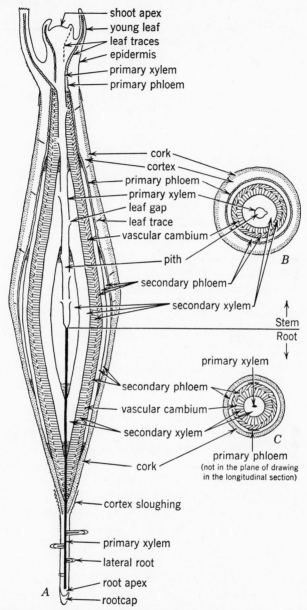

- shoot apex
- young leaf
- leaf traces
- epidermis
- primary xylem
- primary phloem

- cork
- cortex
- primary phloem
- primary xylem
- leaf gap
- leaf trace
- vascular cambium
- pith

secondary phloem

secondary xylem

B

Stem
Root

primary xylem

secondary phloem

vascular cambium

secondary xylem

C

primary phloem
(not in the plane of drawing
in the longitudinal section)

cork

cortex sloughing

primary xylem

lateral root

root apex

rootcap

A

FIG. 1.2. Diagrams showing the relation between primary and secondary growth in a dicotyledonous plant. *A*, longitudinal view of entire plant. *B*, transection of stem. *C*, transection of root. The thickest part of the axis has three increments of secondary xylem and phloem. The usual increase in thickness of the primary plant body, from the base upward (see chapter 15), has been disregarded. (Adapted from Strasburger, 1891.)

entire growth of the successively formed roots and vegetative and reproductive shoots, from the time of their initiation by the apical meristems until their expansion is completed, is commonly termed *primary growth*. The plant body formed by this growth is the *primary plant body* consisting of *primary tissues*. In most vascular cryptogams and monocotyledons, the entire life cycle of the sporophyte is completed in a primary plant body. The gymnosperms, most dicotyledons, and some monocotyledons show an increase in thickness of stem and root by means of *secondary growth*. Thus a *secondary body* composed of *secondary tissues* is added to the primary. A special meristem, the *vascular cambium*, is concerned with the secondary thickening. In addition, a *cork cambium*, or *phellogen*, commonly develops in the peripheral region of the expanding axis and produces a periderm, a secondary tissue system assuming a protective function when the primary epidermal layer is disrupted during the secondary increase in thickness. Figure 1.2 illustrates in a highly diagrammatic manner the relation between primary and secondary growth in a dicotyledonous plant.

INTERNAL ORGANIZATION

The morphologic units of the multicellular plant body, the *cells*, are associated in various ways with each other, forming coherent masses, or *tissues*. In vascular plants the cells are of many different kinds, and their combinations into tissues are such that different parts of the same organ may vary considerably from one another. The arrangement of cells and tissues is not random. It is possible to recognize larger units of tissues which show topographic continuity, or physiologic similarity, or both together. Such tissue units may be called *tissue systems* (De Bary, 1884; Foster, 1949, p. 53; Haberlandt, 1914; Lundengårdh, 1922; Sachs, 1875). Thus the structural complexity of the plant body results from variation in the form and function of cells and also from differences in the manner of combination of cells into tissues and tissue systems.

Despite the long-time concern of botanists with the classification of cells, tissues, and tissue systems, agreement on the subject has not been reached. (For a critical review of the problems of such classification, see Foster, 1949, Exercise IV.) If one attempts to separate cells and tissues into distinct categories, the difficulties are fundamental. The different kinds of cells intergrade in their characters. Living cells are capable of changing their function and structure.

Cells of common origin may differ greatly from each other, and cells derived from different meristems may be basically similar. Tissues also often grade one into the other and overlap in structure and function. Cells of a certain kind may form a coherent tissue, or they may occur in groups or individually among other kinds of cells of contrasting structure and function. No one single criterion, such as structure, origin, or function of cells, or even simple topographic continuity, can be applied consistently to express the complex inter-relationships of plant-body cells in terms of categories of cells and tissues.

In the following discussion the principal tissues of a vascular plant are reviewed with reference to their arrangement in a dicotyledonous plant (fig. 1.3). According to Sachs' (1875) old but convenient classification based on topographic continuity of tissues, the body of a vascular plant may be pictured as composed of three systems of tissues, the *dermal*, the *vascular*, and the *fundamental* (or *ground* system). The dermal system forms the outer protective covering of the plant and is represented, in the primary plant body, by the *epidermis*. During secondary growth the epidermis may be replaced by another dermal system, the *periderm*, with the cork cells forming the new protective tissue. The vascular system is composed of the two principal conducting tissues, the *phloem* and the *xylem*. These tissues contain many types of cells. Some of these are peculiar to the vascular tissues; others have counterparts in the fundamental and dermal systems as well.

The system of fundamental tissues includes all tissues other than dermal and vascular. *Parenchyma* is one of the most common ground tissues. Some of the parenchyma may be modified as a thick-walled supporting tissue, the *collenchyma*. Still other modifications of parenchyma cells are found in the various secretory structures which may occur in the ground system as individual cells or as more or less extensive cell complexes. The fundamental system often contains highly specialized, mechanical elements combined in coherent masses as *sclerenchyma* tissue or dispersed as individual sclerenchyma cells.

The three vegetative organs, stem, root, and leaf, are distinguished by the relative distribution of the vascular and ground tissues (fig. 1.3). The vascular system of the stem frequently occupies a restricted position between the epidermis and the center of the axis. Such an arrangement leaves some ground tissue—the *cortex* (meaning bark or rind in Latin)—between the epidermis and the vascular region, and some—the *pith*—in the center of the stem (fig. 1.3, *B, C*).

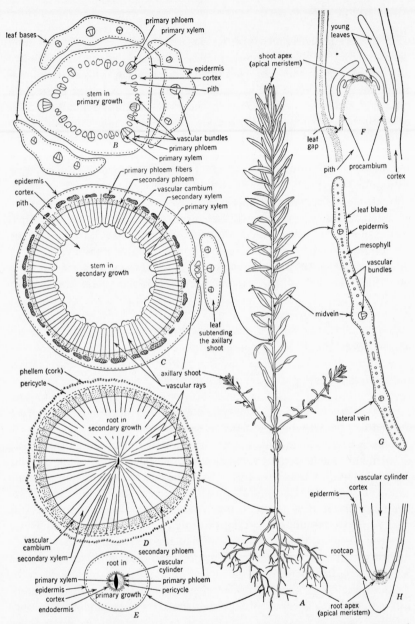

FIG. 1.3. The organization of a vascular plant. *A*, habit sketch of a plant of *Linum usitatissimum* L. (flax) in vegetative state. Transections of stem at *B* and *C* and of root at *D* and *E*. *F*, longitudinal section of the terminal part of the shoot with the apical meristem and developing leaves. *H*, longitudinal section of the terminal part of the root with the apical meristem (covered by the rootcap) and subjacent root regions. *G*, transection of a fully developed leaf blade. (*A*, ×⅛; *B*, *E*, *F*, *H*, ×43; *C*, ×27; *D*, ×6; *G*, ×16. *A*, drawn by R. H. Miller.)

In the root, pith may be absent (fig. 1.3, *E*), and the cortex is commonly shed during secondary growth (fig. 1.3, *D*). The arrangement of primary vascular tissues in the form of a ring of bundles in a transection of a stem (fig. 1.3, *B*) is one of many possible patterns in vascular plants. In the secondary state the original structure of the primary vascular system may be obscured by an interpolation of secondary vascular tissues between the primary xylem and the primary phloem (fig. 1.3, *C*). In the leaf the vascular system consists of numerous interconnected strands imbedded in the ground tissue, which in this organ is usually differentiated as photosynthetic parenchyma, the *mesophyll* (fig. 1.3, *G*).

The three tissue systems of the primary body are derived from the apical meristems (fig. 1.3, *F, H*). When the derivatives of these meristems are partly differentiated, they may be classified into *protoderm, procambium,* and *ground meristem.* These are meristematic precursors of the *epidermal, vascular,* and *fundamental* systems, respectively. The vascular tissue system is enlarged secondarily by secondary growth originating in the *vascular cambium* (fig. 1.3, *C, D*). The periderm, if present, is derived from a separate meristem, the *phellogen* or cork cambium.

SUMMARY OF CELL TYPES AND TISSUES

The familiar types of cells and tissues of a seed plant are summarized here with no attempt to revise existing classifications or to establish a new one. (Cf. Foster, 1949, pp. 58–61.) The cells of a plant derived from a meristem acquire their distinctive characteristics through developmental changes. Some cells undergo more profound changes than others. In other words, cells become specialized to varied degrees. On the one hand, there are the relatively little specialized cells retaining living protoplasts and having the ability to change in form and function (various kinds of parenchyma cells). On the other, there are the highly specialized cells that develop thick rigid walls, become devoid of living protoplasts, and cease to be capable of structural and functional changes (various kinds of sclerenchyma and related cells). Between these two extremes are cells with varying levels of metabolic activity and different degrees of structural and functional specialization. The distinctions among cells and tissues given in the summary below serve to delimit the typical structures, but the occurrence of intermediate structures must be borne in mind in evaluating the distinctions.

Epidermis. Epidermal cells form a continuous layer on the surface of the plant body in the primary state. They show various special characteristics related to their superficial position. The main mass of epidermal cells, the epidermal cells proper, vary in shape but are often tabular. Other epidermal cells are guard cells of the stomata and various trichomes, including root hairs. The epidermis may contain secretory and sclerenchyma cells. The principal distinctive feature of the epidermal cells of the aerial parts of the plant is the presence of cuticle on the outer wall and the cutinization of some or all of the other walls. The epidermis gives mechanical protection and is concerned with restriction of transpiration and with aeration. In the stems and roots having secondary growth, the epidermis is commonly supplanted by the periderm.

Periderm. The periderm comprises cork tissue or *phellem*, cork cambium or *phellogen*, and *phelloderm*. The phellogen occurs near the surface of axial organs having secondary growth. It arises in the epidermis, the cortex, the phloem, or the root pericycle and produces phellem toward the outside, phelloderm toward the inside. Phelloderm may be absent. The cork cells are commonly tabular in form, are compactly arranged, lack protoplasts at maturity, and have suberized walls. The phelloderm cells are usually parenchymatous.

Parenchyma. Parenchyma cells form continuous tissues in the cortex of stem and root and in the leaf mesophyll. They also occur as vertical strands and rays in the vascular tissues. They are primary in origin in the cortex, the pith, and the leaf; primary or secondary in the vascular tissues. Parenchyma cells are characteristically living cells, capable of growth and division. The cells vary in shape, are often polyhedral, but may be stellate or much elongated. Their walls are commonly primary, but secondary walls may be present. Parenchyma is concerned with photosynthesis, storage of various materials, wound healing, and origin of adventitious structures. Parenchyma cells may be specialized as secretory or excretory structures.

Collenchyma. Collenchyma cells occur in strands or continuous cylinders near the surface of the cortex in stems and petioles, and along the veins of foliage leaves. Collenchyma is a living tissue closely related to parenchyma; in fact, it is commonly regarded as a form of parenchyma specialized as supporting tissue of young organs. The shape of cells varies from short prismatic to much elongated. The most distinctive feature is the presence of unevenly thickened primary walls.

Sclerenchyma. Sclerenchyma cells may form continuous masses, or they may occur in small groups or individually among other cells. They may develop in any or all parts of the plant body, primary and secondary. They are strengthening elements of mature plant parts. Sclerenchyma cells have thick, secondary, often lignified walls and commonly lack protoplasts at maturity. Two forms of cells are distinguished, sclereids and fibers. The sclereids vary in shape from polyhedral to elongated and often are branched. Fibers are generally long slender cells.

Xylem. Xylem cells form a structurally and functionally complex tissue which, in association with the phloem, is continuous throughout the plant body. It is concerned with water conduction, storage, and support. The xylem may be primary or secondary in origin. The principal water-conducting cells are the tracheids and the vessel members. Storage occurs in the parenchymatous cells, which are arranged in vertical files and, in the secondary xylem, also in the form of rays. Mechanical cells are fibers and sclereids.

Phloem. Phloem cells form a complex tissue. The phloem tissue occurs throughout the plant body, together with the xylem, and may be primary or secondary in origin. It is concerned with support and with conduction and storage of food. The principal conducting cells are the sieve cells and sieve-tube members, both enucleate at maturity. Sieve-tube members are associated with parenchymatous cells, the companion cells. Phloem parenchyma cells occur in vertical files. Secondary phloem also contains parenchyma in the form of rays. Supporting cells are fibers and sclereids.

Laticifers. These peculiar elements do not form clearly delimited tissues but occur within other tissues as systems of branched or anastomosing tubes. They contain latex and are multinucleate. Their function has not been definitely determined, but they are known to contain food and waste materials. Two kinds of laticifers are recognized, articulated and nonarticulated. The articulated laticifers arise through union of cells in which parts of the walls are dissolved. The nonarticulated are single cells, usually much branched. The laticifers may occur in all parts of the plant, but they are restricted to certain families. The nonarticulated laticifers are primary in origin; the articulated may be primary or secondary.

REFERENCES

Arber, A. *The natural philosophy of plant form.* Cambridge, Cambridge University Press. 1950.

Arnold, C. A. *An introduction to paleobotany.* New York, McGraw-Hill Book Company. 1947.

De Bary, A. *Comparative anatomy of the vegetative organs of the phanerogams and ferns.* Oxford, Clarendon Press. 1884.

Eames, A. J. *Morphology of vascular plants. Lower groups.* New York, McGraw-Hill Book Company. 1936.

Foster, A. S. *Practical plant anatomy.* 2nd ed. New York, D. Van Nostrand Company. 1949.

Haberlandt, G. *Physiological plant anatomy.* London, Macmillan and Company. 1914.

Lundegårdh, H. *Zelle und Cytoplasma.* In: K. Linsbauer. *Handbuch der Pflanzenanatomie.* Band 1. Lief. 1 and 2. 1922.

Sachs, J. *Textbook of botany.* Oxford, Clarendon Press. 1875.

Strasburger, E. *Über den Bau und die Verrichtungen der Leitungsbahnen in den Pflanzen. Histologische Beiträge.* Band 3. Jena, Gustav Fischer. 1891.

Troll, W. *Vergleichende Morphologie der höheren Pflanzen.* Band 1. *Vegetationsorgane.* Heft 1. Berlin, Gebrüder Borntraeger. 1937.

THE CONCEPT OF THE CELL

The study of cells, the units of organic structure, constitutes the field of science called *cytology* and is treated in detail in various specialized texts and reference works (e.g., Guilliermond, 1941; Guilliermond et al., 1933; Küster, 1935; Sharp, 1934, 1943). Cells compose the bodies of plants and animals. The differences in structure and function of cells and the diversities in their groupings bring about the differentiation, within the organismal bodies, of organs and tissues of more or less specialized nature. A student of plant anatomy seeks to gain an understanding of the structure, the development, and the morphologic and physiologic interrelations of the tissues and the organs of plants. A working knowledge of cells facilitates this search.

The concept that the cell is the universal elementary unit of organic structure and function forms the basis of the so-called *cell theory*, whose formulation is usually connected with the names of Schleiden and Schwann, two German biologists of the early nineteenth century. The fundamental features of this concept are, however, older than the formulation of the cell theory, and many other workers have contributed to the important recognition of cells as units of living organisms (cf. Conklin, 1940).

The word *cell* (from the Latin *cellula*, a small apartment) was introduced by the English microscopist Robert Hooke in the seventeenth century. Hooke first used the term with reference to the small units delimited by walls visible in magnified views of cork tissue. Later he recognized cells in other plant tissues and saw that the cavities of the living cells were filled with "juices" (cf. Conklin, 1940, and Matzke, 1943).

With further studies of cells the protoplasm and its inclusions received increasing attention, and the view developed that the protoplasm was the essential part of the cell, the wall being not a necessary component. In plant cells the cell wall appeared to be a secretion of the protoplast, that is, dependent on the protoplast for its origin and structure (see chapter 3), and the animal cells had no rigid envelopes at all.

The substance within the cell received the name of *protoplasm* (from the Greek words for first and moulded), meaning living matter in its simplest form (cf. Studnička, 1937, and Weber, 1936). In 1880 Hanstein introduced the term *protoplast* to designate one unit of this protoplasm contained within one cell and suggested that it be used instead of the term cell. The latter term persisted, however. If one recalls that the word cell may be related not only to the Greek *cytos* (kutos), meaning hollow place, but also to the Roman *cella*, which designated receptacles with contents (cf. Matzke, 1943), it is not an inappropriate designation for the protoplast with its envelopes, at least with reference to the cells of plants.

The component parts of the protoplast were recognized one by one. In 1831, Robert Brown, an English botanist, became aware of the general occurrence of a clear spherical body in each cell and named it the *nucleus* (from the Latin word for kernel). In 1846 Hugo von Mohl introduced a distinction between the protoplasm and cell sap, and in 1862 Kölliker applied the name of *cytoplasm* to the material surrounding the nucleus. Discoveries of other details followed (cf. Sharp, 1934).

At present the following parts are commonly recognized in the protoplast of plant cells (fig. 2.1). First, a group of *protoplasmic components: cytoplasm*, the general protoplasmic material in which the other protoplasmic bodies and nonprotoplasmic materials are located; *nucleus*, a protoplasmic body interpreted as the center of synthetic and regulatory activity and as the seat of hereditary units; *plastids*, organized portions of protoplasm concerned with certain specific activities; *mitochondria*, small bodies apparently structurally related to the other protoplasmic bodies and of somewhat uncertain function. Second, the *nonprotoplasmic components: vacuoles* (cavities with cell sap) and various more or less solid inclusions, such as crystals, starch grains, and oil droplets. The nonprotoplasmic substances in the cytoplasm and vacuoles constitute nutritive materials or other products of metabolism and are generally classified as *ergastic materials* (from the Greek *erg*, meaning work). The cell wall may be considered as composed of ergastic substances that do not remain in the protoplast but occur eventually on its surface.

In classifying the parts of the protoplast it is customary to describe the protoplasmic components as living, the nonprotoplasmic as non-living. To draw a sharp distinction between living and nonliving constituents is obviously impossible, because the property or prop-

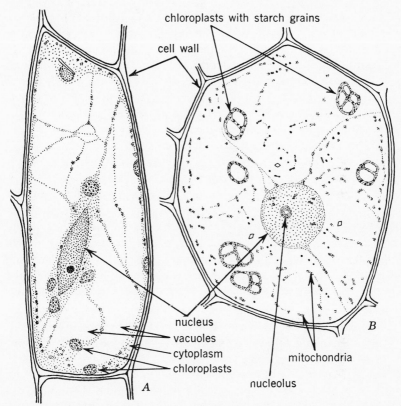

Fɪɢ. 2.1. Components of plant cells. *A*, cell from the petiole of a sugar-beet leaf. It has vacuolated cytoplasm with fine and coarse granules (some of these are mitochondria), a nucleus, and granular chloroplasts. *B*, starch-sheath cell from young stem of tobacco. The chloroplasts contain starch grains (left white in the drawing). (Both, ×1,190.)

erties that are the cause of the living state of protoplasm are not known. The individual substances composing the protoplasm, such as proteins, fats, and water, taken separately, are not alive. Yet they are in a sense alive when they are part of the protoplasm. The nonprotoplasmic substances, such as crystals, oil bodies, or starch, are lifeless even when they are imbedded in the protoplasm, but they or their component parts may become incorporated in the living protoplasm through metabolic changes. Nevertheless, it is tenable to designate nonprotoplasmic substances as nonliving when they are not obviously incorporated in the protoplasm or when they appear to be temporarily inactive.

Thus, the cell may be defined as a protoplast with or without a nonliving envelope, the cell wall, and consisting of the protoplasmic components and of the nonprotoplasmic materials, the latter intimately connected with the vital activities of the protoplast. For convenience the term cell is applied, in plants, also to the dead remains of a cell consisting largely of cell wall.

Nuclei as discrete bodies have not been seen in cells of certain lower groups of plants, but in the higher plants the absence of nuclei is rare and is associated with a specialized condition of the protoplast, as is exemplified by the sieve elements of the phloem tissue. Still other cells may contain more than one nucleus. Multinucleate cells are difficult to interpret with reference to the ordinary uninucleate protoplasts. They may constitute entire organisms remaining multinucleate all their lives, as certain fungi and algae. Sometimes, however, the multinucleate state is only a stage in the development of a tissue or an organ, as in the endosperm of certain angiosperms or in embryos of gymnosperms. The multinucleate state may also occur in the development of cells attaining considerable dimensions, such as fibers or laticiferous tubes. The view has been advanced that in some multinucleate structures each nucleus and the adjacent cytoplasm represent a cell, and the whole structure is an aggregation of protoplasmic units termed *coenocyte*, after the Greek words *coeno*, in common, and *cyte*, a vessel.

Disregarding the multinucleate protoplasmic masses, the concept of the cell as a unit of structure has a considerable theoretical significance because it enables one to define the structure and morphologic origin of plant tissues and organs. The value of interpreting the cell as a physiological unit, however, may be questioned. Physiologically, the plant or animal body is not an aggregation of independent units but an organism in which the various parts are interrelated in their growth and activities. This consideration and certain others have resulted in the evolution of the *organismal theory*, which, in contrast to the cell theory, emphasizes the unity of the protoplasmic mass of the organism as a whole, rather than the division of this mass into cells (cf. Sharp, 1934).

PROTOPLASMIC COMPONENTS

The Cytoplasm

The cytoplasm is the visibly least differentiated part of the protoplasm and appears as the ground mass enclosing all the other components of the protoplast (fig. 2.1, *A*). The word cytoplasm is often used to designate all the living matter in the cell exclusive of the nucleus (Guilliermond, 1941; Sharp, 1934). In this book plastids and mitochondria are treated as protoplasmic bodies separate from the cytoplasm, although the close developmental, structural, and functional relation between the various protoplasmic components is fully recognized. The cytoplasm and the various protoplasmic bodies have the same fundamental characteristics. The following description of the cytoplasm covers, therefore, many properties of the protoplasm in general.

The cytoplasm appears as a transparent semifluid substance denser than water, with granules and vesicles of various sizes imbedded in it. It is highly complex, both physically and chemically. Water constitutes the basic medium and is the most abundant ingredient of the active cytoplasm (85 to 90 per cent of fresh weight; Crafts et al., 1949; Sponsler and Bath, 1942). The various organic and inorganic substances occur in the aqueous medium either in true solution or in a colloidal state. Salts, carbohydrates, and other water-soluble substances are in a dissolved state; that is, they are in molecular and ionic dispersion. The other organic substances, mainly proteins and fats, are dispersed in the aqueous medium in particles usually small enough not to be seen through an ordinary microscope, but larger than molecules (Seifriz, 1936). They are in a colloidal state. The outstanding characteristic of colloidal systems is that the dispersion of one substance in another enormously increases the surface of the components of the system. This condition is favorable for enzymatic reactions and makes it possible, in part, for so many different processes to occur simultaneously within the confines of a single cell.

The cytoplasm has often been characterized as an emulsion, a colloidal system of two immiscible liquids in which one liquid is finely dispersed in the other. Fats and like matter do form an emulsion in the cytoplasm, but side by side with this system there is another having proteins as one of the components and behaving not as an emulsion. Studies of various chemical and physical properties of the cytoplasm, including those revealed by ultraviolet microscopy and polarization optics (Frey-Wyssling, 1948; Moyer, 1942; Schmitt, 1939; Seifriz, 1935, 1936, 1945; Sharp, 1943; Sponsler and Bath, 1942) suggest the presence of a continuous but labile framework of proteins interpenetrated by the aqueous component of the system. The framework consists of chain-like molecules of simple proteins, the polypeptide chains. By bonding between side chains, a reticulum of loosely interwoven strands of protein chains is formed. This open sponge-like system is thought to be capable of thermal movement and of constant readjustment through changes in the cross-linkages between the bundles of chains. The perpetual change in form is the essence of structure of the living protein. Protoplasmic streaming (Seifriz, 1943) is one of the external evidences of this change in form.

Plasma Membranes. An important feature of structural differentiation of the cytoplasm is the presence of surface films where the cytoplasm is in contact with other protoplasmic bodies and with the nonprotoplasmic constituents of the cell (or with the external medium, if the cell has no wall). In plant cells the two most widely discussed surface films are: the *ectoplast* (Scarth, 1942), or *plasma membrane*, that occurs on the outer boundary of the protoplast, next to the wall; and the *tonoplast*, or *vacuolar membrane*, that acts as the limiting layer between the vacuole and the cytoplasm (plate 1, *B*). Plasma membranes apparently occur on the surface of the other protoplasmic bodies of the protoplast, such as plastids and nucleus. Whether these membranes belong to the cytoplasm proper or to the bodies or to both is a debated question (Scarth, 1942).

The development of cytoplasmic membranes is commonly compared with the formation of surface films at interfaces between different physical systems in contact with each other (Guilliermond, 1941; Seifriz, 1936; Sharp, 1934). At such interfaces there is a selective accumulation of certain molecules, and their orientation may be different from that in the interior of the system. In the cytoplasm, fatty substances, particularly those called lipids, and certain proteins appear to take part in the formation of the plasma membrane. Thus, the chemical composition of the plasma membrane is somewhat different from that of the interior cytoplasm, and this difference is probably combined with that resulting from a characteristic orientation of molecules in the membrane. Regardless of its difference from the inner cytoplasm in structure and in chemical properties, the plasma membrane is interpreted as a living layer intimately related to the inner cytoplasm and continually changing in relation to the environment and to the activities of the cell.

The tonoplast is regarded by some as having a composition and structure similar to those of the plasma membrane (Scarth, 1942); others think that the two may be unlike structurally and functionally (Frey-Wyssling, 1948; Zirkle, 1937). All agree, however, that the tonoplast is a distinct entity that differs from the inner cytoplasm.

Interfacial films, whatever their comparative structures and functions, are associated with the important physiological characteristic of the living protoplast, its semipermeability (more exactly, its selective permeability) with regard to substances that enter and leave the cell. All parts of the living cell determine its permeability, but the membranes are chiefly responsible for the regulation of this property.

The Nucleus

The nondividing or metabolic nucleus is usually a spheroidal or ellipsoidal protoplasmic body enclosed within the cytoplasm; that is, it does not touch the vacuole or the cell wall (figs. 2.1; 2.2, *A*, *B*; plate 1, *A*). As was mentioned in connection with the plasma membranes, the nucleus is bounded by a film generally spoken of as the *nuclear membrane*. Within the membrane are the nuclear liquid, or *karyolymph* (also called nuclear sap), the thread-like *chromonemata* arranged in the form of a reticulum, and one or more *nucleoli*. In the living state the internal structure of the nondividing nucleus is difficult to discern, and the body usually appears homogeneous, except where the nucleoli are located. After fixation the reticulum may be readily revealed and, in well-fixed material, it appears as a system of interconnected threads with a variable number of swellings on the threads. Plant cytologists now generally treat the reticulum as an actual structure and not as a fixation artifact (Sharp, 1943). The chromonemata forming the reticulum in a metabolic nucleus are the filamentous constituents of the *chromosomes*. Both received their names from their basic constituent, *chromatin*, meaning a highly stainable substance.

Because of the large amount of karyolymph, the nucleus may be characterized as more or less fluid, but its viscosity is higher than that of the cytoplasm. On the other hand, the proportion of proteins is higher in the cytoplasm than in the nucleus. One of the important chemical distinctions between the nucleus and the cytoplasm is based on the nature and the amounts of *nucleic acids* (combinations of phosphoric acid with certain carbohydrates and bases) in the two parts of the protoplast.

The nucleoli (Gates, 1942) are typical intranuclear bodies, which are usually very distinct. They disappear during nuclear division and then, at telophase, arise again from certain chromosomes. Each nucleus in nearly all organisms has at least one pair of chromosomes, each member of which gives rise to one nucleolus. The number of nucleoli is as characteristic for a species as the number of chromosomes. As many as ten have been counted in some plants. In a given tissue the number of nucleoli seems variable because soon after the telophase the nucleoli may fuse when they touch each other, and they may form a single large nucleolus before the next mitosis. The nucleoli are viscous and semisolid, denser than the karyolymph. They frequently contain vacuoles and crystal-like bodies.

The nuclei vary in size and shape not only in different plants but also in the different tissues of the same plant (Geitler, 1941; Scott, 1940; Trombetta, 1942). The differences in nuclear size may depend on the number of chromosomes, the volume of individual chromosomes, and the amount of karyolymph. The nucleoli also vary in size and may show diurnal fluctuations in their dimensions (Gates, 1942; Geitler, 1941).

Plastids

Plastids are protoplasmic bodies of specialized structure and function (Guilliermond, 1941; Küster, 1935; Schürhoff, 1924; Sharp, 1934). Plastids have not been found in bacteria, blue-green algae, myxomycetes, and certain fungi. They have no exact counterpart in the animal cell. In certain lower plants one or two plastids may occur in each cell, but in the higher plants each protoplast commonly contains many plastids. The plastids are viscous bodies that may show amoeboid changes in shape (fig. 2.2, *B*, *C*). They do not mix with the cytoplasm in which they are located. It is generally considered that a membrane, similar to the plasma membrane, separates a plastid from the cytoplasm (plate 3, *B*).

Although plastids vary in structure and function, they appear to be all interrelated through origin from similar primordial structures in meristems, and one kind of plastid may become changed into another. The entire plastid complex of an organism is sometimes referred to as the *plastidome* (Dangeard, 1935).

The classification of plastids is based on the presence or absence of pigments in these bodies. Colorless plastids are called *leucoplasts;*

pigmented ones, *chromoplasts*. Among the chromoplasts, green plastids termed *chloroplasts* are the most common and the most important physiologically because of their role in photosynthesis. Other chromoplasts carry pigments other than green but have no special names. Some cytologists prefer to use the term chromoplast only

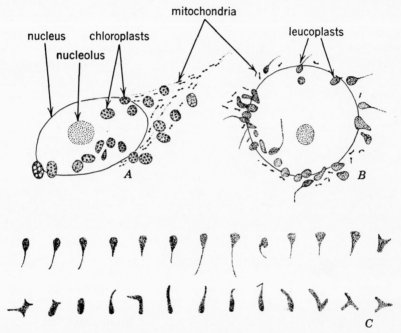

Fig. 2.2. Components of plant cells. *A*, nucleus, granular chloroplasts, and mitochondria from the petiole of a sugar-beet leaf. *B*, nucleus, leucoplasts, and mitochondria from the pith of a sugar-beet hypocotyl. *C*, series of drawings of the same leucoplast of a sugar beet showing amoeboid changes in shape that occurred during 15 minutes of observation. (All, ×1,110. From Esau, 1944.)

with reference to the colored plastids having no chlorophyll and consider chloroplasts as a separate group (Küster, 1935). This convenient classification is observed in this book.

Leucoplasts. Leucoplasts are not a clearly defined group of plastids. They occur in mature cells that are not exposed to light, as, for example, in the pith of stems or in underground organs. They are nearly universally present in immature cells where they may be chromoplasts or chloroplasts in their early stages of development. The plastids of the epidermis frequently appear nonpigmented and are then classified as leucoplasts.

Most present evidence suggests that plastids develop from self-perpetuating mitochondria-like structures. In the youngest cells, these

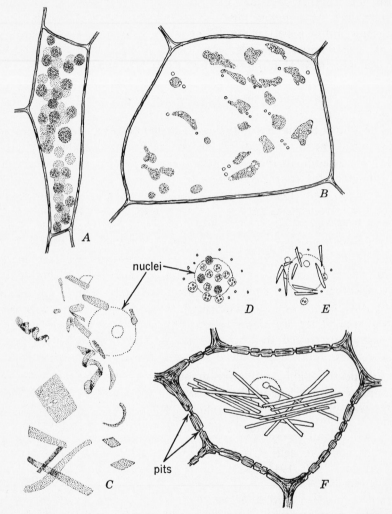

FIG. 2.3. Chromoplasts (*A, B, D*) and related pigment bodies (*C, E, F*). *A*, from
the petal of *Calendula*. *B*, from the fruit of *Pyracantha*. *C*, from the root of
Daucus (carrot). *D, E,* and *F*, from the fruit of *Lycopersicon* (tomato).
(All, ×880.)

structures are not readily distinguished from bodies that always retain their mitochondrial characteristics. In older cells the plastids
become distinct from the mitochondria, particularly the highly

pigmented ones, *chromoplasts*. Among the chromoplasts, green plastids termed *chloroplasts* are the most common and the most important physiologically because of their role in photosynthesis. Other chromoplasts carry pigments other than green but have no special names. Some cytologists prefer to use the term chromoplast only

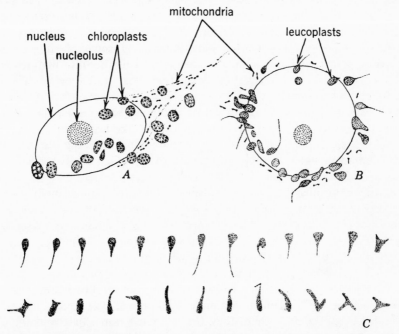

Fig. 2.2. Components of plant cells. *A*, nucleus, granular chloroplasts, and mitochondria from the petiole of a sugar-beet leaf. *B*, nucleus, leucoplasts, and mitochondria from the pith of a sugar-beet hypocotyl. *C*, series of drawings of the same leucoplast of a sugar beet showing amoeboid changes in shape that occurred during 15 minutes of observation. (All, ×1,110. From Esau, 1944.)

with reference to the colored plastids having no chlorophyll and consider chloroplasts as a separate group (Küster, 1935). This convenient classification is observed in this book.

Leucoplasts. Leucoplasts are not a clearly defined group of plastids. They occur in mature cells that are not exposed to light, as, for example, in the pith of stems or in underground organs. They are nearly universally present in immature cells where they may be chromoplasts or chloroplasts in their early stages of development. The plastids of the epidermis frequently appear nonpigmented and are then classified as leucoplasts.

Leucoplasts are relatively fragile and in fresh preparations break down more readily than the chloroplasts. In permanent preparations they are best preserved by the same nonacid fixatives that are used for demonstrating mitochondria. The leucoplasts often appear as small masses of protoplasm, variable and unstable in form (fig. 2.2, *C*). They commonly aggregate near the nucleus (fig. 2.2, *B*). Leucoplasts form starch in granules of variable sizes. If the leucoplasts are specialized as starch-storing bodies, they are called *amyloplasts*.

Chloroplasts. These plastids have been the object of many detailed investigations, and much information is available about their chemistry and structure (Frey-Wyssling, 1948; Granick, 1949; Guilliermond, 1941; Küster, 1935; Weier, 1938). Chloroplasts are most characteristically found in the principal photosynthetic tissue, the mesophyll of leaves, but they also occur in other green parts of the plant body. Sometimes chloroplasts are encountered in deep tissues, removed from light, as in parenchyma cells of the vascular tissues or even in embryos enclosed within seed coats and fruits.

The chloroplasts of higher plants are usually disc-shaped bodies (plate 2, *B*), sometimes curved like a saucer. They are relatively constant in shape and size, more so than the leucoplasts, and also more stable. In many plants the chloroplasts measure between 4 and 6 microns in diameter, although smaller and larger plastids may be found. They occur as a single layer in the cytoplasm, oriented so that one flat side is turned toward the interior of the cell, the other toward the wall. Under certain environmental conditions they are rounded off; under others they are flattened out. In the flattened state they may, in lining the wall, touch and deform each other and appear angular in outline. In some cells the chloroplasts aggregate near the nucleus like the leucoplasts (fig. 2.2, *A*).

As seen through an ordinary microscope the chloroplasts seem either granular or homogeneous in structure. Both appearances are interpreted as normal by certain workers (Weier, 1939). Recent studies with the electron microscope have confirmed the existence of the chloroplast granules, or *grana* (e.g., Frey-Wyssling and Mühlethaler, 1949; Granick, 1949; plate 3, *A*). The granules are usually orderly and uniformly arranged within the chloroplast (fig. 2.2, *A*). They may become aligned in rows so that the plastid appears striped (Heitz, 1936; Weier, 1938). One of the common interpretations is that the chlorophyll is contained in the grana, whereas the matrix or *stroma*, in which the granules are imbedded, is colorless (Weier, 1938). The chloroplast contains much protein, and because of the large numbers of chloroplasts in leaf cells 30 to 40 per cent of the total leaf nitrogen may be localized in the chloroplasts (Granick, 1949).

Chromoplasts. These plastids are bodies of varied shapes—elongated, lobed, angled, spheroidal (fig. 2.3)—and are usually colored yellow or orange. The pigments responsible for these colors belong to the large group of carotenoids (Zscheile, 1941), whose relation to the stroma of the plastid is not clearly understood. Sometimes the pigment is diffused in the plastid, sometimes it occurs in granules, sometimes it appears to be crystalline. In the carrot the pigment bodies occur as optically anisotropic ribbons, plates, or spirals (fig. 2.3, *C*), sometimes connected with starch grains. There is some question whether such bodies should be classified as plastids in the usual sense of the term (Weier, 1942).

Elaioplasts. In considering the plastids, it is proper to mention the structures called *elaioplasts*, which are thought to be concerned with the formation of fatty substances. Fats have been described as arising in the elaioplasts, or directly in the cytoplasm, or through the activity of mitochondria (Sharp, 1934). Elaioplasts are particularly common in the liverworts and the monocotyledons. A careful developmental study of these bodies in *Iris* (Faull, 1935) has suggested that they are definitely functional plastids, capable of forming starch, in addition to oil, during the active season. The oil in the elaioplasts is regarded as reserve food supply imbedded as globules in the plastid matrix.

Frequently highly refractive granules, showing the same staining reactions as oil, occur in chromoplasts and chloroplasts. These granules are referred to as fatty or lipid granules. They are interpreted as an intermediate product contributing to the formation of starch or pigment, or as a product resulting from a disorganization of plastids (Guilliermond, 1941).

Origin of Plastids. Plastids are capable of multiplying by division in cells of various ages (Granick, 1949; Küster, 1935; Sharp, 1934, 1943). These divisions are usually not correlated with mitoses of the nuclei. Meristems have small, granular or thread-like bodies that appear to be the precursors of plastids. The nature of these plastid precursors, or plastid primordia, is a matter of considerable debate in the cytological literature (Guilliermond, 1941; Guilliermond et al., 1933; Küster, 1935; Newcomer, 1940, 1946, 1951; Sharp, 1934; Sorokin, 1938, 1941; Weier, 1938).

Most present evidence suggests that plastids develop from self-perpetuating mitochondria-like structures.   In the youngest cells, these

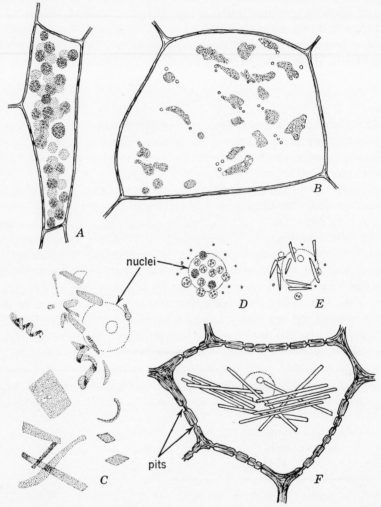

Fig. 2.3.   Chromoplasts (*A, B, D*) and related pigment bodies (*C, E, F*).   *A,* from
the petal of *Calendula*.   *B,* from the fruit of *Pyracantha*.   *C,* from the root of
Daucus (carrot).   *D, E,* and *F,* from the fruit of *Lycopersicon* (tomato).
(All, ×880.)

structures are not readily distinguished from bodies that always retain their mitochondrial characteristics.   In older cells the plastids
become distinct from the mitochondria, particularly the highly

specialized chloroplasts. Despite their varied degrees of specialization, the plastids remain interrelated. They can change from one form into another, and they can produce different substances at different times or simultaneously. The recognition of their interrelationships and of their plasticity with regard to structure and function is of utmost importance for the understanding of the nature of plastids (Faull, 1935; Newcomer, 1946).

Mitochondria

The mitochondria are almost universally classified with the living components of the protoplast, but their structure, chemistry, function, and relation to the other protoplasmic components are matters of disagreement in the cytological literature (Guilliermond, 1941; Newcomer, 1940, 1946; Sharp, 1943). *Mitochondria* (singular, *mitochondrion*, from the Greek *mitos*, thread, and *chondrion*, small grain) is one of several names given to these bodies, another common one being *chondriosome* (grain-like body). The whole complement of these structures in an organism is referred to as the *chondriome*.

Mitochondria appear as small granules, rods, or filaments in the cytoplasm in nearly all animal and plants cells (figs. 2.1, *B*; 2.2, *A, B*; plate 2, *C, D*). They are somewhat more viscous and dense than the cytoplasm. They are highly sensitive to changes in environment and are easily destroyed by many ordinary cytological fixatives, especially those containing acids. Mitochondria are largely composed of protein and lipid. It is the presence of lipid that makes them so susceptible to acids and fat solvents. Although in their chemistry mitochondria are closely related to cytoplasm, many workers consider them a separate category of small protoplasmic bodies, multiplying by division and transmitted from generation to generation through the reproductive cells (Anderson, 1936, 1939; Guilliermond, 1941; Newcomer, 1940, 1946, 1951; Sorokin, 1938, 1941). The idea that the mitochondria arise anew from the cytoplasm is commonly rejected by modern cytologists, though it is admitted that initially they may have arisen as cytoplasmic condensations (Newcomer, 1940, 1946, 1951).

Mitochondria are said to be connected with such activities as those of secretory, enzymatic, or respiratory nature. Because of their small size they have a relatively high surface-to-volume ratio and may be expected to be the site of important interfacial energy changes. These physical properties, together with the abundance of mitochondria in young, highly metabolic tissues, suggest that these bodies may be involved in a variety of physiological activities, carried on side by side, without mutual interference.

NONPROTOPLASMIC COMPONENTS

Vacuoles

Vacuoles (from the Latin *vacuus*, empty) are cavities within the cytoplasm filled with a liquid, the *cell sap*, whose composition may vary in different cells and even in the different vacuoles of the same cell. In sections of living tissue the vacuoles are colorless or pigmented (plate 1, *B*); in well-fixed material they appear as clear areas bounded by the stained cytoplasm (plate 1, *A*). All the vacuoles of a cell or an organism may be regarded as a system and referred to as the *vacuome*.

The principal component of the cell sap is water, and in it are various substances either in true solution or in the colloidal state (Crafts et al., 1949; Seifriz, 1936; Sharp, 1934, 1943; Zirkle, 1937). Salts, sugars, organic acids and other soluble compounds, proteins, and even fatty substances have been identified in plant vacuoles. Tannins are commonly found (plate 2, *A*). Bluish and reddish pigments of the anthocyanin type are also characteristically dissolved in the vacuolar liquid (Blank, 1947; Möbius, 1937). The materials present in the vacuoles are classified as ergastic. They are either reserve substances that may again be utilized by the protoplast for vital activities at a suitable time, or they are by-products of metabolism. The vacuolar liquid is more or less viscous, but usually less so than the cytoplasm. The viscosity of the cell sap is probably associated with the presence of colloids, which may sometimes appear in the form of true gels. Vacuoles containing tanniferous compounds are often highly viscous. The vacuoles are delimited from the cytoplasm by the vacuolar membrane or tonoplast.

Much has been learned about the nature of vacuoles by studies of cells in the living state and by staining them with noninjurious vital dyes. With regard to *p*H, two types of vacuoles have been recognized. The relatively alkaline types stain reddish orange with neutral red, and the markedly acid ones assume a bluish magenta color with the same dye (Zirkle, 1937). The concentration of the vacuolar sap varies, and when a substance accumulates beyond its saturation point it may crystallize out. An increase in concentration may occur also through withdrawal of water, as, for example, in the drying of seeds (Sharp, 1934). Water can be withdrawn artificially from a vacuole by placing living cells into a hypertonic solution. As is well known, such treatment causes cell plasmolysis. The protoplast loses water and shrinks away from the wall (plate 1, *B*). If a cell is restored to its natural state by a change in the bathing solution, it is spoken of as being deplasmolyzed.

Vacuoles vary in shape and size in relation to the stage of development and the metabolic state of the cell. In meristematic cells they are often numerous and small. In mature cells commonly one single vacuole occupies the central part of the protoplast, whereas the cytoplasm and the other protoplasmic components are restricted to a parietal position, that is, next to the wall. Some meristematic cells have a very extensive vacuolar system. The cells of the vascular cambium, for example, may be as highly vacuolated as plant hairs, which serve as best examples of highly vacuolated plant cells (Bailey, 1930). Formerly meristematic cells were thought to be nonvacuolated, and it was customary to speak of a cell as "becoming vacuolated" when it began to show conspicuous vacuoles during development. Now, the occurrence of vacuoles is considered to be almost universal in plant cells, including those of meristems (Bailey, 1930; Zirkle, 1937). If a cell develops from a type of meristematic cell having many small vacuoles, these vacuoles increase in size through uptake of water and gradually coalesce as the cell enlarges and ages. Thus the enlargement of a plant cell involves both an increase in the amount of its cell sap and an extension of its wall. The protoplasm may also grow in amount (Frey-Wyssling, 1948; Heyn, 1940). Vacuoles are less characteristic of animal cells, and the enlargement of these cells is associated mainly with an increase in the amount of protoplasm.

The origin of vacuoles is variously interpreted (Guilliermond, 1941; Sharp, 1934; Zirkle, 1937). According to one hypothesis, certain colloidal products having a strong attraction for water become separated from the cytoplasm and by taking up large amounts of water are converted into vacuolar sap. Other workers consider the vacuolar system to be permanent and self-perpetuating. They assume the existence, in meristematic cells, of small units resembling mitochondria in shape (but not in staining reactions), which multiply by division and change into vacuoles through absorption of water. The origin of vacuoles from special bodies, however, seems very doubtful (Zirkle, 1937).

Ergastic Substances

Ergastic substances are products of metabolism. These substances may appear and disappear at different times in the life of the cell. They are reserve or waste products resulting from cellular activities and are usually simpler in structure than protoplasmic bodies. Some of the well-known ergastic substances are the visible carbohydrates, cellulose and starch; protein bodies; fats and related substances; and mineral matter in the form of crystals. They include also many other organic substances, such as tannins, resins, gums (Howes, 1949), rubber, and alkaloids, whose nature or function or both are known imperfectly. Ergastic substances occur in the vacuoles, in the cell wall, and may be associated with the protoplasmic components of the cell.

Carbohydrates. Cellulose and starch are the principal ergastic substances of the protoplast. Cellulose is the chief component of plant cell walls, whereas starch occurs as reserve material in the protoplast itself. Both these carbohydrates are composed of long chain-like molecules, whose basic units are anhydrous glucose residues of the formula $C_6H_{10}O_5$. In both, these basic units show an orderly arrangement, forming a space lattice. The symmetrical spacing of the building units gives cellulose and starch certain crystalline properties, as, for example, optical anisotropy and double refraction, which may be revealed by the use of polarized light (plate 4, *A*).

Glucose residues are associated with water in the two carbohydrates, starch having more of it than cellulose. In the walls of plant cells other materials beside water usually accompany cellulose. (See chapter 3.) In their combination with water and other materials starch and cellulose show colloidal characteristics, such as ability to imbibe water and to swell, well exemplified by the formation of pastes and jellies from starch treated with hot water.

The morphologic variation of starch grains is so extensive that they may be used for the identification of seeds and other starch-containing plant parts (fig. 2.4; Küster, 1935). The following figures (in microns) exemplify their variations in size: 70 to 100 in potato, 30 to 45 in wheat, 12 to 18 in maize. Starch grains of many plants show conspicuous concentric layering because of the alternation of more and less diffractive layers. These layers are successively deposited around a point, the *hilum*, the position of which may be central in some grains, acentric in others. Compound grains with two or more hila are characteristic of some plants.

The layering of starch in the grains is interpreted as resulting from diurnal periodicity in the activity of the plastid forming the starch grain. The successive lamellae differ from each other in density and in water content (Frey-Wyssling, 1948). The innermost part of the grain is said to be particularly rich in water, and this feature would explain the commonly observed cracking in the hilum region of desiccated grains.

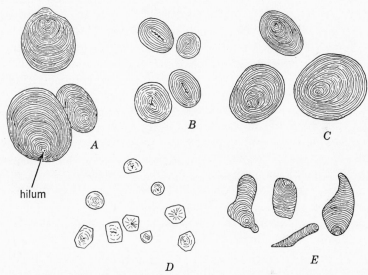

hilum

Fig. 2.4. Starch grains from the following organs and plants: *A*, root of arrow-root (*Maranta*). *B*, seed of bean (*Phaseolus*). *C*, tuber of potato (*Solanum*). *D*, grain of maize (*Zea*). *E*, fruit of banana (*Musa*). (All, ×285.)

Starch arises almost exclusively in plastids, mainly leucoplasts and chloroplasts. The chloroplasts commonly synthesize *assimilation starch* (Sharp, 1934), a temporary product which remains in the plastid as long as there is an excess of carbohydrate in the cell. Leucoplasts often produce *storage starch*. One or more starch grains may arise in one plastid (fig. 2.1, *B*). The starch grains contained in one plastid may remain discrete, or they may grow together into a compound grain. As the grain increases in size, the plastid becomes distended and its mass is often pushed to one side of the grain. The rest of the grain then appears to be covered by a very thin layer of plastid material. If the plastid forming the starch grain is a chloroplast, it frequently remains clearly visible even after it is much distended. The leucoplast in a similar state becomes inconspicuous.

Starch deposition occurs widely in the plant body, but the particularly common places of its accumulation are seeds, the parenchyma of the secondary vascular tissues in stems and roots, and the
parenchyma of specialized storage organs, such as fleshy roots, tubers,
rhizomes, and corms.

Proteins. Proteins are the main ingredients of the living protoplasmic bodies, but they also occur as temporarily inactive ergastic
substances. Ergastic protein is known as a storage material and is
found deposited in amorphous or crystalline form. Amorphous protein forms globules or shapeless masses (in gymnosperm egg cells,
algae, fungi). Like starch and cellulose, crystalline protein combines
crystalline and colloidal properties, and therefore the individual units
of this material are spoken of as *crystalloids* (meaning crystal-like)
rather than as crystals (Küster, 1935).

A well-known amorphous ergastic protein is gluten, which is
combined with starch in the endosperm of wheat. Cuboidal protein
crystalloids occur within parenchyma cells in the peripheral regions
of the potato tuber. Crystalloids are often combined with amorphous
protein in the *aleuron* grains (aleuron means wheaten flour in Greek),
which are ergastic bodies found in the endosperm, the perisperm, and
the embryo of many seeds (Sharp, 1934).

The origin of protein inclusions, which was studied mainly by
following the development of aleuron grains (Frey-Wyssling, 1948;
Guilliermond, 1941; Sharp, 1934; Wieler, 1943), is still a controversial
matter. Some investigators claim that protoplasm or plastid-like
bodies are concerned with the formation of these grains; others report that the ergastic protein first occurs in vacuoles; then, upon
withdrawal of water from these vacuoles, the remaining contents are
transformed into bodies of protein nature.

Fats and Related Substances. Fats and oils are widely distributed
in the plant body, and they probably occur in small amounts in
every plant cell. The term fat may be used to describe not only
the fats proper, that is, esters of fatty acids with glycerol, but also
related substances grouped under the name of lipids; and oils may be
regarded as liquid fats (Seifriz, 1936). Waxes, suberin, and cutin
are fatty in nature and often occur as protective substances in and
on the cell wall. Phosphatids and sterols are also related to fats.

As protoplasmic inclusions, fats and oils are common reserve materials in seeds, spores, and embryos, in meristematic cells, and occasionally in differentiated tissues of the vegetative body (Sharp, 1934,
p. 102). They occur as solid bodies or more frequently as fluid

droplets of various sizes either dispersed in the cytoplasm or aggregated in larger masses. Fatty substances are thought to be elaborated directly by the cytoplasm and also by elaioplasts.

The essential oils, a class of highly volatile and aromatic substances, have a widespread occurrence in plants (McNair, 1932). In certain plants as, for example, in the conifers, they occur in all tissues; in others they may develop only in petals (rose), petals and fruit skin (orange), bark and leaves (cinnamon), or fruit (nutmeg).

Tannins. Tannins, in the wide sense of the term, are a heterogenous group of phenol derivatives, usually related to glucosides. (In a restricted sense the term tannin refers to a specific category of phenolic compounds.) The anhydrous derivatives of tannins, the phlobaphenes (Gortner and Gortner, 1949, p. 750), are yellow, red, or brown amorphous substances which are very conspicuous in sectioned material. They appear as coarsely or finely granular masses, or as bodies of various sizes. In the following discussion and throughout the book, the term tannin is used in a wide sense, including the phlobaphenes and other tannin derivatives.

Tannins are particularly abundant in leaves of many plants; in the xylem, the phloem, and the periderm of stems and roots; in unripe fruits; in the testa of seeds; and in pathological growths like galls (Küster, 1935; Sperlich, 1939). No tissue, however, appears to lack tannins entirely, and they may be identified in meristematic cells. Sometimes tannin-containing cells are conspicuously associated with vascular bundles and occur abundantly in areas where the vascular tissue terminates beneath storage tissues or beneath secretory cells of nectaries. The monocotyledons are notably poor in tannins (Sperlich, 1939).

Tannins may be present in individual cells or in special containers termed tannin sacs. The tannin-containing cells often form connected systems. In the individual cells the tannins occur in the protoplast and may also impregnate the walls as, for example, in cork tissue. Within the protoplast, tannins are a common ingredient of the vacuoles (plate 2, *A*), or they may occur in the cytoplasm proper in the form of small droplets (tannin vacuoles) which eventually fuse.

With regard to their function, the tannins are interpreted as substances protecting the protoplast against desiccation, decay, or injury by animals; as reserve substances related in some undetermined manner to the starch metabolism; as substances associated with the formation and transport of sugars; as antioxidants; and as protective colloids maintaining the homogeneity of the cytoplasm (Hauser, 1935, 1936a, b).

Crystals (Frey-Wyssling, 1935; Netolitzky, 1929; Pobeguin, 1943). In contrast to animals, which normally eliminate excess inorganic materials to the exterior, plants deposit such materials almost entirely in their tissues. The inorganic deposits in plants consist mostly of calcium salts and of anhydrids of silica. Among the calcium salts the most common is calcium oxalate, which is found in the majority of plant families. Calcium oxalate occurs as mono- and trihydrate

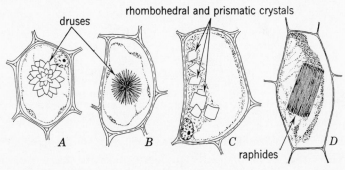

FIG. 2.5. Cells with different types of crystals. *A* and *B*, druses from the cortex of *Gnetum gnemon*. *C*, prismatic and rhombohedral crystals from cortex of *Gnetum indicum*. *D*, raphides from leaf of *Vitis vinifera*. (*A–C*, ×800; *D*, ×625.)

salts in many crystalline forms. There are solitary rhombohedrons or octahedrons (prismatic or bipyramidal) (fig. 2.5, *C*; plate 4, *B*). The occurrence of so-called crystal sand results from the formation of many small crystals in one cell. Crystals may be united into compound structures, the druses and the sphaerites (fig. 2.5, *A*, *B*; plate 4, *D*). Elongated crystals are termed styloids and raphides. The raphides are aggregated into bundles (fig. 2.5, *D*; plate 4, *C*).

Calcium oxalate crystals may be commonly observed in vacuoles. Some workers, however, report that crystals are formed in the cytoplasm (Küster, 1935; Netolitzky, 1929; Scott, 1941). Some oxalate crystals arise in cells that resemble adjacent, crystal-free cells. Others are formed in specialized cells, the crystal *idioblasts* (that is, cells markedly differing from other constituents of the same tissue in form, structure, or contents; from the Greek *idio*, peculiar). Still other crystals are deposited in the cell walls. Crystals may be much smaller than the cells containing them, or they may completely fill and even deform the cells. Raphides often occur in remarkably large cells which, at maturity, are dead structures filled with mucilage capable of swelling. Parts of the cell wall of such raphide idioblasts remain thin, and, if the mucilage swells, the thin wall bursts and the raphides are ejected (Cheavin, 1938). Calcium oxalate crystals may be deposited uniformly throughout the tissue, or they may be rather restricted to certain tissue regions (e.g., in cells surrounding the fiber strands in the secondary phloem of *Robinia* or in cells along the margins of the phloem rays in *Vitis*).

Calcium carbonate rarely occurs in well-formed crystals. The best-known calcium carbonate formations are the *cystoliths* (from the Greek *kustis*, a bag, and *lithos*, a stone), which are outgrowths of the cellulose wall impregnated with the mineral (Beyrich, 1944). They occur in ground parenchyma and in the epidermis. In the epidermis they may be formed in hairs or in special enlarged cells, the lithocysts. (See chapter 7.)

Silica is deposited mostly in cell walls, but sometimes it forms bodies in the lumen of the cell. The Gramineae is the best-known example of a plant group having silica in both the walls and the cell lumina (Küster, 1935; Netolitzky, 1929).

REFERENCES

Anderson, L. E. Mitochondria in the life cycles of certain higher plants. *Amer. Jour. Bot.* 23:490–500. 1936.

Anderson, L. E. Cytoplasmic inclusions in the male gametes of *Lilium. Amer. Jour. Bot.* 26:761–766. 1939.

Bailey, I. W. The cambium and its derivative tissues. V. A reconnaissance of the vacuome in living cells. *Ztschr. f. Zellforsch. u. Mikros. Anat.* 10:651–682. 1930.

Beyrich, H. Neue Beiträge zur Entwicklungsgeschichte und Morphologie der Zystolithen. *Protoplasma* 38:287–313. 1944.

Blank, F. The anthocyanin pigments of plants. *Bot. Rev.* 13:241–317. 1947.

Cheavin, W. H. S. The crystals and cystoliths found in plant cells. Part I: Crystals. *Microscope, Brit. Jour. Micros. and Photomicrogr.* 2:155–158. 1938.

Conklin, E. G. Cell and protoplasm concepts: historical account. In: *Cell and Protoplasm. Amer. Assoc. Adv. Sci. Publ.* 14:6–19. 1940.

Crafts, A. S., H. B. Currier, and C. R. Stocking. *Water in the physiology of plants.* Waltham, Mass., Chronica Botanica Company. 1949.

Dangeard, P. A. Note sur les principaux constituants de la cellule. *VI Internatl. Bot. Congr. Proc.* 2:33–36. 1935.

Esau, K. Anatomical and cytological studies on beet mosaic. *Jour. Agr. Res.* 69:95–117. 1944.

Faull, A. F. Elaioplasts in *Iris:* a morphological study. *Arnold Arboretum Jour.* 16:225–267. 1935.

Frey-Wyssling, A. *Die Stoffausscheidung der höheren Pflanzen. Monographien aus dem Gesamtgebiet der Physiologie der Pflanzen und der Tiere.* Band 32. Berlin, Julius Springer. 1935.

Frey-Wyssling, A. *Submicroscopic morphology of protoplasm and its derivatives.* New York, Elsevier Publishing Company. 1948.

Frey-Wyssling, A., and K. Mühlethaler. Über den Feinbau der Chlorophyllkörner. *Naturf. Gesell. in Zürich, Vrtljschr.* 94:181–183. 1949.

Gates, R. R. Nucleoli and related nuclear structures. *Bot. Rev.* 8:337–409. 1942.

Geitler, L. Das Wachstum des Zellkerns in tierischen und pflanzlichen Geweben. *Ergeb. der Biol.* 18:1–54. 1941.

Gortner, R. A., Jr., and W. A. Gortner. *Outlines of biochemistry.* 3rd ed. New York, John Wiley & Sons. 1949.

Granick, S. The chloroplasts: their structure, composition, and development. In: J. Frank and W. E. Loomis. Editors. *Photosynthesis in plants. Amer. Soc. Plant Physiol. Monogr.* 1949.

Guilliermond, A. *The cytoplasm of the plant cell.* Waltham, Mass., Chronica Botanica Company. 1941.

Guilliermond, A., G. Mangenot, and L. Plantefol. *Traité de cytologie végétale.* Paris, Librarie E. Le François. 1933.

Hauser, W. Zur Physiologie des Gerbstoffes in der Pflanzenzelle. *Protoplasma* 24:219–224. 1935; 26:413–417. 1936*a*; 27:125–130. 1936*b*.

Heitz, E. Untersuchungen über den Bau der Plastiden. I. Die gerichteten Chlorophyllscheiben der Chloroplasten. *Planta* 26:134–163. 1936.

Heyn, A. N. J. The physiology of cell elongation. *Bot. Rev.* 6:515–574. 1940.

Howes, F. N. *Vegetable gums and resins.* Waltham, Mass., Chronica Botanica Company. 1949.

Küster, E. *Die Pflanzenzelle.* Jena, Gustav Fischer. 1935.

Matzke, E. B. The concept of cells held by Hooke and Grew. *Science* 98:13–14. 1943.

McNair, J. B. The interrelation between substances in plants: essential oils and resins, cyanogen and oxalate. *Amer. Jour. Bot.* 19:255–272. 1932.

Möbius, M. Pigmentation in plants, exclusive of the algae. *Bot. Rev.* 3:351–363. 1937.

Moyer, L. S. Proteins and protoplasmic structure. In: *A Symposium on the Structure of Protoplasm. Amer. Soc. Plant Physiol. Monogr.* Pp. 23–40. 1942.

Netolitzky, F. Die Kieselkörper. Die Kalksalze als Zellinhaltskörper. In: K. Linsbauer. *Handbuch der Pflanzenanatomie.* Band 3. Lief. 25. Pp. 1–80. 1929.

Newcomer, E. H. Mitochondria in plants. *Bot. Rev.* 6:85–147. 1940. II. *Bot. Rev.* 17:53–89. 1951.

Newcomer, E. H. Concerning the duality of the mitochondria and the validity of the osmiophilic platelets in plants. *Amer. Jour. Bot.* 33:684–697. 1946.

Pobeguin, T. Les oxalates de calcium chez quelques Angiospermes. *Ann. des Sci. Nat. Bot.* Ser. 11. 4:1–95. 1943.

Scarth, G. W. Structural differentiation of cytoplasm. In: *A Symposium on the structure of Protoplasm. Amer. Soc. Plant Physiol. Monogr.* Pp. 99–107. 1942.

Schmitt, F. O. The ultrastructure of protoplasmic constituents. *Physiol. Revs.* 19:270–302. 1939.

Schürhoff, P. N. Die Plastiden. In: K. Linsbauer. *Handbuch der Pflanzenanatomie.* Band 1. Lief. 10. 1924.

Scott, F. M. Size of nuclei in the shoot of *Ricinus communis. Bot. Gaz.* 101:625–636. 1940.

Scott, F. M. Distribution of calcium oxalate crystals in *Ricinus communis* in relation to tissue differentiation and presence of other ergastic substances. *Bot. Gaz.* 103:225–246. 1941.

Seifriz, W. The structure of protoplasm. *Bot. Rev.* 1:18–36. 1935.

Seifriz, W. *Protoplasm.* New York, McGraw-Hill Book Company. 1936.

Seifriz, W. Protoplasmic streaming. *Bot. Rev.* 9:49–123. 1943.

Seifriz, W. The structure of protoplasm. II. *Bot. Rev.* 11:231–259. 1945.

Sharp, L. W. *Introduction to cytology.* 3rd ed. New York, McGraw-Hill Book Company. 1934.

Sharp, L. W. *Fundamentals of cytology.* New York, McGraw-Hill Book Company. 1943.

Sorokin, H. Mitochondria and plastids in living cells of *Allium cepa. Amer. Jour. Bot.* 25:28–33. 1938.

Sorokin, H. The distinction between mitochondria and plastids in living epidermal cells. *Amer. Jour. Bot.* 28:476–485. 1941.

Sperlich, A. Das trophische Parenchym. B. Exkretionsgewebe. In: K. Linsbauer. *Handbuch der Pflanzenanatomie.* Band 4. Lief. 38. 1939.

Sponsler, O. L., and J. D. Bath. Molecular srtucture in protoplasm. In: *A Symposium on the Structure of Protoplasm. Amer. Soc. Plant Physiol. Monogr.* Pp. 41–79. 1942.

Studnička, F. K. Noch einiges über das Wort Protoplasma. *Protoplasma* 27:619–625. 1937.

Trombetta, V. V. The cytonuclear ratio. *Bot. Rev.* 8:317–336. 1942.

Weber, F. Das Wort Protoplasma. *Protoplasma* 26:109–112. 1936.

Weier, T. E. The structure of the chloroplast. *Bot. Rev.* 4:497–530. 1938.

Weier, T. E. The microscopic appearance of the chloroplast. *Protoplasma* 32:147–152. 1939.

Weier, T. E. A cytological study of the carotene in the root of *Daucus carota* under various experimental treatments. *Amer. Jour. Bot.* 29:35–44. 1942.

Wieler, A. Der feinere Bau der Aleuronkörner und ihre Entstehung. *Protoplasma* 38:21–63. 1943.

Zirkle, C. The plant vacuole. *Bot. Rev.* 3:1–30. 1937.

Zscheile, F. P. Plastid pigments. *Bot. Rev.* 7:587–648. 1941.

CHAPTER

3

The Cell Wall

The presence of nonprotoplasmic walls is considered the outstanding characteristic differentiating the cells of plants from those of animals. Few plant cells lack walls, and few animal cells (these belong to the lower organisms) have nonprotoplasmic envelopes comparable to the walls of plant cells. Examples of cells without walls in plants are the motile spores in algae and fungi and the sexual cells in lower and higher plants. The sexual reproductive cells of higher plants, however, remain imbedded, throughout their existence, within the cytoplasm of other cells (Küster, 1935).

The cell wall was discovered before the protoplast, and in the early history of botany it received more attention than the cell contents. Later the protoplast became the main object of study. In the present century research on cell walls has received a new impetus through the discovery of manifold industrial uses of cellulose and its derivatives and through the development of new and improved techniques in cell-wall investigations. The microchemical tests of wall materials have been further refined, and the use of polarized light, of X-rays, and of the electron microscope has become common practice in cell-wall research (cf. Berkley, 1941; Frey-Wyssling, 1948; Ott, 1943).

The term *cell wall* is now commonly used in the botanical literature written in English, but in some of the older publications in this language and in most of the German literature the term *cell membrane* is employed instead.

CELL WALL AS A COMPONENT OF THE PROTOPLAST

Among the parts of the protoplast the wall is characterized (in chapter 2) as a nonprotoplasmic component, and the materials forming it are classified as ergastic. This classification implies that the wall is essentially nonliving. The question whether the wall should be considered a lifeless secretion of the protoplast or a structure endowed with its own life has always interested students of cell behavior, and the results of modern work on growth substances have again brought this question into prominence, particularly with reference to the growth of walls in surface area. Two contrasting views on the causal relationships in such growth have been expressed. According to one, the extension of the wall is regulated by the protoplast; according to the other, the wall is living and capable of independent growth (Frey-Wyssling, 1950; Heyn, 1940).

Pollen grains and some spores of Pteridophyta develop part of their wall at the expense of the outside medium, which may or may not be living (Küster, 1935, p. 436; Sharp, 1934, p. 181). Usually, however, the wall grows only when it is in contact with living cytoplasm. It has become a common concept that the cytoplasm interpenetrates the wall undergoing extension growth (Frey-Wyssling, 1950; Preston and Wardrop, 1949). In such protoplasm-wall complex the wall material may still be visualized as an ergastic substance separated from the vital activities of the protoplast. This interpretation is even easier to apply to cell walls that have ceased to grow and from which, presumably, the cytoplasm withdraws except where the cytoplasmic strands, the plasmodesmata, are retained.

GROSS MICROSCOPIC STRUCTURE

Classification of Wall Layers

The interpretation of the plant cell as consisting of the protoplast and its envelope, the cell wall, agrees with the common observation that each cell within a tissue has its own wall. The recognition of the dual nature of the partitions between the contiguous protoplasts is not always possible, but it may be revealed by appropriate microchemical tests and maceration techniques (Kerr and Bailey, 1934). From the time of their inception, the walls of contiguous cells are held together by an intercellular substance, which may be stained differentially or dissolved out. In the latter instance the tissue becomes macerated and falls apart into the individual cells.

The cell walls of plants vary much in thickness in relation to age and type of cell (figs. 3.1, 3.2, 3.3; plate 5). Generally, young cells have thinner walls than the fully developed ones, but in some cells the wall does not thicken much after the cell ceases to grow.

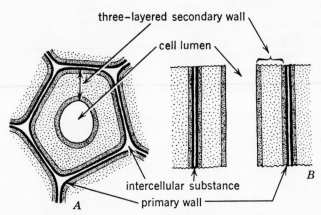

FIG. 3.1. Diagrams illustrating the common type of wall structure in cells with secondary wall layers in transverse (*A*) and longitudinal (*B*) sections. The wall layers are classified according to the concept of Kerr and Bailey (1934).

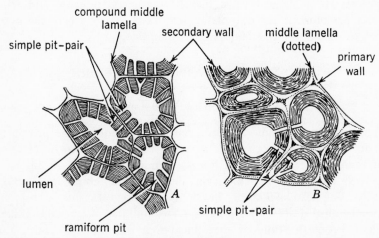

FIG. 3.2. Cells with secondary walls and simple pits. *A*, sclereids from a transection of *Cydonia* (quince) fruit. *B*, phloem fibers from a transection of *Nicotiana* (tobacco) stem. (Both, ×560.)

Whether thin or thick, the walls are of complex structure and often permit the recognition of layers variable in chemistry and structure. On the basis of development and structure, three fundamental parts may be recognized in plant cell walls: the intercellular substance or middle lamella, the primary wall, and the secondary wall (fig. 3.1; Anderson, 1935; Bailey, 1938; Kerr, 1946; Kerr and Bailey, 1934). The intercellular substance cements together the primary walls of two contiguous cells, and the secondary wall is laid over the primary, that is, next to the *lumen* (the central cavity, from the Latin, meaning light or opening) of the cell.

The *middle* lamella is amorphous, colloidal, and optically inactive (isotropic, plate 5, *B*). It is composed mainly of a pectic compound which appears to be a mixture of calcium and magnesium pectate (Bonner, 1950). In woody tissues the middle lamella is commonly lignified. In mature tissues the intercellular substance is difficult to identify, and, as a consequence, the term middle lamella has been used in the literature without much consistency (cf. Kerr and Bailey, 1934). The distinction between the intercellular lamella and the primary wall is frequently obscured during the extension growth of the cell. In such cells as tracheids and fibers, which typically develop prominent secondary walls, the intercellular layer becomes extremely tenuous. As a result, the two primary walls of contiguous cells and the intervening middle lamella appear as a unit, particularly when all three become strongly impregnated with lignin (fig. 3.3, *A*). This triple structure has often been called middle lamella. The matter is still more complicated when the first layer of the secondary wall cannot be distinguished by ordinary microscopy from the primary wall, because then middle lamella, if the term is employed loosely, might refer to this compound structure consisting of five layers. In this book the term middle lamella is used only with reference to the intercellular substance, following Kerr and Bailey (1934). A term of convenience, *compound middle lamella*, may be substituted if the intercellular substance is obscured, but this term would mean sometimes the three-ply, sometimes the five-ply, structure described above (Foster, 1949, p. 12; Kerr and Bailey, 1934).

The *primary wall* is the first wall proper formed in a developing cell, and in many types of cells it is the only wall. It consists of cellulose and of true pectic compounds and usually contains variable amounts of noncellulosic polysaccharides and hemicelluloses (Bonner, 1950). It also may become lignified. The primary wall is optically anisotropic (plate 4, *A*). Since the primary wall is initiated before the cell enlarges, it passes through a period of growth in surface area, which may be succeeded or temporarily interrupted by a period or periods of growth in thickness; or, possibly, the two types of growth may be combined. Thus the primary wall may have a complex history and also a complex structure. If the wall is thick, it often shows conspicuous lamination, indicating that growth in thickness has occurred by a successive deposition of layers (see chapter 9).

Primary walls are usually associated with living protoplasts. The walls of dividing and growing meristematic cells are primary, and so are those of most of the cells which retain living protoplasts during the height of their physiological maturity. The changes that occur in primary walls are therefore reversible. The wall may lose a thickening previously acquired, and chemical substances may be removed or replaced by others. Cambial walls, for example, show seasonal changes in thickness and in colloidal properties (Kerr and Bailey, 1934), and the thick primary walls of the endosperm in certain seeds are digested during germination.

Like the term middle lamella, the designation primary wall is also treated inconsistently in the literature. There is, notably, an attempt to restrict the concept of primary wall to a very thin layer of the cell wall initially laid down (Frey-Wyssling, 1948, p. 174; 1950; Mühlethaler, 1950), probably the earliest part of the primary wall in the sense of the classification adopted in this book. Sometimes the additional primary layers of cell walls like those in the collenchyma tissue (see chapter 9) are interpreted as a special kind of primary wall or as secondary wall (Bloch, 1944; Majumdar, 1944–45; Priestley and Scott, 1939).

As its name implies, the *secondary wall* follows the primary in the order of appearance. It consists mainly of cellulose or of varying mixtures of cellulose, noncellulosic polysaccharides, and hemicelluloses. It may be modified through deposition of lignin and various other substances. Because of its high content of cellulose the secondary wall is strongly anisotropic (plate 5, *B*). The complexity and the lack of homogeneity in structure are strongly pronounced in the secondary wall. Generally, the secondary walls of tracheary cells and fibers are distinctly three-layered (fig. 3.1; plate 5, *B*), and there are physical and chemical differences between the layers. The number of layers may exceed three, and the innermost sometimes consists only of a helical band. (Such bands are called tertiary wall by some authors; cf. Eames and MacDaniels, 1947, p. 30.)

Secondary walls are laid down after the cell has ceased to enlarge, and therefore they do not undergo growth in surface like the primary walls. The secondary wall may be considered a supplementary wall whose principal function is mechanical. Often the cells with secondary walls are devoid of protoplasts at maturity (certain fibers, tracheids, vessel elements). Secondary walls are, in other words, most characteristic of cells that are highly specialized and undergo irreversible changes in their development (Bailey, 1938). However, cells with active, living protoplasts, such as the xylem ray and xylem parenchyma cells, also may have secondary walls; on the other hand, cells definitely specialized as mechanical (sclerenchyma) elements may long retain their protoplasts (see chapter 10). Information is meager on the ability of protoplasts to reduce the thickness of the secondary wall or to modify its chemistry, after the cell has completed its development. Delignification and dissolution of secondary walls under normal and pathological conditions have been reported in the literature (Bloch, 1941; cf. also Foster, 1949, p. 99), but the accuracy of some of the observations has been questioned (Jaeger, 1928).

Pits

Secondary cell walls are commonly characterized by the presence of depressions or cavities varying in depth, expanse, and detailed structure. Such cavities are termed *pits*. Primary walls also may have conspicuous depressions. However, because of the differences in structure and formation of primary and secondary walls the recesses in the two wall categories differ in their development and structure. According to the wood anatomists, therefore, the cavities in the secondary walls and the depressions in the primary walls should not be called by the same name. Only the secondary walls have *pits*, whereas the primary walls have *primary pit fields* (Committee on Nomenclature, 1933). Thus, according to this terminology, the meristematic cells and those of their derivatives that form no secondary walls have primary pit fields (fig. 3.3, *D*); cells with secondary walls have pits (fig. 3.3, *A*, *B*).

The primary pit fields of a meristematic cell may be so deeply depressed and so numerous that the wall appears beaded in sectional views. During the differentiation of cells having only primary walls (e.g., some types of parenchyma cells) the primary pit fields may be but slightly modified. In contrast, in certain specialized cells with primary walls (e.g., sieve elements of the phloem) the primary pit fields are considerably modified as the cell matures. In primary pit fields, whether modified more or less during cell differentiation, the primary wall is relatively thin but continuous across the pit area.

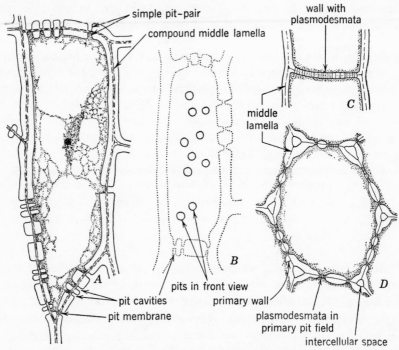

Fig. 3.3. Primary pit fields, simple pits, and plasmodesmata. *A* and *B*, ray cells, with secondary walls (left white in drawing), from a radial section of apple wood showing simple pits and pit-pairs in sectional and face (or front) views. *C* and *D*, parenchyma cells, without secondary walls, from tobacco stem showing distribution of plasmodesmata: dispersed throughout the wall in *C* and restricted to primary pit fields in *D*. (*A*, *B*, ×865; *C*, ×420; *D*, ×325; adapted from Livingston, 1935.)

Furthermore, while the cell is alive, the primary pit fields show concentrations of plasmodesmata (fig. 3.3, *D*).

The distinguishing feature of a pit is that the secondary wall layers are completely interrupted at the pit; that is, the primary wall is not covered by secondary layers in the pit region (fig. 3.3, *A*). Pits may be formed over primary pit fields, one or more pit over one field. Such primary pit fields may remain in evidence after the development of the secondary wall, or they may be obscured when, during the extension growth of the cell, the primary wall is reduced in thickness (Kerr and Bailey, 1934). Pits arise also over primary wall parts that bear no primary pit fields, and, inversely, some primary pit fields are completely covered by secondary wall layers (information by Professor I. W. Bailey). Thus, there is no absolute interdependence between the position of the primary pit fields in the primary wall and the development of pits in the secondary wall.

The distinction between pits and primary pit fields has a sound morphological basis, but frequently primary and secondary walls cannot be distinguished with ordinary microscopic observation. If an uncertainty exists regarding the exact nature of a wall, neither term, pit or primary pit field, may be applied without classifying the wall by implication. A substitute term that would include pits and primary pit fields, however, is not available in the literature. In this book the distinction between pits and primary pit fields is maintained whenever the nature of the wall is known. If this information is not available but the wall is thick and bears clearly circumscribed cavities, these cavities are termed pits. The adjective *pitted* is applied here either to secondary walls having pits or to primary walls with primary pit fields.

It is customary to include in the definition of the pit in a secondary wall not only the cavity but also the part of the primary wall that occurs at the bottom of the cavity (Committee on Nomenclature, 1933). Thus, fundamentally, a pit consists of a *pit cavity* and a *pit membrane* (or *pit-closing* membrane). The pit cavity is open internally to the lumen of the cell and is closed by the pit membrane along the line of junction of two cells (figs. 3.2 and 3.3, *A*).

Two principal types of pits are recognized in cells with secondary walls: *simple pits* and *bordered pits*. The most fundamental difference between the two kinds of pits is that in the bordered pit the secondary wall arches over the pit cavity—this part of the wall constitutes the border—and narrows down its opening to the lumen of the cell (fig. 3.4; plate 7); in the simple pit no such overarching occurs (figs. 3.2 and 3.3, *A*).

A pit in a wall of a given cell usually occurs opposite a complementary pit in the wall of an adjacent cell; that is, two pits are combined into a paired structure, the *pit-pair* (figs. 3.2, 3.3, *A*, 3.4). The pit membrane is common to both pits of a pair and consists of two primary walls and a lamella of intercellular substance (fig. 3.4). Two bordered pits make up a *bordered pit-pair* (fig. 3.4; plate 7); two simple pits, a *simple pit-pair* (figs. 3.2 and 3.3, *A*). A bordered pit may be complemented by a simple pit, the two constituting a *half-bordered pit-pair* (plate 9). A pit may have no complementary structure, as, for example, when it occurs opposite an intercellular space. Such a structure is called a *blind pit*. Sometimes two or

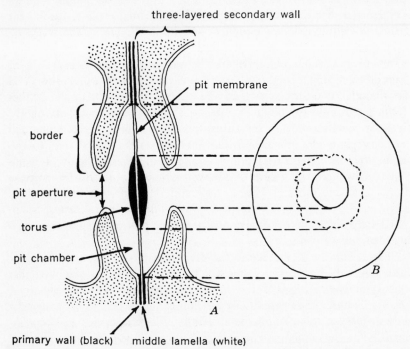

Fig. 3.4. Diagrams of bordered pit-pairs of *Pinus* seen in sectional (*A*) and face (*B*) views. The wall details in *A* are represented according to the concept of Kerr and Bailey (1934). The pit membrane consists of two primary walls and the intercellular lamella but is thinner than the same triple structure in the unpitted part of the wall. The torus is formed by thickenings of the primary wall. *B* shows that in face view the outline of the torus is uneven. Note that the outer and inner layers of the secondary wall are connected into a rim about the pit aperture.

more small pits are combined with one pit in the opposite wall, a combination that has been named *unilaterally compound pitting*.

Simple pits occur in certain parenchyma cells (fig. 3.3, *A*, *B*; plate 6, *B*), in phloem fibers, and in sclereids. In a simple pit the cavity may be uniform in width, or it may be slightly wider or slightly narrower toward the lumen of the cell. If it narrows down toward the lumen, the simple pit intergrades with the bordered pit in its structure. The simple pits of thin walls are shallow. In thick walls the cavity of a simple pit may have the form of a canal passing from the lumen of the cell toward the pit membrane (fig. 3.2). A cavity that appears as a single structure at its opening to the lumen of the cell may break up into two or more cavities deeper in the wall and give the impression of a branched canal (fig. 3.2, *A*). Such pits are called *ramiform pits* (that is, pits shaped like branches, from the Latin *ramus*, branch). These pits develop by fusion of two or more canal-like cavities, of as many pits, into one cavity. This fusion results from the decrease in the circumference of the successive wall layers as the lumen gradually becomes reduced during the centripetal growth of the wall.

Bordered pits are more complex and more variable in structure than simple pits. They occur mainly in the water-conducting and mechanical cells of the xylem, such as vessel elements, tracheids, and various fibers, but may be found in some fibers and sclereids outside the xylem also. All these elements are highly specialized cell types that commonly undergo irreversible changes during their development.

The part of the cavity enclosed by the overarching secondary wall, the *pit border*, is called the *pit chamber*, and the opening in the border is the *pit aperture* (fig. 3.4). The pit aperture may be circular, lenticular, or linear (figs. 3.4–3.6). The shape of the aperture may agree with the outline of the pit chamber, or it may not. Vessel elements in the angiosperms often have oval bordered pits with oval apertures (fig. 3.6, *B*). Some tracheary cells of ferns have transversely much-elongated bordered pits with linear apertures (see chapter 11). In the bordered pits of the gymnosperms, circular, oval, or linear apertures may be associated with pit chambers and borders circular in outline (figs. 3.4 and 3.5).

If the secondary wall and the border are relatively thick, the border divides the cavity into the *pit chamber*, the space between the pit membrane and the overarching border, and the *pit canal*, the passage from the cell lumen into the pit chamber (fig. 3.5). Such a canal has an *outer aperture* opening into the pit chamber and an *inner aperture* facing the cell lumen. The two apertures are commonly unlike in shape and size: the inner is rather large lenticular or linear, the outer small and circular. The thicker the cell wall, the smaller and thicker is the border, the smaller the pit chamber, and the longer and narrower the inner pit aperture. With the increase in wall thickness, the inner aperture may become so long in one direction that it may reach laterally the limits of the pit cham-

ber and even surpass these (fig. 3.5). If the inner aperture is relatively large and linear or lenticular in outline and the outer is small
and circular, the pit canal has the shape of a flattened funnel (Eames
and MacDaniels, 1947, p. 47). The circular pit apertures in a bordered pit-pair appear exactly opposite each other. In a bordered
pit-pair with elongated inner pit apertures the apertures may cross
each other symetrically (fig. 3.5, *A*), or they may coincide in orientation.

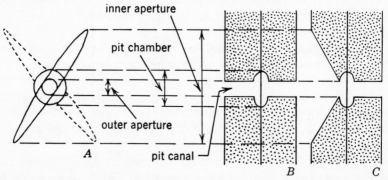

Fig. 3.5. Diagrams of bordered pit-pairs with extended pit apertures, flattened
canals, reduced borders, and small pit cavities. Such pits occur in thick-walled
tracheids and fiber tracheids of conifer wood. *A*, face view of pit-pair showing
the extension of the pit apertures beyond the limits of the pit chamber (or border),
the crossed arrangement of the apertures of the two pits of the pair, and the
contrast in the shape and size of the inner and outer apertures. *B*, sectional view
exposing the pit canal along its narrow diameter. *C*, sectional view exposing the
pit·canal along its wide diameter. The diagrams of *A* and *C* together show that
the canal has the shape of a flattened funnel, with the wide opening representing
the inner aperture, the narrow opening, the outer aperture.

The bordered pit-pairs of conifer tracheids are particularly elaborate in their structural details (fig. 3.4; plates 7 and 8). In the large,
relatively thin-walled tracheids of the early wood, these pit-pairs,
as seen in face views, have large circular or oval borders with conspicuous lenticular or circular apertures. The pit chambers are also
correspondingly large, with the pit canals practically absent. The
pit membrane has a thickening of primary nature, the *torus*, which
is somewhat larger in diameter than the pit apertures. The pit
membrane is flexible, and under certain conditions the torus occurs
in a lateral position, appressed to one or the other pit aperture of
the pit-pair (plate 7, *C–F*). The movements of the pit membranes
and the changes in the position of the torus are reportedly influenced
by pressure relations within the tracheids. When the torus occurs

in median position (plate 7, *B*), water passing through the bordered pit-pair presumably moves through the torus-free portion of the pit membrane, which appears to have pores (Bailey, 1916; Frenzel, 1929). If the torus is in lateral position, the movement of the water through the pit-pair is restricted. In addition to the torus, the pit membranes may bear other thickenings, some forming radial patterns (plate 7, *A*; Bannan, 1941). The torus is particularly characteristic of the bordered pits in the Gnetales, *Ginkgo*, and the Coniferales (with certain exceptions). It occurs only rarely in the angiosperms and has been described in the Ophioglossaceae (Wright, 1920).

In certain dicotyledons the pits of vessels develop minute outgrowths from the free surface of the secondary wall of the borders and give the pits a sieve-like appearance. The processes are highly refractive, vary in number, shape, and size, and occur not only in the pit chambers but also on the inner surface of the secondary wall of vessels. In half-bordered pit-pairs they occur only in the bordered member of the pair. Bordered pits with such processes have been named *vestured pits* (Bailey, 1933).

The pits are variously arranged in different cells, and they are not spaced uniformly, even in a single cell. Moreover, they vary in structure within one cell. The distribution and structure of the pits within a cell depend much on the type of cells to which it is joined in a tissue. Simple pits may occur in all walls of a given cell or only in certain ones. A tracheary cell may have no pits in parts of walls joined to a fiber, large prominently bordered pits where it is connected to another tracheary cell, and much reduced borders where it is joined to a parenchyma cell. The pit-pairs between two pine tracheids have well-differentiated tori, but in the half-bordered pit-pairs which occur between tracheids and the parenchymatous members of the xylem tori are usually absent.

Pits may form definite patterns that have special names (Committee on Nomenclature, 1933; Record, 1947). The bordered pits in tracheary cells show three main types of arrangement: scalariform, opposite, and alternate. If the pits are elongated or linear and form ladder-like series (fig. 3.6, *A*), the arrangement is called *scalariform pitting* (from the Latin *scalaris*, pertaining to a ladder). Pits arranged in horizontal pairs or short horizontal rows characterize *opposite pitting* (fig. 3.6, *B*). If such pits are crowded, their borders assume rectangular outlines in face view. When the pits occur in diagonal rows, the arrangement is *alternate pitting* (fig. 3.6, *C*), and crowding gives the borders hexagonal outlines in face view. Small

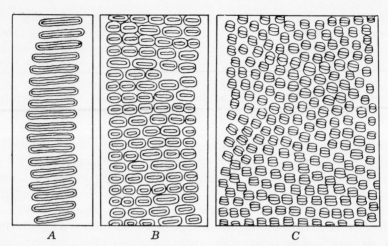

FIG. 3.6. Arrangement of bordered pits in vessel walls of angiosperms seen in face view. *A*, scalariform in *Magnolia;* *B*, opposite in *Liriodendron;* *C*, alternate in *Salix*. (All, ×375. Drawn from photomicrographs in S. J. Record, *Identification of the Timbers of Temperate North America*, John Wiley & Sons, 1947.)

simple pits are often aggregated in clusters. Such an arrangement is called *sieve pitting*.

Plasmodesmata

With special techniques it is possible to demonstrate in many living plant tissues strand-like structures extending from the protoplasts into the cell walls (fig. 3.3, *C*, *D*; plate 6, *C–E*). These structures are commonly interpreted as cytoplasmic threads, the *plasmodesmata* (from the Greek *desmos*, strand), interconnecting the living protoplasts of the plant body into an organic whole. The name plasmodesmata (singular *plasmodesma*), dates back to Strasburger (1901), but there is yet no agreement on the proper use of the word (Note, 1941). The interpretation of structure and morphologic nature of plasmodesmata is likewise a matter of disagreement (Meeuse, 1941).

Some workers are uncertain that the strands are continuous from one cell to the other (Livingston and Bailey, 1946; Schumacher, 1942). Others deny their cytoplasmic nature, first, because wall markings and certain artifacts developing during the treatment of the sections resemble plasmodesmata and, second, because the demonstration of plasmodesmata usually requires special techniques involving such drastic treatment as swelling of the walls by means of sulphuric acid. There is, however, some evidence that plasmodesmata might be cytoplasmic strands: these structures occur only in living cells; they and the cytoplasm have an affinity for the same dyes; they show a positive test for oxidases; and, when the protoplast is plasmolyzed, it withdraws from the wall except where it is connected by plasmodesmata (Meeuse, 1941; Sharp, 1943). The report that plasmodesmata have been recognized in the living cambium and ray cells of certain gymnosperms. (Livingston and Bailey, 1946) gives the best support to their interpretation as cytoplasmic structures.

Plasmodesmata have been seen in red algae, hepatics, mosses, vascular cryptogams, gymnosperms, and angiosperms (Meeuse, 1941). When a given plant is thoroughly investigated for their presence, they are found throughout all living tissues, including the meristematic (Livingston, 1935). Plasmodesmata either occur in groups or are distributed throughout a wall (fig. 3.3, C, D; plate 6, C–E). When they are grouped, they are frequently localized in the primary pit fields. In fact, the common concept is that all primary pit fields of living cells are traversed by plasmodesmata. They have been definitely seen in the primary pit fields of the cambial walls (Kerr and Bailey, 1934; Livingston and Bailey, 1946). The relation of the plasmodesmata to primary pit fields is characteristic: in two adjoining cells cytoplasmic processes extend into the cavities of a pair of pit fields, and the thin wall of the pit field is traversed by very fine threads connecting the two small masses of cytoplasm filling the depressions of the pit fields (fig. 3.3, D). It seems that these extensions of cytoplasm into the depressions of the pit fields are sometimes mistaken for plasmodesmata themselves, but they are obviously much larger than plasmodesmata, whose diameters lie within the range of a few tenths of a micron (Livingston, 1935; Livingston and Bailey, 1946; Roelofsen and Houwink, 1951).

Counts of the numbers of plasmodesmata in various cells are available for the tobacco plant (Livingston, 1935). For example, the end walls (walls perpendicular to the vertical axis of the stem) in the outer cortex showed 21 to 24 threads per 100 square microns, uniformly distributed; in the side walls (walls parallel to the vertical axis of the stem) 7 to 9 threads per 100 square microns, arranged in groups. Particularly abundant plasmodesmata were found in the epidermal cells. The anticlinal walls, more or less perpendicular to the vertical axis of the organ (leaf or stem), had about 31 to 36 strands per 100 square microns; the anticlinal walls, parallel to the vertical axis of the organ, 18 to 25 strands per 100 square microns.

The threads were sparse in the inner periclinal walls, and none were seen in the outer walls.

The origin of plasmodesmata is uncertain. It has been suggested that young, growing walls are permeated with cytoplasm which later withdraws except in localized areas where it then constitutes the plasmodesmata. There is also a possibility that plasmodesmata are formed anew in older walls, since they are known to arise where cells form new contacts as during cellular readjustment in tissue differentiation, in graft unions, and in junctions of tyloses (p. 237) entering vessels from different parenchyma cells (Meeuse, 1941; Sharp, 1934).

Plasmodesmata are thought to be concerned with material transport and conduction of stimuli. Some workers assert that plasmodesmata are present in the outer epidermal walls and that such distribution not only suggests their connection with sensitive reactions of plants but also emphasizes the close relation between protoplast and wall (Schumacher, 1942). Plasmodesmata are also regarded as channels permitting the movement of viruses from cell to cell, but direct proof of this assumption is lacking (Esau, 1948). The presence of plasmodesmata between the haustoria-like structures of such parasites as *Viscum, Cuscuta,* and *Orobanche* and the cells of their host plants is also thought to be related to food and virus movement (Esau, 1948).

CHEMISTRY OF WALLS

The most common compound in plant cell walls is the carbohydrate cellulose. This substance received its name because it is the basic constituent of almost all cell walls in vascular plants (Ott, 1943). It is associated with various substances, most often with other compound carbohydrates, and many walls, particularly those of woody tissues, are impregnated with lignin. The common carbohydrate constituents of the cell walls other than cellulose are noncellulosic polysaccharides, hemicelluloses, and pectic compounds (Bonner, 1950). The fatty compounds, cutin, suberin, and waxes, occur in varying amounts in the walls of many types of cells, especially abundantly in those that are located on the periphery of the plant body. Various other organic compounds and mineral substances may be present, but they rarely play an essential part in wall structure. Water is a common constituent of cell walls and often is found in considerable amounts (Crafts et al., 1949). Part of it occurs in microcapillaries and is relatively free; the remainder is associated with hydrophilic substances.

Cellulose is a relatively hydrophilic crystalline compound having the general empirical formula $(C_6H_{10}O_5)_n$. As a polysaccharide hexosan it is closely related to starch (see chapter 2), and its molecules are chain- or ribbon-like structures with 100 or more of the glucose residues held together by oxygen bridges (fig. 3.7, *E* and *F*). The length of individual chains appears to vary greatly. Among the other wall substances the *noncellulosic polysaccharides*, the mannans, the galactans, the xylans, and the arabans, are most closely allied to cellulose (Bonner, 1950).

Pectic substances are derivatives of polygalacturonic acid and occur in three general types, protopectin, pectin, and pectic acid (Bonner, 1936, 1946, 1950). *Hemicelluloses* have certain constituents in common with the pectic compounds, but the two groups of substances are distinguishable by their solubilities (Bonner, 1950). Pectic compounds are amorphous colloidal substances, plastic and highly hydrophilic. The latter property suggests a possible function of maintaining a state of high hydration in the young walls. Because of the outstanding ability of pectin to jell, it is an important industrial product (Woodmansee, 1948). As was mentioned previously, pectic compounds not only constitute the intercellular substance that binds together the walls of individual cells but also occur associated with cellulose in the other wall layers, notably the primary.

Gums and *mucilages* should also be mentioned among the compound carbohydrates of the cell walls. These substances are related to the pectic compounds, and both have the property of swelling in water (Bonner, 1950). Gums appear in plants mainly as a result of physiological or pathological disturbances that induce a breakdown of walls and cell contents (gummosis or gummous degeneration). The mucilages occur in some gelatinous or mucilaginous types of cell walls. Such walls are common in the outer cell layers of plant bodies of many aquatic species and in seed coats (Meyer and Anderson, 1939).

Lignin, one of the most important wall substances, has been studied for over one hundred years, but nevertheless its chemistry is known imperfectly (Brauns, 1948; Gortner and Gortner, 1949). It is an organic compound of high carbon content, distinct from the carbohydrates. Lignin may be present in all three wall layers—the middle lamella, the primary wall, and the secondary wall. The impregnation with lignin usually starts in the intercellular lamella and then spreads centripetally through the primary and secondary walls (Kerr and Bailey, 1934). In woody tissues the middle lamella and the primary wall are more strongly lignified than the secondary wall (Anderson, 1935).

Mineral substances like silica and calcium carbonate, and diverse organic compounds like tannins, resins, fatty substances, volatile oils, and acids, as well as crystalline pigments, may impregnate walls. Silica is a common component of walls of grasses and horsetails (Bonner, 1950). Organic compounds are frequently deposited in the xylem walls when this tissue changes from sapwood into heartwood (Eames and MacDaniels, 1947; Wise, 1944).

The most important fatty substances are *cutin, suberin,* and *waxes.* Waxes melt readily and are easily extracted by fat solvents, whereas cutin and suberin are not meltable and show considerable insolubility in fat solvents (Priestley, 1943). Suberin and cutin are closely related, highly polymerized compounds consisting of fatty acids (Frey-Wyssling, 1935). Suberin occurs in association with the cellulose in cork cells of the periderm. Cutin forms a continuous layer—the cuticle—on the surface of the epidermis of all aerial parts (see chapter 7). Cutin also occurs with the cellulose in the outer walls of the epidermis. These walls often show gradations from pure cellulose on the inside through layers having varying amounts of pectic compounds and fatty substances to an outermost layer of cuticle, free of cellulose and probably also without pectic compounds (Priestley, 1943). The phenomena of impregnation of walls with suberin and cutin are referred to as *suberization* and *cutinization,* respectively, and the formation of cuticle as *cuticularization.* Waxes are associated with suberin and cutin and may appear on the surface of the cuticle in various forms (see chapter 7). Such deposition of wax is responsible for the glaucus condition (bloom) of many fruits, leaves, and stems (Priestley, 1943).

Because of their chemical nature and their peripheral position in the plant body, the fatty wall substances are considered to be effective in reducing transpiration and in protecting the foliage from leaching effects of rain. The relatively hard, varnish-like cuticle, specifically, may protect against penetration of living tissues by potential parasites and against mechanical injuries (Priestley, 1943).

Fatty materials are not restricted to the peripheral layers of the plant body. Suberin occurs in the specialized layers like the endodermis and the exodermis (see chapter 17). Inner cuticles develop in seeds during the transformation of the integuments into seed coats (see chapter 20). Fatty substances, identified as cutin (Häusermann, 1944; Priestley, 1943) and as suberin (Scott, 1948) occur as a coating on the mesophyll cell walls facing the internal air-space system of the leaf.

MICROSCOPIC AND SUBMICROSCOPIC STRUCTURE

The various chemical substances of cell walls combine physically and chemically with each other. Therefore, to recognize the individual compounds and their relations to each other a variety of physical and chemical methods must be employed (Anderson, 1935; Kerr and Bailey, 1934). Investigators combine observations on differential staining; differential solubilities; coarse and fine structural variations; reaction to polarized and fluorescent light, to X-rays, and to dark-field illumination; refractive indices; and composition of ash (Anderson, 1935). Lately, the electron miscroscope has been added as a tool for the study of cell walls (Frey-Wyssling, 1948). By the various techniques mentioned, much has been learned about the fine structural details of cell walls, particularly of secondary walls, and a clearer understanding of their properties has been gained.

Micellar and Intermicellar Systems

The structural organization of cell walls is based on cellulose. The fundamental units of the system are the chain-like cellulose molecules of variable length. These chains are not dispersed at random but occur in aggregates, usually referred to as *micelles*. The chain molecules have a parallel arrangement in a micelle, and the glucose residues within a chain are spaced at uniform distances from each other. Thus a bundle of cellulose molecules, the micelle, is comparable to a crystal in that its units are arranged symmetrically.

Formerly the cellulose micelles were thought to be individual units arranged in an orderly manner in an intermicellar material. This concept (and the term *micelle*) was introduced by Nägeli in the nineteenth century (Frey-Wyssling, 1936). The prevalent modern view is that the bundles of cellulose molecules are interconnected by means of the longer chain molecules extending beyond the limits of the bundles and form a porous coherent system, the *micellar system*, interpenetrated by an equally coherent *intermicellar system* in which various wall substances other than the cellulose are present (fig. 3.7, *D*; Bailey, 1940; Frey-Wyssling, 1948; Meyer and Anderson, the micelle are distributed *anisotropically*, that is, arranged dissimilarly in different directions. This anisotropy is expressed in certain properties of cellulose. When, for example, cellulose is made to swell, it expands much more strongly in the direction at right angles to the long axis of the micelles than in planes parallel to this axis (Bailey, 1940); or, when light is passed through cellulose, the light is variously affected, depending on the direction from which it strikes the micelles. In other words, cellulose shows swelling anisotropy and optical anisotropy.

Optically anisotropic substances are *doubly refractive* or *birefringent*. These terms refer to the manner in which the light entering the anisotropic material is deflected (refracted) from its original course. When a beam of light strikes such material obliquely, the part of the beam that enters it (the other part is reflected) is refracted not as a single beam but as two beams deflected to different degrees. When the angle formed by the two refracted beams is large, the material is said to be strongly birefringent. The birefringence of a substance is readily revealed by its effect upon polarized light. As is well known, such light is interpreted as vibrating in one plane only: it is plane polarized light. A device for using polarized light incorporates two crystalline prisms, or polaroids, one of which, the polarizer, produces polarized light, and the other, the analyzer, aids the observer to determine whether the object illuminated by the light from the polarizer has any effect upon this light (fig. 3.8). If in the absence of any object the analyzer is rotated 90 degrees with respect to the polarizer, no light will pass through the system. The two prisms are said to be crossed.

An isotropic object has no effect upon polarized light, and, therefore, when it is inserted between the crossed prisms, the field seen through the microscope remains dark (middle lamellae in plate 5, B). If a doubly refractive substance is substituted for the isotropic specimen, in certain orientations it will so affect the incident light that the light will pass the analyzer and the object will appear bright (primary walls and parts of secondary walls in plate 5, B).

As was mentioned previously, birefringent material diffracts one beam of light as two. Both of these are polarized in mutually perpendicular planes. If the doubly refractive material placed between the crossed elements of a polarizing system is so oriented that neither of its planes of polarization coincides with the plane of polarization of the polarizer, the ray coming from the polarizer is resolved into two mutually perpendicular components. The planes of these com-

(see chapter 20). Fatty substances, identified as cutin (Häusermann, 1944; Priestley, 1943) and as suberin (Scott, 1948) occur as a coating on the mesophyll cell walls facing the internal air-space system of the leaf.

MICROSCOPIC AND SUBMICROSCOPIC STRUCTURE

The various chemical substances of cell walls combine physically and chemically with each other. Therefore, to recognize the individual compounds and their relations to each other a variety of physical and chemical methods must be employed (Anderson, 1935; Kerr and Bailey, 1934). Investigators combine observations on differential staining; differential solubilities; coarse and fine structural variations; reaction to polarized and fluorescent light, to X-rays, and to dark-field illumination; refractive indices; and composition of ash (Anderson, 1935). Lately, the electron miscroscope has been added as a tool for the study of cell walls (Frey-Wyssling, 1948). By the various techniques mentioned, much has been learned about the fine structural details of cell walls, particularly of secondary walls, and a clearer understanding of their properties has been gained.

Micellar and Intermicellar Systems

The structural organization of cell walls is based on cellulose. The fundamental units of the system are the chain-like cellulose molecules of variable length. These chains are not dispersed at random but occur in aggregates, usually referred to as *micelles*. The chain molecules have a parallel arrangement in a micelle, and the glucose residues within a chain are spaced at uniform distances from each other. Thus a bundle of cellulose molecules, the micelle, is comparable to a crystal in that its units are arranged symmetrically.

Formerly the cellulose micelles were thought to be individual units arranged in an orderly manner in an intermicellar material. This concept (and the term *micelle*) was introduced by Nägeli in the nineteenth century (Frey-Wyssling, 1936). The prevalent modern view is that the bundles of cellulose molecules are interconnected by means of the longer chain molecules extending beyond the limits of the bundles and form a porous coherent system, the *micellar system*, interpenetrated by an equally coherent *intermicellar system* in which various wall substances other than the cellulose are present (fig. 3.7, *D*; Bailey, 1940; Frey-Wyssling, 1948; Meyer and Anderson,

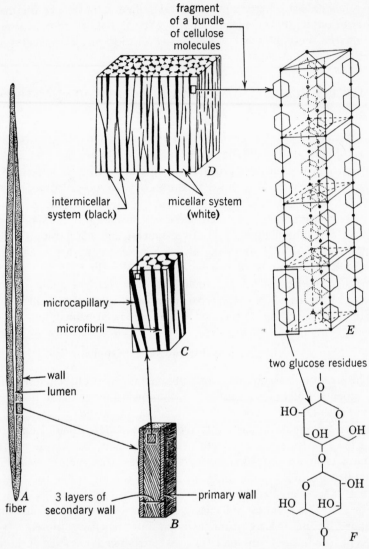

FIG. 3.7. Diagrams illustrating the common concept of microscopic and sub-microscopic structure of secondary cellulose wall. A fragment (*B*) of a fiber (*A*) shows upon magnification the presence of a primary wall and a three-layered secondary wall. A fragment of the thick central layer of the secondary wall reveals upon further magnification (*C*) two continuous systems, one consisting of microfibrils of cellulose (white in the drawing), the other of microcapillaries (black in the drawing) containing various noncellulosic wall constituents. The microfibrils grade down to smaller and smaller units and are in themselves complex in structure so that in the field beyond the range of ordinary microscopes (submicroscopic field) they may be resolved into a system of finest microfibrils—

1939). In view of this concept the old term micelle (sometimes interchanged with *crystallite*), referring to a particle with definite boundaries, is obsolete. The term nevertheless persists in the literature but in a modified form. The micelles of the micellar system represent not units with a closed surface but the more voluminous parts of a framework where cellulose molecules of indeterminate length combine into crystalline lattices. Outside the latticed areas the bars of the framework can become finer and finer until they are reduced to molecular dimensions, so that in places the framework is of the thickness of one chain of cellulose.

Evidence of Crystalline Nature of Cellulose

The orderly arrangement of the molecular units of cellulose determining its crystalline properties has been revealed by means of X-ray studies (Bragg and Bragg, 1934; Frey-Wyssling, 1935; Sponsler, 1933). The wave lengths of the X-rays are smaller than the dimensions of cellulose molecules, and, therefore, when a beam of X-rays is allowed to impinge on a block of cellulose, a large part of the beam goes through, but part of the rays strike the atoms and groups of atoms and are scattered, or *diffracted*. The diffracted waves of light appear as reflections of the incident waves, and, when the X-ray beam strikes the crystalline material at a proper angle, the scattered waves from all points reinforce each other, and a strong beam is diffracted. For convenience, the diffracted beams are often referred to as reflections. They are reflections of the X-rays from the atoms and groups of atoms, and when caught on a photographic plate they leave a diffraction pattern. By obtaining such diffraction patterns from various sides of the same block of cellulose, one can determine the three-dimensional configuration of the molecular groups of cellulose. This configuration was found to be that of a space lattice (fig. 3.7, *E*).

Since the distances between the points on the cellulose space lattice vary in different planes, it may be said that the constituent parts of

the micellar system—interpenetrated by finest microporosities—the intermicellar system (*D*). The intermicellar system contains noncellulosic wall constituents, whereas the micellar system is composed of bundles of chain-like cellulose molecules (*E*). These bundles vary in thickness and grade down to the size of individual chain molecules. The bundles of cellulose chains, the micelles or crystallites, show an orderly arrangement of the glucose residues (*F*) that constitute the basic units of the cellulose chain molecules. (Based on Bailey, 1939, and Frey-Wyssling, 1935, 1948.)

the micelle are distributed *anisotropically*, that is, arranged dissimilarly in different directions. This anisotropy is expressed in certain properties of cellulose. When, for example, cellulose is made to swell, it expands much more strongly in the direction at right angles to the long axis of the micelles than in planes parallel to this axis (Bailey, 1940); or, when light is passed through cellulose, the light is variously affected, depending on the direction from which it strikes the micelles. In other words, cellulose shows swelling anisotropy and optical anisotropy.

Optically anisotropic substances are *doubly refractive* or *birefringent*. These terms refer to the manner in which the light entering the anisotropic material is deflected (refracted) from its original course. When a beam of light strikes such material obliquely, the part of the beam that enters it (the other part is reflected) is refracted not as a single beam but as two beams deflected to different degrees. When the angle formed by the two refracted beams is large, the material is said to be strongly birefringent. The birefringence of a substance is readily revealed by its effect upon polarized light. As is well known, such light is interpreted as vibrating in one plane only: it is plane polarized light. A device for using polarized light incorporates two crystalline prisms, or polaroids, one of which, the polarizer, produces polarized light, and the other, the analyzer, aids the observer to determine whether the object illuminated by the light from the polarizer has any effect upon this light (fig. 3.8). If in the absence of any object the analyzer is rotated 90 degrees with respect to the polarizer, no light will pass through the system. The two prisms are said to be crossed.

An isotropic object has no effect upon polarized light, and, therefore, when it is inserted between the crossed prisms, the field seen through the microscope remains dark (middle lamellae in plate 5, B). If a doubly refractive substance is substituted for the isotropic specimen, in certain orientations it will so affect the incident light that the light will pass the analyzer and the object will appear bright (primary walls and parts of secondary walls in plate 5, B).

As was mentioned previously, birefringent material diffracts one beam of light as two. Both of these are polarized in mutually perpendicular planes. If the doubly refractive material placed between the crossed elements of a polarizing system is so oriented that neither of its planes of polarization coincides with the plane of polarization of the polarizer, the ray coming from the polarizer is resolved into two mutually perpendicular components. The planes of these com-

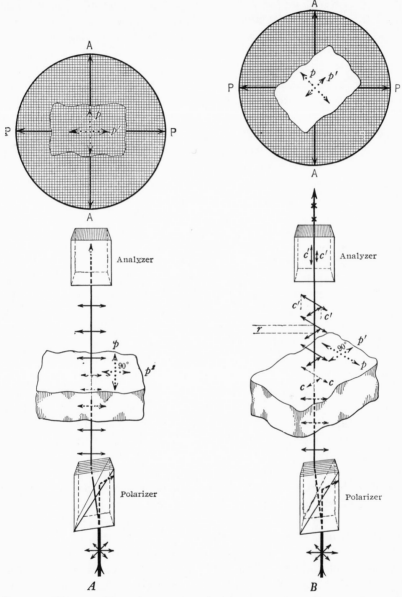

Fig. 3.8. Diagrams illustrating passage of light through an optically anisotropic substance placed between crossed prisms of a polarizing system. The substance is in the position of "extinction" in *A*, in the position of "brightness" in *B*. (From Chamot and Mason, *Handbook of Chemical Microscopy*, Vol. I, John Wiley & Sons, 1938.)

ponent rays are not exactly crossed with respect to the analyzer, and, therefore, both component vibrations are partially transmitted by the analyzer. The specimen appears bright on a dark background (fig. 3.8, *B*). When one or the other of the planes of polarization of the material is in alignment with the plane of polarization of the incident light, no light passes through the analyzer and the phenomenon of extinction is exhibited (fig. 3.8, *A*; central layer of secondary walls in plate 5, *B*). The material now does not reveal its anisotropy. In cellulose the brightest light (strongest birefringence) is seen when the light passes through it at right angles to the long axis of the molecular chains. Parallel to this position cellulose does not affect the light and remains dark between crossed prisms (Chamot and Mason, 1938; Gage, 1941; Schmitt, 1939).

Microfibrillar and Microcapillary Structure

The interpretation of cellulose of plant cell walls as a combination of two interpenetrating systems, the micellar framework and the intermicellar substance, refers only to the realm of the submicroscopic. The students of cell walls have made the striking observation that the structure visible with ordinary microscopy appears like an enlarged image of the postulated submicroscopic structure. The walls contain a porous matrix of cellulose consisting of very fine, coalesced fibrils, the *microfibrils,* and an interfibrillar system of *microcapillaries* containing various noncellulosic wall constituents (Bailey, 1939, 1940). Like the micelles in the submicroscopic field, the microfibrils of the microscopic realm are not discrete entities but represent the elongated parts of a continuous porous matrix.

In view of the similarity between the microscopic structure of cellulose walls and the postulated ultramicroscopic structure, the question has been raised as to what intervenes between the units of the micellar and the microfibrillar systems. Do the two systems belong to two distinct size classes, or are they connected by units of intermediate sizes? In other words, are the microfibrils composed directly of anastomosing micelles, or are they divided into still finer fibrils, which ultimately grade down to the dimensions of the micellar framework? Similarly, are there two size classes of porosities, or are the microcapillaries and the intermicellar spaces connected by interstices of intermediate or transitional dimensions (Bailey, 1939)? The second alternative, that there is a gradual transition of microscopic units, measuring 250 Å (Ångstrom unit, 0.0001 micron) and less, to submicroscopic micelles, measuring 60 Å and less, is now being supported by evidence obtained by the use of the electron microscope (plates 10 and 11, *D*; Frey-Wyssling, 1950; Frey-Wyssling and Mühlethaler, 1947; Kinsinger and Hock, 1948). Within the microfibrils the micelles and consequently also the chain molecules occur approximately parallel to the long axis of the fibrils (Bailey, 1939, 1940). Thus the microscopically visible microfibrillar arrangements serve as an indication of the orientation of the cellulose chains in the plant cell wall.

The microcapillaries within the cellulose framework may contain liquids, lignin, waxes, cutin, suberin, hemicelluloses, pectic substances, other less common organic compounds, and even crystals and silica (Bailey, 1940). A striking demonstration of the relation between the microfibrillar and microcapillary systems can be made on heavily lignified secondary walls. In such walls it is possible to remove the lignin and leave a coherent matrix of cellulose; and, conversely, it is possible to remove the cellulose and leave a coherent matrix of lignin. The two matrices appear like positive and negative images of the original structural pattern (Bailey, 1940; Bailey and Kerr, 1937; Freudenberg, 1932).

Certain investigators consider that in secondary walls cellulose does not form a continuous matrix but appears as discrete particles cemented by isotropic material (e.g., Farr, 1947; Wergin, 1943). This view conflicts with many data on secondary wall structure (Bailey, 1938, 1939, 1940) and particularly with the picture of this structure obtained by means of the electron microscope (Frey-Wyssling and Mühlethaler, 1947). Views are divided on the structure of the primary wall also. Some workers interpret it as having a coherent system of cellulose (Frey-Wyssling and Mühlethaler, 1947; Mühlethaler, 1950); others visualize a dispersed phase of cellulose in a continuous phase of protopectin (Kerr, 1951).

Although the interstices of the cellulose matrix are filled with various substances, the cell walls are porous, as evidenced by the passage of substances through them. Studies of penetrability using organic compounds, basic and acid dyes, India ink, and colloidal gold have suggested the following values for different walls. The pores appear to be below 1 micron in cutinized walls of hairs, at least 1 micron in the intermicellar spaces of vessel walls, and about 500 micromicrons in the pit fields of *Sambucus* pith and in the pit membranes of bordered pits of *Pinus* tracheids (Frenzel, 1929).

Orientation of Microfibrils in the Wall

As was outlined on p. 56, the degree of birefringence of wall layers, which is revealed by the polarizing microscope, is determined by the orientation of molecular chains of cellulose with reference to the beam of incident light. Since the long axes of the molecular chains and those of the microfibrils are approximately parallel, the degree of birefringence can serve to determine the orientation of the microfibrils. In addition, the fibrillar orientation may be reliably studied by observing the microscopically visible striations and the orientation of the planes of hydrolysis caused by enzymatic activity of certain fungi (plate 11, *A*, *B*), or by inducing the formation of crystals in the elongated porosities of the cellulose matrix, where the crystals become oriented parallel to the fibrils and are microscopically visible (Bailey, 1940; Bailey and Kerr, 1935, 1937; Bailey and Vestal, 1937*a*, *b*).

These methods and others have furnished a large body of data that give a comprehensive picture of the structure of the crystalline cellulose in secondary walls. In general the patterns are highly variable. They vary in different woods, in wood from different parts of the tree, in different cells of the same tissue, in different layers of the same cell, and in different lamellae of the same layer (Bailey and Berkley, 1942).

In the three-layered walls of certain vessels, tracheids, and wood fibers the fibrillar orientations of the inner and outer layers vary between transverse and helical, the helices being of comparatively low pitch, and those of the central layer fluctuate between longitudinal and relatively steeply pitched helical (fig. 3.9; Bailey and Berkley, 1942; Berkley, 1948; Wardrop and Preston, 1947). Characteristic patterns occur about the large bordered pits of the early wood tracheids (Bailey and Vestal, 1937*a*). In the cotton fiber the bulk of the secondary wall consists of microfibrils oriented at an angle of 45 degrees and less with respect to the longitudinal axis of the fiber (Hock, 1942; Kerr, 1946). In the consecutive lamellae of the flax fiber the helices are wound in opposite directions (Anderson, 1927). In tracheary cells with annular and scalariform secondary thickenings the crystalline regions of these thickenings have a horizontal, ring-like orientation (Frey-Wyssling, 1948). Although the pitch of the helices of microfibrils varies in the secondary walls of different cells and

among the layers of the same wall, within a given layer the microfibrils are usually parallel to one another and always parallel to the
surface of the cell. The secondary walls may be said to have a
parallel texture (fig. 3.9; plate 11, *D*; Frey-Wyssling, 1950; Frey-
Wyssling et al., 1948).

Information on the microfibrillar structure of primary walls is
less abundant than that on the secondary walls. The earliest part

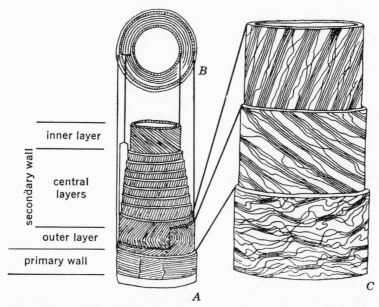

inner layer

central
layers

outer layer

primary wall

secondary wall

B

A

C

Fig. 3.9. Diagrams of wall structure in the cotton fiber. *A*, telescoped segment,
and *B*, transverse section, of fiber, showing the spatial relation of the various
layers and the orientation of microfibrils in these layers. *C*, enlarged diagram
showing the primary wall with its reticulate microfibrillar structure, the outer
layer of the secondary wall combining a reticulate and parallel orientation of
microfibrils, and the first central layer of the secondary wall with predominantly
parallel microfibrillar structure. (After Berkley, 1948.)

of a primary wall shows a scattered texture in electron micrographs,
with the microfibrils crisscrossing each other in a reticulate manner
(plate 10, *A*; Frey-Wyssling et al., 1948; Mühlethaler, 1950). In
the subsequent primary wall layers the microfibrils of a particular
layer are oriented parallel to one another, although the successive
layers may crisscross each other (plate 6, *A*).

The Coarse Patterns in Walls

The presence or absence of secondary walls, the relative thickness of primary and secondary walls, and the differentiation of the secondary wall into three or more layers cause the most conspicuous variations in the appearance of walls. In addition, the secondary walls, particularly the wide central layer of the three-layered types, show diverse patterns coarser than the microfibrillar network. In cells cut at right angles to their long axes the most common patterns are: concentric layering (fig. 3.9), radial and branching lamellations, and combinations of radial and concentric lamellations. Some of these arrangements of lamellae are determined by the distribution of the noncellulosic constituents of the walls, but many specific configurations result from variations in densities and porosities in the different parts of the cellulosic matrix. In many tracheary cells and xylem fibers the denser parts of walls have more numerous fibrils per unit volume, and these are more intimately coalesced than the fibrils of the more porous parts (Bailey, 1940; Bailey and Kerr, 1935, 1937). In the cotton fiber the concentric lamellation has been correlated with the alternation of day and night. Every 24 hours one compact and highly birefringent and one porous and weakly anisotropic lamella are formed. If the cotton fibers are grown under continuous illumination, they have no growth rings (Hock, 1942).

Sometimes the concentric layering is caused by actual discontinuities in the cellulose matrix. In the fibers of compression wood of some gymnosperms, in the gelatinous fibers of dicotyledons, and in certain sclereids and phloem fibers, layers of truly isotropic material divide layers of cellulose (Bailey, 1938; Bailey and Kerr, 1935). Some phloem fibers appear to have no cementing material between the concentric lamellae of cellulose, and the lamellae may be readily separated from one another (plate 24, *A*; Anderson, 1927). Tracheids in the compression wood of gymnosperms often develop a helically striate inner layer of secondary wall (plate 11, *C*; Record, 1947, p. 28).

PROPERTIES OF WALLS

Cell walls show varying degrees of *plasticity* (property of becoming permanently deformed when subjected to changes in shape or size), *elasticity* (property of recovery of the original size and shape after deformation), and *tensile strength* in relation to their chemical composition and their microscopic and submicroscopic structure. Plasticity of walls is well illustrated by their permanent extension in certain stages of growth of cells in volume (Heyn, 1940); elasticity, by the reversible changes in volume (30 per cent or more in mesophyll cells) in response to changes in turgor pressure (Meyer and Anderson, 1939, p. 68). Notable tensile strength is characteristic of mechanical cells, particularly of the extraxylary fibers of monocotyledons and dicotyledons.

Some of the conspicuous differences in optical and other physical properties of walls are correlated with the orientation of the micro-fibrils. Thus, for example, walls or wall layers in which the micro-fibrils are oriented parallel to the long axis of the cell do not ex-hibit their anisotropy in transverse sections and do not contract longitudinally; on the contrary, walls having the microfibrils oriented at right angles to the long axis of the cell are strongly birefringent in transverse sections and contract longitudinally on drying (Bailey, 1939).

Because of its abundance in cell walls cellulose has a major influ-ence upon their properties. Other substances add their properties or modify those imparted by the cellulose. Tensile strength is one of the remarkable characteristics of cellulose. Lignin, on the other hand, increases the resistance of walls to pressure and protects the cellulose fibrils from becoming creased (Frey-Wyssling, 1935).

FORMATION OF WALLS

Initiation of Wall during Cell Division

The process of somatic division of a protoplast into two daughter protoplasts may be separated into two stages: the division of the nucleus, or *mitosis* (also called karyokinesis, Sharp, 1934, p. 439), and the division of the extranuclear part of the protoplast, or *cytokinesis* (also called cell division). In cells having cell walls the new wall is formed during cytokinesis.

The divisions of the nucleus and the cell may follow each other so closely that mitosis and cytokinesis appear as one phenomenon; or the two may be separated in time. The ordinary somatic divisions, characterizing vegetative growth from the meristems, usually show a close correlation between nuclear and cellular divisions. In con-trast, the two phenomena are widely separated in the formation of pollen and endosperm in many angiosperms, and in the development of the female gametophyte and the proembryo in gymnosperms (Sharp, 1934, p. 110).

The partition between the new protoplasts, when first evident, is referred to as the *cell plate*. If cytokinesis follows the nuclear division immediately, the cell plate arises in the equatorial plane of a fibrous spindle, the *phragmoplast*, extending between the two groups of chromosomes that move apart during the anaphase of mitosis (plate 12, *A*; Küster, 1935, p. 571). As these two groups develop into the telophase nuclei, the phragmoplast widens out in the equatorial plane and assumes the shape of a barrel. When the cell plate appears in the median part of the equatorial plane of the phragmoplast, the fibers of the phragmoplast disappear in this position but remain evident at the margins, until the cell plate appears here too (plate 12, *B*, *C*).

If the diameter along which the cell is dividing is so short that the phragmoplast, after a slight widening, reaches the walls that are oriented perpendicularly to the plane of division, the phragmoplast appears to be connected to the two nuclei for the duration of cytokinesis. If, however, this diameter is longer than the original phragmoplast is wide, the phragmoplast extends laterally until it comes in contact with the cell walls, and during this extension it completely separates from the nuclei (plate 12, *E*, *F*). As seen from the side, such a phragmoplast appears as two groups of fibers, disconnected from the nuclei but connected with each other by the cell plate, which follows the phragmoplast in its lateral extension. In face views the phragmoplast has a somewhat varied appearance, depending on the shape and size of the dividing cells and also on the original position of the nucleus (plate 12, *E*, *F*, cell to the right; Bailey, 1920*b*; Goldstein, 1925; Sharp, 1934).

The progress of the phragmoplast and cell plate through the cell lumen is particularly striking in very long cells, for example, fusiform cambial cells, dividing longitudinally. The process of cell-plate formation in such cells is greatly extended in time and space and is clearly dissociated from the nuclear mitosis (Bailey, 1920*b*; see also chapter 6).

The exact nature of the fibers that form the phragmoplast and their relation to the cell plate are not known, but the phragmoplast and the mitotic spindle are not supposed to be identical (Becker, 1938; Sharp, 1943). The phragmoplastic fibers appearing at the margins of the cell plate are sometimes called kinoplasmasomes, a term reflecting the old concept of the existence of a special kind of active, fibrous cytoplasm, the kinoplasm (Bailey, 1920*b*; Sharp, 1934, p. 44).

The views of cell-plate formation have been misinterpreted by some workers, and this, in turn, has led to misconceptions regarding the numbers of nuclei in ordinary somatic cells. The erroneous reports have been reviewed and corrected by several investigators (Bailey, 1920*a*; Esau, 1938; Wareham, 1936).

Cytokinesis is not limited to meristematic cells with dense protoplasts. Some of the meristematic cells themselves are highly vacuolated, and, furthermore, enlarging and prominently vacuolated cells are known to divide actively during the growth of roots, shoots, leaves, and fruits of higher plants. The explanation of the progress of the phragmoplast through vacuolated cells is complicated by the fact that the new cell plate eventually occurs in the region formerly occupied by the vacuole. In some instances it has been observed that during the early prophase of the nuclear division, that is, long before the beginning of cytokinesis, a cytoplasmic plate, the *phragmosome*, is formed across the cell in the plane of cell division. It is derived from strands of parietal cytoplasm and thus forms a living medium in which the phragmoplast and the cell plate develop (fig. 3.10; Sinnott and Bloch, 1941).

If a cell plate is not formed immediately after the nuclear division, phragmoplasts may arise later. Sometimes no phragmoplast is formed; instead, the cell divides by a process called *furrowing*. Such division has been described in lower plants and in pollen and endosperm development in higher plants. It consists of the formation of cleavage furrows within the protoplast, starting at the existing walls and advancing inwardly until they meet and divide the protoplast into two or more cells.

Although cell-plate formation has been studied in living and fixed material (Becker, 1934, 1938), the origin and nature of this structure are still subjects of speculation (Frey-Wyssling, 1948). It seems well substantiated that substances in semi-fluid state accumulate in in the equatorial plane of the phragmoplast and cleave the protoplast in two (plate 12, *D*). The two new cytoplasmic surfaces become parts of the protoplasmic membranes of the two new cells. It is likely that pectic substances occur in the semifluid partition in the equatorial plane (Frey-Wyssling, 1948). These substances can be thought of as forming the new middle lamella. A deposition of cellulose on both sides of this middle lamella and externally to the new protoplasmic membranes would initiate the formation of the two primary wall layers of the two sister cells. Basically similar phenomena might be involved in cell division by furrowing.

Thus the partition that appears between the two sister protoplasts at cytokinesis undergoes different physical and chemical changes during the progress of cell division. There is no agreement regarding the stage of the process at which the visible partition should be

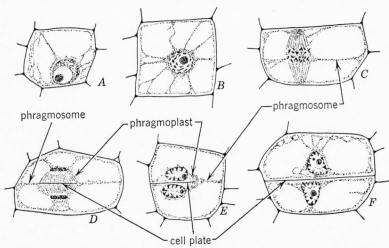

FIG. 3.10. Division of highly vacuolated cells. Drawn from section of young pith of *Ligustrum* and arranged to show the successive stages in the process. *A*, cell in a nondividing state. *B*, nucleus in prophase and located in the middle of the cell. *C*, nucleus in early anaphase; laterally the mitotic spindle is connected to the parietal cytoplasm by a prominent cytoplasmic layer, the phragmosome. *D*, daughter nuclei in telophase; the barrel-shaped spindle between the nuclei is the phragmoplast; the cell plate appears in its equatorial plane. *E*, cell plate intersects one of the walls of the mother cell. *F*, cell division is completed and the cell plate occupies the former position of the phragmosome. (All, ×940.)

called cell plate. The term has, therefore, no precise definition and merely serves, at present, as a designation for the first visible structure delimiting the two sister protoplasts from one another.

Growth of Walls

In considering the mechanism of wall growth it is necessary to differentiate between growth in surface area and growth in thickness. The former process is much more difficult to explain than the latter. Growth in thickness is particularly obvious in secondary walls but is common also in primary walls (as classified according to Kerr and

Bailey, 1934). It occurs by a successive deposition of wall material, layer upon layer, that is, by a process known as *apposition.*

The explanations of growth of walls in surface area are connected with the ideas about the chemical and submicroscopic structure of meristematic walls. Since these ideas are divergent, the concepts of extension growth are also at variance with one another (cf. Frey-Wyssling, 1950; Kerr, 1951; Mühlethaler, 1950). The extension of the primary wall of enlarging cells is often enormous and may occur without any appreciable loss in thickness. The maintenance of this thickness indicates that new material is added to the wall during its expansion. Some workers visualize a pulling apart of the microfibrils of the previously formed lamellae and an apposition of new layers of coalesced fibrils (Bailey, 1940). Others assume a distinct type of growth called *intussusception* (cf. Frey-Wyssling, 1950). In this type of growth new wall material is thought to be interpolated among the parts of the extending wall. The concept of intussusception is also applied to both wall categories, primary and secondary, with reference to their impregnation with various substances (e.g., lignin, suberin) after they attain a certain thickness.

Growth of walls by apposition is usually centripetal. In other words, it occurs from the outside and toward the lumen of the cell. Sometimes, however, wall growth has a centrifugal course, that is, in the direction away from the lumen. Centripetal growth is characteristic of cells forming tissues. Centrifugal growth is a specialized type of growth found in pollen grains and other spores. In such structures, centrifugal growth is responsible for the formation of the characteristic prominences of the exine (the outer wall). The more or less degenerated contents of the tapetal cells (see chapter 18) surrounding the developing spores seem to be involved in the formation of exine (Küster, 1935, p. 436; Sharp, 1934, p. 181).

As was mentioned in the beginning of this chapter, the cytoplasm is probably intimately concerned with cell-wall formation. It is depicted as permeating an expanding meristematic wall (Frey-Wyssling et al., 1948). In the growth of secondary walls the observation has been made, in certain types of cells, that the future pattern of the secondary thickening is clearly foreshadowed in the cytoplasm. In tracheary elements the cytoplasm becomes densely granular next to those portions of the wall that are to be covered with wall material in the form of helices or reticulae (Farr, 1949; Sinnott and Bloch, 1945).

One of the remarkable features of wall growth is the unequal expansion of the different parts of the wall in the same cell (Frey-Wyssling, 1950; see also chapter 4). Often cells grow more in length than in width, a phenomenon that has been associated with

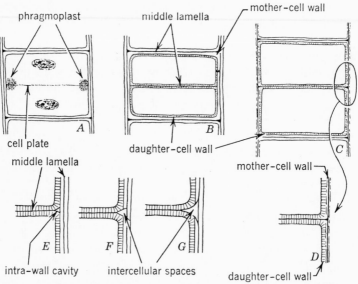

Fig. 3.11. Illustration of concepts regarding the adjustments between new and old cell walls after cell division. *A*, cell plate has been formed. *B*, two primary walls cemented by the intercellular substance occupy the position of the cell plate; primary daughter-cell walls have been laid down on the inside of the primary mother-cell wall. *C* and *D*, the daughter cells have expanded vertically, and the mother-cell wall has been stretched and ruptured opposite the new wall which separates the daughter protoplasts. This change has permitted the junction of the old and the new intercellular lamellae. (Based on Priestley and Scott, 1939.) *E* to *G*, establishment of continuity between the old and the new middle lamellae through formation of an intercellular space. *E*, appearance of cavity between daughter- and mother-cell walls. *F*, dissolution of mother-cell wall next to cavity. *G*, completion of change of the intra-wall cavity into an intercellular space. (Based on Martens, 1937.)

the predominantly horizontal orientation of microfibrils in primary walls. Some cells continue to grow at their tips after the rest of the wall has ceased to expand. Still others show part of a given wall expanding rapidly in conformity with the growth of a contiguous cell, and another part growing slowly or not at all because of the similar behavior of the wall of the adjacent cell. The differential growth of different parts of the same wall is best explained by the concept that the cytoplasm is intimately associated with the wall undergoing an increase in surface.

Another complex aspect of wall growth has to do with the establishment of continuity between the new intercellular lamella and that located outside the primary wall of the mother cell. Workers visualize an extension and breakdown of the parent wall opposite the new middle lamella (fig. 3.11, *A–D*; Priestley and Scott, 1939). The formation of intercellular spaces might be associated with this phase of wall growth (fig. 3.11, *E–G*; Martens, 1937, 1938).

FORMATION OF INTERCELLULAR SPACES

Although the cells in the meristematic tissues are generally closely packed, during tissue differentiation the intimate connection between walls of adjacent cells may be partly broken, with the appearance of intercellular spaces. The most common intercellular spaces result from a separation of cell walls from each other along more or less extended areas of their contact (fig. 3.12, *A*; plate 5, *A*). These are the *schizogenous* intercellular spaces, so called because formerly the mechanism of their formation was thought to involve a splitting of the middle lamella (*schizo*, split; *genesis*, beginning; both from the Greek).

The origin of the schizogenous intercellular spaces is described as follows: Martens, 1937, 1938; Sifton, 1945; fig. 3.11, *E–G*. When the new primary walls are formed between two sister protoplasts, the middle lamella between these walls comes in contact with the original mother-cell wall and not with the middle lamella cementing the mother-cell wall to that of its neighbor. A small cavity arises at the point of contact between the new middle lamella and the parent wall; then the parent wall becomes dissolved opposite the cavity. Thus the intra-wall cavity develops into an intercellular space. If a similar space is present between the mother cell and its neighbor, the new cavity and the old intercellular space may join to form one large space. In this process of space formation the intercellular substance is perhaps partly dissolved, but it does not disappear. The intercellular space remains lined by intercellular material (plate 5, *A*; Sifton, 1945). Certain plants, such as the submerged water plants, develop particularly large air spaces which, in the internodes, may extend like canals from node to node. These spaces are initiated like ordinary schizogenous spaces but later are

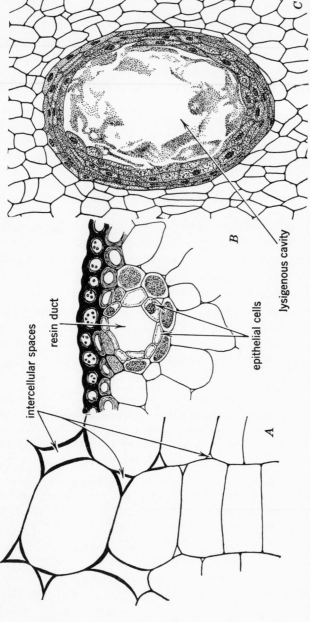

Fig. 3.12. Intercellular spaces. *A*, ordinary schizogenous intercellular spaces in different stages of development in ray parenchyma of *Bryophyllum* stem, with the youngest cells and spaces appearing below. *B*, a specialized schizogenous intercellular space in the form of a resin duct in a leaf of *Sequoia sempervirens*. Secretory epithelial cells line the duct. *C*, a lysigenous intercellular space in the form of a pigment cavity in the ovary of *Gossypium*. The detached fragments in the lumen of the cavity are derived from broken-down cells. The densely stippled flattened cells lining the cavity are secretory cells. (*A*, ×1,005; *B*, ×310; *C*, ×320.)

enlarged by cell divisions perpendicular to the circumference of the air space (Hulbary, 1944).

Some of the schizogenous intercellular spaces form specialized structures, the *secretory ducts.* Examples are the resin ducts in the Coniferae (fig. 3.12, *B*) and the secretory ducts in the Compositae and the Umbelliferae (Sifton, 1945). They are initiated similarly to the air spaces just described for aquatic plants. Since many cells in longitudinal or transverse series form spaces in the same position, these spaces take the form of long intercellular canals that may become connected into an intercommunicating system (De Bary, 1884, pp. 445–450). The cells lining the duct cavity are secretory and release their product into the canal.

Another type of intercellular space arises through dissolution of entire cells, which are therefore called *lysigenous* (from *lysis,* loosening, in Greek) intercellular spaces (fig. 3.12, *C*). Examples are the large air spaces in water plants and in some monocotyledonous roots (*Zea;* Sifton, 1945), and secretory cavities in *Eucalyptus, Citrus,* and *Gossypium* (De Bary, 1884; Stanford and Viehoever, 1918). In the secretory cavities the cells that break down release the secretion into the space and remain, themselves, in partly collapsed or disintegrated state around the periphery of the cavity.

REFERENCES

Anderson, D. B. A michrochemical study of the structure and development of flax fibers. *Amer. Jour. Bot.* **14**:187–211. 1927.

Anderson, D. B. The structure of the walls of the higher plants. *Bot. Rev.* **1**:52–76. 1935.

Bailey, I. W. The structure of the bordered pits of conifers and its bearing upon the tension hypothesis of the ascent of sap in plants. *Bot. Gaz.* **62**:133–142. 1916.

Bailey, I. W. Phragmospheres and binucleate cells. *Bot. Gaz.* **70**:469–471. 1920*a.*

Bailey, I. W. The cambium and its derivative tissues. III. A reconnaissance of cytological phenomena in the cambium. *Amer. Jour. Bot.* **7**:417–434. 1920*b.*

Bailey, I. W. The cambium and its derivative tissues. VIII. Structure, distribution, and diagnostic significance of vestured pits in dicotyledons. *Arnold Arboretum Jour.* **14**:259–273. 1933.

Bailey, I. W. Cell wall structure of higher plants. *Indus. and Engin. Chem.* **30**:40–47. 1938.

Bailey, I. W. The microfibrillar and microcapillary structure of the cell wall. *Torrey Bot. Club Bul.* **66**:201–213. 1939

Bailey, I. W. The walls of plant cells. *Amer. Assoc. Adv. Sci. Publ.* 14:31–43. 1940.

Bailey, I. W., and E. E. Berkley. The significance of X-rays in studying the orientation of cellulose in the secondary wall of tracheids. *Amer. Jour. Bot.* 29:231–241. 1942.

Bailey, I. W., and T. Kerr. The visible structure of the secondary wall and its significance in physical and chemical investigations of tracheary cells and fibers. *Arnold Arboretum Jour.* 16:273–300. 1935.

Bailey, I. W., and T. Kerr. The structural variability of the secondary wall as revealed by "lignin" residues. *Arnold Arboretum Jour.* 18:261–272. 1937.

Bailey, I. W., and M. R. Vestal. The orientation of cellulose in the secondary wall of tracheary cells. *Arnold Arboretum Jour.* 18:185–195. 1937a.

Bailey, I. W., and M. R. Vestal. The significance of certain wood-destroying fungi in the study of the enzymatic hydrolysis of cellulose. *Arnold Arboretum Jour.* 18:196–205. 1937b.

Bannan, M. W. Variability in wood structure in roots of native Ontario conifers. *Torrey Bot. Club Bul.* 68:173–194. 1941.

Becker, W. A. Experimentelle Untersuchungen über die Vitalfärbung sich teilender Zellen: III Mitt. Weitere Studien über die Zytokinese. *Soc. Bot. Poloniae Acta* 11:139–203. 1934.

Becker, W. A. Recent investigations *in vivo* on the division of plant cells. *Bot. Rev.* 4:446–472. 1938.

Berkley, E. E. Plant cell wall structures. *Chron. Bot.* 6:364–365. 1941.

Berkley, E. E. Cotton, a versatile textile fiber. *Textile Res. Jour.* 18:71–88. 1948.

Bloch, R. Wound healing in higher plants. *Bot. Rev.* 7:110–146. 1941.

Bloch, R. Developmental potency, differentiation and pattern in meristems of *Monstera deliciosa. Amer. Jour. Bot.* 31:71–77. 1944.

Bonner, J. The chemistry and physiology of the pectins. *Bot. Rev.* 2:475–497. 1936.

Bonner, J. The chemistry and physiology of the pectins. II. *Bot. Rev.* 12:535–537. 1946.

Bonner, J. *Plant biochemistry.* New York, Academic Press. 1950.

Bragg, W. H., and W. L. Bragg. *The crystalline state.* Vol. 1. *A general survey.* New York, The Macmillan Company. 1934.

Brauns, F. E. Lignin—a botanical raw material. *Econ. Bot.* 2:419–435. 1948.

Chamot, E. M., and C. W. Mason. *Handbook of chemical microscopy.* Vol. 1. 2nd ed. New York, John Wiley & Sons. 1938.

Committee on Nomenclature. International Association of Wood Anatomists. Glossary of terms used in describing woods. *Trop. Woods* 1933 (36):1–12. 1933.

Crafts, A. S., H. B. Currier, and C. R. Stocking. *Water in the physiology of plants.* Waltham, Mass., Chronica Botanica Company. 1949.

De Bary, A. *Comparative anatomy of the vegetative organs of the phanerogams and ferns.* Oxford, Clarendon Press. 1884.

Eames, A. J., and L. H. MacDaniels. *An introduction to plant anatomy.* 2nd ed. New York, McGraw-Hill Book Company. 1947.

Esau, K. The multinucleate condition in fibers of tobacco. *Hilgardia* 11:427–434. 1938.

Esau, K. Some anatomic aspects of plant virus disease problems. II. *Bot. Rev.* 14:413–449. 1948.

Farr, W. K. Cell wall and synthetic fibers. *Econ. Bot.* 1:98–113. 1947.

Farr, W. K. The tertiary membrane of the plant cell wall. *Jour. Phys. and Colloid. Chem.* 53:260–274. 1949.

Foster, A. S. *Practical plant anatomy.* 2nd ed. New York, D. Van Nostrand Company. 1949.

Frenzel, P. Über die Porengrössen einiger pflanzlicher Zellmembranen. *Planta* 8:644–665. 1929.

Freudenberg, K. The relation of cellulose to lignin in wood. *Jour. Chem. Ed.* 9:1171–1180. 1932.

Frey-Wyssling, A. *Die Stoffausscheidung der höheren Pflanzen. Monographien aus dem Gesamtgebiet der Physiologie der Pflanzen und der Tiere.* Band 32. Berlin, Julius Springer. 1935.

Frey-Wyssling, A. Der Aufbau der pflanzlichen Zellwände. *Protoplasma* 25:261–300. 1936.

Frey-Wyssling, A. *Submicroscopic morphology of protoplasm and its derivatives.* New York, Elsevier Publishing Company. 1948.

Frey-Wyssling, A. Physiology of cell wall growth. *Ann. Rev. Plant Physiol.* 1:169–182. 1950.

Frey-Wyssling, A., and K. Mühlethaler. Use of supersonics in the preparation of fiber samples for electron-microscope studies. *Textile Res. Jour.* 17:32–33. 1947.

Frey-Wyssling, A., K. Mühlethaler, and R. W. G. Wyckoff. Mikrofibrillenbau der pflanzlichen Zellwände. *Experientia* 4:475–476. 1948.

Gage, S. H. *The microscope.* 17th ed. Ithaca, New York, Comstock Publishing Company. 1941.

Goldstein, B. A study of progressive cell plate formation. *Torrey Bot. Club Bul.* 52:197–219. 1925.

Gortner, R. A., Jr., and W. A. Gortner. *Outlines of Biochemistry.* 3rd ed. New York, John Wiley & Sons. 1949.

Häusermann, E. Über die Benetzungsgrösse der Mesophyllinterzellularen. *Schweiz. Bot. Gesell. Ber.* 54:541. 1944.

Heyn, A. N. J. The physiology of cell elongation. *Bot. Rev.* 6:515–574. 1940.

Hock, C. W. Microscopic structure of the cell wall. In: *A symposium on the structure of protoplasm. Amer. Soc. Plant Physiol. Monogr.* Pp. 11–12. 1942.

Hulbary, R. L. The influence of air spaces on the three-dimensional shapes of cells in *Elodea* stems, and a comparison with pith cells of *Ailanthus. Amer. Jour. Bot.* 31:561–580. 1944.

Jaeger, M. Untersuchungen über die Frage des Wachstums und der Entholzung verholzter Zellen. *Jahrb. f. Wiss. Bot.* 68:345–381. 1928.

Kerr, T. The outer wall of the cotton fiber and its influence on fiber properties. *Textile Res. Jour.* 16:249–254. 1946.

Kerr, T. Growth and structure of the primary wall. In: Folke Skoog. Editor. *Plant Growth Substances.* Madison, Wisc., University of Wisconsin Press. 1951.

Kerr, T., and I. W. Bailey. The cambium and its derivative tissues. X. Structure, optical properties and chemical composition of the so-called middle lamella. *Arnold Arboretum Jour.* 15:327–349. 1934.

Kinsinger, W. G., and C. W. Hock. Electron microscopical studies of natural cellulose fibers. *Indus. and Engin. Chem.* 40:1711–1716. 1948.

Küster, E. *Die Pflanzenzelle.* Jena, Gustav Fischer. 1935.

Livingston, L. G. The nature and distribution of plasmodesmata in the tobacco plant. *Amer. Jour. Bot.* 22:75–87. 1935.

Livingston, L. G., and I. W. Bailey. The demonstration of unaltered plasmodesmata in the cambium of *Pinus strobus* and in ray cells of *Sequoia sempervirens.* Abst. *Amer. Jour. Bot.* 33:824. 1946.

Majumdar, G. P. The cell wall and importance of its study in modern researches. *Science and Culture* 10:466–472. 1944–45.

Martens, P. L'origine des espaces intercellulaires. *Cellule* 46:357–388. 1937.

Martens, P. Nouvelles recherches sur l'origine des espaces intercellulaires. *Bot. Centbl. Beihefte* 58:349–364. 1938.

Meeuse, A. D. J. Plasmodesmata. *Bot. Rev.* 7:249–262. 1941.

Meyer, B. S., and D. B. Anderson. *Plant physiology.* New York, D. Van Nostrand Company. 1939.

Mühlethaler, K. Electron microscopy of developing plant cell walls. *Biochim. et Biophys. Acta* 5:1–9. 1950.

Note on the use of the term "plasmodesmata." *Bot. Rev.* 7:333. 1941.

Ott, E. *Cellulose and cellulose derivatives.* New York, Interscience Publishers. 1943.

Preston, R. D., and A. B. Wardrop. The fine structure of the wall of the conifer tracheid. IV. Dimensional relationships in the outer layer of the secondary wall. *Biochim. et Biophys. Acta* 3:585–592. 1949.

Priestley, J. H. The cuticle in angiosperms. *Bot. Rev.* 9:593–616. 1943.

Priestley, J. H., and L. I. Scott. The formation of a new cell wall at cell division. *Leeds Phil. Lit. Soc. Proc.* 3:532–545. 1939.

Record, S. J. *Identification of timbers of temperate North America.* New York, John Wiley & Sons. 1947.

Roelofsen, P. A., and A. L. Houwink. Cell wall structure of staminal hairs of *Tradescantia virginica* and its relation with growth. *Protoplasma* 40:1–22. 1951.

Schmitt, F. O. The ultrastructure of protoplasmic constituents. *Physiol. Revs.* 19:270–302. 1939.

Schumacher, W. Über plasmodesmenartige Strukturen in Epidermisaussenwänden. *Jahrb. f. Wiss. Bot.* 90:530–545. 1942.

Scott, F. M. Internal suberization of plant tissues. *Science* 108:654–655. 1948.

Sharp, L. W. *Introduction to cytology.* 3rd ed. New York, McGraw-Hill Book Company. 1934.

Sharp, L. W. *Fundamentals of cytology.* New York, McGraw-Hill Book Company. 1943.

Sifton, H. B. Air-space tissue in plants. *Bot. Rev.* 11:108–143. 1945.

Sinnott, E. W., and R. Bloch. Division in vacuolate plant cells. *Amer. Jour. Bot.* 28:225–232. 1941.

Sinnott, E. W., and R. Bloch. The cytoplasmic basis of intercellular patterns in vascular differentiation. *Amer. Jour. Bot.* 32:151–156. 1945.

Sponsler, O. L. The molecule in biological structures as determined by X-ray methods. *Quart. Rev. Biol.* 8:1–30. 1933.

Stanford, E. E., and A. Viehoever. Chemistry and histology of the glands of the cotton plant, with notes on the occurrence of similar glands in related plants. *Jour. Agr. Res.* 13:419–436. 1918.

Strasburger, E. Über Plasmaverbindungen pflanzlicher Zellen. *Jahrb. f. Wiss. Bot.* 36:493–610. 1901.

Wardrop, A. B., and R. D. Preston. Organization of the cell walls of tracheids and wood fibers. *Nature* 160:911–913. 1947.

Wareham, R. T. "Phragmospheres" and the "multinucleate phase" in stem development. *Amer. Jour. Bot.* 23:591–597. 1936.

Wergin, W. Über den Feinbau der Zellwände höherer Pflanzen. *Biol. Zentbl.* 63:350–370. 1943.

Wise, L. E. *Wood chemistry.* New York, Reinhold Publishing Company. 1944.

Woodmansee, C. W. Pectin–its extraction and utilization. *Econ. Bot.* 2:88–91. 1948.

Wright, G. Pit-closing membranes in Ophioglossaceae. *Bot. Gaz.* 69:237–247. 1920.

4

Meristems and Tissue Differentiation

MERISTEMS AND GROWTH OF THE PLANT BODY

Beginning with the division of the fertilized egg cell, the vascular plant generally produces new cells and forms new organs until it dies. In the early embryonic stages of development cell division occurs throughout the young organism, but as the embryo enlarges and develops into an independent plant the addition of new cells is gradually restricted to certain parts of the plant body, while other parts become concerned with activities other than growth. Thus, portions of embryonic tissue persist in the plant throughout its life, and the adult plant is a composite of adult and juvenile tissues. These perpetually young tissues, primarily concerned with growth, are the *meristems*.

The restriction of growth to certain parts of the plant body seems to have evolved with the phylogenetic increase in elaboration of the plant organism. In the most primitive nonvascular plants all cells are essentially alike, all take part in metabolism, photosynthesis, building of new protoplasm, and multiplication by division. With the progressive evolutionary specialization of tissues the function of cell division became largely separated from other functions and eventually confined to the meristems and their immediate derivatives. The presence of meristems strikingly differentiates the plant from the animal. In the plant, growth resulting from meristematic activity is possible throughout the life of the organism, whereas in the animal body the multiplication of cells mostly ceases after the organism attains adult size and the number of organs is fixed.

The term *meristem* (from the Greek *meristos*, meaning divisible) emphasizes the cell-division activity characteristic of the tissue which bears this name. Obviously, the synthesis of new living substance is a fundamental part of the process of the formation of new cells by division. Living tissues other than the meristems may produce new cells, but the meristems carry on such activity indefinitely, because they not only add cells to the plant body but also perpetuate themselves; that is, some of the products of division in the meristems do not develop into adult cells but remain meristematic.

Since meristems occur at the apices of all shoots and roots, main and lateral, their number in a single plant may be large. Furthermore, plants characterized by secondary increase in thickness possess additional extensive meristems, the vascular and cork cambia, responsible for the secondary growth. The combined activities of all these meristems give rise to a complex, and often large, plant body. The primary growth, initiated in the apical meristems, expands the plant body, increases its surface and its area of contact with air and soil, and eventually produces the reproductive organs. The cambia, on the other hand, aid in maintenance of the expanding body by increasing the volume of the conducting system and forming supporting and protecting cells.

Not all apical meristems present on a given plant are necessarily active. One of the well-known examples of inhibition of growth in such meristems is that dependent on the hormonal relationship between the main shoot and the lateral buds. In some plants the growth of the lateral buds is suppressed as long as the terminal shoot is actively growing. The activity of the cambia also varies in intensity, and both the apical meristems and the cambia may show seasonal fluctuations in their meristematic activity, with a slowing down or a complete cessation of cell division in the temperate zones during the winter.

MERISTEMS AND MATURE TISSUES

In the preceding discussion the meristems were described as formative tissues adding new cells to the plant body and at the same time perpetuating themselves as such. Thus, in active meristems a continuous separation occurs between cells that remain meristematic—the *initiating cells*—and those that develop into the various tissue elements—the *derivatives* of the initiating cells. In this development the derivatives gradually change, physiologically and morphologically, and assume more or less specialized characteristics. In other words, the derivatives *differentiate* into the specific elements of the various tissue systems. The developing cell becomes different in two senses: first, it assumes characteristics that distinguish it from its meristematic precursors, and, second, it diverges from cells of similar age by following different lines of specialization.

Since the cells of vascular plants vary so much in their function and their morphologic characteristics, they also vary in details of differentiation. Moreover, different types of cells attain different degrees of differentiation as compared with their common meristematic precursors. Some diverge relatively little from the meristematic cells and retain the power of division to a high degree (e.g., various parenchyma cells); others are more thoroughly modified and lose most, or all, of their former meristematic potentialities (e.g., sieve elements, fibers, tracheary elements).

These variously differentiated cells may be considered *mature* in the sense that they have reached the degree of specialization and physiological stability that normally characterizes them as components of certain tissues of an adult plant part. Such a concept of maturity includes the qualification that living cells may resume meristematic activities when properly stimulated. The literature contains numerous examples of fully differentiated but living cells changing morphologically and physiologically as a result of changes in the environmental conditions, such as may be induced by various stimuli (Küster, 1925), wounding (Bloch, 1941, 1944), or physiological isolation (Buvat, 1944, 1945; Camus, 1949; Gautheret, 1945; White, 1943, 1946). Some workers visualize a combination of the processes of *dedifferentiation* (loss of previously developed characteristics) and a *redifferentiation* (development of new characteristics) in this assumption of new characteristics by a cell (Bloch, 1941).

For variable lengths of time, during the differentiation of tissues from meristems, the derivatives of meristematic cells synthesize protoplasm, enlarge, and divide. These processes of growth may persist to some degree even after the derivatives show evidences of differentiation into specific kinds of cells. It is, therefore, difficult to delimit the meristem proper from its recent derivatives, and the term meristem is often used broadly to designate not only the cell complexes that show no evidence of specialization but also those whose future course of development is partly determined. The development of meristematic derivatives into mature cells also is gradual. Some activities characteristic of mature tissues (for example, photosynthesis, starch storage) may occur while these tissues are still developing. Such overlapping of adult and juvenile characteristics makes it impossible to delimit the different stages of development. Differentiation, in other words, is a continuous process.

CLASSIFICATION OF MERISTEMS

Apical and Lateral Meristems

One of the most common groupings of plant meristems is based on their position in the plant body. It divides the formative tissues into *apical meristems*, that is, meristems located at the apices of main and lateral shoots and roots, and *lateral meristems*, that is, meristems arranged parallel with the sides of the organ in which they occur. The vascular cambium and the cork cambium (or *phellogen*) are lateral meristems. (See figs. 1.2 and 1.3.)

Primary and Secondary Meristems

Another classification divides the meristems into primary and secondary, according to the nature of the cells that give origin to these meristems. If these cells are the direct descendants of the embryonic cells that never ceased to be concerned with growth, the meristems are called primary. If, however, the cells first differentiate and function as members of some mature tissue system, then again take up meristematic activity, the resulting meristem is called secondary. This classification of meristems is rapidly becoming obsolete because it is based on the concept that cells returning to a meristematic state undergo a profound readjustment—a dedifferentiation—and that they reacquire the meristematic potentialities. Although experimental studies with living tissues and cells (Gautheret, 1946; Morel, 1948; Prevot, 1948) indicate that the meristematic and histogenetic potentialities of cells are affected by their development as members of certain tissue systems, the degree of such physiological differentiation is highly variable, and no means have been found as yet to distinguish between an acceleration of meristematic activity that had never ceased and a resumption of such activity after a period of inactivity.

The classification of meristems into primary and secondary on the basis of their origin is not employed in this book. Instead, the expressions *primary meristems* and *secondary meristems* are used if it is necessary to indicate the relative time of origin of the meristem in a given plant or one of its organs. This classification is related to the equally simple distinction into primary and secondary parts of the plant body (see chapter 1). The fundamental parts of this body, its root and stem axes, their branches and appendages, constitute the primary parts, and they originate from primary meristems. The additional vascular and protective tissues that may be formed subsequently to primary growth are secondary and arise from secondary meristems. If this classification is correlated with the topographical classification, the apical meristems correspond to the primary meristems, the lateral to the secondary meristems.

The System of Primary Meristems

In descriptions of the primary differentiation at the apices of root and shoot the initiating cells and their most recent derivatives are often distinguished, under the name of *promeristem*, from the partly differentiated but still meristematic subjacent tissues, and the meristematic tissues are segregated according to the tissue systems that are derived from them. These tissues are: the *protoderm* (*a* in plate 13, *A–C*), which differentiates into the epidermal system; the *procambium* (sometimes called *provascular tissue; b* in plate 13, *A–C*), which gives rise to the primary vascular tissues; and the *ground meristem* (*c* in plate 13, *A–C*), the precursor of the fundamental or ground tissue system. If the term meristem is used broadly, the protoderm, the procambium, and the ground meristem are referred to as the primary meristems (Haberlandt, 1914, pp. 94–98). In a more restricted sense, these three cell complexes constitute the partly determined primary meristematic tissues (Foster, 1949, p. 35), although in many plants the procambium shows also the property of self-perpetuation (some of the procambial cells become the cambial initials in plants with secondary growth), an outstanding characteristic of the meristems.

The terms protoderm, procambium, and ground meristem serve well for describing the pattern of differentiation in plant organs, and they are correlated with the equally simple and convenient classification of mature tissues into the three systems, epidermal, vascular, and fundamental, reviewed in the first chapter. It seems immaterial whether the protoderm, the procambium, and the ground meristem are called meristems or meristematic tissues as long as it is understood that they are tissues whose future course of development is partly determined.

Intercalary Meristems

The term *intercalary meristem* is used to designate an actively growing primary tissue region somewhat removed from the apical meristem. The word intercalary implies that the meristem is inserted between more or less differentiated tissue regions. The intercalary meristems are often grouped with the apical and the lateral meristems on the basis of position. Such grouping is not to be recommended. Since the intercalary growth regions contain differentiated tissue elements and since eventually they are completely transformed into mature tissues, they deserve the appellation of meristems only if the term is used in its wide connotation, and as meristems they are not of the same rank as the apical and lateral meristems.

The best-known examples of intercalary meristems are those found in internodes and leaf sheaths of many monocotyledons, particularly grasses (fig. 4.1; Artschwager, 1948; Lehmann, 1906; Prat, 1935), and in *Equisetum* (Golub and Wetmore, 1948). The relation between the apical meristem and the intercalary meristem is well understood in grasses (e.g., Sharman, 1942). The youngest portion of the shoot originating from the apical meristem has no internodes as such. These develop through cell division at the bases of the leaf insertions. The superposed leaf insertions or nodes thus are separated from each other by intercalary growth. The intercalated portions are the internodes. At first the cells divide throughout the young internode, but later the meristematic activity becomes confined to their bases (fig. 4.1). The leaf elongates similarly, and in it, too, cell division gradually becomes confined to the lowermost region of the sheath. After the internodes and the leaf sheaths complete their elongation, their basal parts retain, for an extended time, the potentiality for further growth, although fully differentiated vascular and supporting cells are present in these parts (Artschwager, 1948; Lehmann, 1906). At this stage of development the potentially meristematic regions of the plant are known as *joints* (plate 58, B; Lehmann, 1906). They often exhibit their meristematic potentiality when the culm rises, after lodging, by curving away from the ground (plate 58, C). This curvature results from growth and division of cells located on the lower side of the lodged culm. Such growth in a joint is not unlimited. As the plant ages, the joint also becomes mature throughout and loses its meristematic potentialities (Lehmann, 1906).

Being inserted between mature tissue regions, an intercalary meristem would interrupt the continuity of the vascular tissues and would

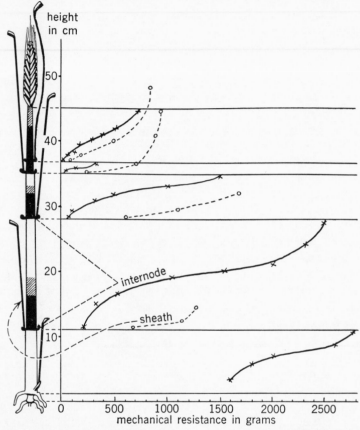

Fig. 4.1. Distribution of growth regions in a culm of a rye plant. The plant illustrated to the left has five internodes and a spike borne at the top. Leaf sheaths are represented diagrammatically as extending upward from each node and terminating where the leaf blades (shown only in part) diverge from them. The youngest tissue in the internodes (intercalary meristems) is represented in black, the somewhat older tissue is hatched, the most mature is left white. The curves to the right indicate the mechanical resistance of internodal tissues (solid lines) and of the sheaths (broken lines) at the various levels of the shoot. The resistance was measured by determining the pressure, expressed in grams, necessary to make a transverse cut through the internode or sheath. (After Prat, 1935.)

weaken the structure of leaf and stem if it were completely undifferentiated. It has been shown in many monocotyledonous stems (Buchholz, 1920; Lehmann, 1906) and in *Arachis* gynophore—an organ which elongates through the meristematic activity at the base of the ovary and forces the fruit, the peanut, beneath the ground (Jacobs, 1947)—that the intercalary meristems have vascular tissues while they are actively growing. The joints of grasses, which are active in growth only under certain conditions, have vascular and supporting cells of such a nature that they are capable of some extension and do not greatly hinder the elongation, if such is taking place (Artschwager, 1948; Lehmann, 1906).

The activity of the intercalary meristems is not an isolated phenomenon but is merely an intensified and localized expression of the primary growth that is responsible for the final form and size of plant organs. Leaves, flowers, and fruits show cell division for some time after they are initiated at the apex, and their prolonged increase in size may be regarded as an intercalary growth, less localized than that found in grasses, horsetails, or the peanut.

CYTOLOGIC CHARACTERISTICS OF MERISTEMS

Modern research on meristems has led to the realization that meristems show variable cytologic structure and are not fundamentally different from mature living tissues. Generally, the protoplasts of meristematic cells are relatively undifferentiated. During active divisions meristematic cells mostly lack ergastic inclusions, and their plastids are in proplastid stages. But cork cambium may have chloroplasts, starch and tannins may occur in the cambial ray initials (Esau, 1948), and various storage materials are found in meristems of embryos.

The degree of vacuolation of the meristematic cells varies greatly. The cells in the apical meristems of many plants, particularly among the angiosperms, have dense protoplasts (plate 13, *A, B*), with small, inconspicuous vacuoles dispersed in the cytoplasm (Zirkle, 1932). Many other vascular plants, notably the cryptogams and some gymnosperms, have conspicuously vacuolated cells in the apical meristems (plates 13, *C, D*, and 14, *C, D*; Foster, 1938, 1941), and the initials in the vascular cambium may be as highly vacuolated as plant-hair cells (plates 18 and 19; Bailey, 1930). In general, the larger the meristematic cell, the greater is the relative amount of vacuolar material (Zirkle, 1932). Sometimes the cells farther removed from the initial region of an apical meristem are more densely cytoplasmic than the initials themselves and their most recent derivatives. This condition is found in many lower vascular plants and in certain gymnosperms (plates 13, *D*, and 14, *C*).

Meristematic cells are usually described as having large nuclei. However, the ratio between the size of the cell and the size of the nucleus—the cytonuclear ratio—varies considerably (Trombetta, 1942). In general, the nuclei of large meristematic cells are relatively smaller in proportion to the size of the cell than those of the smaller cells. The sizes of entire meristematic cells and their shapes are also variable characteristics. One extreme is the small, nearly isodiametric cell of some apical meristems, the other, the long narrow fusiform initial in the vascular cambium. No less striking are the differences in wall thickness. Although commonly the meristematic cells have thin walls (plate 14, *A*), certain zones of the apical meristems may have thick walls (plate 14, *C, D*) with conspicuous primary pit fields; and the cambial initials sometimes develop remarkably thick walls with deeply depressed primary pit fields. Intercellular spaces are generally absent in the meristems, but they may appear very early among the still-dividing derivatives (this feature is particularly well illustrated by the roots; fig. 5.13, *B*).

The foregoing statements show that it would be erroneous to emphasize a certain set of characteristics as being typical of the meristematic cells. Nevertheless, the lack of conspicuous vacuolation is most commonly encountered in the meristematic tissues, and small, essentially isodiametric cells with thin walls occur in the meristems more usually than in other kinds of tissues. In recognition of the variability in the characteristics of the meristems, the term *eumeristem*, that is, true meristem, has been suggested for the designation of a meristem composed of small, approximately isodiametric cells, with thin walls, and rich in cytoplasm (Kaplan, 1937). This term, used judiciously, with the understanding that in a morphologic or physiologic sense a "typical meristematic cell" does not exist, often serves well for descriptive purposes.

GROWTH PATTERNS IN MERISTEMS

Meristems and meristematic tissues show varied arrangements of cells resulting from varied patterns of cell division. Apical meristems having only one initiating cell (for example, *Equisetum* and many ferns, fig. 5.1) have an orderly distribution of cells (Golub and Wetmore, 1948). In the higher plants the sequence of cell divisions in the apices is less precise, but it is not random either, for an apical

meristem grows as an organized whole and the divisions and enlargement of individual cells are related to the internal distribution of
growth and to the external form of the apex (Wardlaw, 1945; Wetmore and Wardlaw, 1951). These correlative influences bring about
a differentiation of distinctive zones in the meristems. In some parts
of the meristem the cells may divide sluggishly and attain considerable dimensions; in others they may divide frequently and remain
small (plate 14, *C, D*). Some cell complexes divide in various planes
(volume growth), others only by walls at right angles to the surface
of the meristem (*anticlinal* divisions, surface growth).

The lateral meristems are particularly distinguished by divisions
parallel with the nearest surface of the organ (*periclinal* divisions),
which result in establishment of rows of cells parallel with the radii
of the axes (radial seriation) and an increase in the thickness of the
organ. Radial alignment is so characteristic of the immediate derivatives of the vascular cambium (plates 17 and 18), and those of the
phellogen (plate 42, *A*), that it is often regarded as an invariable
indication of secondary growth. However, radial alignment of cells
may originate during various stages of primary growth (cf. Esau,
1943).

In cylindrical bodies, such as stems and roots, the term *tangential*
division (or tangential longitudinal) is commonly used instead of
periclinal division; the *anticlinal* division is *radial* (or radial longitudinal) if it occurs parallel with the radius of the cylinder, and
transverse if the new wall is laid down at right angles to the longitudinal axis of the cylinder.

Organs arising at the same apical meristem may subsequently assume varied forms because the still-meristematic derivatives of the
apical meristems (primary meristems in the wide sense) often exhibit
distinct patterns of growth. Indeed, some of these growth patterns
are so characteristic that the meristematic tissues showing them have
received special names. These are: the *mass meristem* (or block meristem), the *rib meristem* (or file meristem), and the *plate meristem*
(Schüepp, 1926). The mass meristem grows by divisions in all planes
and produces bodies that are isodiametric or spheroidal or have no
definite shape. The best examples of such growth are found in
reproductive organs during the formation of spores, sperms (in lower
vascular plants), and endosperm, and in young embryos of some
plants. The rib meristem (plates 13, *C*, and 14, *B*) gives rise to a
complex of parallel longitudinal files ("ribs") of cells by divisions
at right angles to the longitudinal axis of the cell row and also to

appreciably through lignification, suberization, or silicification. In certain cell types, such as the vessel elements, parts of the wall are removed.

One of the first gross differences that appear among the developing cells is the unequal increase in size. Some cells continue to divide without significant increase in size; others cease dividing and enlarge. Examples of differential growth in size are found in the elongation of the procambial cells in contrast to the lack of similar elongation of cells in the adjacent pith and cortex; or of the elements of the first sieve tubes in contrast to that of the adjacent parenchyma cells (fig. 4.2, *A*). Size differences between two adjacent cells also may result from unequal divisions. In some plants, for example, root hairs develop from cells which are the smaller of two sister cells formed by the division of protodermal cells (fig. 4.2, *B*, *C*; see also chapter 7, and Sinnott and Bloch, 1939).

The increase in size of a cell may be relatively uniform, but frequently the cell enlarges more in one direction than in another and thereby assumes a new form. Some cells are strikingly different in shape from their meristematic precursors (primary phloem fibers, branched sclereids, laticiferous cells); many, however, become modified in a less spectacular manner, with simply a change in the number of facets and a retention of the general shape (Hulbary, 1944).

The predominant cell arrangement in a tissue may be determined early by the growth form of its meristem (e.g., rib meristem, plate meristem). The relative position of walls in adjacent cell rows also gives a distinctive appearance to a tissue (Sinnott and Bloch, 1941). Most commonly new walls alternate with the old ones in the adjacent cell row (fig. 4.2, *A*), but in some tissues (cork, cortex of certain roots) a new wall is formed opposite the point of insertion of a previous one in the adjacent row (plate 41).

The enlargement and the change in the shape of cells in a differentiating tissue are accompanied by various readjustments in the relation of the cells to each other. One of the most familiar phenomena is the appearance of intercellular spaces along the line of union of three or more cells (see chapter 3). The development of intercellular spaces sometimes does not change the general arrangement of the cells, but sometimes it profoundly modifies the appearance of the developing tissue (Hulbary, 1944).

With regard to the growth of walls during the differentiation of a tissue, two possibilities are recognized: (1) the growth of walls of adjacent cells is so adjusted that no separation of the walls occurs;

meristem grows as an organized whole and the divisions and enlargement of individual cells are related to the internal distribution of growth and to the external form of the apex (Wardlaw, 1945; Wetmore and Wardlaw, 1951). These correlative influences bring about a differentiation of distinctive zones in the meristems. In some parts of the meristem the cells may divide sluggishly and attain considerable dimensions; in others they may divide frequently and remain small (plate 14, *C*, *D*). Some cell complexes divide in various planes (volume growth), others only by walls at right angles to the surface of the meristem (*anticlinal* divisions, surface growth).

The lateral meristems are particularly distinguished by divisions parallel with the nearest surface of the organ (*periclinal* divisions), which result in establishment of rows of cells parallel with the radii of the axes (radial seriation) and an increase in the thickness of the organ. Radial alignment is so characteristic of the immediate derivatives of the vascular cambium (plates 17 and 18), and those of the phellogen (plate 42, *A*), that it is often regarded as an invariable indication of secondary growth. However, radial alignment of cells may originate during various stages of primary growth (cf. Esau, 1943).

In cylindrical bodies, such as stems and roots, the term *tangential* division (or tangential longitudinal) is commonly used instead of *periclinal* division; the *anticlinal* division is *radial* (or radial longitudinal) if it occurs parallel with the radius of the cylinder, and *transverse* if the new wall is laid down at right angles to the longitudinal axis of the cylinder.

Organs arising at the same apical meristem may subsequently assume varied forms because the still-meristematic derivatives of the apical meristems (primary meristems in the wide sense) often exhibit distinct patterns of growth. Indeed, some of these growth patterns are so characteristic that the meristematic tissues showing them have received special names. These are: the *mass meristem* (or block meristem), the *rib meristem* (or file meristem), and the *plate meristem* (Schüepp, 1926). The mass meristem grows by divisions in all planes and produces bodies that are isodiametric or spheroidal or have no definite shape. The best examples of such growth are found in reproductive organs during the formation of spores, sperms (in lower vascular plants), and endosperm, and in young embryos of some plants. The rib meristem (plates 13, *C*, and 14, *B*) gives rise to a complex of parallel longitudinal files ("ribs") of cells by divisions at right angles to the longitudinal axis of the cell row and also to the longitudinal axis of the plant organ. This pattern of growth occurs notably in the development of the cortex of the root and of the pith and the cortex of stems. The plate meristem (see chapter 16) grows chiefly by anticlinal divisions so that the number of layers originally established in the young organ does not increase any further and a plate-like structure is produced. The result of growth by a plate meristem is well illustrated by the flat blades of angiospermous leaves (plate 62). The plate meristem and the rib meristem are growth forms that occur mainly in the ground meristem. They determine the two basic forms of the plant body, the thin spreading lamina (blade) of the leaf-like organs, on the one hand, and the elongated cylindrical structures found in the root, the stem, the petiole, and the leaf rib, on the other.

HISTOLOGIC ASPECTS OF TISSUE DIFFERENTIATION

Concept of Differentiation

In a preceding part of this chapter differentiation was interpreted as the development of the derivatives of meristems into the elements of the various tissue systems of the adult plant body. In this sense differentiation comprises the many interrelated processes of physiological and morphological nature which bring about the specialization of cells. Since the degree and kind of specialization vary in different cells, cellular differentiation ultimately results in the histological diversity characteristic of the bodies of higher plants.

Tissues that have completed their development are differentiated tissues (or mature tissues, in the sense defined on p. 76). Frequently the term *differentiated* is used to express not only the attainment of a certain state of development but also the occurrence of variations in structure and function resulting from developmental changes within a given cell, tissue, tissue system, or organ. One might say, for example, that certain walls of the sieve-tube elements are differentiated into sieve plates; that the xylem tissue is differentiated into tracheary elements, fibers, and parenchyma, and the vascular tissue system into xylem and phloem; or that the plant body is differentiated into root, stem, and leaf. In this sense it is appropriate to speak of differentiation in the meristem itself, if it shows variations in the nature of the component cells.

The variation in the degree of specialization of developing cells has been previously emphasized. Many cells are so much modified during differentiation that they ultimately reach an irreversible state. Such a state is usually associated with a profound alteration of the protoplast or its complete disappearance. The cell thus loses the capacity to dedifferentiate and to resume meristematic activity.

The presence of an active protoplast, however, does not prove that a given cell has not undergone irreversible changes. Experiments with tissues cultured in isolation from the plant body, and studies on phenomena of regeneration and wound repair suggest that living cells may attain degrees of specificity limiting their meristematic potentialities (Bloch, 1941, 1944; Buvat, 1944, 1945; Gautheret, 1946; Morel, 1948; Prevot, 1948).

The acquisition of histological diversity in the presence of nuclear uniformity, that is, genetical identity of cells, is the most important unsolved problem of differentiation. At present, the concept is emerging that cell behavior during differentiation depends more directly on the constitution of the cytoplasm than that of the nucleus (Beadle, 1948; Mather, 1948). It has been suggested that cells contain semiautonomic cytoplasmic units which undergo systematic changes (Beadle, 1948) and perhaps are segregated during cell division (Bloch, 1948). If such changes and segregation occur, they are apparently not random but are subject to the control of the organism as a whole, for cells differentiate in relation to their position in the plant body (Bloch, 1943; Bünning, 1951; Prat, 1948). They may show a different behavior when released, in the form of tissue cultures, from the original plan of organization (Morel, 1948).

Morphologic Expressions of Differentiation

During the differentiation of tissues, histologic diversity results from changes in the characteristics of individual cells and from readjustments in the intercellular relationships. The common alterations in the contents of differentiating cells have been mentioned in chapter 2 and need but a brief recapitulation here. There is the conspicuous increase in the amount of vacuolar sap, if the meristematic cell itself is not yet highly vacuolated; the accumulation of various ergastic substances; the development of plastids from the proplastids; and the acquisition of color by the plastids. In highly specialized cells the protoplast or parts of it may disappear.

The changes in wall structure have also been considered (chapter 3). The increase in thickness, primary or secondary, often produces striking differences among cells. The chemistry of walls may change appreciably through lignification, suberization, or silicification. In certain cell types, such as the vessel elements, parts of the wall are removed.

One of the first gross differences that appear among the developing cells is the unequal increase in size. Some cells continue to divide without significant increase in size; others cease dividing and enlarge. Examples of differential growth in size are found in the elongation of the procambial cells in contrast to the lack of similar elongation of cells in the adjacent pith and cortex; or of the elements of the first sieve tubes in contrast to that of the adjacent parenchyma cells (fig. 4.2, *A*). Size differences between two adjacent cells also may result from unequal divisions. In some plants, for example, root hairs develop from cells which are the smaller of two sister cells formed by the division of protodermal cells (fig. 4.2, *B*, *C*; see also chapter 7, and Sinnott and Bloch, 1939).

The increase in size of a cell may be relatively uniform, but frequently the cell enlarges more in one direction than in another and thereby assumes a new form. Some cells are strikingly different in shape from their meristematic precursors (primary phloem fibers, branched sclereids, laticiferous cells); many, however, become modified in a less spectacular manner, with simply a change in the number of facets and a retention of the general shape (Hulbary, 1944).

The predominant cell arrangement in a tissue may be determined early by the growth form of its meristem (e.g., rib meristem, plate meristem). The relative position of walls in adjacent cell rows also gives a distinctive appearance to a tissue (Sinnott and Bloch, 1941). Most commonly new walls alternate with the old ones in the adjacent cell row (fig. 4.2, *A*), but in some tissues (cork, cortex of certain roots) a new wall is formed opposite the point of insertion of a previous one in the adjacent row (plate 41).

The enlargement and the change in the shape of cells in a differentiating tissue are accompanied by various readjustments in the relation of the cells to each other. One of the most familiar phenomena is the appearance of intercellular spaces along the line of union of three or more cells (see chapter 3). The development of intercellular spaces sometimes does not change the general arrangement of the cells, but sometimes it profoundly modifies the appearance of the developing tissue (Hulbary, 1944).

With regard to the growth of walls during the differentiation of a tissue, two possibilities are recognized: (1) the growth of walls of adjacent cells is so adjusted that no separation of the walls occurs;

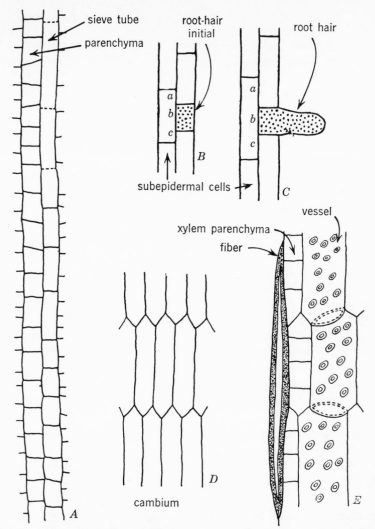

FIG. 4.2. Diagrams illustrating different kinds of intercellular adjustment during tissue differentiation. *A*, series of cells from a root tip of tobacco. Parenchyma cells continued dividing; the sieve elements ceased dividing and began elongating. *B* and *C*, development of a root hair in a species in which the root hair is formed from the smaller of two sister cells resulting from a transverse division of a proto-dermal cell. In *C* the root-hair cell is shown extended at a right angle to the root but not in the direction of elongation of the root. Apparently in the sub-epidermal cell adjacent to the root hair the wall parts *a* and *c* continued to elongate, whereas the part *b* ceased to elongate after the root hair was initiated. *D* and *E*, some cambium and some xylem that could develop from such cambium, both in tangential sections. *E* shows the results of the following developmental changes in cambial derivatives. The xylem parenchyma cells were formed by transverse divisions of such derivatives. The vessel elements expanded laterally. The fiber elongated by apical intrusive growth.

87

(2) a separation of the walls occurs, and the growing cell comes to occupy the space formed through the separation. The first method of growth, sometimes called *symplastic growth* (Priestley, 1930), is common in organs expanding during their primary growth. Whether all cells in a complex are still dividing, or whether some have ceased to divide and are elongating (fig. 4.2, *A*), the walls of adjacent cells appear to grow in unison, for there is no evidence of separation or buckling of walls. In this coordinated growth it is possible that part of a given wall is expanding and another is not, if the two parts are associated with walls of two cells, one of which is still growing while the other has ceased to do so (fig. 4.2, *B*, *C*; Sinnott and Bloch, 1939).

The second type of intercellular adjustment, that involving an intrusion of cells among others, is called *intrusive growth* (Sinnott and Bloch, 1939) or *interpositional growth* (Schoch-Bodmer, 1945). The occurrence of such growth in the elongation of cambial initials, of primary and secondary fibers (fig. 4.2, *D*, *E*), of tracheids, and of certain other cells has been well established by careful observations (Bailey, 1944; Bannan and Whalley, 1950; Klinken, 1914; Neeff, 1914, 1920, 1922; Schoch-Bodmer and Huber, 1946, 1949; and others). One of the most spectacular examples of elongation by intrusive growth is found in certain woody Liliaceae in which the secondary tracheids may become 15 to 40 times longer than the original meristematic cells (Cheadle, 1937). The elongating cells grow at their apices *(apical intrusive growth)*, usually at both ends. The intercellular material seems to change in front of the advancing tip, and the primary walls of the adjacent cells become separated from each other in the same manner as they do during the formation of intercellular spaces. The common assumption is that, if plasmodesmata are present in front of the advancing tip, they are ruptured. This phenomenon has not been actually observed, but the separation of members of pairs of primary pit fields has been noted (Neeff, 1914). Pit-pairs later appear between pairs of cells that come in contact through intrusive growth (Bannan, 1950; Bannan and Whalley, 1950). Intrusive growth also occurs in connection with the lateral expansion of cells attaining considerable width (e.g., vessel members, fig. 4.2, *E*; see chapter 11).

Early botanists assumed the occurrence of a gliding or sliding growth in the process of adjustment among differentially elongating or laterally expanding cells. The concept of gliding growth implies that a large part of a wall of a given cell expands in area and glides over the walls of other cells with which the enlarging cell is in contact before the growth begins (Krabbe, 1886; Neeff, 1914). Intrusive growth, on the contrary, is visualized as a localized extension of a wall without severance of contacts between the enlarging cell and its neighbors. Whether such localized extension involves some gliding of the new wall part over the walls of cells with which new contacts are established (cf. Bannan, 1951) or whether the new wall is apposed along the outer surfaces of the cells that are being pushed apart (Schoch-Bodmer, 1945) is still problematical. Certain intercellular readjustments are best explained by an assumption of severance of contacts and gliding of walls (Bannan, 1951; Neeff, 1914), but intrusive growth appears to be by far the more common phenomenon. Some workers attempt to explain all intercellular adjustments by symplastic growth (Meeuse, 1942) despite the availability of strong evidence supporting the concept of intrusive growth.

REFERENCES

Artschwager, E. Anatomy and morphology of the vegetative organs of *Sorghum vulgare. U. S. Dept. Agr. Tech. Bul. 957.* 1948.

Bailey, I. W. The cambium and its derivative tissues. V. A reconnaissance of the vacuome in living cells. *Ztschr. f. Zellforsch. u. Mikros. Anat.* 10:651–682. 1930.

Bailey, I. W. The development of vessels in angiosperms and its significance in morphological research. *Amer. Jour. Bot.* 31:421–428. 1944.

Bannan, M. W. The frequency of anticlinal divisions in fusiform cambial cells of *Chamaecyparis. Amer. Jour. Bot.* 37:511–519. 1950.

Bannan, M. W. The reduction of fusiform cambial cells in *Chamaecyparis* and *Thuja. Canad. Jour. Bot.* 29:57–67. 1951.

Bannan, M. W., and B. E. Whalley. The elongation of fusiform cambial cells in *Chamaecyparis. Canad. Jour. Res. Sect. C., Bot. Sci.* 28:341–355. 1950.

Beadle, G. M. Genes and biological enigmas. *Amer. Scientist* 36:69–74. 1948.

Bloch, R. Wound healing in higher plants. *Bot. Rev.* 7:110–146. 1941.

Bloch, R. Polarity in plants. *Bot. Rev.* 9:261–310. 1943.

Bloch, R. Developmental potency, differentiation and pattern in meristems of *Monstera deliciosa. Amer. Jour. Bot.* 31:71–77. 1944.

Bloch, R. The development of the secretory cells of *Ricinus* and the problem of cellular differentiation. *Growth* 12:271–284. 1948.

Buchholz, M. Über die Wasserleitungsbahnen in den interkalaren Wachstumszonen monokotyler Sprosse. *Flora* 14:119–186. 1920.

Bünning, E. Über die Differenzierungsvorgänge in der Cruciferenwurzel. *Planta* 39:126–153. 1951.

Buvat, R. Recherches sur la dédifférenciation des cellules végétales. I. Plantes entières et boutures. *Ann. des Sci. Nat., Bot.* Ser. 11. 5:1–130. 1944.

Buvat, R. Recherches sur la dédifférenciation des cellules végétales. II. Cultures des tissus et tumeurs. *Ann. des Sci. Nat., Bot.* Ser. 11. **6**:1–119. 1945.

Camus, G. Recherches sur le rôle des bourgeons dans les phénomènes de morphogénèse. *Rev. de Cytol. et de Biol. Vég.* **11**:1–199. 1949.

Cheadle, V. I. Secondary growth by means of a thickening ring in certain monocotyledons. *Bot. Gaz.* **98**:535–555. 1937.

Esau, K. Origin and development of primary vascular tissues in seed plants. *Bot. Rev.* **9**:125–206. 1943.

Esau, K. Phloem structure in the grapevine, and its seasonal changes. *Hilgardia* **18**:217–296. 1948.

Foster, A. S. Structure and growth of the shoot apex in *Ginkgo biloba. Torrey Bot. Club Bul.* **65**:531–556. 1938.

Foster, A. S. Comparative studies on the structure of the shoot apex in seed plants. *Torrey Bot. Club Bul.* **68**:339–350. 1941.

Foster, A. S. *Practical plant anatomy.* 2nd ed. New York, D. Van Nostrand Company. 1949.

Gautheret, R. J. La culture des tissus végétaux. *Assoc. Franç. pour l'Avanc. des Sci. Compt. Rend.* Sess. 64. **3**:204–226. 1945.

Gautheret, R. J. *Plant tissue culture.* Sixth Symposium on Development and Growth. Suppl. to Vol. 10. 1946.

Golub, S. J., and R. H. Wetmore. Studies of development in the vegetative shoot of *Equisetum arvense* L. I. The shoot apex. *Amer. Jour. Bot.* **35**:755–767. 1948.

Haberlandt, G. *Physiological plant anatomy.* London, Macmillan and Company. 1914.

Hulbary, R. L. The influence of air spaces on the three-dimensional shapes of cells in *Elodea* stems, and a comparison with pith cells of *Ailanthus. Amer. Jour. Bot.* **31**:561–580. 1944.

Jacobs, W. P. The development of the gynophore of the peanut plant, *Arachis hypogaea* L. I. The distribution of mitoses, the region of greatest elongation, and the maintenance of vascular continuity in the intercalary meristem. *Amer. Jour. Bot.* **34**:361–370. 1947.

Kaplan, R. Über die Bildung der Stele aus dem Urmeristem von Pteridophyten und Spermatophyten. *Planta* **27**:224–268. 1937.

Klinken, J. Über das gleitende Wachstum der Initialen im Kambium der Koniferen und den Markstrahlenverlauf in ihrer sekundären Rinde. *Biblioth. Bot.* **19**(84):1–41. 1914.

Krabbe, G. *Das gleitende Wachsthum bei der Gewebebildung der Gefässpflanzen.* Berlin, Gebrüder Borntraeger. 1886.

Küster, E. *Pathologische Pflanzenanatomie.* 3rd ed. Jena, Gustav Fischer. 1925.

Lehmann, E. Zur Kenntnis der Grassgelenke. *Deut. Bot. Gesell. Ber.* **24**:185–189. 1906.

Mather, K. Nucleus and cytoplasm in differentiation. In: *Growth in relation to differentiation and morphogenesis. Soc. Expt. Biol. Symposia* **1948**:196–216. 1948.

Meeuse, A. D. J. A study of intercellular relationships among vegetable cells with special reference to "sliding growth" and to cell shape. *Rec. des Trav. Bot. Néerland.* **38**:18–140. 1942.

Morel, G. Recherches sur la culture associée de parasites obligatoires et de tissus végétaux. *Ann. des Epiphyt.* **14**, Mém. 5. 1948.

Neeff, F. Über Zellumlagerung. Ein Beitrag zur experimentellen Anatomie. *Ztschr. f. Bot.* **6**:465–547. 1914.

Neeff, F. Über die Umlagerung der Kambiumzellen beim Dickenwachstrum der Dicotylen. *Ztschr. f. Bot.* **12**:225–252. 1920.

Neeff, F. Über polares Wachstum von Pflanzenzellen. *Jahrb. f. Wiss. Bot.* **61**:205–283. 1922.

Prat, H. Recherches sur la structure et le mode de croissance des chaumes. *Ann. des Sci. Nat., Bot.* Ser. 10. **17**:81–145. 1935.

Prat, H. Histo-physiological gradients and plant organogenesis. *Bot. Rev.* **14**:603–643. 1948.

Prevot, P. C. Contribution à l'histologie des phénomènes de néoformations chez *Begonia Rex* Putz. *Rev. Sci. (Paris)* **86**:275–285. 1948.

Priestley, J. H. Studies in the physiology of cambial activity. II. The concept of sliding growth. *New Phytol.* **29**:96–140. 1930.

Schoch-Bodmer, H. Interpositionswachstum, symplastisches und gleitendes Wachstum. *Schweiz. Bot. Gesell. Ber.* **55**:313–319. 1945.

Schoch-Bodmer, H., and P. Huber. Wachstumstypen plastischer Pflanzenmembranen. *Naturf. Gesell. Schaffhausen, Mitt.* **21**:29–43. 1946.

Schoch-Bodmer, H., and P. Huber. Spitzenwachstum und Gabelbildung bei secundären Fasern. *Schweiz. Ztschr. f. Forstw.* **100**:551–567. 1949.

Schüepp, O. Meristeme. In: K. Linsbauer. *Handbuch der Pflanzenanatomie*. Band 4. Lief. 16. 1926.

Sharman, B. C. Developmental anatomy of the shoot of *Zea mays* L. *Ann. Bot.* **6**:245–282. 1942.

Sinnott, E. W., and R. Bloch. Changes in intercellular relationships during the growth and differentiation of living plant tissues. *Amer. Jour. Bot.* **26**:625–634. 1939.

Sinnott, E. W., and R. Bloch. The relative position of cell walls in developing plant tissues. *Amer. Jour. Bot.* **28**:607–617. 1941.

Trombetta, V. V. The cytonuclear ratio. *Bot. Rev.* **8**:317–336. 1942.

Wardlaw, C. W. The shoot apex in pteridophytes. *Biol. Rev.* **20**:100–114. 1945.

Wetmore, R. H., and C. W. Wardlaw. Experimental morphogenesis in vascular plants. *Ann. Rev. Plant Physiol.* **2**:269–292. 1951.

White, P. R. *A handbook of plant tissue culture.* Lancaster, Pa., Jaques Cattell Press. 1943.

White, P. R. Plant tissue cultures. II. *Bot. Rev.* **12**:521–529. 1946.

Zirkle, C. Vacuoles in primary meristems. *Ztschr. f. Zellforsch. u. Mikros. Anat.* **16**:26–47. 1932.

5

Apical Meristems

DELIMITATION

In this book the concept of apical meristem is applied to include the meristematic initials and their immediate derivatives at the apex of a shoot or a root. The apical meristem, thus delimited, is thought to correspond approximately to the promeristem, and to contrast with the partly determined derivatives of the promeristem: the protoderm, the ground meristem, and the procambium. A more precise delimitation of the apical meristem is hardly possible. It would be impracticable, for instance, to think of the apical meristem as consisting of the initiating cells only because such cells may be poorly differentiated from their most recent derivatives.

The terms *shoot apex* and *root apex* are convenient expressions that may be employed in place of apical meristem of the shoot and apical meristem of the root, respectively. Shoot apex and root apex are also appropriate substitutions for the somewhat inaccurate term growing point (cf. Foster, 1949, p. 29). Growth in the sense of cell division, which is so characteristic of the meristematic state, is not restricted to the so-called growing point but occurs abundantly—and may be even more intense—at some distance from the apical meristem (Dermen and Bain, 1944; Goodwin and Stepka, 1945; Schüepp, 1926; Wardlaw, 1945). Similarly, growth in the sense of increase in size of cells, tissues, and organs is most pronounced, not in the apical meristem, but in its derivatives.

INITIALS AND DERIVATIVES

An *initial*, or initiating cell (p. 75), is a cell that remains within the meristem indefinitely by combining self-perpetuation with the addition of cells to the plant body. The inference about the existence of apical initials is generally based on microscopic views (e.g., Clowes,

1950) and on theoretical considerations. Recently, however, some experimental evidence has been obtained regarding this matter by treatments with colchicine. This treatment makes it possible to change the number of chromosomes in individual cells (Baker, 1943; Dermen, 1945, 1947; Satina et al., 1940). When certain cells of the shoot apices are thus affected, the change becomes detectable and is perpetuated indefinitely in more or less extended parts of the plant body developing after the treatment, and the alterations may be traced directly to the cells in the apical meristem. These cells obviously fit the definition of initials. However, there is also evidence that changes in growth may cause a shift in the relative position of the cells in the apical meristem so that an initial is displaced and ceases to act as such (Bain and Dermen, 1944). The concept of meristematic initials, therefore, implies that a cell is an initial, not because of its inherent characteristics, but simply because of its particular position in the meristem, a position that cannot be considered permanent. The initials, moreover, rather than dominate the growth of the apical meristem, appear to be correlated in their activity with the other cells of the meristem (Foster, 1941*a*).

The number of initials in root and shoot apices is variable. In many vascular cryptogams a single initial cell occurs at the apex (fig. 5.1); in other lower vascular plants, as well as in the higher, several initials are present. The single initial is morphologically quite distinct from its derivatives and is customarily spoken of as the *apical cell*. If the initials are more or less numerous, they are called *apical initials*. Their recognition under the microscope, in contrast to the single apical cells, is uncertain (plates 13 and 14).

The apical initials may occur in one or more tiers. If there is only one tier, all cells of a plant body are ultimately derived from it. In the alternative situation, different parts of a plant body are derived from different groups of initials. The existence of more than one independent layer of initials in certain plants has been clearly demonstrated in the previously mentioned experiments with colchicine. The treatment may induce polyploidy in one or more superficial layers of the apical meristem (fig. 5.2) and thus convert the plant into a cytochimera (Jones, 1937). Induced cytochimeras in *Datura* (Satina et al., 1940), *Solanum* (Baker, 1943), and *Vaccinium* (Dermen and Bain, 1944) and spontaneous chimeras in *Citrus* (Frost and Krug, 1942) and apple (Blaser and Einset, 1948) showed that polyploidy was perpetuated indefinitely if any one of the three superficial layers in the apical meristem were polyploid, and these three layers behaved independently in the transmission of their characteristic chromosome numbers. These plants obviously had three tiers of initials.

Induced polyploidy has served to demonstrate also the presence of more than one initial cell in each tier. In addition to periclinal

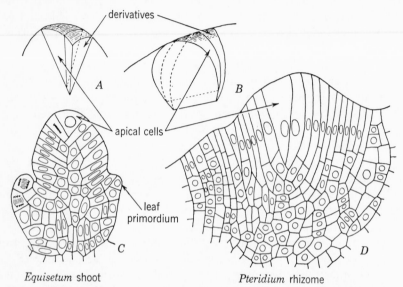

Equisetum shoot   *Pteridium* rhizome

Fig. 5.1. Apical cells. *A* and *B*, diagrams illustrating two forms of apical cell, pyramidal (*A*) and lenticular (*B*). The cells are cut off from three sides in the pyramidal initial (from four, if the cell is located in the root and certain of its derivatives form a rootcap), from two in the lenticular (from three, if the cell is located in the root). In each drawing a derivative cell is shown attached to right side of the apical cell. *C* and *D*, shoot apices with apical cells of *Equisetum* shoot and *Pteridium* rhizome in longitudinal views. Note apical cells in leaf primordia in *C*. In the primordium to the left, the apical cell is dividing. (*A* and *B*, adapted from Schüepp, 1926. *C* and *D*, ×230.)

chimeras, continuous sectorial polyploidy was observed in *Vaccinium* (Bain and Dermen, 1944). The restriction of polyploidy to individual sectors of the stem is possible only if the initials occur in groups, with each component cell capable of becoming polyploid independently of the others.

EVOLUTION OF THE CONCEPT OF APICAL ORGANIZATION

As has been discussed by several writers (Foster, 1939*a*, 1941*a*; Schüepp, 1926; Sifton, 1944; Wardlaw, 1945), the view concerning

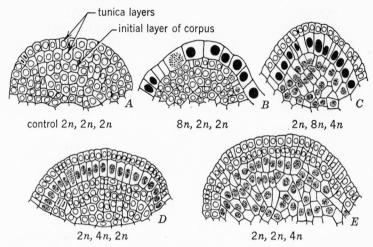

control 2*n*, 2*n*, 2*n*   8*n*, 2*n*, 2*n*   2*n*, 8*n*, 4*n*

2*n*, 4*n*, 2*n*   2*n*, 2*n*, 4*n*

FIG. 5.2. Shoot apices of *Datura* from a diploid plant (*A*) and from several periclinal cytochimeras. The chromosomal combinations in the various apices are indicated by the values given below each drawing. The first figure of each group of three refers to the first tunica layer; the second, to the second tunica layer; the third, to the initial layer of the corpus. The octoploid cells are the largest, and their nuclei are shown in black for emphasis; the tetraploid cells are somewhat smaller, and their nuclei are stippled; the diploid cells are the smallest, and their nuclei are shown by circles. The chromosomal characteristics of the tunica layers are perpetuated only in these layers and their derivatives; those of the initial layer of the corpus are immediately transmitted to the subjacent layers. This difference in the behavior results from the manner of division: in the tunica layers the divisions are anticlinal, in the corpus they occur in various planes. (Adapted from Satina et al., 1940.)

the number, the arrangement, and the activity of the initial cells and their recent derivatives in the apical meristems has undergone profound changes since the shoot apex was first recognized by Wolff (1759) as an undeveloped region from which growth of the plant proceeded.

The discovery of the apical cell in cryptogams led to the concept that such cells exist in phanerogams as well. The apical cell was interpreted as a constant structural and functional unit of apical meristems governing the whole process of growth. Subsequent researches refuted the assumption of a universal occurrence of apical cells and replaced it by a concept of independent origin of different parts of the plant body. The *apical-cell theory* was superseded by the *histogen theory*.

The histogen theory was developed by Hanstein (1868, 1870) on the basis of extensive studies of angiospermous shoot apices and embryos. Its basic theses are, first, that the main body of the plant arises, not from superficial cells, but from a mass of meristem of considerable depth, and, second, that this mass consists of three zones, the *histogens*, which may be differentiated by their origin and course of development. The uppermost, the *dermatogen* (from the Greek words meaning skin and to bring forth), is the primordial epidermis; the second, the *periblem* (from the Greek, clothing), gives rise to the cortex; the third, the *plerome* (from the Greek, that which fills), forms the entire inner mass of the axis. The dermatogen and the periblem form mantle-like layers covering the massive plerome. The dermatogen, each layer of the periblem, and the plerome begin with one or several initials distributed in superposed tiers in the uppermost part of the apical meristem. These initials, however, are of minor importance in determining the configuration of the apex. The configuration depends on the distribution of growth in the apex as a whole. Thus Hanstein had a modern dynamic view of the activity of an apical meristem, but his theory had one serious weakness in that it included an assumption that the destinies of the different regions of the plant body were determined from the very origin of these regions. According to the present view, strongly supported by the results obtained with cytochimeras, the histogenesis and the organogenesis have no obligate relationship to the segmentation and the layering of cells in the apical meristems. Furthermore, in shoot apices of gymnosperms and in those of many angiosperms a distinction between a periblem and a plerome, in the sense of Hanstein, does not exist (Foster, 1949, p. 33).

The apical-cell and the histogen theories have been developed with reference to both the root apex and the shoot apex. Later, attention became centered largely on shoot apices. The third theory of apical growth, the *tunica-corpus theory*, was an outcome of observations on these apices. According to this theory, two tissue zones occur in the apical meristem: the *tunica*, consisting of one or more peripheral layers of cells, and the *corpus*, a mass of cells enclosed by the tunica (fig. 5.5 and plate 13, *A–C*). The demarcation between these two zones results from the contrasting modes of cell division in the tunica and the corpus. The layers of the tunica show predominantly anticlinal divisions; that is, they are undergoing surface growth. The corpus cells divide in various planes, and the whole mass grows in volume. Each layer of the tunica arises from a group of separate initials, and the corpus has one layer of such initials. In other words, the number of tiers of initials is equal to the number of tunica layers plus one, the tier of corpus initials. In contrast to the histogen theory, the tunica-corpus theory does not imply any relation between the configuration of the cells at the apex and histogenesis below the apex. Although the epidermis usually arises from the outermost tunica layer, the underlying tissues may have their origin in the tunica or the corpus or both, depending on plant species and the number of tunica layers.

It will be useful at this point to correlate some of the terms reviewed thus far. Hanstein's "dermatogen" is not equivalent with Haberlandt's "protoderm." The protoderm refers to the outermost layer of the apical meristem, regardless of whether this layer arises from independent initials or not, and regardless of whether it gives rise to the epidermis only or to some subepidermal tissue also. The dermatogen, as conceived by Hanstein, has its own initials and develops into the epidermis. Thus, dermatogen is a more restricted term than protoderm. If the protoderm arises from individual initials and remains uniseriate in its future development, it corresponds to the dermatogen. In apices with a tunica, the outermost layer of the tunica coincides with the dermatogen, if it gives rise to no internal cell layers.

The introduction of the tunica-corpus concept of structure and growth of shoot apices stimulated a renewed interest in apical meristems and caused the appearance of a considerable body of literature on the subject. In the original statement of the theory by Schmidt (1924), the tunica and the corpus were clearly regarded as two interdependent growth zones, but some of the later proponents of the theory began to show a formalized attitude towards the problem by treating the tunica and the corpus as morphological entities. Owing largely to the efforts of Foster (1938, 1941, 1943, 1949) and his students (e.g., Ball, 1941; Boke, 1940, 1941, 1944, 1951; Gifford, 1950, 1951; Reeve, 1942, 1943, 1948; Sterling, 1944–1946) the concept of the tunica and corpus organization, instead of losing its plasticity, has become more fluid and retained its usefulness for the purposes of description of growth patterns in shoot apices of angiosperms.

The tunica-corpus concept was developed with reference to the angiosperms and proved to be largely unsuitable for the characterization of the apical meristem of gymnosperms (cf. Foster, 1941*a*, 1949, p. 30; Johnson, 1950). In this group of plants the shoot apices show a more or less pronounced differentiation into several regions distinguishable from one another by cell arrangement, cell size, reaction to staining, thickness of wall, and direction of cell division (figs. 5.3 and 5.4; plate 14, *C, D*). However, this complex zonation does not make the apical organization of gymnosperms fundamentally different from that of angiosperms. An increasing number of angiosperms is found to have a cytohistologic differentiation in the apical meristem similar to that of gymnosperms (cf. Foster, 1949; Philipson, 1949).

Few researches have dealt with the origin of the characteristic growth patterns in apical meristems during the development of a plant from a fertilized egg. The available information suggests that the apical meristems become localized during the development of the embryo, but that their more or less stable patterns are established during the early stages of growth of the plant from an embryo (Allen, 1946, 1947*a, b*; Nast, 1941; Reeve, 1948; Spurr, 1949).

The recognition of cytohistologic complexity of apical meristems has been one of the important results of studies on shoot apices during the last twenty-five years. It has brought an understanding that apical meristems are not simple and homogeneous in structure, but have a complex organization and are composed of parts distinguishable by their morphology and manner of growth. However, despite the visible segregation into zones, an apical meristem grows as a whole, with a close coordination between the activities of the different parts and without a precise and rigid relationship between the planes of division at the apex and the genesis of tissues and organs (Bower, 1935, p. 328; Foster, 1941*a*; Wardlaw, 1945, 1947).

Some workers are presently directing their efforts toward the determination of the role of the apical meristems in the development of the general form and organization of the plant as a whole. Basically, two assumptions are made concerning this role (see literature in Ball, 1946, and Snow and Snow, 1947). According to one, the apex is a self-determining and dominant center of development controlling the growth of the parts derived from it; the other assumption regards the apex as a plastic region operating under the control of stimuli sent to it from the mature subjacent tissues.

The interpretation of the apex as a self-determining region is emerging as a result of experimental studies of two kinds: (1) cultures of isolated apical meristems and (2) partial isolation of apical meristems and leaf primordia by operations on growing plants. The culture studies have shown that apical meristems of roots are capable of forming any tissue elements of the root, but within a short distance this capacity appears to be lost (Robbins et al., 1936). Apical meristems of shoots including the youngest leaf primordia may grow into entire plants, whereas the subjacent regions form only vasculated masses of cells (Ball, 1946). Operations on shoot apices indicate a high degree of independence of the apex, for the apex may continue growth and formation of primordia after its procambial connection with the subjacent region is severed (Ball, 1948; Snow and Snow, 1947; Wardlaw, 1947). The view that the activities of the apical meristem are controlled by events in the subjacent regions is largely based on the observations that the appearance of leaves at the shoot apices may be preceded by the differentiation of the procambium which later becomes associated with the emerging leaves (see chapter 15).

VEGETATIVE SHOOT APEX

The vegetative shoot apices vary in shape, size, and cytohistologic structure, and in their relation to the lateral organs. The shoot apices of conifers are commonly narrow and conical in form (fig. 5.4). In *Ginkgo* (fig. 5.3 and plate 14, *C, D*) and in the cycads they are rather broad and flat. The apical meristem of a grass and some other monocotyledons is elevated above the youngest leaf primordium (plate 14, *A*). In many dicotyledons it barely rises above the primordia (fig. 5.5), and in some it appears sunken below them (Gifford, 1950). The diameters of apices range from 90 microns in some angiosperms to 3.5 millimeters in *Cycas revoluta* (Foster, 1949, p. 30). The shape and the size of the apex change markedly during the development of the plant.

Vascular Cryptogams

In the lower Tracheophyta growth at the apex proceeds either from one or few initial cells, which are usually distinctive in their morphology (Bower, 1889–90, 1935; Härtel, 1938; Schüepp, 1926; Wardlaw, 1945). Most commonly the single apical cell is pyramidal (tetrahedral) in shape (e.g., Psilotales, Equisetaceae, certain ferns). The base of this pyramid is turned toward the free surface, and the new cells are formed at the other three sides (fig. 5.1, *A*). Some of the water ferns (*Salvinia* and *Azolla*) have three-sided apical cells, with two sides from which new cells are cut off (fig. 5.1, *B*). In *Selaginella* growth occurs from a single three- or four-sided apical cell or from a group of initials, and the two situations may be encountered in the same individual. The eusporangiate ferns have two to four initials, the leptosporangiates have one, but there is no sharp line of division between the two groups with reference to this character. Much information supports the view that in the ferns the type of apex with several initials is more primitive than the one with a single apical cell (Bower, 1889–91, 1935; Wardlaw, 1945).

Gymnosperms

The Gymnosperms commonly show several interrelated growth zones that are ultimately derived from a group of surface initials (Foster, 1941*a*; Kemp, 1943; figs. 5.3 and 5.4; plates 13, *D*, and 14, *C*, *D*). These initials divide periclinally to give rise to a subsurface group of cells, termed *mother cells*. Cell division is sluggish in the interior of this group but is active on its periphery. The products of the divisions along the flanks of the mother-cell group combine with derivatives resulting from anticlinal divisions of the apical initials. All together these lateral derivatives form a mantle-like peripheral zone of densely staining and relatively small cells which appear less differentiated (eumeristem) than the mother cells and sometimes even less than the cells of the initiating zone. The derivatives produced at the base of the mother-cell zone become pith cells, and usually they pass through a rib-meristem form of growth. (Part of the pith may arise from the peripheral zone.) The peripheral mantle of cells, rich in cytoplasm, is the seat of origin of the leaf primordia and of the epidermis, the cortex, and the vascular tissues of the axis.

The details of this structural pattern vary in the different groups of gymnosperms. The cycads have very wide apices (from 400 to 860 microns in *Zamia* to 2,018 to 3,305 microns in *Cycas*) with a relatively large number of cells in the initiating zone (Foster, 1939*b*, 1940, 1941*b*, 1943; Johnson, 1939, 1944*a*, *b*). The initiating zone, therefore, occupies a considerable portion of the surface of the meristem, and its periclinal derivatives converge toward the center of the meristematic mound. This convergence of cell layers from the initiating toward the derivative zones is a distinguishing characteristic of the cycads. In other seed plants investigated thus far, the cell layers typically diverge from the point of initiation (Foster, 1943). The peripheral zone of the shoot apex in a cycad shows no pronounced stratification, and the mother-cell zone is ill defined. The rib meristem derived from the base of the central zone is conspicuous, except in *Cycas revoluta*.

In *Ginkgo* (Foster, 1938, 1941*a*; fig. 5.3 and plate 14, *C*, *D*) the zones are much more sharply delimited than in the cycads. The central mother-cell zone differentiates close to the apical initials, and the renewal of meristematic activity on the periphery of this zone is so well expressed and definitely localized that the youngest derivatives are arranged in series radiating from the central cells in a

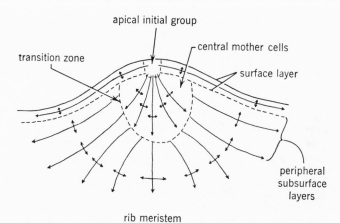

Fig. 5.3. Diagram delimiting the zones and their mode of growth in the shoot apex of *Ginkgo biloba* as seen in a longitudinal section. Arrows indicate the prevailing direction of growth. The apical initial group gives rise to the surface layer by anticlinal divisions. It also adds cells, by periclinal divisions, to the central mother-cell group. Growth in volume by cell enlargement and occasional divisions in various planes predominate in the central mother-cell zone. The outermost products of divisions in the mother-cell zone become displaced toward the transition zone where they divide by walls periclinal with reference to the mother-cell zone. The derivatives of these divisions form the peripheral subsurface layers and the prospective pith, the rib meristem zone. (After Foster, 1938. Compare with plate 14, *C*.)

manner characteristic of cambial derivatives. The rib meristem and the peripheral zones are, consequently, definitely set off from the central zone.

The apical zonation in the Coniferales is less diversified than in the cycads and less well defined than in *Ginkgo* (Cross, 1939, 1941, 1942, 1943*a*, *b*; Kemp, 1943; Korody, 1937; Sterling, 1945, 1946). Fundamentally, however, this zonation is similar to that in the lower gymnosperms (fig. 5.4 and plate 13, *D*). Many of the coniferous apices have been found to vary in their appearance in relation to seasonal variations in meristematic activity. Sometimes the outermost layer of cells of the meristem appears as discrete as a layer of the tunica of angiosperms, but this arrangement has not been found consistently in any one species studied thus far.

In contrast to the other gymnosperms, the Gnetales show a definite separation into a surface layer and an inner core derived from its own initials. Therefore, the shoot apices of *Ephedra* (Gifford, 1943) and *Gnetum* (Johnson, 1950) have been described as having a tunica-corpus pattern of growth. The tunica is uniseriate, and the corpus is

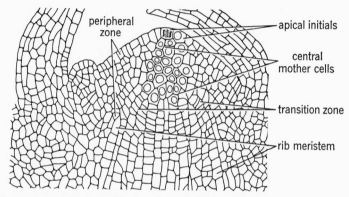

peripheral zone

apical initials

central mother cells

transition zone

rib meristem

Fig. 5.4. Drawing of a shoot apex of *Pinus strobus* in longitudinal view. Apical initials contribute cells to the surface layer by anticlinal divisions and to the central mother-cell zone by periclinal divisions. The mother-cell zone (cells with nuclei) contributes cells to the transition zone composed of actively dividing cells arranged in series radiating from the mother-cell zone. The products of these divisions form the rib meristem and the subsurface layers of the peripheral zone. (×150. From a slide by A. R. Spurr.)

comparable to the central mother-cell zone in its morphology and manner of division.

The data on the shoot apices in the gymnosperms suggest some possible trends in the evolution of apical structure in this group of plants (Foster, 1941*a*, 1943; Johnson, 1944*b*, 1950). The large apex of the cycads with its extensive initiation zone, massive core of mother cells, and generally diversified growth zones is probably primitive. Evolutionary advancement seems to have involved a refinement of the meristem in the sense that it became simpler, with less diversity in growth zones, and at the same time with a more precise separation of zones of surface and volume growth, each derived from independent initials. If this concept is correct, the Gnetales could be regarded as having the most advanced type of apical organization in the gymnosperms, a type essentially similar to that of the angiosperms.

Angiosperms

The main features of the tunica-corpus organization of the angio-spermous shoot apex have been discussed in a foregoing part of this chapter. One to five layers of tunica have been observed in the dicotyledons, one to three in the monocotyledons (Foster, 1939*a*; Rüdiger, 1939; Schalscha-Ehrenfeld, 1940; Thielke, 1951). An absence of tunica-corpus organization, with the outermost layer dividing periclinally, has been observed in *Saccharum officinarum* (Thielke, 1951). To draw the limits between the tunica and the corpus is no simple matter. The number of parallel periclinal layers in the shoot apex may vary during the ontogeny of the plant and under the influence of seasonal growth changes. There also may be periodic changes in stratification in relation to the initiation of leaves (plate 13, *A, B*; Cross and Johnson, 1941; Gifford, 1950; Reeve, 1942, 1948; Rouffa and Gunckel, 1951*a*; Schmidt, 1924; Schnabel, 1941). Some workers interpret such fluctuations as evidence of variations in the thickness of the tunica (Reeve, 1948; Rouffa and Gunckel, 1951*a*); others think that they are reflections of changes in the stratification of the corpus (Kliem, 1937; Schnabel, 1941; Zimmermann, 1928). A comparative study of representatives of the family Rosaceae suggests that possibly many layers of tunica is a more advanced condition than few layers (Rouffa and Gunckel, 1951*a*).

Evidence is accumulating that the apices of angiosperms may show a cytohistologic zonation like that in the gymnosperm apices: a somewhat vacuolated large-celled central zone enclosed in a denser staining, small-celled peripheral zone (plate 13, *C*). This zonation is combined with a tunica and corpus organization. The central zone may be restricted to the corpus or may extend into the tunica (Ball, 1941; Boke, 1941, 1951; Gifford, 1950; Majumdar, 1942; Millington and Gunckel, 1950; Philipson, 1949; Rouffa and Gunckel, 1951*a*).

ORIGIN OF LEAVES

In this chapter only those features of leaf origin are considered that are related to the structure and activity of the apical meristem. A leaf is initiated by periclinal divisions in a small group of cells at the side of an apical meristem. In angiosperms the tunica and the corpus are variously concerned with leaf initiation, depending on their quantitative relationship in a given apex (Cross and Johnson,

1941; Schmidt, 1924). In the dicotyledons the periclinal divisions initiating the leaves occur, not in the surface layer, but in one or more layers beneath it (fig. 5.5, C^3). If the tunica consists of a single layer, such divisions are located within the corpus; otherwise they may occur in both tunica and corpus or in the tunica only (Foster, 1936). In certain monocotyledons the superficial tunica layer undergoes periclinal divisions and gives rise to some or most of the tissue of the leaf (plate 14, *A*; Foster, 1936; Hsü, 1944; Sharman, 1945; Thielke, 1951). The leaves of gymnosperms generally arise from the peripheral tissue zone, and sometimes the surface layer appears to participate in the formation of the internal tissue of the leaf (Cross, 1939, 1942; Korody, 1937). In the vascular cryptogams the leaves arise either from single superficial cells or from groups of such cells, one of which soon enlarges and becomes the conspicuous apical cell of the primordium (fig. 5.1, *C*; Härtel, 1938; Sifton, 1944; Wardlaw, 1949).

The divisions initiating a leaf primordium cause the formation of a lateral prominence on the side of the shoot apex (plate 13, *A*, and fig. 5.5, *D*). This prominence constitutes the leaf base or the so-called *leaf buttress* (cf. Foster, 1936). Subsequently the leaf grows upwardly from the buttress (see chapter 16). The level at which a leaf buttress appears, in relation to the initiating region of the apical meristem, varies in different species (Chouard, 1937). In some species the apical meristem has the form of a relatively high cone, with the divisions that initiate the leaf appearing low on its sides (fig. 16.18, *A*). In others the apical meristem is less prominently elevated above the youngest leaf buttress (fig. 5.5, *D*). In still others it appears practically at one level with such a buttress (plate 13, *A*), or in a depression below it (e.g., *Drimys Winteri*, Gifford, 1950). Depending on the level at which a leaf primordium is initiated, the shoot apex shows more or less pronounced changes in shape during the period between the initiation of two successive leaf primordia (or pairs of primordia in plants with an opposite leaf arrangement, fig. 5.5). Such a period has been designated *plastochron* (Schmidt, 1924), a term originally formulated in a rather general sense for a time interval between two successive similar events that are repeated periodically (Askenasy, 1880). The changes in the morphology of the shoot apex occurring during one plastochron may be referred to as plastochronic changes.

Plastochronic changes may be illustrated most graphically by a shoot apex of a plant with a decussate (opposite, with the alternate pairs at right angles to each other) leaf arrangement, as depicted in fig. 5.5. Before the initiation of a new leaf primordium the apical meristem appears as a rounded mound (fig. 5.5, *A*). It gradually widens (fig. 5.5, *B, C*). Then leaf buttresses are initiated on its sides (fig. 5.5, *D*). While the new leaf primordia grow upward from the buttresses, the apical meristem again assumes the appearance of a small mound (fig. 5.5, *E*).

Thus, from plastochron to plastochron the shoot apex undergoes periodic changes in width. To characterize these changes, the expressions minimal-area and maximal-area phases were introduced (Schmidt, 1924). Since the distinction between the leaf buttresses in the process of formation and the apical meristem proper is not equally clear in different plants, some workers include the loci of leaf initiation in measuring the widest diameter of the shoot apex (Gifford, 1950; Schmidt, 1924, p. 355); others attempt to exclude these loci (Johnson, 1950; Popham and Chan, 1950; Rouffa and Gunckel, 1951*b*). Plastochronic changes may be expressed also in the cyto-histologic organization and in the distribution and intensity of mitotic activity in the apical meristem (Gifford, 1950; Popham and Chan, 1950; Zimmermann, 1928).

The study of cellular divisions during plastochronic changes reveals the mode of leaf initiation but gives no information regarding the causes determining the emergence of leaf primordia in their characteristic sequence (see chapter 15). To detect the causal relationships in leaf initiation, workers resort to experimental methods, such as the application of growth-regulating substances to the apices and the making of various incisions designed to affect the normal development of a leaf (Ball, 1944; Snow and Snow, 1947; Wardlaw, 1949). Several hypotheses have been advanced regarding the factors causing the primordia to arise in certain positions (cf. Philipson, 1949; Wetmore and Wardlaw, 1951). Some workers emphasize the possibility that the existing primordia determine the position of the new primordium (e.g., Plantefol, 1948; Wardlaw, 1949). Others seek the ultimate causes determining leaf arrangement, not in the apical meristem itself, but in the organization of the subjacent regions (see chapter 15). The determination of the position of leaves is only one of the many facets of the problem of apical organization. The study of this problem requires the consideration of both physical and physiological factors (Philipson, 1949; Wardlaw, 1949).

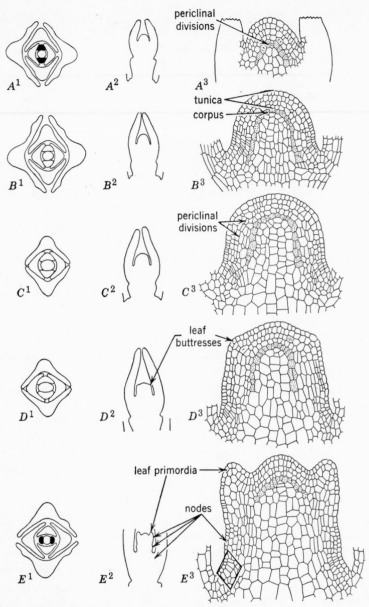

Fɪɢ. 5.5. Drawings illustrating leaf initiation in the shoot apex of *Hypericum uralum*, a dicotyledon with opposite leaves. The low-power views A^1–E^2 compare shoot apices in different stages of leaf initiation. Sections are transverse in A^1–E^1, longitudinal in A^2–E^2. The leaves are in pairs at each node and the median planes of the successive pairs cross each other at right angles (decussate arrange-

ORIGIN OF BRANCHES

In the lower vascular plants, such as *Psilotum, Lycopodium,* and *Selaginella,* branching occurs at the apex, without reference to the leaves. It is described as *dichotomous* when the original apical meristem undergoes a median division into two equal parts; as *monopodial* when a branch arises laterally at the apical meristem (Sifton, 1944). In seed plants, branches commonly are formed in close association with the leaves—they appear to originate in the axils of the leaves—and in their nascent state they are referred to as *axillary buds.* Judging from most investigations the term axillary is somewhat inaccurate because the buds generally arise on the stem (figs. 5.5, E^3, and 5.6) but become displaced closer to the leaf base, or even onto the leaf itself, by subsequent growth readjustments. Such relationship has been observed in the ferns (Wardlaw, 1943*b*), the dicotyledons (Garrison, 1949; Gifford, 1951; Koch, 1893), and the Gramineae (Evans and Grover, 1940; Sharman, 1945). In the grasses, the lack of developmental relation between the bud and the subtending (axillant) leaf is particularly clear. The bud originates close to the leaf located above it (fig. 5.7, *A*). Later the bud becomes separated from this leaf by the interpolation of an internode between it and the leaf.

Axillary buds are commonly initiated somewhat later than the leaves subtending them. Therefore, it is not always clear whether the meristem of the axillary bud is derived directly from the apical meristem of the main shoot or whether it originates from partly differentiated tissue of the internode. Both situations probably occur, because plants vary with regard to the time of appearance of axillary buds (Garrison, 1949; Gifford, 1951; Majumdar, 1942; Philipson, 1949; Sifton, 1944; Wardlaw, 1943*a*). On the one hand, the axillary buds may be directly related to the apical meristem of the parent shoot; on the other, they may intergrade, ontogenetically, with

---

ment). The protrusions in the axis below the leaves in $A^2–E^2$ are the leaf bases of the next lower pair of leaves. $A^3–E^3$, histologic details of apices from longitudinal sections similar to those shown in $A^2–E^2$. The stippling indicates the outer boundary of the corpus and its immediate derivatives. $A^1–E^3$ illustrate changes in the shape and histology of shoot apex through approximately one plastochron, starting with the phase shortly after the emergence of the leaf pair shown in black in A^1, and ending with the phase shortly after the emergence of the next higher leaf pair shown in black in E^1. The 4-sided figure in E^3 indicates the presumptive place of origin of an axillary bud. (Adapted from Zimmermann, 1928.)

the adventitious buds which arise in obviously differentiated tissue regions (Link and Eggers, 1946; Priestley and Swingle, 1929).

The initiation of the bud in higher vascular plants is characterized by a combination of anticlinal divisions, in one or more of the superficial layers of the young axis, and of various divisions, sometimes

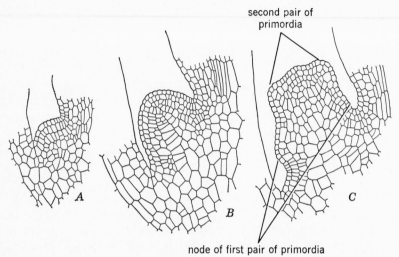

node of first pair of primordia

Fɪɢ. 5.6. Drawings illustrating origin of an axillary bud in *Hypericum uralum*. The axillary bud is formed by the derivatives of the three outer layers of tunica of the main shoot (see fig. 5.5). The two outer layers divide anticlinally and maintain their individuality as the two outer layers of tunica of the bud (*A–C*). The third layer of the main shoot divides periclinally and otherwise and gives rise to the third and fourth layers of tunica and to the corpus of the bud. The third tunica layer is evident in the bud in *C*, but the fourth has not been organized yet. In *C*, the second pair of leaf primordia is being initiated. The first pair was oriented in a plane perpendicular to the surface of the drawing. (Adapted from Zimmermann, 1928.)

predominantly periclinal, in the deeper layers (figs. 5.6 and 5.7). This coordinated growth in surface of the peripheral region and growth in volume at greater depth causes the bud to protrude above the surface of the axis. Sometimes the divisions initiating a bud are quite regular and result in the formation of a series of layers approximately parallel to each other (fig. 5.7, *C*). Because of this configuration the early bud meristem has been named shell zone (Garrison, 1949; Gifford, 1951; Reeve, 1943; Schmidt, 1924). Depending on the quantitative relationships between the tunica and the corpus in the shoot apices of angiosperms, the derivatives of the two zones variously participate in the formation of the axillary bud meri-

stem, and not necessarily in the same proportions as in the formation of the leaves of the same plant, because the buds may arise in
deeper layers than the leaves (Schmidt, 1924; Sharman, 1942, 1945;

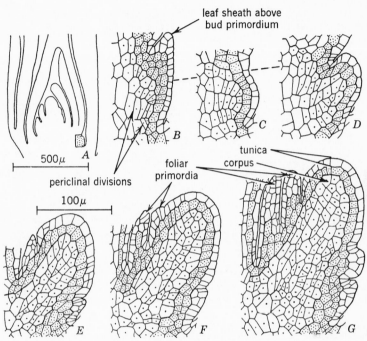

FIG. 5.7. Drawings depicting the development of an axillary bud in *Agropyron
repens* (quackgrass). Median longitudinal sections in the plane of leaves. *A*, low-
power view of the shoot apex with several leaf primordia. The stippled part
indicates the position of the axillary bud. *Agropyron* has a two-layered tunica
(see fig. 16.18). The axillary bud is formed by the derivatives of tunica and
corpus. The derivatives of the second layer of tunica are stippled, and those of
the corpus are indicated by a single dot in each cell in *B–G*. The bud is initiated
by periclinal divisions in the corpus derivatives (*B* and *C*). This growth is accompanied by anticlinal divisions in the tunica derivatives. The bud emerges
above the surface of the stem (*D*). By enlargement and rib meristem growth
the corpus derivatives elongate the core of the axillary bud (*E–G*). They also
organize its corpus. The tunica derivatives remain in a biseriate arrangement at
the apex of the bud and form its two-layered tunica (*E* and *G*). Leaf primordia
arise on the bud (*E–G*). (Adapted from Sharman, 1945.)

Zimmermann, 1928). If the axillary bud develops into a shoot, its
apical meristem is gradually organized—commonly duplicating the
pattern found in the parent shoot apex—and proceeds with the
formation of leaves (figs. 5.6 and 5.7).

Axillary buds are described as arising *exogenously*, that is, in relatively superficial tissues. This appears to be an entirely appropriate interpretation, when the origin of such buds is compared with that of lateral roots (plate 15, *B*), which are initiated deeply in the parent axis (*endogenous* origin). However, an example of endogenous initiation of adventitious buds, in the carob tree, is recorded in the literature (Thompson, 1943-44).

FLORAL APEX

In the reproductive state, the floral apices replace the vegetative, sometimes directly, but more frequently through the development of inflorescences (fig. 5.8). It would seem plausible to assume that the vegetative apex becomes reorganized, more or less abruptly, into the floral apex and that the two are merely different growth forms of the same meristem. However, the idea that the floral meristem is fundamentally different from the vegetative has been presented in the literature (Grégoire, 1938; see also reviews by Foster, 1939a, and Philipson, 1949), and many authors would base the development of the flower on this concept. Usually the floral meristem is found to be different from the vegetative in varying degrees in the manner of its growth and its cytologic and histologic characteristics, but most workers think that these differences are not fundamental (e.g., Boke, 1947; Lawalrée, 1948; Philipson, 1947b, 1949; Reeve, 1943; Satina and Blakeslee, 1941; Schüepp, 1942).

Before considering the structural differences between vegetative and floral meristems it is necessary to recall that the flowers may be borne on a wide variety of inflorescences. The cytohistologic structure which characterizes the apical meristem during the reproductive state (that is, the floral-apex structure) appears sometime during the development of the inflorescence apex.

The change from the vegetative to the floral form of apex is readily detected at low magnifications by changes in the growth pattern and shape of the apex and by the morphology of lateral organs. In some plants, like the soy bean, the inflorescences are borne on axillary branches, and therefore the first sign of approaching flowering is the accelerated production of buds in the axils of leaf primordia of the lateral shoots (Murneek and Gomez, 1936). In many grasses the apex rapidly elongates before the differentiation of the inflorescence (Bonnett, 1936; plate 81). Frequently, the inflorescence and flower apices are conspicuously flatter and wider than the vegetative (Borthwick et al., 1931; Philipson, 1946, 1947a, b; fig. 5.8).

Histologically the floral meristem differs from the vegetative in varying degrees. It may retain the same quantitative relationship

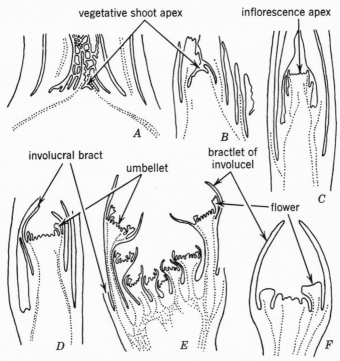

FIG. 5.8. Transformation of the apical meristem during the shift from vegetative growth to the development of flowers in *Daucus carota*. The inflorescence of the carrot is a compound umbel. It consists of an axis bearing several small umbels (umbellets) in an umbellate arrangement. *E* depicts such a compound umbel in a young state. *A*, vegetative shoot apex at the base of the rosette of leaves. *B*, shoot apex at approach of reproductive stage raised above the ground level by internodal elongation. *C* and *D*, flattened inflorescence (umbel) apices producing bracts and primordia of umbellets. The apex of each umbellet assumes an appearance similar to that of the apex of the umbel and produces bractlets and floral primordia (*E*). Each flower of the umbellet also develops a flattened apex and forms the floral organs (*F*). (*A–E*, ×13; *F*, ×46. After Borthwick et al., 1931.)

between the tunica and the corpus as was present in the vegetative apex (plate 78, *A*, *B*), or the number of discrete surface layers may be reduced or augmented (Philipson, 1949). The most frequently described change concerns the distribution of the eumeristematic and the more highly vacuolated cells (fig. 5.9). In many species the floral apex shows a uniform, densely staining, small-celled peripheral zone of one or more layers enclosing a lighter-staining, larger-celled core. The distinctive features of the floral meristem were emphasized by Grégoire (1938) when he advanced his concept of a fundamental

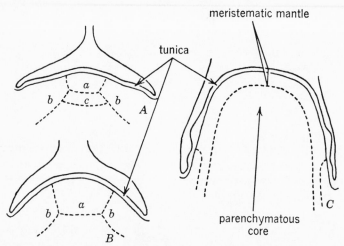

Fig. 5.9. Diagrams illustrating the modification in the zonation of a vegetative apex during the change into an inflorescence apex in *Succisa pratensis*. *A*, apex in the spring when it is forming foliage leaves; *B*, in early stage of enlargement to form an inflorescence primordium; *C*, in later stage of development of inflorescence. Details are: *a*, central zone of large cells; *b*, peripheral zone; *c*, rib meristem. *a* and parts of *b* and *c* constitute the corpus. Initiation of inflorescence is associated with cessation of growth in length and disappearance of rib meristem (*B*). Later, the central and peripheral zones are reorganized to form, together with the tunica, a meristematic mantle enclosing a parenchymatous core which now has no trace of rib meristem activity (*C*). (After Philipson, 1947.)

dissimilarity between the floral and the vegetative apices. However, they may also be interpreted as expressions of determinate growth and of the shift in the direction of growth during the organization of the floral apex. Axis elongation becomes limited, and therefore the characteristic activity of the corpus, resulting in the formation of the rib meristem, is discontinued. The cells of the central tissue enlarge and vacuolate prominently, and intercellular spaces sometimes appear among them (Philipson, 1946, 1949; Reeve, 1943). Meristematic activity becomes restricted to the peripheral mantle-like zone, which apparently is derived from the cell layers corresponding to the tunica and part of the corpus of the vegetative apex (Lawalrée,

1948; Philipson, 1947*b*, 1949). This activity is concerned, not with the elongation of the shoot and the maintenance of the initial region of the apical meristem, but only with the production of floral organs. In the absence of axial elongation the flower parts appear in close sequence.

The change from the vegetative to the flowering state not only affects the apical meristems concerned with flower production but alters, physiologically and morphologically, other parts of the plant as well (Melchers and Lang, 1948; Murneek and Gomez, 1936; Philipson, 1949). This change is associated with a shift in the balance between meristematic activity and cell maturation in favor of the latter. It usually signifies the end of growth at the given apical meristem because of the determinate nature of the flower, and in annual plants it means the end of growth and the approach of death of the entire plant. The change is not irreversible, however, and may be interrupted or prevented by subjecting the plant to influences that favor vegetative growth. Even such a typical characteristic of the flower as determinate growth is not fixed, and the floral meristem occasionally resumes vegetative growth after the floral parts have been formed (Thompson, 1943–44). Thus, the visible change from the vegetative to the floral meristem is a reflection of a physiologic change in the plant, and the floral apex appears as an ontogenetic modification of the vegetative apex (Foster, 1939*a*; Schüepp, 1942).

ROOT APEX

The apical meristem of the root, like that of the shoot, shows diverse patterns of growth, and there is no constant relation between the structure of the initial region and the delimitation of the primary tissues of the axis (fig. 5.10; Kroll, 1912; Schüepp, 1926; Wagner, 1939). In contrast to the apical meristem of the shoot, that of the root produces cells not only toward the axis but also away from it, for it initiates the rootcap. Because of the presence of the rootcap the root meristem is not terminal but subterminal in its position, in the sense that it is located beneath the rootcap (plate 15, *A*). It further differs from the shoot meristem in that it forms no lateral appendages comparable to the leaves, and no branches. The root branches are usually initiated beyond the region of most active growth, and, as was pointed out previously, they arise endogenously. (See also chapter 17.) Because of the absence of leaves, the root apex shows no such periodic changes in shape and structure as may occur in shoot apices in relation to leaf initiation. It also produces no nodes and internodes, and, therefore, the root grows more uniformly in length than the shoot, in which the internodes elongate much more than the nodes. The rib-meristen type of growth is characteristic of the elongating root cortex (fig. 5.13 and plate 14, B; Wagner, 1937).

The apical meristem of the root, like that of the shoot, may be termed *promeristem* and, as such, contrasted with the subjacent primary meristematic tissues. The young root axis is more or less clearly separated into the future central cylinder and cortex. In their meristematic state, the tissues of these two regions are the *procambium* and the *ground meristem*, respectively. The term procambium may be applied to the entire central cylinder of the root, if this cylinder eventually differentiates into a solid vascular core. Many roots, however, have a pith-like area in the center. This area is sometimes regarded as potentially vascular and therefore procambial in its meristematic state, sometimes as ground tissue similar to that of the pith in stems and differentiating from a ground meristem (Guttenberg, 1940; see also chapter 17). The term *protoderm*, if used, according to Haberlandt (1914), to designate the surface layer, regardless of its developmental relation to other tissues, may be applied to the outer layer of the young root. Usually the root protoderm becomes distinct some distance from the promeristem because of its common origin with either the cortex or the rootcap.

Some workers continue to use Hanstein's histogen terms to characterize the organization of the young root (Clowes, 1950; Eames and MacDaniels, 1947; Guttenberg, 1940, 1941). In this book the structure of the differentiating root is analyzed in terms of the mature regions to be formed: the epidermis, the cortex, and the central (or vascular) cylinder. If it is necessary to emphasize the meristematic state of the tissues in these regions, the terms protoderm, ground meristem, and procambium are used. If the root has a distinct pith, the pith is treated as ground tissue.

The principal source of information on the detailed structure and growth of the apical meristems of roots is the literature of the past century. (See reviews by Kroll, 1912, and Schüepp, 1926.) In contrast to the apical meristems of the shoots, those of the roots have received relatively little attention in modern times, and therefore the information on the apical meristems of the shoot and the root has not been coordinated. The first attempt at such a coordination (Allen, 1947a, b) for an individual species (*Pseudotsuga taxifolia*) shows that the comparative structure of the apical meristems of the shoot and the root is part of the large problem of homologies between the tissue regions of the two organs.

The root apices have been divided into so-called types on the basis of the developmental relation between the initiating region and the primary tissue regions. In the lower vascular plants (Bower, 1889–90, 1935; Johnson, 1933), all tissues are derived either from a single apical cell (e.g., Equisetaceae, Polypodiaceae; fig. 5.10, *A*) or from several initials arranged in one tier (e.g., Marattiaceae). These plants usually have the same apical structure in both the root and the shoot. In gymnosperms and angiosperms either all the primary tissue regions appear to arise from a common poorly defined meristematic layer, or one or more of these regions can be traced to separate initials. The principal patterns of apical organization that have been described for roots are briefly summarized on the basis of the review by Schüepp (1926).

Many gymnosperms and some dicotyledonous families (e.g., Proteaceae, Casuarinaceae, and certain Leguminosae) have two sets of initials, one forming the central cylinder, the other giving rise to the cortex and the rootcap. The outermost layer of the cortex becomes the epidermis. A more complicated pattern is found in some Rosaceae, some Leguminosae, the Juglandaceae, the Tiliaceae, and the Umbelliferae. The central cylinder and the inner cortex arise from one set of initials, the rest of the cortex and the rootcap from another. In these plants, too, the epidermis is the outer layer of the cortex.

In certain dicotyledons (Ranalian families, some Leguminosae and Amentiferae, and others) all parts of the root appear to arise from a common initial region, the epidermis eventually differentiating outside the cortex from cells ontogenetically related to the rootcap cells (comparable to fig. 5.10, *C*).

The most precise organization of the meristem in the dicotyledons is based on three tiers of initials. One gives origin to the central cylinder, the second to the cortex, and the third to the epidermis and the rootcap (figs. 5.10, *E*, and 5.13, *A*; plate 16, *A*). Representatives of many dicotyledonous families of various taxonomic groups have this kind of apical structure. Some specific examples may be found among the Rosaceae, the Solanaceae, the Cruciferae, the Scrophulariaceae, and the Compositae.

Four structural patterns have been described in the monocotyledons. In one, the central cylinder has separate initials, the cortex and

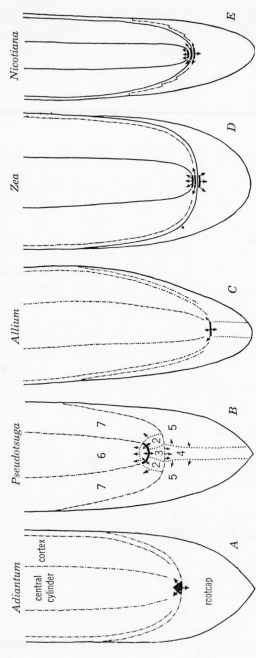

Fig. 5.10. Diagrams of root tips showing structure of apical meristems in relation to the derivative regions. *A*, a single apical cell (black triangle) forms all parts of the root and the rootcap. *B*, the initial zone (black arc) gives derivatives to the mother-cell zones of the various root parts as follows: 1 (below 6, not marked) of central cylinder (6); 2, of cortex (7); 3, of column of rootcap (4). Longitudinal divisions on the periphery of the column give cells to the peripheral part of the rootcap (5). (Adapted from Allen, 1947b.) *C*, initial region with poorly individualized initials gives rise to the central cylinder, the cortex, and the column. Longitudinal divisions on the periphery of the column form the peripheral parts of the rootcap, the epidermis, and probably part of the cortex. (Cf. fig. 5.11 and plate 16, *B*.) *D*, three tiers of initials in the initial zone. One gives rise to the central cylinder; the second, to the cortex; the third, to the rootcap. The epidermis differentiates from the outermost layer of the cortex. (Cf. fig. 5.12 and plate 72, *B*.) *E*, three tiers of initials, one forming the central cylinder; the second, the cortex; the third, the rootcap. The epidermis originates from the root-cap by periclinal divisions. (Cf. fig. 5.13, *A*, and plate 16, *A*.)

the rootcap have common initials, and the epidermis arises as part of the rootcap. (This pattern is supposed to agree with that found in the gymnosperms and certain dicotyledons.) In the second, the central cylinder, the cortex, and the rootcap have separate initials,

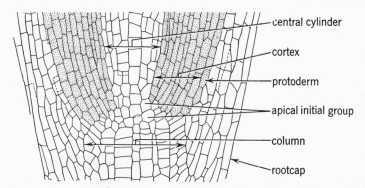

FIG. 5.11. Root tip of *Allium sativum* in longitudinal section. Note longitudinal divisions in the outer layers of the column. These divisions contribute cells to the peripheral part of the rootcap. For further details see legends to fig. 5.10, *C*, and plate 16, *B*. (×210.)

and the epidermis constitutes the outermost layer of the cortex (figs. 5.10, *D*, 5.12, and 5.13, *B*). In the third, all four regions—the central cylinder, the cortex, the epidermis, and the rootcap—have separate initials. The fourth pattern was found in *Allium sativum* (Mann, 1952; fig. 5.11 and plate 16, *B*). It resembles that found in those dicotyledons in which all parts of the root appear to arise from a

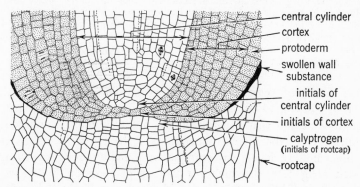

FIG. 5.12. Root tip of *Zea mays* in longitudinal section. The epidermis arises from the same initials as the cortex. Compare with fig. 5.10, *D*. The swollen wall substance originates through the gelatinization of the wall between the rootcap and the protoderm, a phenomenon associated with the sloughing of the rootcap (see chapter 17). (×205.)

common initial region (fig. 5.10, *C*). Thus, two of the monocotyledonous patterns are characterized by an independent origin of rootcap, and the meristem concerned with the formation of this structure is referred to as *calyptrogen* (from the Greek *calyptra*, veil, and *genos*, offspring).

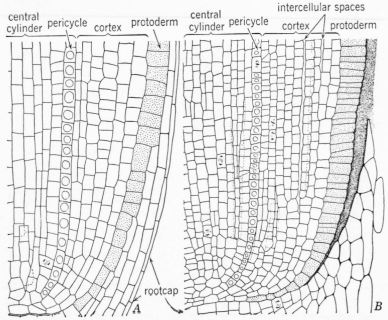

Fig. 5.13. Drawings of longitudinal sections of root tips of *Nicotiana tabacum* (*A*) and of *Zea mays* (*B*), illustrating two contrasting methods of origin of epidermis. In *A* the epidermis separates from the rootcap by periclinal divisions. In *B* the epidermis arises from the same initials as the cortex through an early periclinal division in one of the recent derivatives of a cortical initial. The densely stippled area in *B* indicates the gelatinized wall between the rootcap and the protoderm. (*A*, ×300; *B*, ×228.)

The results of two modern investigations on root apices (Allen, 1947*a*, *b*; Clowes, 1950) show that recognition of the initials may be quite difficult and that zonation in the apices is more complex than it appears from the mere enumeration of the initial layers given in the preceding review. An example of a highly complex zonation is given in fig. 5.10, *B*, which is a diagram of the root tip of *Pseudotsuga taxifolia* (Allen, 1947*b*). In this root, two kinds of initials are recognized: the "permanent" (black arc in the figure), which remain in their position indefinitely, and the "temporary" (zones 1, 2, and 3) which give origin to the various root regions and are from time to time replaced by derivatives from the permanent initials. *Fagus sylvatica* appears to have a basically similar apical organization, but, judging from the description (Clowes, 1950), the initials of the various regions are more independent than those of *Pseudotsuga*.

A distinct departure from the modern view on the structure of the initial region is expressed in the recently advanced concept that the roots of dicotyledons have an apical cell which renews the so-called initials of the various root regions (Guttenberg, 1947).

The structure of root apices requires further investigation, particularly by the use of artificial and spontaneous chimeras that have yielded such significant results in the study of shoot apices. The first attempt at such an approach to the study of roots has yielded only sectorial chimeras in seedling roots of *Vicia* and *Crepis* (Brumfield, 1943). These results were taken as an indication that the roots possessed very few initials, all located in one layer of the meristem.

The tips of growing roots are commonly used to illustrate the principal steps in tissue differentiation: cell division, cell elongation, and cell maturation. However, the demarcation of the regions in which each of the three processes predominate may be made only very approximately. At the same level of the root, these processes overlap not only in the different tissue regions but also in the different cells of the same tissue region, and even in individual cells (Esau, 1943; Wagner, 1937). The meristematic cortex vacuolates and develops intercellular spaces very close to the apex, where the central-cylinder meristem still appears dense. In the central cylinder the precursors of the innermost xylem vessels cease dividing, enlarge, and vacuolate considerably in advance of the other vascular precursors (plate 15, *A*), and the first sieve tubes mature in the part of the root where cell division is still in progress (fig. 17.7). In individual cells, division, elongation, and vacuolation are combined.

REFERENCES

Allen, G. S. Embryogeny and development of the apical meristems of *Pseudotsuga*. I. Fertilization and early embryogeny. *Amer. Jour. Bot.* 33:666–677. 1946.

Allen, G. S. Embryogeny and the development of the apical meristems of *Pseudotsuga*. II. Late embryogeny. *Amer. Jour. Bot.* 34:73–80. 1947*a*.

Allen, G. S. Embryogeny and the development of the apical meristems of *Pseudotsuga*. III. Development of the apical meristems. *Amer. Jour. Bot.* 34:204–211. 1947*b*.

Askenasy, E. Über eine neue Methode, um die Vertheilung der Wachsthumsintensität in wachsenden Theilen zu bestimmen. *Naturhist. Medic. Ver. Heidelberg, Verhandl. N. S.* 2:70–153. 1880.

Bain, H. F., and H. Dermen. Sectorial polyploidy and phyllotaxy in the cranberry (*Vaccinium macrocarpon* Ait.). *Amer. Jour. Bot.* 31:581–587. 1944.

Baker, R. E. Induced polyploid, periclinal chimeras in *Solanum tuberosum.* *Amer. Jour. Bot.* 30:187–195. 1943.

Ball, E. The development of the shoot apex and of the primary thickening meristem in *Phoenix canariensis* Chaub., with comparisons to *Washingtonia filifera* Wats. and *Trachycarpus excelsa* Wendl. *Amer. Jour. Bot.* 28:820–832. 1941.

Ball, E. The effect of synthetic growth substances on the shoot apex of *Tropaeolum majus* L. *Amer. Jour. Bot.* 31:316–327. 1944.

Ball, E. Development in sterile culture of stem tips and subjacent regions of *Tropaeolum majus* L. and *Lupinus albus* L. *Amer. Jour. Bot.* 33:301–318. 1946.

Ball, E. Differentiation in the primary shoots of *Lupinus albus* L. and *Tropaeolum majus* L. *Soc. Expt. Biol. Symposia.* No. 2. *Growth.* 1948:246–262. 1948.

Blaser, H. W., and J. Einset. Leaf development in six periclinal chromosomal chimeras of apple varieties. *Amer. Jour. Bot.* 35:473–482. 1948.

Boke, N. H. Histogenesis and morphology of the phyllode in certain species of *Acacia.* *Amer. Jour. Bot.* 27:73–90. 1940.

Boke, N. H. Zonation in the shoot apices of *Trichocereus spachianus* and *Opuntia cylindrica.* *Amer. Jour. Bot.* 28:656–664. 1941.

Boke, N. H. Histogenesis of the leaf and areole in *Opuntia cylindrica.* *Amer. Jour. Bot.* 31:299–316. 1944.

Boke, N. H. Development of the adult shoot apex and floral initiation in *Vinca rosea* L. *Amer. Jour. Bot.* 34:433–439. 1947.

Boke, N. H. Histogenesis of the vegetative shoot in *Echinocereus.* *Amer. Jour. Bot.* 38:23–38. 1951.

Bonnett, O. T. The development of the wheat spike. *Jour. Agr. Res.* 53:445–451. 1936.

Borthwick, H. A., M. Phillips, and W. W. Robbins. Floral development in *Daucus carota.* *Amer. Jour. Bot.* 18:784–796. 1931.

Bower, F. O. The comparative examination of meristems of ferns as a phylogenetic study. *Ann. Bot.* 3:305–392. 1889–90.

Bower, F. O. Is the eusporangiate or the leptosporangiate the more primitive type in the ferns? *Ann. Bot.* 5:109–134. 1890–91.

Bower, F. O. *Primitive land plants.* London, Macmillan and Company. 1935.

Brumfield, R. T. Cell-lineage studies in root meristems by means of chromosome rearrangements induced by X-rays. *Amer. Jour. Bot.* 30:101–110. 1943.

Chouard, P. Le méristème des pousses végétatives de quelques Monocotylédones. *Ann. des Sci. Nat., Bot.* Ser. 10. 19:83–92. 1937.

Clowes, F. A. L. Root apical meristems of *Fagus sylvatica. New Phytol.* 49:248–268. 1950.

Cross, G. L. The structure and development of the apical meristem in the shoots of *Taxodium distichum. Torrey Bot. Club Bul.* 66:431–452. 1939.

Cross, G. L. Some histogenetic features of the shoot of *Cryptomeria japonica. Amer. Jour. Bot.* 28:573–582. 1941.

Cross, G. L. Structure of the apical meristem and development of the foliage leaves of *Cunninghamia lanceolata. Amer. Jour. Bot.* 29:288–301. 1942.

Cross, G. L. The shoot apices of *Athrotaxis* and *Taiwania*. *Torrey Bot. Club Bul.* 70:335–348. 1943a.

Cross, G. L. A comparison of the shoot apices of the sequoias. *Amer. Jour. Bot.* 30:130–142. 1943b.

Cross, G. L., and T. J. Johnson. Structural features of the shoot apices of diploid and colchicine-induced, tetraploid strains of *Vinca rosea* L. *Torrey Bot. Club. Bul.* 68:618–635. 1941.

Dermen, H. The mechanism of colchicine-induced cytohistological changes in cranberry. *Amer. Jour. Bot.* 32:387–394. 1945.

Dermen, H. Periclinal cytochimeras and histogenesis in cranberry. *Amer. Jour. Bot.* 34:32–43. 1947.

Dermen, H., and H. F. Bain. A general cytological study of colchicine polyploidy in cranberry. *Amer. Jour. Bot.* 31:451–463. 1944.

Eames, A. J., and L. H. MacDaniels. *An introduction to plant anatomy.* 2nd ed. New York, McGraw-Hill Book Company. 1947.

Esau, K. Origin and development of primary vascular tissues in seed plants. *Bot. Rev.* 9:125–206. 1943.

Evans, M. W., and F. O. Grover. Developmental morphology of the growing point of the shoot and the inflorescence in grasses. *Jour. Agr. Res.* 61:481–520. 1940.

Foster, A. S. Leaf differentiation in angiosperms. *Bot. Rev.* 2:349–372. 1936.

Foster, A. S. Structure and growth of the shoot apex in *Ginkgo biloba*. *Torrey Bot. Club Bul.* 65:531–556. 1938.

Foster, A. S. Problems of structure, growth and evolution in the shoot apex of seed plants. *Bot. Rev.* 5:454–470. 1939a.

Foster, A. S. Structure and growth of the shoot apex of *Cycas revoluta*. *Amer. Jour. Bot.* 26:372–385. 1939b.

Foster, A. S. Further studies on zonal structure and growth of the shoot apex of *Cycas revoluta* Thunb. *Amer. Jour. Bot.* 27:487–501. 1940.

Foster, A. S. Comparative studies on the structure of the shoot apex in seed plants. *Torrey Bot. Club Bul.* 68:339–350. 1941a.

Foster, A. S. Zonal structure of the shoot apex of *Dioon edule* Lindl. *Amer. Jour. Bot.* 28:557–564. 1941b.

Foster, A. S. Zonal structure and growth of the shoot apex in *Microcycas calocoma* (Miq.) A. Dc. *Amer. Jour. Bot.* 30:56–73. 1943.

Foster, A. S. *Practical plant anatomy.* 2nd ed. New York, D. Van Nostrand Company. 1949.

Frost, H. B., and C. A. Krug. Diploid-tetraploid periclinal chimeras as bud variants in *Citrus*. *Genetics* 27:619–634. 1942.

Garrison, R. Origin and development of axillary buds: *Syringa vulgaris* L. *Amer. Jour. Bot.* 36:205–213. 1949.

Gifford, E. M., Jr. The structure and development of the shoot apex of *Ephedra altissima* Desf. *Torrey Bot. Club Bul.* 70:15–25. 1943.

Gifford, E. M., Jr. The structure and development of the shoot apex in certain woody Ranales. *Amer. Jour. Bot.* 37:595–611. 1950.

Gifford, E. M., Jr. Ontogeny of the vegetative axillary bud in *Drimys Winteri* var. *chilensis*. *Amer. Jour. Bot.* 38:234–243. 1951.

Goodwin, R. H., and W. Stepka. Growth and differentiation in the root tip of *Phleum pratense*. *Amer. Jour. Bot.* 32:36–46. 1945.

Grégoire, V. La morphogénèse et l'autonomie morphologique de l'appareil floral. I. Le carpelle. *Cellule* 47:287–452. 1938.

Guttenberg, H. von. Der primäre Bau der Angiospermenwurzel. In: K. Linsbauer *Handbuch der Pflanzenanatomie*. Band 8. Lief. 39. 1940.

Guttenberg, H. von. Der primäre Bau der Gymnospermenwurzel. In: K. Linsbauer. *Handbuch der Pflanzenanatomie*. Band 8. Lief. 41. 1941.

Guttenberg, H. von. Studien über die Entwicklung des Wurzelvegetationspunktes der Dikotyledonen. *Planta* 35:360–396. 1947.

Haberlandt, G. *Physiological plant anatomy*. London, Macmillan and Company. 1914.

Hanstein, J. Die Scheitelzellgruppe im Vegetationspunkt der Phanerogamen. *Festschr. Niederrhein. Gesell. Natur- und Heilkunde* 1868:109–134. 1868.

Hanstein, J. Die Entwicklung des Keimes der Monokotylen und der Dikotylen. *Bot. Abhandl.* 1(1):1–112. 1870.

Härtel, K. Studien an Vegetationspunkten einheimischer Lycopodien. *Beitr. z. Biol. der Pflanz.* 25:125–168. 1938.

Hsü, J. Structure and growth of the shoot apex of *Sinocalamus Beecheyana* McClure. *Amer. Jour. Bot.* 31:404–411. 1944.

Johnson, M. A. Origin and development of tissues in *Equisetum scirpoides*. *Bot. Gaz.* 94:469–494. 1933.

Johnson, M. A. Structure of the shoot apex in *Zamia*. *Bot. Gaz.* 101:189–203. 1939.

Johnson, M. A. Zonal structure of the shoot apex in *Encephalartos, Bowenia, and Macrozamia*. *Bot. Gaz.* 106:26–33. 1944a.

Johnson, M. A. On the shoot apex of the cycads. *Torreya* 44:52–58. 1944b.

Johnson, M. A. Growth and development of the shoot of *Gnetum gnemon* L. I. The shoot apex and pith. *Torrey Bot. Club Bul.* 77:354–367. 1950.

Jones, W. N. Chimaeras: a summary and some special aspects. *Bot. Rev.* 3:545–562. 1937.

Kemp, M. Morphological and ontogenetic studies on *Torreya californica* Torr. I. The vegetative apex of the megasporangiate tree. *Amer. Jour. Bot.* 30:504–517. 1943.

Kliem, F. Vegetationspunkt und Blattanlage bei *Avena sativa*. *Beitr. z. Biol. der Pflanz.* 24:281–310. 1937.

Koch, L. Die vegetative Verzweigung der höheren Gewächse. *Jahrb. f. Wiss. Bot.* 25:380–488. 1893.

Korody, E. Studien am Spross-Vegetationspunkt von *Abies concolor, Picea excelsa* und *Pinus montana*. *Beitr. z. Biol. der Pflanz.* 25:23–59. 1937.

Kroll, G. H. Kritische Studie über die Verwertbarkeit der Wurzelhaubentypen für die Entwicklungsgeschichte. *Bot. Centbl. Beihefte* 28:134–158. 1912.

Lawalrée, A. Histogénèse florale et végétative chez quelques Composées. *Cellule* 52:215–294. 1948.

Link, G. K. K., and V. Eggers. Mode, site, and time of initiation of hypocotyledonary bud primordia in *Linum usitatissimum* L. *Bot. Gaz.* 107:441–454. 1946.

Majumdar, G. P. The organization of the shoot of *Heracleum* in the light of development. *Ann. Bot.* 6:49–81. 1942.

Mann, L. K. Anatomy of the garlic bulb and factors affecting bulb development. *Hilgardia* 21:195–251. 1952.

Melchers, G., and A. Lang. Die Physiologie der Blütenbildung. *Biol. Zentbl.* 67:105–174. 1948.

Millington, W. F., and J. E. Gunckel. Structure and development of the vegetative shoot tip of *Liriodendron tulipifera* L. *Amer. Jour. Bot.* 37:326–335. 1950.

Murneek, A. E., and E. T. Gomez. Influence of length of day (photoperiod) on development of the soy bean plant var. Biloxi. *Mo. Agr. Exp. Sta. Res. Bul.* 242. 1936.

Nast, C. G. The embryogeny and seedling morphology of *Juglans regia* L. *Lilloa* 6:163–205. 1941.

Philipson, W. R. Studies in the development of the inflorescence. I. The capitulum of *Bellis perennis* L. *Ann. Bot.* 10:257–270. 1946.

Philipson, W. R. Studies in the development of the inflorescence. II. The capitula of *Succisa pratensis* Moench. and *Dipsacus fullonum* L. *Ann. Bot.* 11: 285–297. 1947*a*.

Philipson, W. R. Some observations on the apical meristems of leafy and flowering shoots. *Linn. Soc. London, Jour. Bot.* 53:187–193. 1947*b*.

Philipson, W. R. The ontogeny of the shoot apex in dicotyledons. *Biol. Rev.* 24:21–50. 1949.

Plantefol, L. La distribution des feuilles sur les tiges. *Nature* (Paris). 76(3160): 230–233. 1948.

Popham, R. A., and A. P. Chan. Zonation in the vegetative stem tip of *Chrysanthemum morifolium* Bailey. *Amer. Jour. Bot.* 37:476–484. 1950.

Priestley, J. H., and C. F. Swingle. Vegetative propagation from the standpoint of plant anatomy. *U. S. Dept. Agr. Tech. Bul.* 151. 1929.

Reeve, R. M. Structure and growth of the vegetative shoot apex of *Garrya elliptica* Dougl. *Amer. Jour. Bot.* 29:697–711. 1942.

Reeve, R. M. Comparative ontogeny of the inflorescence and the axillary vegetative shoot in *Garrya elliptica*. *Amer. Jour. Bot.* 30:608–619. 1943.

Reeve, R. M. The "tunica-corpus" concept and development of shoot apices in certain dicotyledons. *Amer. Jour. Bot.* 35:65–75. 1948.

Robbins, W. J., M. Bartley, and V. B. White. Growth of fragments of excised root tips. *Bot. Gaz.* 97:554–579. 1936.

Rouffa, A. S., and J. E. Gunckel. A comparative study of vegetative shoot apices in the Rosaceae. *Amer. Jour. Bot.* 38:290–300. 1951*a*.

Rouffa, A. S., and J. E. Gunckel. Leaf initiation, origin, and pattern of pith development in the Rosaceae. *Amer. Jour. Bot.* 38:301–307. 1951*b*.

Rüdiger, W. Die Sprossvegetationspunkte einiger Monokotylen. *Beitr. z. Biol. der Pflanz.* 26:401–433. 1939.

Satina, S., A. F. Blakeslee, and A. G. Avery. Demonstration of the three germ layers in the shoot apex of *Datura* by means of induced polyploidy in periclinal chimeras. *Amer. Jour. Bot.* 27:895–905. 1940.

Satina, S., and A. F. Blakeslee. Periclinal chimeras in *Datura stramonium* in relation to development of leaf and flower. *Amer. Jour. Bot.* 28:862–871. 1941.

Schalscha-Ehrenfeld, M. von. Spross-Vegetationspunkt und Blattanlage bei einigen monokotylen Wasserpflanzen (*Potamogeton crispus, Heteranthera dubia, Typha angustifolia*). *Planta* 31:448–477. 1940.

Schmidt, A. Histologische Studien an phanerogamen Vegetationspunkten. *Bot. Arch.* 8:345–404. 1924.

Schnabel, V. Der Bau der Sprossvegetationspunkte von *Honckenya peploides*, *Silene maritima*, *Dianthus caryophyllus* und *Clematis paniculata*. *Bot. Arch.* 42:461-502. 1941.

Schüepp, O. Meristeme. In: K. Linsbauer. *Handbuch der Pflanzenanatomie*. Band 4. Lief. 16. 1926.

Schüepp, O. Beschreibung von Blütenständen auf Grund des zeitlichen Verlaufs der Anlage, des Wachstums and des Aufblühens. *Schweiz. Bot. Gesell. Ber.* 52:273-316. 1942.

Sharman, B. C. Developmental anatomy of the shoot of *Zea mays* L. *Ann. Bot.* 6:245-282. 1942.

Sharman, B. C. Leaf and bud initiation in the Gramineae. *Bot. Gaz.* 106:269-289. 1945.

Sifton, H. B. Developmental morphology of vascular plants. *New Phytol.* 43:87-129. 1944.

Snow, M., and R. Snow. On the determination of leaves. *New Phytol.* 46:5-19. 1947.

Spurr, A. R. Histogenesis and organization of the embryo in *Pinus strobus* L. *Amer. Jour. Bot.* 36:629-641. 1949.

Sterling, C. On the shoot apex of *Chlorogalum pomeridianum* (DC.) Kunth. *Madroño* 7:188-192. 1944.

Sterling, C. Growth and vascular development in the shoot apex of *Sequoia sempervirens* (Lamb.) Endl. I. Structure and growth of the shoot apex. *Amer. Jour. Bot.* 32:118-126. 1945.

Sterling, C. Organization of the shoot of *Pseudotsuga taxifolia* (Lamb.) Britt. I. Structure of the shoot apex. *Amer. Jour. Bot.* 33:742-750. 1946.

Thielke, C. Über die Möglichkeiten der Periklinalchimärenbildung bei Gräsern. *Planta* 39:402-430. 1951.

Thompson, J. McLean. Towards a modern physiological interpretation of flowering. *Linn. Soc. London, Proc.* 156:46-68. 1943-44.

Wagner, N. Wachstum und Teilung der Meristemzellen in Wurzelspitzen. *Planta* 27:550-582. 1937.

Wagner, N. Über die Entwicklungsmechanik der Wurzelhaube und des Wurzel-rippenmeristems. *Planta* 30:21-66. 1939.

Wardlaw, C. W. Experimental and analytical studies of pteridophytes. I. Preliminary observations on the development of buds on the rhizome of the ostrich fern (*Matteuccia struthiopteris* Tod.). *Ann. Bot.* 7:171-184. 1943*a*.

Wardlaw, C. W. Experimental and analytical studies of pteridophytes. II. Experimental observations on the development of buds in *Onoclea sensibilis* and in species of *Dryopteris*. *Ann. Bot.* 7:357-377. 1943*b*.

Wardlaw, C. W. The shoot apex in pteridophytes. *Biol. Rev.* 20:100-114. 1945.

Wardlaw, C. W. Experimental investigations of the shoot apex of *Dryopteris aristata* Druce. *Roy. Soc. London, Phil. Trans.* 232:343-384. 1947.

Wardlaw, C. W. Experimental and analytical studies of Pteridophytes. XIV. Leaf formation and phyllotaxis in *Dryopteris aristata* Druce. *Ann. Bot.* 13:163-198. 1949.

Wetmore, R. H., and C. W. Wardlaw. Experimental morphogenesis in vascular plants. *Ann. Rev. of Plant Physiol.* 2:269-292. 1951.

Wolff, C. F. *Theoria generationis*. Leipzig, Wilhelm Engelman. 1759.

Zimmermann, W. A. Histologische Studien am Vegetationspunkt von *Hypericum uralum*. *Jahrb. f. Wiss. Bot.* 68:289-344. 1928.

CHAPTER

6

The Vascular Cambium

LOCATION IN THE PLANT BODY

The vascular cambium is the lateral meristem that forms the secondary vascular tissues. It is located between the xylem and the phloem (fig. 1.3 and plate 17) and, in stems and roots, commonly has the shape of a cylinder. When the secondary vascular tissues of an axis are in discrete strands, the cambium may remain restricted to these strands in the form of strips (e.g., *Cucurbita*, plate 45, *B*). It also appears in strips in most petioles and leaf veins that show secondary growth.

CELL TYPES

The tissues differentiating from apical meristems contain many cell types which differ strikingly from the meristematic cells in shape and size. In contrast, there is a general resemblance between the cambium cells and their derivatives, and the shape and arrangement of cells in the secondary xylem and the secondary phloem are foreshadowed in the shape and arrangement of the cambial cells (plate 17 and figs. 11.10, 11.11, 12.7, 12.8).

The vascular cambium contains two types of cells: elongated cells with tapering ends, the *fusiform initials* (that is, spindle-shaped initials), and nearly isodiametric, relatively small cells, the *ray initials* (figs. 6.1 and 6.2; plate 19). The exact shape of the fusiform initials of *Pinus silvestris* has been determined as that of long, pointed, tangentially flattened cells with an average of 18 faces (Dodd, 1948). The fusiform initials give rise to all the cells of xylem and phloem that are arranged with their long axes parallel to the long axis of the organ in which they occur; in other words, they form the longitudinal or vertical systems of xylem and phloem (figs. 11.10, 11.11, 12.7, 12.8). Examples of elements in this system are tracheids, fibers, and xylem parenchyma in the xylem; and sieve cells, fibers, and phloem parenchyma in the phloem. The ray initials give origin to the ray cells, that is, elements of the transverse or horizontal system of the xylem and the phloem. (See chapters 11 and 12.)

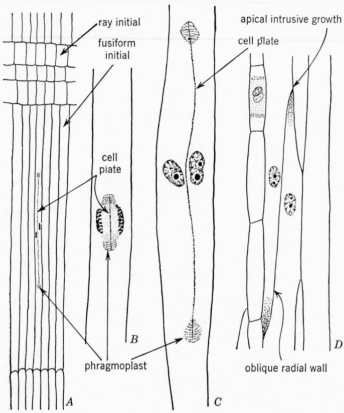

Fig. 6.1. Diagrams illustrating the vascular cambium of *Nicotiana tabacum* as seen in radial (*A–C*) and tangential (*D*) sections. The divisions in *A–C* are tangential and appear in side views. *B* shows an early stage of division; *C*, a later stage. *D* illustrates a ray initial in tangential division, with the cell plate appearing in surface view, and an oblique radial wall recently formed in a fusiform initial. The densely stippled areas in *D* indicate the apices of the two new cells which were growing by apical intrusive growth, one downward, the other upward. (*A*, ×120; *B, C*, ×600; *D*, ×300.)

Table 6.1 gives information on the comparative characteristics of the two kinds of initials of *Pinus strobus*. These initials differ from each other most notably in length and volume, the fusiform cells being much larger than the ray initials. However, in one dimension, the radial, the ray initials surpass the fusiform. In the 60-year-old stem both kinds of initials are larger than in the 1-year-old stem. The initials are uninucleate, and, although the nuclei of the fusiform in-

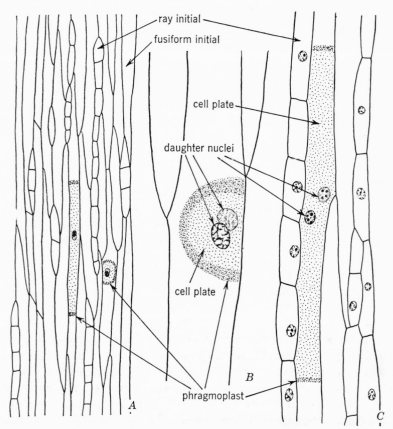

Fig. 6.2. Diagrams illustrating the vascular cambium of *Nicotiana tabacum* as seen in tangential sections. The divisions depicted in these diagrams are tangential, and they show the partly formed cell plates in surface view. In *B* the new cell plate has intersected one of the radial longitudinal walls of the parent cell; in *C* both radial walls are intersected. (*A*, ×120; *B*, ×600; *C*, ×300.)

itials may be markedly larger than those of the ray initials, their volumes do not increase in proportion to the cell volumes so that the ratio of nuclear volume to cell volume is much smaller in the fusiform cells (table 6.1, last column).

The fusiform initials show a wide range of variation in their dimensions and volume (Bailey, 1920*a*). Some of these variations

TABLE 6.1

DIMENSIONS OF CAMBIAL INITIALS OF *Pinus strobus*

(Adapted from Bailey, 1920*b*)

Age of axis in years	Kind of initial	Diameters in microns			Volume in microns[3]	Ratio between volumes of nucleus and cell
		Vertical	Radial	Tangential		
1	Ray	22.9	17.8	13.8	5,000	1:14
1	Fusiform	870.0	4.3	16.0	60,000	1:60
60	Ray	24.8	26.6	17.0	10,000	1:12
60	Fusiform	4000.0	6.2	42.4	1,000,000	1:286

depend on plant species. The following figures, expressed in millimeters, exemplify differences in the lengths of fusiform initials in several plants: *Pinus strobus,* 3.20; *Ginkgo,* 2.20; *Myristica,* 1.31; *Pyrus,* 0.53; *Populus,* 0.49; *Fraxinus,* 0.29; *Robinia,* 0.17 (Bailey, 1920*a*). Certain size variations of fusiform initials are associated with developmental phenomena. Generally, the length of fusiform initials increases with the age of the axis, but after this length reaches a certain maximum it remains relatively stable (table 6.1; Bailey, 1920*a*). There also may be seasonal fluctuations in length (Bannan, 1951*b*). The changes in the size of fusiform initials bring about similar changes in the secondary xylem and phloem cells derived from these initials. The ultimate size of these cells, however, depends only partly on that of the cambial initials, because changes in size occur also during the differentiation of cells (see chapter 4).

The cambial cells are highly vacuolated (plates 18, *B,* and 19; Bailey, 1930). Their walls have primary pit fields with plasmodesmata. The radial walls are thicker than the tangential walls, and their primary pit fields are deeply depressed.

CELL ARRANGEMENT

During active growth in the cambium, the initials and their immediate derivatives form a zone of similar unexpanded meristematic cells, the *cambial zone* (plate 18, *A*). As seen in transections the cells in the cambial zone are arranged in radial series. On either side of the cambial zone, cambial derivatives expand and gradually assume the characteristics of the various xylem and phloem cells. The prevailing concept is that the initials are arranged in one layer, one cell in thickness. In a strict sense, only the initials constitute the cambium (Bailey, 1943), but frequently the term is used with reference to the cambial zone, because it is difficult to distinguish the initials from their recent derivatives (plate 18, *B*).

In tangential views the arrangement of cambial cells shows two basic patterns. In one, the fusiform initials occur in horizontal tiers with the ends of the cells of one tier appearing at approximately the same level (plate 19, *B*). Such meristem is called *storied* or *stratified cambium*. It is characteristic of plants with short fusiform initials. In the second type, the fusiform initials are not arranged in horizontal tiers, and their ends overlap (plate 19, *A*). This type is termed *nonstoried* or *nonstratified cambium*. It is common in plants with long fusiform initials. Various intergrading types of arrangement occur in different plants. The nonstratified type is considered to be phylogenetically more primitive than the stratified. The former is found in fossil pteridophytes, in fossil and living gymnosperms, and in structurally primitive dicotyledons; the latter, in highly specialized dicotyledons (Bailey, 1923).

CELL DIVISION

The phloem and the xylem are formed by tangential (periclinal) divisions of cambial initials. The vascular tissues are laid down in two opposite directions, the xylem cells toward the interior of the axis, the phloem cells toward its periphery. The consistent tangential orientation of the planes of division during the formation of vascular tissues determines the arrangement of cambial derivatives in radial rows (plates 17 and 18). Such radial seriation may persist in the developing xylem and phloem (plate 17), or it may be disturbed through various kinds of growth readjustments during the differentiation of these tissues (xylem in plate 18, *A*).

Tangential divisions that occur during the formation of xylem and phloem cells are not limited to the initials but are encountered also in varied numbers of derivatives, sometimes several times within the progeny of the same derivative (Bannan, 1951*b*; Raatz, 1892). During the winter rest, xylem and phloem cells mature more or less closely to the initials; sometimes only one cambial layer is left between the mature xylem and phloem elements (Esau, 1948).

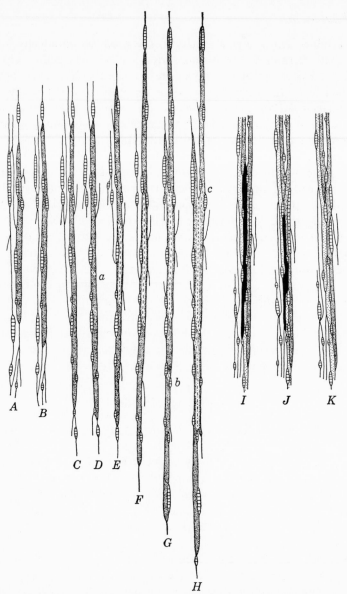

FIG. 6.3. Two series (A–H and I–K) of tangential sections through the secondary phloem of *Taxus baccata*, illustrating developmental changes in the vascular cambium that produced this phloem. In both series the cells to the left (A and I) are farthest from the cambium. Series A–H shows that the cambial initial, which gave origin to the stippled cells, elongated (A–C), then divided (D at a). The resulting sister cells elongated (E–F), then each divided, the lower at b in G, the upper at c in H. The series in I–K shows stages in the disappearance of the initial that gave rise to the cell shown in black. (Adapted from Klinken, 1914.)

As the xylem cylinder increases in thickness by secondary growth, the cambial cylinder also grows in circumference. The principal cause of this growth is the increase in the number of cells in tangential direction, followed by a tangential expansion of these cells. In stratified cambia the increase in the number of fusiform initials occurs by radial (anticlinal) longitudinal divisions. In nonstratified cambia, however, the fusiform initials divide by more or less oblique anticlinal walls, and then the resulting cells elongate at their apices (apical intrusive growth; figs. 6.1, *D*, and 6.3, *D–H*) until each cell is as long as, or longer than, the mother cell.

In the various longitudinal divisions of the cambial initials and their derivatives, cytokinesis is a process extended in time and space. The cell plate is initiated between the two new nuclei and then spreads through the entire length of the cell, preceded by the phragmoplast fibers (figs. 6.1 and 6.2; see also chapter 3).

DEVELOPMENTAL CHANGES IN THE CAMBIUM

Detailed studies of the vascular cambium of conifers have shown that the increase in circumference of the meristem is accompanied by profound changes in size, number, and arrangement of cells. Table 6.2 illustrates some of the changes that occur in the nonstrati-

TABLE 6.2

DIFFERENCE BETWEEN A 1-YEAR-OLD AND A 60-YEAR-OLD STEM OF *Pinus strobus* IN CIRCUMFERENCE OF CAMBIUM AND SIZE AND NUMBER OF INITIALS

(Adapted from Bailey, 1923)

Item	Age of Stem	
	1 year	60 years
Radius of woody cylinder	2,000 microns	200,000 microns
Circumference of cambium	12,566 microns	1,256,640 microns
Average length of fusiform initials	870 microns	4,000 microns
Average tangential diameter of fusiform initials	16 microns	42 microns
Number of fusiform initials in cross section of stem	724	23,100
Average tangential diameter of ray initials	14 microns	17 microns
Number of ray initials in cross section of stem	70	8,796

fied cambium of a pine stem as the stem increases in girth. Both the fusiform and the ray initials are greatly multiplied in number.

The fusiform initials enlarge notably along their tangential diameters, whereas the ray initials become only slightly larger in this dimension. There is also a remarkable increase in the length of the fusiform initials. The increase in number of the fusiform initials, as seen in transections, results, in part, from intrusive apical elongation without division (fig. 6.3, *A–C*), but most of it occurs through oblique radial divisions followed by apical intrusive growth (fig. 6.3, *D–H*). Since the rays in the pine are mostly uniseriate (one cell in width), the increase in the number of ray initials, as shown for the older stem in table 6.2, is a result, not of divisions of the existing ray initials, but of the addition of new ray initials.

New ray initials originate from fusiform initials. According to some observations, ray initials of conifers arise mostly as segments from the tips of fusiform initials (Barghoorn, 1940*a*). In *Chamae-cyparis* and *Thuja*, however, nearly all new ray initials originate by subdivision of fusiform initials (Bannan, 1950, 1951*a*).

The high degree of plasticity of the vascular cambium of conifers is evidenced also by the continuous loss of individual initials from the meristem (Bannan, 1950, 1951*a*, *b*; Bannan and Whalley, 1950; Klinken, 1914; Whalley, 1950). Both fusiform and ray initials are frequently displaced by other initials. The displaced initials may mature into xylem or phloem elements. A shortening of a fusiform initial may take place before its final disappearance from the cambium (fig. 6.3, *I–K*; Bannan, 1950, 1951*a*, *b*).

The vascular cambium of the dicotyledons appears to have a degree of plasticity similar to that of the conifer cambium. Various changes of ray structure occur during the increase in circumference of a dicotyledonous tree, fusiform and ray initials displacing one another. There is also a loss of initials from the cambium (Barghoorn, 1940*b*, 1941*a*, *b*).

SEASONAL ACTIVITY

The secondary growth originating in the vascular cambium is intimately connected with the activities of the primary parts of the plant body and shows fluctuations in relation to the changes in the physiologic state of the plant. Herbaceous plants commonly have a regular sequence of vegetative phase, reproductive phase, somatic death, and seed dispersal. Between the vegetative and reproductive phases, the plant body may attain various dimensions and its vascular tissues may be increased in amount by secondary growth. This growth ceases, however, during the transition to the reproductive stage, since the cambial activity appears to be closely associated with the vegetative phase (Wilton and Roberts, 1936). In woody species there is a repetition of vegetative and reproductive phases, without somatic death of the whole individual. As is well known, in woody species growing in temperate regions periods of growth and reproduction alternate with periods of relative inactivity during the winter. The seasonal periodicity finds its expression in the cambial activity also. Production of new cells by the vascular cambium slows down or ceases entirely during the rest period, and the vascular tissues mature more or less closely to the initial layer.

In the spring the winter rest period is succeeded by a reactivation of the cambium. From the anatomic aspect, the phenomenon of reactivation may be divided into two stages: (1) expansion of the cambial cells in the radial direction ("swelling" of the cambium) and (2) initiation of cell division. The radial enlargement is accompanied by a weakening of the radial walls so that a slight external force applied to the stem will cause these walls to break (Esau, 1948). The separation of the bark from the wood resulting from such a break is commonly called slipping of the bark. Such a slipping may also be induced later, during the cell division and tissue differentiation in the cambial zone. At this time, however, the break occurs most commonly through the young xylem where the tracheary elements have attained their maximum diameters but are still without secondary walls (Bailey, 1943).

The xylem and the phloem have been reported as arising from the cambium simultaneously or one before the other. Whatever the order of differentiation, the amount of xylem increment formed during one season is characteristically wider than the phloem increment of the same season.

The resumption of cambial activity in the spring has often been found related to the new primary growth from buds (cf. Wareing, 1951). In many dicotyledons cambial activity of the stem begins beneath the emerging new shoots and spreads from here basipetally toward the main branches, the trunk, and the root. As an example, the data obtained with *Acer pseudo-platanus*, as growing in England, may be cited (Cockerham, 1930). In this tree 9 to 10 weeks elapse between the inception of xylem differentiation in the twigs (late in April) and that in the roots (early in July). Activity ceases in the same order. The formation of xylem stops in the twigs in late July; in the roots, in late September. Thus, 8 to 9 weeks elapse between the cessation of cambial activity in the branches and that in the root. The inception of cambial reactivation beneath the new shoots and its basipetal progress explains why, in a dicotyledon, the portion of a twig that might be left in pruning above the uppermost bud dries up and forms a "snag" (Wray, 1934).

In conifers and in the dicotyledonous species that form numerous large vessels in the early part of an annual xylem increment (ring-porous wood, plate 31, *B*) cambial reactivation in the spring is less closely associated with bud development than in *Acer* and other dicotyledons with the so-called diffuse-porous wood (plate 28, *C*, and chapter 11). The conifers and the dicotyledons with ring-porous wood show an early and rapid spread of cambial reactivation throughout the trunk in the presence of only a small amount of bud growth (Messeri, 1948; Münch, 1937; Priestley, 1930; Wareing, 1951).

Although the growing buds may have some regulatory influence upon the inception of secondary activity in the spring, they do not appear to be concerned with the maintenance of cambial activity through the summer (Münch, 1937; Priestley, 1930). The initial stimulation of cambial activity has been related to the distribution of growth substances in the spring (cf. Wareing, 1951). Such substances were found to be formed in the growing buds and then to appear in measurable amounts at successively lower levels in the tree in advance of the cambial activity (e.g., Avery et al., 1937). The vascular cambium can be stimulated into activity by wounding also, possibly in relation to formation of wound hormones as a result of injury (Brown, 1937).

REFERENCES

Avery, G. S., P. R. Burkholder, and H. B. Creighton. Production and distribution of growth hormone in shoots of *Aesculus* and *Malus*, and its probable role in stimulating cambial activity. *Amer. Jour. Bot.* 24:51–58. 1937.

Bailey, I. W. The cambium and its derivative tissues. II. Size variations of cambial initials in gymnosperms and angiosperms. *Amer. Jour. Bot.* 7:355–367. 1920*a.*

Bailey, I. W. The cambium and its derivative tissues. III. A reconnaissance of cytological phenomena in the cambium. *Amer. Jour. Bot.* 7:417–434. 1920*b.*

Bailey, I. W. The cambium and its derivative tissues. IV. The increase in girth of the cambium. *Amer. Jour. Bot.* 10:499–509. 1923.

Bailey, I. W. The cambium and its derivative tissues. V. A reconnaissance of the vacuome in living cells. *Ztschr. f. Zellforsch. u. Micros. Anat.* 10:651–682. 1930.

Bailey, I. W. Some misleading terminologies in the literature of "plant tissue culture." *Science* 98:539. 1943.

Bannan, M. W. The frequency of anticlinal divisions in fusiform cambial cells of *Chamaecyparis*. *Amer. Jour. Bot.* 37:511–519. 1950.

Bannan, M. W. The reduction of fusiform cambial cells in *Chamaecyparis* and *Thuja*. *Canad. Jour. Bot.* 29:57–67. 1951*a*.

Bannan, M. W. The annual cycle of size changes in the fusiform cambial cells of *Chamaecyparis* and *Thuja*. *Canad. Jour. Bot.* 29:421–437. 1951*b*.

Bannan, M. W., and B. E. Whalley. The elongation of fusiform cambial cells in *Chamaecyparis*. *Canad. Jour. Res. Sect. C., Bot. Sci.* 28:341–355. 1950.

Barghoorn, E. S., Jr. Origin and development of the uniseriate ray in the Coniferae. *Torrey Bot. Club Bul.* 67:303–328. 1940*a*.

Barghoorn, E. S., Jr. The ontogenetic development and phylogenetic specialization of rays in the xylem of dicotyledons. I. The primitive ray structure. *Amer. Jour. Bot.* 27:918–928. 1940*b*.

Barghoorn, E. S., Jr. The ontogenetic development and phylogenetic specialization of rays in the xylem of dicotyledons. II. Modification of the multiseriate and uniseriate rays. *Amer. Jour. Bot.* 28:273–282. 1941*a*.

Barghoorn, E. S., Jr. The ontogenetic development and phylogenetic specialization of rays in the xylem of dicotyledons. III. The elimination of rays. *Torrey Bot. Club Bul.* 68:317–325. 1941*b*.

Brown, A. B. Activity of the vascular cambium in relation to wounding in the balsam poplar, *Populus balsamifera* L. *Canad. Jour. Res. Sect. C., Bot. Sci.* 15: 7–31. 1937.

Cockerham, G. Some observations on cambial activity and seasonal starch content in sycamore (*Acer pseudo-platanus*). *Leeds Phil. Lit. Soc. Proc.* 2: 64–80. 1930.

Dodd, J. D. On the shapes of cells in the cambial zone of *Pinus silvestris* L. *Amer. Jour. Bot.* 35:666–682. 1948.

Esau, K. Phloem structure in the grapevine, and its seasonal changes. *Hilgardia* 18:217–296. 1948.

Klinken, J. Über das gleitende Wachstum der Initialen im Kambium der Koniferen und den Markstrahlenverlauf in ihrer secundären Rinde. *Biblioth. Bot.* 19(84):1–41. 1914.

Messeri, A. L'evoluzione della cerchia legnosa in *Pinus halepensis* Mill. in Bari. *Nuovo Giorn. Bot. Ital.* 55:111–132. 1948.

Münch, E. Regelung des Dickenwachstums und der Stammform durch das Längenwachstum bei Nadelbäumen. *Deut. Bot. Gesell. Ber.* 55:109–113. 1937.

Priestley, J. H. Studies in the physiology of cambial activity. III. The seasonal activity of the cambium. *New Phytol.* 29:316–354. 1930.

Raatz, W. Die Stabbildungen im secundären Holzkörper der Bäume und die Initialentheorie. *Jahrb. f. Wiss. Bot.* 23:567–636. 1892.

Wareing, P. F. Growth studies in woody species. IV. The initiation of cambial activity in ring-porous species. *Physiol. Plantarum* 4:546–562. 1951.

Whalley, B. E. Increase in girth of the cambium in *Thuja occidentalis* L. *Canad. Jour. Res. Sect. C., Bot. Sci.* 28:331–340. 1950.

Wilton, O. C., and R. H. Roberts. Anatomical structure of stems in relation to the production of flowers. *Bot. Gaz.* 98:45–64. 1936.

Wray, E. M. The structural changes in a woody twig after summer pruning. *Leeds Phil. Lit. Soc. Proc.* 2:560–570. 1934.

7

The Epidermis

CONCEPT

The term *epidermis* designates the outermost layer of cells on the primary plant body. The word is derived from two words of Greek origin, *epi*, upon, and *derma*, skin. Through the history of development of plant morphology the concept of the epidermis has undergone various changes, and there is still no complete uniformity in the application of the term (Linsbauer, 1930). This superficial system of cells varies in composition, function, and origin and, therefore, does not lend itself to a precise definition based on any one criterion. In this book the term epidermis is used in a broad morphologic-topographic sense. It refers to the superficial layer of cells of all parts of the primary plant body—stems, roots, leaves, flowers, fruits, and seeds. It is considered to be absent on the rootcap and not differentiated as such on the apical meristems.

The inclusion of the surface layer of the root in the concept of epidermis is contrary to the view that the root epidermis belongs to a separate category of tissue and should have its own name, *rhizodermis* or *epiblem* (Allen, 1947; Kroemer, 1903; Linsbauer, 1930; Olivier, 1881). The epidermis of the root differs from that of the shoot in origin, function, and structure, and, therefore, the emphasis of some workers upon the distinctness of the two parts of the epidermis is justified. At the same time, the proper definition of the root epidermis is inseparably connected with the problem of the morphologic relation between root and shoot (Allen, 1947). As long as there is no agreement on this problem, it seems most convenient to use the term epidermis in its broadest sense to mean the primary surface tissue of the entire plant, with due recognition of its multiplicity of functions and variability in structure and origin in the different parts of the plant.

ORIGIN AND DURATION

The details of the origin of epidermis are presented in chapter 5. Briefly, the epidermis of the shoot arises from the outermost cell layer of the apical meristem, either from independent initials or jointly with the subjacent tissue layers. If the shoot apex shows a segregation into zones of surface and volume growth, that is, into a tunica and a corpus, the epidermis originates from the outermost layer of tunica. Such a layer of cells fits the definition of Hanstein's *dermatogen* (cf. chapter 5), since its course of development into the epidermis begins in an independent initial region. In plants showing less precise zonations in the apical meristem, as in most of the gymnosperms, the epidermis does not have separate initials but is a product of the lateral derivatives of the apical initials. These divide both anticlinally and periclinally and are the ultimate sources of the superficial as well as the interior cells of the plant body. In plants with single apical cells the epidermis also has common origin with the deeper lying tissues. In roots the epidermis may be related developmentally to the rootcap or to the cortex.

When the epidermis does not arise from separate initials, it becomes distinct at various distances from the apical meristem, depending on the architecture of the meristem. Haberlandt's term *protoderm* (cf. chapter 5) designates such primordial epidermis, as well as the epidermis arising from separate initials. This term was coined as a morphologic-topographic designation, with no reference to the origin of the tissue. In this book protoderm is used to indicate the undifferentiated epidermis, regardless of its origin.

Organs having little or no secondary growth usually retain the epidermis as long as they exist (De Bary, 1884; Flamm, 1922). An exception is exemplified by some woody monocotyledons having no secondary addition to the vascular system in which a kind of periderm arises and the epidermis is destroyed. In stems and roots of gymnosperms and dicotyledons and of arborescent monocotyledons having secondary growth, the epidermis shows varying longevity, depending on whether it is early supplanted by periderm or whether the formation of the periderm is delayed and the epidermis remains functional for a few or many years. Ordinarily, the periderm arises in the first year of growth of woody stems and roots, but numerous tree species produce no periderm until their axes are many times thicker than they were at the completion of primary growth. In such plants the epidermis, as well as the underlying cortex, continues to grow and thus keeps pace with the increasing circumference of the vascular cylinder. The individual cells enlarge tangentially and divide radially. A striking example of such prolonged growth is found in stems of a maple (*Acer striatum*) in which trunks about 20 years old may attain a thickness of about 20 cm and still remain clothed with the original epidermis (De Bary, 1884, p. 536). The cells of such an old epidermis are not more than twice as wide tangentially as the epidermal cells in an axis 5 mm in thickness. This size relation clearly shows that the epidermal cells are dividing continuously while the stem increases in thickness.

STRUCTURAL CHARACTERISTICS

Composition

In relation to the multiplicity of its functions the epidermis contains a wide variety of cell types. The most abundant are the epidermal cells proper, which may be regarded as the least specialized members of the system constituting the ground mass of the tissue. Dispersed among these cells are the guard cells of the stomata and sometimes other specialized cells. The epidermis may produce a variety of appendages, the trichomes, such as hairs and more complex structures. Trichomes with a specific function, the root hairs, develop from the epidermal cells of the roots.

Epidermal Cells

Morphology and Arrangement. Mature epidermal cells are commonly described as being tabular in shape because of their relatively small extent in depth, that is, in the direction at right angles to the surface of the organ (plate 21, *B*). Deviating types, cells which are much deeper than they are wide, also occur, for example, in the palisade-like epidermis of many seeds (fig. 10.6; Linsbauer, 1930). In surface view the epidermal cells may be nearly isodiametric (fig. 7.1, *B, F*) or elongated (fig. 7.1, *A*). The three-dimensional shape of the epidermal cells has been examined, by modern methods (see chapter 8), in two plants, *Aloe aristata* and *Anacharis densa* (Matzke, 1947, 1948). In general, the number and the kind of faces in the cells investigated suggest a resemblance to a tetrakaidecahedron (fig. 8.2, *A*) cut in half. The form of epidermal cells is sometimes related to differences in position upon the plant organ. Elongated epidermal cells are often found on structures which themselves are elongated, such as stems, petioles, vein ribs of leaves, and leaves of most monocotyledons. Elongated epidermal cells also occur near some hairs and stomata. Frequently epidermal cells are shallow above the strands of subepidermal sclerenchyma. In many leaves the epidermal layers on the

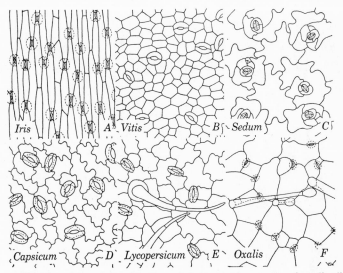

FIG. 7.1. Surface views of abaxial (lower) foliar epidermis showing distribution and position of stomata. *A, Iris,* sunken stomata in longitudinal rows. *B, Vitis,* dispersed stomata, at same level with the other epidermal cells. *C, Sedum,* raised stomata with subsidiary cells. *D* and *E, Capsicum* and *Lycopersicum,* raised stomata. *F, Oxalis,* sunken stomata. Wavy epidermal walls in *C–E.* Nonglandular and glandular hairs in *E* and *F,* respectively. (*A, C, F,* ×93; *B, D, E,* ×168; *B, D, E,* courtesy of Artschwager.)

two surfaces are rather dissimilar in shape and size of cells and in thickness of walls and cuticle.

In many leaves and petals the epidermal cells have wavy anticlinal walls (figs. 7.1, *C–E,* and plate 20, *B*), and the undulations may be present in the entire depth of the walls or only in their outermost parts. The cause of this waviness has been the subject of much study and speculation in the literature (Linsbauer, 1930). One of the explanations of this phenomenon relates the undulations to the development of stresses during the differentiation of the leaf (Avery, 1933). Another concept is that the waviness is caused by the method of hardening of the differentiating cuticle (Watson, 1942). The waviness of the walls is variable, depending on the location in the leaf or petal (often the undulations occur only on the lower side of a leaf or are more pronounced here than on the upper side); it is also affected by environmental conditions (Linsbauer, 1930; Watson, 1942).

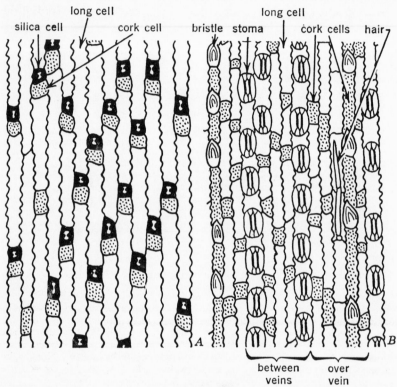

FIG. 7.2. Epidermis of sugarcane in surface view. *A*, epidermis of stem showing alternation of long cells with pairs of short cells, the cork cells and silica cells. *B*, lower epidermis from a leaf blade, showing distribution of stomata in relation to the various kinds of epidermal cells. (*A*, ×500; *B*, ×320. Both adapted from Artschwager, 1940.)

The outer wall of an epidermal cell may be flat or convex. or it may bear one or more localized raised areas.

A striking morphologic variability is encountered in the epidermis of the Gramineae and the Cyperaceae (Artschwager, 1930, 1940; Frohnmeyer, 1914; Grob, 1896; Heinemann, 1925; Prat, 1948). In the Gramineae, for example, the epidermis typically contains long cells and two kinds of short cells, silica cells and cork cells (fig. 7.2,

A). The short cells frequently occur together in pairs. The silica cells are almost filled with SiO_2 and show varied shapes. The cork cells have suberized walls and often contain solid organic material. In some parts of the plant the short cells develop protrusions above the surface of the leaf in the form of papillae, bristles, spines, or hairs. The epidermal cells of the Gramineae are arranged in parallel rows, and the composition of these rows varies in different parts of the plant. The inner face of the leaf sheath at its base, for example, has a homogeneous epidermis composed of long cells only. Elsewhere in the leaves various combinations of the different types of cells may be found. Rows containing long cells and stomata occur over the assimilatory tissue (fig. 7.2, *B*); only elongated cells or such cells combined with cork cells or bristles (fig. 7.2, *B*) or with mixed pairs of short cells follow the veins. In the stem, too, the composition of the epidermis varies, depending on the level on the internode and on the position of the internode in the plant as a whole.

The Gramineae and other monocotyledons possess still another peculiar type of epidermal cell, the bulliform or motor cell. Since this cell type is of considerable interest from the developmental and physiological aspects, it is treated separately in a later part of this chapter.

Some epidermal cells greatly deviate from the main mass of cells. Certain Gramineae, Gymnospermae, Dictoyledoneae and certain lower vascular plants (*Adiantum, Selaginella*) contain fiber-like epidermal cells (Linsbauer, 1930). The longest epidermal fibers—up to 2 mm—were described in the Stylidaceae. In the Gramineae such fibers may be 200 to 375 microns in length. Certain Cruciferae contain sac-like secretory cells (myrosin cells, see chapter 13) scattered in the epidermis. In Acanthaceae, Cucurbitaceae, Moraceae (fig. 7.13, *C*), and Urticaceae epidermal cells may develop cystoliths. Some of these cystolith-containing cells (the lithocysts) are specialized epidermal cells; others appear to be reduced trichomes (Linsbauer, 1930).

Sometimes the entire epidermis consists of highly specialized cells. Thus in certain seeds and scales the epidermis is made up of a solid layer of sclereids (figs. 10.6 and 10.7). The epidermis of the Polypodiaceae is differentiated as a photosynthetic tissue (Meyer, 1923; Wylie, 1948). The epidermal cells border upon prominent and extensive intercellular spaces and bear numerous protuberances projecting into the intercellular spaces and containing chloroplasts.

The epidermal cells are arranged compactly, with rare breaks in their continuity other than those represented by the stomatal pores.

Intercellular spaces occur in the epidermis of petals, but they appear to be closed on the outside by the cuticle.

Contents. In general the contents of the epidermal cells have been incompletely investigated, but since these cells possess living protoplasts they may be expected to include a variety of substances, depending on the degree of their specialization (Linsbauer, 1930). The epidermal plastids of the majority of plants are not definitely differentiated as chloroplasts. Some ferns, water plants, and a number of higher vascular land plants, particularly those of shady habitats, contain well-developed chloroplasts in the epidermis (Linsbauer, 1930; Meyer, 1923; Wylie, 1948). The cell sap of the epidermal cells may contain anthocyanin, for example, in many flowers, in leaves of the purple beech and the red cabbage, and in the stems and petioles of *Ricinus.*

Wall Structure. The epidermal walls of different plants and of different plant parts vary markedly in thickness. In the thinner-walled epidermis the outer wall is frequently the thickest (plate 20, *A*). Epidermis with exceedingly thick walls is found in coniferous leaves (fig. 7.4 and plate 65; Linsbauer, 1930; Marco, 1939). The wall thickening is uneven and so massive in some species that it almost obliterates the lumina of the cells. It has not been determined whether these walls are primary or secondary. Thick secondary walls occur in the epidermal cells differentiated as sclereids in seed coats and scales (see chapter 10).

The radial and the inner tangential walls frequently show primary pit fields. The outer wall also may have thin places and markings resembling primary pit fields (Linsbauer, 1930). Plasmodesmata have been described not only in the radial and the inner tangential walls but also in the outer walls (see chapter 3).

The epidermal cells of leaves and petals in some plants show internal ridges that resemble folds (Marco, 1939). These ridges are interpreted as partial septa originating as ingrowing walls that reach only part of the way into the cell lumen (Küster, 1935, p. 577). The septa apparently consist of two wall layers cemented together by intercellular material. The two layers may split apart with the formation of a schizogenous intercellular space. In such instances a ridge appears as a loop in transection.

The most characteristic feature of epidermal walls is the presence of the fatty substance *cutin* as an impregnation of the walls themselves (cutinization) and as a separate layer—the *cuticle* (cuticularization)—on the outer surface of the cells (plate 20, *A*). The cuticle covers all parts of the shoot, including the apical meristem (Priestley, 1943). It occurs on all floral parts, on nectaries, and on ordinary and glandular trichomes. It is typically absent from the surface of an actively growing root (Kroemer, 1903; Priestley, 1943). The continuity of the cuticle is clearly demonstrated by the observation that it can be removed from plant parts as an unbroken layer (plate 21, *A*).

Cutin has also been identified on the free surfaces of the leaf-mesophyll cells and on the inner walls of the epidermis where these are exposed to the internal air spaces (see chapter 3). The inner layer of cutin is continuous with the superficial cuticle through the stomatal apertures, whose bounding cells, the guard cells, are covered with a cuticle on their free surfaces (Priestley, 1943).

The cuticle attains variable thickness in different plants. Environmental conditions and other unknown factors affect the development of the cuticle (Stevens, 1932). The surface of the cuticle may be smooth, or it may have various protrusions, ridges, or cracks. The origin of the complicated relief pattern in the cuticle of floral parts (plate 21, *A*) has been ascribed to the effects of cell growth (Martens, 1934; Priestley, 1943).

Deposits of wax may occur on the surface of the cuticle in the form of granules, rods, often with hooked ends, crusts, homogeneous glass-like layers, or viscous semiliquid masses (Cunze, 1925; Linsbauer, 1930; Weber, 1942). Other surface deposits are oil, resin, salts in crystalline form (*Cressa cretica, Tamarix, Frankenia*), and caoutchouc (*Eucalyptus*) (Linsbauer, 1930).

The cutinized part of the outer epidermal wall beneath the cuticle has a complicated structure (Priestley, 1943; see also chapter 3). In plants with thick outer walls it consists of many lamellae of cutinized cellulose alternating with layers rich in pectin. The stratified appearance of the cutinized outer wall of the epidermis and the increase in the proportion of the cutin toward the periphery suggest that the fatty substances migrate outwards. At the surface they coalesce to form the continuous cuticle; farther in they remain dispersed in the cellulose lamellae (Priestley, 1943). There is considerable speculation concerning the source of the migrating fatty substances and their path of movement. Some workers assume that they originate in the epidermal cells; others think that the deeper-lying cells also contribute such materials. It has been suggested that the movement of the fatty substances through the walls occurs through special channels and that the fine radial lines often seen in thick epidermal walls are such channels (Priestley, 1943). There is, however, evidence that the cellulose matrix of cell walls is porous and that these pores may be large enough to permit the passage of various substances to the outside (Frenzel, 1929; Rouschal and Strugger, 1940).

The cuticle occurs not only over the surface of the epidermal cells but also often as rib-like projections into the radial walls (fig. 9.2, *A*). Such ribs develop relatively late in the life of an organ. One of the explanations of these ribs is that, when new cells are produced by anticlinal divisions during the development of the epidermis, each of these cells extends tangentially and produces its own complete wall, while the parent wall becomes stretched and torn (Priestley, 1943). Thus, the outer cutinized layers accumulate as interrupted lamellae of cellulose together with pectic substances and cutin. The interruptions occur over the radial walls and are filled with cutin deposits. The stretching and tearing of the outer cellulose lamellae and their thorough permeating with cutin eventually make it difficult to distinguish the cuticle and the cutinized layers from one another (plate 21, *B*, *C*) without special treatment.

Most plants produce only epidermal cuticular layers, even if the periderm is formed very late in the life of the organ and the epidermis continues to grow. In some exceptional plants like the Viscoideae and *Menispermum* (plate 21, *C*) cuticular layers are also formed among cortical cells in successively deeper regions of the cortex (Damm, 1902).

Among other common wall substances, lignin is a relatively infrequent component of the epidermal walls (Linsbauer, 1930). If present, it is sometimes generally distributed, sometimes restricted to a part of the outer wall. Lignification of epidermal cells is comparatively common in the lower vascular plants. It occurs also in the Cycadaceae, in the needles of conifers, in the rhizomes of Gramineae, in the leaves of Gramineae outside the sclerenchyma strands, in Cyperaceae and Juncaceae, and in a few dicotyledons (*Eucalyptus, Quercus, Laurus nobilis, Nerium oleander*). Many plants deposit silica in epidermal cells (e.g., *Equisetum*, ferns, Gramineae, numerous Cyperaceae, palms, and certain dicotyledons; Linsbauer, 1930).

In some dicotyledonous families (Malvaceae, Rutaceae, Loganiaceae, Gentianaceae, Euphorbiaceae) mucilaginous modifications of walls occur in individual epidermal cells, or in groups of cells; sometimes most epidermal cells are more or less mucilaginous, as, for example, in seeds (Linsbauer, 1930).

Bulliform Cells. The bulliform cells, literally "cells shaped like bubbles," are large, thin-walled, highly vacuolated cells which occur in all monocotyledonous orders except the Helobiae (Grob, 1896; Guttenberg, 1926; Linsbauer, 1930; Löv, 1926). Bulliform cells either cover the entire upper surface of the blade or are restricted to grooves between the veins. In the latter situation they form bands, usually several cells wide, arranged parallel with the veins. In transections through such a band the cells often form a fan-like pattern, for the median cells are usually the largest and somewhat wedge-shaped (plate 59, *A*). Bulliform cells may occur on both sides of the leaf. They are not necessarily restricted to the epidermis but are sometimes accompanied by similar cells in the subjacent mesophyll.

Bulliform cells are poor in solid contents. They are mainly water-containing cells, with little or no chlorophyll. Tannins and crystals are rarely found in these cells. Their radial walls are thin, but the outer wall may be as thick or thicker than those of the adjacent ordinary epidermal cells. The walls are of cellulose and pectic substances. The outer walls are cutinized and also bear a cuticle (Burström, 1942; Löv, 1926).

The principal function ascribed to the bulliform cells is that concerned with the unrolling of the developing leaves. Their sudden and rapid expansion during a certain stage of leaf development is assumed to bring about the unfolding of the blade (hence the term expansion cells, often applied to these cells; Löv, 1926; Skutch, 1930). Another common concept is that, by changes in turgor, these cells play a role in the hygroscopic opening and closing movements of mature leaves (hence the alternative term motor cells; Eames and MacDaniels, 1947, p. 338). Still other workers doubt that the cells have any other function than that of water storage (Linsbauer, 1930). An experimental study on the unfolding and the hygroscopic movements of wheat leaves has shown that in this plant the bulliform cells are not actively or specifically concerned with these phenomena (Burström, 1942).

Stomata

The stomata are apertures in the epidermis, each bounded by two guard cells (fig. 7.1 and plate 20). By changes in their shape, the guard cells control the size of the stomatal aperture. In Greek, stoma means mouth, and the term is often used with reference to the stomatal pore only. In this book, the term stoma includes the guard cells and the pore between them. In many plants two or more of the cells adjacent to the guard cells appear to be associated functionally with them and are morphologically distinct from the other epidermal cells. Such cells are called *subsidiary* or *accessory cells* (figs. 7.1, *C*, and 7.5).

The stomata are most common on green aerial parts of plants, particularly leaves. Roots and the aerial parts of some chlorophyll-free land plants (*Monotropa, Neottia*) have no stomata as a rule, but rhizomes have such structures (De Bary, 1884, p. 46). They occur on some submerged aquatic plants, and not on others. The variously colored petals of the flowers often have stomata, sometimes nonfunctional. Stomata are found also on stamens and gynoecia. In green leaves they occur either on both surfaces or on one only, usually the lower (that is, abaxial surface). The numbers of stomata on leaves range between 1,000 to 100,000 per square centimeter in dicotyledonous leaves (Meyer and Anderson, 1946, p. 176–178).

In leaves with parallel veins, such as those of monocotyledons, and in the needles of conifers the stomata are arranged in parallel rows (figs. 7.2, *B*, and 7.4, *A*). The substomatal chambers in each row are coalesced, and the mesophyll cells bounding these chambers form an arch over (or beneath) the intercellular canal (fig. 7.4, *B*, and plate 65, *A*; Haberlandt, 1914, p. 455). In netted veined leaves the stomata are scattered (fig. 7.1, *B–F*).

Guard cells may occur at the same level as the adjacent epidermal cells, or they may protrude above or be sunken below the surface of the epidermis (compare figs. 7.1, 7.3, 7.4, and 7.6). In some plants stomata are restricted to the epidermis lining depressions in the leaf, the stomatal crypts. Epidermal hairs may be also prominently developed in such crypts (fig. 16.2, *A*).

The guard cells are generally kidney-shaped in surface view (figs. 7.1, 7.3, *D*, and 7.6, *C*) and have ledges of wall material on the upper and lower sides. In sectional views such ledges appear like horns (plate 20, *A*, and fig. 7.3, *E, F, H*). Sometimes the ledge occurs only on the upper side (fig. 7.3, *A, G, I*), and sometimes no ledge is present (fig. 7.4, *B, E*). If two ledges are present, the upper delimits the front cavity above the stomatal pore, and the lower encloses the back cavity between the pore and the substomatal chamber (fig. 7.3, *F*).

An outstanding characteristic of stomata is the unevenly thickened walls of the guard cells (figs. 7.3 and 7.4). This feature appears to be related to the changes in shape and volume (and the concomitant changes in the size of stomatal aperture) which occur in the guard cells under the influence of fluctuations in turgor pressure within them.

The primary cause of changes in turgor of the guard cells is not definitely established (Heath, 1949; Wilson, 1948). The immedi-

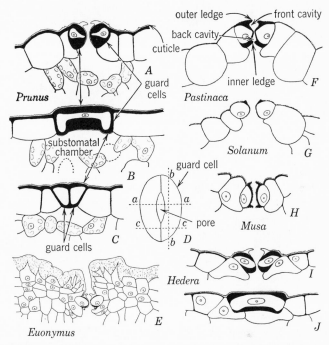

FIG. 7.3. Details of stomatal structure in abaxial epidermis of foliage leaves. *A–C*, stomata and some associated cells from a *Prunus* (peach) leaf sectioned along the planes indicated, in diagram *D*, by the broken lines *aa*, *bb*, and *cc*, respectively. *E–I*, stomata from various leaves cut along the plane *bb*. *J*, a guard cell of *Hedera* (ivy) cut along the plane *bb*. The stomata are raised in *Prunus*, *Pastinaca* (parsnip), and *Solanum* (potato). They are slightly raised in *Hedera*, slightly sunken in *Musa* (banana), and deeply sunken in *Euonymus*. The horn-like protrusions in the various guard cells are sectional views of ledges. Some stomata have two ledges (*E, F, H*); others only one (*A, G, I*). The ledges are entirely cuticular in composition in *Prunus*, *Euonymus*, and *Hedera*. The *Euonymus* leaf has a thick cuticle, and parts of the epidermal cells are occluded with cutin. (*A–D, F–J*, ×485; *E*, ×195.)

ate cause appears to be the condensation and hydrolysis of starch within them. The guard cells contain chloroplasts (Freeland, 1951), and the fluctuations of internal pressure in the cells are commonly associated with the appearance and disappearance of starch in the chloroplasts. Some workers consider that changes in starch content of the guard cells are not autonomous but are correlated (negatively)

with similar changes in the subsidiary and other epidermal cells
(Strugger and Weber, 1926). The guard cells probably vary in the
intensity of their activity (Kaufman, 1927; Sawyer, 1932) and may
become completely functionless in old organs (Flamm, 1922).

Judging by the polymorphism of the guard cells, the mechanisms
responsible for opening and closing of the stomata are varied (Cope-

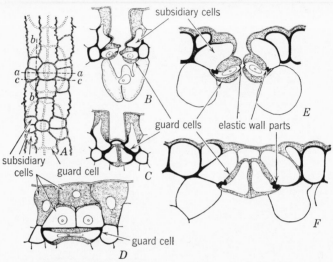

FIG. 7.4. Stomata of conifer leaves. *A*, surface view of the epidermis with two
deeply sunken stomata from *Pinus merkusii*. The guard cells are overarched by
subsidiary and other epidermal cells. Stomata and some associated cells of *Pinus*
in *B–D*, and of *Sequoia* in *E* and *F*. The broken lines in *A* indicate the planes
along which the sections of the stomata were made in *B–F*: *aa*, *B* and *E*; *bb*, *D*;
cc, *C* and *F*. (*A*, ×170; *B–D*, ×255; *E*, *F*, ×480. *A*, adapted from Abagon, 1938.)

land, 1902; Haberlandt, 1914, pp. 447–454). In one common type,
the change in the shape of the guard cells occurs because of the
greater thinness and consequent extensibility of the wall turned away
from the stomatal aperture, the so-called back wall (fig. 7.3, *A*, *E–I*,
and plate 20, *A*). When the turgor increases, the thin wall bulges
away from the aperture, while the front wall (facing the pore) becomes straight or concave. The whole cell appears to bend away
from the aperture, and the aperture increases in size. Reversed
changes occur under decreased turgor.

Another distinct type of stomatal mechanism is illustrated by the
guard cells of the Gramineae and the Cyperaceae. These cells are
bulbous at two ends and straight in the middle (fig. 7.5). The middle
portion has a strongly but unevenly thickened wall; the bulbous ends

are thin walled. Increase in turgor causes a swelling of the bulbous ends and the consequent separation of the straight median portions from each other (compare *E* and *F* in fig. 7.5).

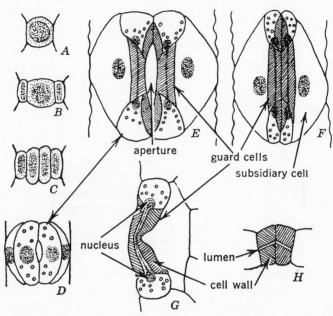

Fig. 7.5. Development and structure of stomata in sugarcane. *A*, stoma mother cell. *B*, stoma mother cell with two subsidiary cells derived from two adjoining cells. *C*, early stage of guard-cell development. *D*, young stoma with two guard cells and two subsidiary cells. The guard cells are kidney-shaped, and the subsidiary cells are much compressed by the expansion of the guard cells. *E* and *F*, mature stomata seen from the outer surface in open (*E*) and closed (*F*) states. Note the change in the shape of guard cells and subsidiary cells, and in structure of walls (hatched parts in *E–H*) between *D* and *E*. *G*, longitudinal section of one guard cell. The nucleus is much extended and appears as two masses connected by a thin thread. *H*, transection·through the central portion of two guard cells from a closed stoma. The small circles in *D–G* represent chloroplasts. (After Flint and Moreland, 1946.)

Coniferous stomata are sunken and appear as though suspended from the subsidiary cells arching over them (fig. 7.4, *B*, *E*). In their median parts the guard cells are elliptical in section and have narrow lumina (fig. 7.4, *B*, *E*). At their ends they have wider lumina and are triangular in section (fig. 7.4, *C*, *F*). The characteristic feature of these guard cells is that their walls and those of the subsidiary cells are partly lignified and partly free of lignin. This combination of more and less rigid wall parts, the manner of connection with the subsidiary cells, and the presence of thin wall parts in the subsidiary cells are features that appear to be involved in the working of the coniferous stomata (Florin, 1931).

The front cavities of stomata in conifers and some angiosperms are often occluded with finely granular or alveolar material interpreted as wax (Wilhelm, 1883), resin (Turrell, 1947), or a physically porous cuticular emulsion (Bailey and Nast, 1944).

The chemistry of the guard-cell walls is comparable to that of the other epidermal cells of the same leaves. They are usually cutinized in the outer layers and covered with a cuticle. As previously mentioned, the cuticle extends through the stomatal aperture into the substomatal chamber where it joins the inner cuticle. (The cuticle is reported to be absent on the thin wall facing the pore in *Citrus;* Turrell, 1947.) The ledges are sometimes formed of cuticle only (fig. 7.3, *A, E, I;* Priestley and Scott, 1938, p. 221; Turrell, 1947). In other plants they consist of guard-cell wall covered with a cuticle (fig. 7.3, *F–H;* Reule, 1937). Guard cells show lignification, at least in parts of their walls, in vascular cryptogams, gymnosperms, Gramineae, Cyperaceae, and certain dicotyledons (Kaufman, 1927).

Stomata arise through differential divisions in the protoderm. After several divisions of a given protodermal cell, one of the products of these divisions becomes the immediate precursor of the guard cells. This is the stoma or guard-cell mother cell (figs. 7.6, *A,* and 7.7, *A*), which eventually divides into the two guard cells. These enlarge and assume the characteristic kidney shape. Even the guard cells of the Gramineae are of this form before they become shaped like dumbbells (fig. 7.5, *D;* Flint and Moreland, 1946). The area which becomes the pore shows a lenticular mass of pectic material just before the walls separate from each other (fig. 7.6, *A;* Ziegenspeck, 1944). This appearance probably results from the swelling of the intercellular material preceding itš dissolution. The mother cells of the guard cells occur at the same level as the adjacent epidermal cells. If the mature stoma is raised above or sunken below the surface of the epidermis, the change in position occurs during the maturation of the stoma through mutual readjustments among the epidermal cells and between the epidermal and the mesophyll cells (fig. 7.7; De Bary, 1884, p. 44). Even in the coniferous leaves, in which the guard cells are so deeply sunken, the stoma mother cells are at one level with the other epidermal cells (Cross, 1942).

The guard-cell mother cell may be produced by a single anticlinal division of a given protoderm cell (e.g., Gramineae, *Iris*), or the protoderm cell may divide several times before the mother cell differentiates (e.g., Begoniaceae, Crassulaceae, Solanaceae, and many others; De Bary, 1884, pp. 39–45; Strasburger, 1866–67; Tognini, 1894). The subsidiary cells commonly originate from protodermal

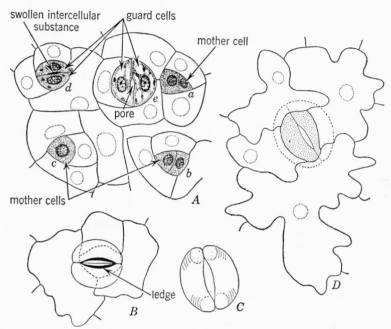

Fig. 7.6. Stomata of *Nicotiana* (tobacco) in surface views. *A*, stages in the development of stomata: *a* and *b*, soon after the division that resulted in the formation of the stoma mother cell; *c*, stoma mother cell enlarging; *d*, stoma mother cell has divided into two guard cells which are still completely joined, but the intercellular substance in the position of the future pore is swollen; *e*, young stoma with pore between the guard cells. *B*, mature stoma seen from the outer side of the adaxial epidermis. *D*, similar stoma seen from the inner side of the abaxial epidermis. Since the guard cells are raised (see fig. 7.7), they appear above the epidermal cells in *B* and below them in *D*. Compare the ledge in *B* with that shown in fig. 7.7, *F*. *C*, guard cells as they appear from the inner side of the epidermis. (*A*, ×620; *B–D*, ×490.)

cells which occur adjacent to the guard-cell mother cell (Campbell, 1881; Porterfield, 1937; Ziegenspeck, 1944). They may be sister cells of the mother cell, or they may arise through division of the cells adjacent to the mother cell (fig. 7.5). Sometimes the subsidiary cells are products of divisions of a protoderm cell that occur before the appearance of the mother cell (Strasburger, 1866–67; Tognini, 1894).

During their development, the guard cells of Gramineae and Cyperaceae show a peculiar change in shape of the nuclei (Flint and Moreland, 1946; Ziegenspeck, 1944). As the guard cell assumes its characteristic shape, with the two bulbous ends and a narrow middle part, the nucleus becomes much extended and simulates the shape of

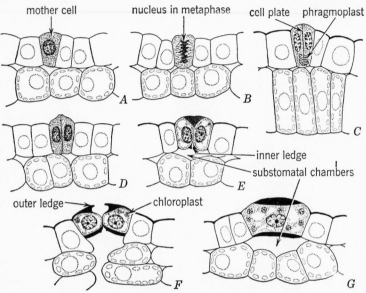

Fig. 7.7. Development of the stoma of *Nicotiana* (tobacco) as seen in sections. (Compare with surface views in fig. 7.6, *A*.) *C*, from adaxial (upper) epidermis with some palisade cells; others from abaxial (lower) epidermis. *A–C*, stoma mother cell before and during division into two guard cells. *D*, two young guard cells with thin walls. *E*, guard cells have extended laterally and have begun to thicken their walls. The inner ledge and the substomatal chamber have been formed. *F*, mature guard cells with upper and lower ledges and unevenly thickened walls. *G*, one mature guard cell cut parallel with its long axis and at right angles to the leaf surface. (All, ×490.)

the cell. It becomes transformed into a structure with two enlarged portions, one at each end of the cell, and a thread-like connection passing through the thick-walled median part of the cell (fig. 7.5, *G*). Apparently the two portions of the nucleus located in the bulbous ends of the cell may separate from each other entirely (Flint and Moreland, 1946).

In a given leaf the stomata arise not all at once but in succession, through a considerable period of leaf growth. Two principal patterns may be distinguished in the development of the stomata in the leaf as a whole (Ziegenspeck, 1944). In leaves with parallel veins, having the stomata in longitudinal rows, the developmental stages of the stomata are observable in sequence in the successively more differentiated portions of the leaf. (This sequence is basipetal, that is, from the tip of the leaf downward; see chapter 16.) In the netted veined leaves the different developmental stages are mixed in mosaic fashion so that mature stomata occur side by side with immature ones. The first pattern is characteristic of most monocotyledons and of a few dicotyledons (e.g., *Tragopogon, Thesium*); the second, of most dicotyledons and a few monocotyledons (e.g., Araceae, Smilacoideae, Taccaceae, Dioscoreaceae). Both developmental patterns are found among the vascular cryptogams.

The mode of development of stomata, their spatial relation to neighboring cells, and the absence or presence and numbers of subsidiary cells are characteristics that are employed with reference to problems of classification and phylogeny in the angiosperms and the conifers (Florin, 1931; Foster, 1949, p. 67; Metcalfe and Chalk, 1950, p. XV).

Trichomes on Aerial Plant Parts

Trichomes (a word of Greek origin, meaning a growth of hair) are epidermal appendages of diverse form, structure, and functions (figs. 7.8–7.12). They are represented by protective, supporting, and glandular hairs, by scales, by various papillae, and by the absorbing hairs of the roots.

Trichomes are usually distinguished from the so-called emergences (e.g., prickles, De Bary, 1844, p. 58) on the basis that the emergences are formed from both epidermal and subepidermal tissues. The distinction between such emergences and trichomes is not sharp, however, because some plant hairs are raised upon a base originating by division of subepidermal cells (Netolitzky, 1932). Trichomes also intergrade with nontrichomatous epidermal cells having protrusions in the form of papillae and with cells differentiated as "water vesicles" (Haberlandt, 1914, p. 116).

Trichomes may occur on all parts of a plant. Either they persist throughout the life of an organ, or they are ephemeral. Some persisting hairs remain alive; others become devoid of protoplasts and are retained in dry state. The epidermal trichomes usually develop early in relation to the growth of the organ.

Trichomes may show wide variations within families and the smaller plant groups, and even in the same plant (fig. 7.9, *D*, *E*). On the other hand, there is sometimes considerable uniformity in tri-

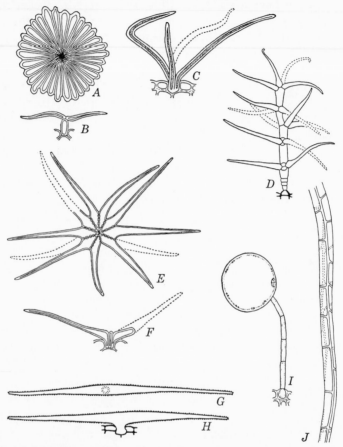

Fig. 7.8. Trichomes. *A* and *B*, peltate scale of *Olea* in surface (*A*) and side (*B*) views. *C*, tufted hair of *Quercus*. *D*, branched, candelabra hair of *Platanus*. *E* and *F*, stellate hair of *Sida* in surface (*E*) and side (*F*) views. *G* and *H*, two-armed, T-shaped unicellular hair of *Lobularia* in surface (*G*) and side (*H*) views. *I*, vesiculate hair of *Chenopodium*. *J*, part of multicellular shaggy hair of *Portulaca*. (*A–C*, *F*, *I*, ×180; *D*, *E*, *G*, *H*, *J*, ×90.)

chomes within a plant group (Metcalfe and Chalk, 1950, pp. 1326–1329). Plant-hair types have been successfully used in the classification of genera and even of species in certain families and in the recognition of interspecific hybrids (Heintzelmann and Howard, 1948; Hoff, 1950; Metcalfe and Chalk, 1950; Rollins, 1944).

Trichomes may be classified into different morphological categories (cf. Foster, 1949, p. 73). One common type is referred to as *hair*.

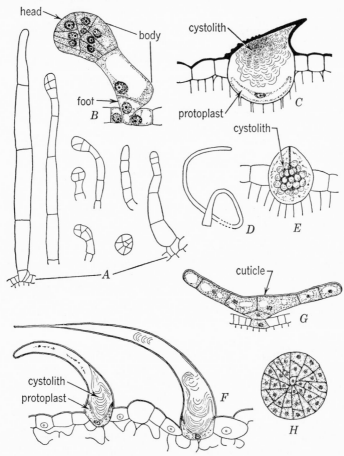

FIG. 7.9. Trichomes. *A*, group of ordinary and glandular (with multicellular heads) hairs of *Nicotiana* (tobacco). *B*, enlarged view of glandular hair of tobacco, showing the characteristic density of contents of the glandular head. *C*, hooked hair with cystolith of *Humulus*. *D*, long coiled unicellular hair, and *E*, short bristle with cystolith of *Boehmeria*. *F*, hooked hairs with cystoliths of *Cannabis*. *G* and *H*, glandular peltate trichome of *Humulus* seen in sectional (*G*) and surface (*H*) views. (*H* from younger trichome than *G*.) (*A, H,* ×100; *B, D, E,* ×310; *C, G,* ×245; *F,* ×490.)

Structurally, hairs may be subdivided into unicellular and multicellular. The unicellular hairs may be unbranched (fig. 7.9, *D, F*) or branched (fig. 7.8, *G, H*). Multicellular hairs may consist of a single row of cells (figs. 7.8, *I*, and 7.9, *A*) or of several layers (fig. 7.8, *J*). Some multicellular hairs are branched in dendroid (tree-like) manner (fig. 7.8, *D*); others have the branches oriented largely in one plane (stellate hairs, fig. 7.8, *E*). Commonly a multicellular hair can be divided into a foot, which is imbedded in the epidermis, and a body projecting above the surface (fig. 7.9, *B*). The cells surrounding the foot are sometimes morphologically distinct from other epidermal cells (Netolitzky, 1932).

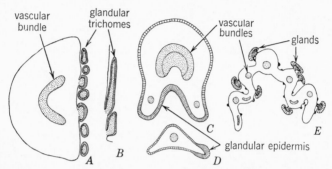

FIG. 7.10. Glandular structures on leaves. *A* and *B*, multicellular glandular trichomes with palisade-like secretory layer of *Nerium oleander*. *C* and *D*, glandular epidermis on leaf and stipule of *Salix*. *E*, leaf from a winter bud of *Betula* with peltate glands bearing a palisade-like glandular epidermis. *A, C–E*, from transverse, *B*, from longitudinal sections of leaves. (*A, B*, ×21.5; *C, D, E*, ×37.)

Another common type of trichome is the *scale*, also called *peltate hair* (from the Latin *peltatus*, target-shaped or shield-like, and attached by its lower surface). A scale consists of a discoid plate of cells, often borne on a stalk or attached directly to the foot (figs. 7.8, *A, B*, and 7.9, *G, H*).

Unicellular, multicellular, and peltate hairs may be glandular. Some of the simple multicellular glandular hairs consist of a stalk and a unicellular or multicellular head (fig. 7.9, *B*). The head constitutes the secretory part of the hair. In a peltate glandular trichome the discoid plate is composed of glandular cells (fig. 7.9, *G, H*). Some glandular trichomes consist of a multicellular core of cells covered with a palisade-like layer of secretory cells, for example, shaggy glandular hairs of *Nerium* (fig. 7.10, *A, B*). Glandular trichomes with a multicellular stalk and a usually multicellular head are sometimes classified as *colleters* (cf. Foster, 1949, p. 74), a term derived from the Greek *colla*, glue, referring to the sticky secretion from these structures. Examples of such colleters are the glandular trichomes on foliar organs of buds of certain genera (*Aesculus, Rosa, Carya*). In its original usage the term colleter was applied to all kinds of glandular structures from the simplest glandular hairs to the most complex multicellular structures consisting of derivatives of epidermal and subepidermal cells (Hanstein, 1868).

A trichome is initiated as a protuberance from an epidermal cell. The protuberance elongates, and if it develops into a multicellular

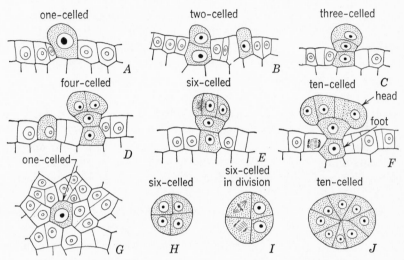

FIG. 7.11. Development of glandular trichomes (stippled cells) of *Ligustrum* as seen in sectional (*A–F*) and surface (*G–J*) views. (×490.)

structure various divisions may follow the initial elongation (fig. 7.11; Cooper, 1932; Netolitzky, 1932).

The cell walls of trichomes are commonly of cellulose and are covered with a cuticle. They may be lignified. Plant hairs often produce thick secondary walls as, for instance, the cotton seed hairs (Anderson and Kerr, 1938) or the "climber hairs" of *Humulus* (fig. 7.9, *C*; Franz, 1935). The walls of trichomes are sometimes impregnated with silica or calcium carbonate (Beyrich, 1943). Their contents are varied in relation to function; the most complex are probably those of the glandular cells. Chloroplasts are often present, though they may be small and not persisting (Netolitzky, 1932). Plant hair cells, other than the glandular, are characteristically highly vacuolated. Cystoliths and other crystals may develop in hairs (fig. 7.9, *C, E, F*).

Cotton seed hairs, commonly known as cotton fibers, are extremely long epidermal hairs with thick secondary walls of almost pure cellulose (Berkley, 1948; Matthews, 1947). They are formed from the protoderm of the ovule during flowering and continue to arise for about 10 days after anthesis (Anderson and Kerr, 1938; Farr, 1931). The elongation lasts for 15 to 20 days, and the hairs become ½ to 2½ in. long, depending on the variety of cotton. A number of other plants produce commercially usable hairs on the seeds or other parts of the fruit (Dewey, 1943; Pearson, 1948).

Among glandular hairs, the stinging hairs of the nettle (*Urtica*) have a rather unusual wall structure, with a special mechanism for releasing the contents of the hair (Emmelin and Feldberg, 1947; Haberlandt, 1914, pp. 129–130). The hair is like a fine capillary tube, calcified at its lower end and silicified at its upper end. At the base, a bladder-like end is imbedded in epidermal cells, somewhat raised above the surface. At the upper end the tube is closed by means of a spherical tip which breaks off along a predetermined line when the hair comes in contact with the skin. The sharp edge left after the separation of the tip readily penetrates the skin, and the contents of the tube escape into the wound. The poisonous material of the nettle is highly complex and contains a histamine and an acetyl-choline (Feldberg, 1950).

Active secretory cells of glandular trichomes have dense proto-plasts and elaborate various substances, such as volatile oils, resins, mucilages, and gums. These substances are excreted and accumulate between the wall and the cuticle. Their final removal from the hair occurs by rupture of the cuticle (Netolitzky, 1932; Van Horne and Zopf, 1948). In young organs the cuticle is supposedly re-generated, and the accumulation of the secretion is repeated (Haber-landt, 1914, p. 513).

Glandular trichomes are one of many types of glandular struc-tures, the *glands* (De Bary, 1884, pp. 92–101; Haberlandt, 1914, pp. 511–516), that may be found on the surface of the plant body. These structures vary in degree of complexity, and the most elaborate intergrade with the simple glandular hairs by transitional structures. Some of the glandular structures are emergences in the sense that they develop partly from the epidermis, partly from the subepi-dermal tissue. In the mature state they may resemble some of the complex trichomes (fig. 7.10, *E*). Glandular surfaces may occur independently of any trichomes or emergences, simply as a glandular epidermis covering the leaf teeth (*Prunus*) or other parts of foliar organs (fig. 7.10, *C*, *D*; Böhmker, 1916; Schwendt, 1907). Special glands, the *nectaries,* producing a sugary secretion, occur on flowers and also on other plant parts (Böhmker, 1916; see also chapter 18). Many of the glandular structures are excretory organs discharging terpenes (ethereal oils, balsams, resins, camphors). These substances are end products of metabolism, particularly of processes associated with growth. This circumstance makes understandable the particular abundance of glandular structures on young, growing organs (Frey-Wyssling, 1935). Glands secreting mucilage and mixtures of this substance with resins are commonly formed in buds and cover the scales and leaf primordia in the latter with a foamy sticky emulsion (Brick, 1914). Such glands reduce their activity or cease to function after the leaves expand; frequently they fall off entirely.

Root Hairs

As was previously mentioned, the epidermis of the root typically lacks a cuticle and stomata but commonly bears root hairs. These are tubular structures constituting direct lateral extensions of the cells that originate them. They are rarely branched (Linsbauer, 1930). In a study involving 37 species in 20 families, the root hairs were found to vary between 5 and 17 microns in diameter and between 80 and 1,500 microns in length (Dittmer, 1949). The root hairs are highly vacuolate, and their walls are thin. The chemistry of the walls has been variously interpreted. The best evidence indicates that an inner cellulose lamella is covered on the outside by calcium pectate (Cormack, 1949). In young root hairs the pectic covering is mucilaginous, but, according to recent electron microscope studies, it is permeated by microfibrils of cellulose (Frey-Wyssling and Mühlethaler, 1950).

The development of root hairs has been studied in much detail (Cormack, 1949). The root hairs develop acropetally, that is, toward the apex of the root, and apparently never originate among preexisting hairs. Because of the acropetal sequence of initiation, in most seedlings the length of root hairs shows a uniform gradation in size, beginning with those nearest the apex. The hairs are initiated in the part of the root located behind the zone of most active cell division, but where the longitudinal extension of the epidermal cells may still be in progress. Usually the root hair emerges as a small papilla at or near the apical end of a cell. If the cell continues to elongate, after the appearance of the papilla, the root hair eventually occurs some distance from this end; otherwise its position remains terminal. According to most observations, the root hair grows at the tip where, during growth, the wall is softer and more

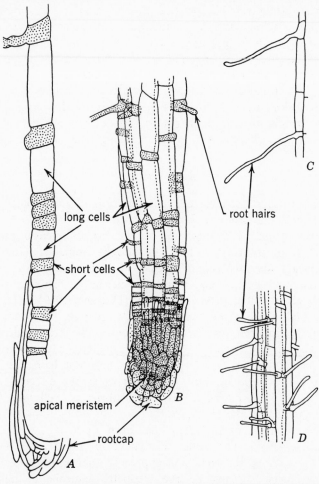

Fɪɢ. 7.12. Root-hair development. Views of parts of roots showing development of root hairs from specialized protodermal cells (short cells, or trichoblasts). *A* and *C, Cyperus; B* and *D, Anigozanthos.* (*A, B,* ×240; *D,* ×175. Redrawn from Leavitt, *Boston Soc. Nat. Hist. Proc.* **31,** 1904.)

delicate than along the sides. The nucleus is usually located close behind the growing tip.

The mechanism of root-hair formation has been variously interpreted in the literature, but there is general agreement that the emergence of root hairs follows a retardation in vertical elongation of the epidermal cells (Cormack, 1949). Considerable evidence has been obtained that the decrease in the rate of this elongation and the associated emergence of root hairs are related to the mode of transformation of the plastic pectic acid on the surface of these cells into the harder calcium pectate (Cormack, 1949).

In some plants the root epidermis shows a morphologic differentiation into hair-forming cells (*trichoblasts*) and cells that do not form hairs (fig. 7.12). This differentiation may be strong or weak (Cormack, 1949; Sinnott and Bloch, 1939). In general, the root hair-forming cells are shorter than the others (fig. 7.12, *C, D*). When strongly expressed, this difference may be visible at the origin of a trichoblast (fig. 7.12, *A, B*). In such instances a given protodermal cell divides into a longer and a shorter cell, the shorter being characterized by denser cytoplasm than the longer cell (Leavitt, 1904).

In plants having a homogeneous root epidermis all epidermal cells are potential trichomatous cells, but not all necessarily produce root hairs. The nontrichomatous cells of a root with a heterogenous epidermis may be induced to form root hairs by suitable changes in the environment, and conversely the potentially trichomatous cells may be prevented from developing such structures (Cormack, 1949).

Root hairs are short lived. Their longevity is commonly measured in days (Linsbauer, 1930). Old root hairs collapse, and the walls of the epidermal cells, if the cells are not sloughed off, become suberized and lignified. Persisting root hairs have been observed in a number of plant species (Artschwager, 1925; Cormack, 1949; Hayward and Long, 1942). Such hairs become thick-walled and are then probably not concerned with absorption.

MULTIPLE EPIDERMIS

One or more layers of cells beneath the epidermis in leaf, stem, and root may be morphologically and physiologically distinct from the deeper-lying ground tissue. The older plant anatomists designated all distinctly characterized subepidermal layers as *hypodermis* (from the Greek *hypo*, below, and *derma*, skin; De Bary, 1884, p. 225; Guttenberg, 1943). The specialized subsurface tissue may be part of the ground tissue, or it may be derived from the protoderm by periclinal divisions. The recognition of the latter possibility has prompted workers to separate the hypodermis originating in the ground tissue from the subsurface layers of protodermal origin by introducing the concept of *multiple* or *multiseriate epidermis* (cf. Linsbauer, 1930). A study of mature structures rarely permits the identification of the tissue either as multiple epidermis or as a combination of epidermis and a hypodermis. The origin of the subsurface layers can be properly revealed only by developmental studies.

The outermost layer of a multiple epidermis resembles the ordinary uniseriate epidermis in having a cuticle. The inner layers are commonly differentiated as water-storage tissue lacking chlorophyll (Linsbauer, 1930). The multiple epidermis varies in thickness from 2 to 16 layers of cells (De Bary, 1884, p. 33). Sometimes only individual cells of the epidermis undergo periclinal divisions. Representatives with multiple epidermis may be found among the Moraceae (fig. 7.13, most species of *Ficus*), the Pittosporaceae, the Piperaceae (*Peperomia*), the Begoniaceae, the Malvaceae, the Monocotyledoneae (palms, orchids), ferns, and others (Linsbauer, 1930). The *velamen* (from the Latin word for covering) of the aerial and terrestrial roots of orchids is a multiple epidermis (Engard, 1944; Linsbauer, 1930).

The periclinal divisions initiating the multiple epidermis in leaves occur at different stages of leaf growth but usually when a leaf is several internodes below the apex (Linsbauer, 1930). In *Ficus*, for example, the leaf has a uniseriate epidermis until the stipules are shed (Pfitzer, 1872). Then periclinal divisions occur in the epidermis (fig. 7.13, *A*). Similar divisions are repeated in the outer row of daughter cells, sometimes once, sometimes twice (fig. 7.13, *B*). During the expansion of the leaf, anticlinal divisions occur also, and, since these divisions are not synchronized in the different layers, the ontogenetic relation between these layers becomes more or less obscured (fig. 7.13, *B, C*). The inner cells expand more than the outer. The outer cells remain particularly small because they expand less and undergo more numerous anticlinal divisions than the inner. The cystolith-containing cells characteristic of *Ficus* leaves (see chapter 3) do not divide but keep pace with the increasing depth of the epidermis and even overtake it by expansion and intrusion into the mesophyll (fig. 7.13; Ajello, 1941; Pfitzer, 1872). In some plants (e.g., *Peperomia*) the cells of the multiple epidermis remain arranged in radial rows and clearly reveal their common origin (Linsbauer, 1930).

The histogenetic relation between the epidermis and the subepidermal layers is quite variable. In some plants, for example, in grasses, the mesophyll or part of it has common origin with the epidermis, whereas in the roots the epidermis is often the outermost layer of

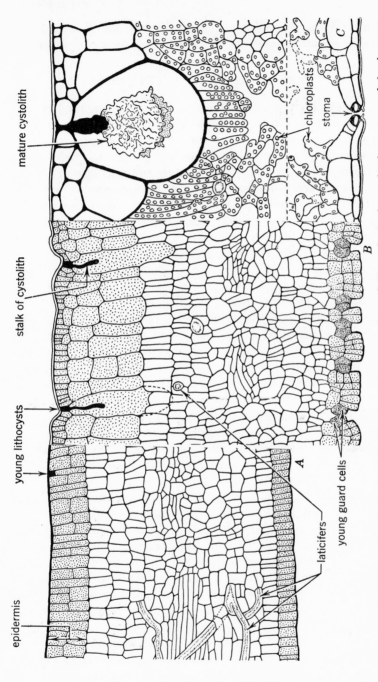

FIG. 7.13. Multiple epidermis (on both leaf surfaces) in transections of *Ficus elastica* leaves in three stages of development. Epidermis stippled in *A* and *B*, with thick walls in *C*. Part of leaf omitted along broken line in *C*. Cystolith development: *A*, wall thickens in lithocyst; *B*, cellulose stalk appears; *C*, calcium carbonate is deposited on stalk. Unlike other epidermal cells, lithocyst undergoes no periclinal divisions. (*A*, ×265; *B*, ×210; *C*, ×300.)

the cortex. Thus, the multiple epidermis is just one of several expressions of a common origin of the surface and subsurface layers.

STRUCTURE IN RELATION TO FUNCTION

The multiplicity of functions ascribed to the epidermis is thoroughly reviewed in the literature (Linsbauer, 1930). The normal functions of the epidermis of the aerial plant parts are considered to be restriction of transpiration, mechanical protection, gaseous exchange through stomata, and storage of water and metabolic products. However, some accessory functions may predominate to such an extent that the epidermis assumes characteristics typical, not of this tissue, but of some other. In this category of functions are included photosynthesis (Wylie, 1948), secretion, absorption (other than that of the root epidermis), and possibly also the perception of stimuli and causal association with the movements of plant parts. Some of the functions of the epidermis appear to be related to certain specialized anatomic characteristics (Linsbauer, 1930).

The restriction of transpiration is largely the result of the cuticularization and cutinization of the outer epidermal walls. The efficiency of the cuticle in this respect is indicated by the lower values obtained for the cuticular transpiration as contrasted with that occurring through the stomata (Linsbauer, 1930). The waxes which are frequently deposited on the surface of the cuticle are also important in reducing the loss of water by transpiration (Cunze, 1925). At the same time, the existence of cuticular transpiration shows that the restriction of water loss by the epidermis is by no means absolute. Moreover, the presence of cuticle is only one of many factors affecting transpiration (Priestley, 1943).

Recently, evidence has been presented that in some leaves the epidermis plays an important role in conduction within the leaf (Wylie, 1943, 1948; see also chapter 16). In many species the epidermis is intimately connected with the vascular bundles by special parenchymatous extensions from the sheaths surrounding the vascular bundles. The water apparently is readily translocated through this parenchyma to the epidermis where it spreads horizontally and eventually reaches the mesophyll cells lying somewhat distant from the vascular bundles.

The root epidermis is particularly adapted for absorption. The ability of root hairs to absorb water has been demonstrated experimentally by the use of a seedling root of the radish (Rosene, 1943).

However, the hairless epidermal cells also absorb water with a range of velocity comparable to that of cells bearing root hairs. The principal function of the root hairs is considered to be the extension of the absorbing surface of the root, and from this standpoint the available information pertaining to their numbers and surface area in a rye plant is of interest (Dittmer, 1937). In this plant the 13,815,672 roots had a surface area of 2,554.09 sq ft. Living root hairs numbered 14,335,568,288 and had a total surface area of 4,321.31 sq ft. Thus the combined surface area of the roots and root hairs was 6,875.40 sq ft, and it was packed in less than 2 cu ft of soil. This total root surface was 130 times that exposed to the outside air by the aerial parts of the same plant. If the surface of the mesophyll cells of a foliage leaf facing the intercellular spaces was taken in consideration, the root surface was still 22 times that of the transpirational area of the top.

The meristematic potentialities of the epidermis merit a brief mention. In general, this tissue is relatively passive with regard to meristematic activities (Linsbauer, 1930). Nevertheless, the epidermis is known to resume such activity during the normal course of development (e.g., formation of phellogen, see chapter 14) and after injuries (Foster, 1949, pp. 66–67; Linsbauer, 1930; McVeigh, 1938).

REFERENCES

Abagon, M. A. A comparative anatomical study of the needles of *Pinus insularis* Endlicher and *Pinus merkusii* Junghun and de Vriese. *Philippine Univ. Nat. and Appl. Sci. Bul.* **6**:29–58. 1938.

Ajello, L. Cytology and cellular interrelations of cystolith formation in *Ficus elastica*. *Amer. Jour. Bot.* **28**:589–594. 1941.

Allen, G. S. Embryogeny and the development of the apical meristems of *Pseudotsuga*. II. Late embryogeny. *Amer. Jour. Bot.* **34**:73–80. 1947.

Anderson, D. B., and T. Kerr. Growth and structure of cotton fiber. *Indus. and Engin. Chem.* **30**:48–54. 1938.

Artschwager, E. Anatomy of the vegetative organs of sugar cane. *Jour. Agr. Res.* **30**:197–221. 1925.

Artschwager, E. A comparative study of the stem epidermis of certain sugar-cane varieties. *Jour. Agr. Res.* **41**:853–865. 1930.

Artschwager, E. Morphology of the vegetative organs of sugarcane. *Jour. Agr. Res.* **60**:503–549. 1940.

Avery, G. S., Jr. Structure and development of the tobacco leaf. *Amer. Jour. Bot.* **20**:565–592. 1933.

Bailey, I. W., and C. G. Nast. The comparative morphology of the Winteraceae. V. Foliar epidermis and sclerenchyma. *Arnold Arboretum Jour.* **25**:342–348. 1944.

Berkley, E. E.   Cotton, a versatile textile fiber.   *Textile Res. Jour.* **18**:71–88. 1948.

Beyrich, H.   Über die Membranverkieselung einiger Pflanzenhaare.   *Flora* **36**: 313–324. 1943.

Böhmker, H.   Beiträge zur Kenntnis der floralen und extrafloralen Nektarien. *Bot. Centbl. Beihefte* **33**:169–247. 1916.

Brick, E.   Die Anatomie der Knospenschuppen in ihrer Beziehung zur Anatomie der Laubblätter.   *Bot. Centbl. Beihefte* **31**:209–308. 1914.

Burström, H.   Über die Entfaltung und Einrollen eines mesophilen Grassblattes. *Bot. Notiser* **1942**:351–362. 1942.

Campbell, D. H.   On the development of the stomata of *Tradescantia* and Indian corn.   *Amer. Nat.* **15**:761–766. 1881.

Cooper, D. C.   The development of the peltate hairs of *Shepherdia canadensis. Amer. Jour. Bot.* **19**:423–428. 1932.

Copeland, E. B.   The mechanism of stomata.   *Ann. Bot.* **16**:327–364. 1902.

Cormack, R. G. H.   The development of root hairs in angiosperms.   *Bot. Rev.* **15**:583–612. 1949.

Cross, G. L.   Structure of the apical meristem and development of the foliage leaves of *Cunninghamia lanceolata. Amer. Jour. Bot.* **29**:288–301. 1942.

Cunze, R.   Untersuchungen über die ökologische Bedeutung des Wachses im Wasserhaushalt der Pflanzen.   *Bot. Centbl. Beihefte* **42**:160–185. 1925.

Damm, O.   Über den Bau, die Entwicklungsgeschichte und die mechanischen Eigenschaften mehrjähriger Epidermen bei den Dicotyledonen.   *Bot. Centbl. Beihefte* **7**:219–260. 1902.

De Bary, A.   *Comparative anatomy of the vegetative organs of the phanerogams and ferns.* Oxford, Clarendon Press. 1884.

Dewey, L. H.   Fiber production in the western hemisphere.   *U. S. Dept. Agr. Misc. Pub.* 518. 1943.

Dittmer, H. J.   A quantitative study of the roots and root hairs of a winter rye plant (*Secale cereale*).   *Amer. Jour. Bot.* **24**:417–420. 1937.

Dittmer, H. J.   Root hair variations in plant species.   *Amer. Jour. Bot.* **36**:152– 155. 1949.

Eames, A. J., and L. H. MacDaniels.   *An introduction to plant anatomy.* 2nd ed.   New York, McGraw-Hill Book Company. 1947.

Emmelin, N., and W. Feldberg.   The mechanism of the sting of the common nettle (*Urtica urens*).   *Jour. Physiol.* **106**:440–455. 1947.

Engard, C. J.   Morphological identity of the velamen and exodermis in orchids. *Bot. Gaz.* **105**:457–462. 1944.

Farr, W. K.   Cotton fibers. I. Origin and early stages of elongation.   *Boyce Thompson Inst. Contrib.* **3**:441–458. 1931.

Feldberg, W.   The mechanism of the sting of the common nettle.   *Brit. Sci. News* **3**:75–77. 1950.

Flamm, E.   Zur Lebensdauer und Anatomie einiger Rhizome.   *Akad. der Wiss. Wien, Math.-Nat. Kl. Sitzber.* Abt. 1. **131**:7–22. 1922.

Flint, L. H., and C. F. Moreland.   A study of the stomata in sugarcane.   *Amer. Jour. Bot.* **33**:80–82. 1946.

Florin, R.   Untersuchungen zur Stammesgeschichte der Coniferales und Cordaitales.   *Svenska Vetensk. Akad. Handl.* Ser. 3. **10**:1–588. 1931.

Foster, A. S. *Practical plant anatomy.* 2nd ed. New York, D. Van Nostrand Company. 1949.

Franz, H. Beiträge zur Kenntnis des Dickenwachstums der Membranen. (Untersuchungen an den Haaren von *Humulus lupulus*.) *Flora* 29:287–308. 1935.

Freeland, R. O. The green pigment and physiology of guard cells. *Science* 114:94–95. 1951.

Frenzel, P. Über die Porengrössen einiger pflanzlicher Zellmembranen. *Planta* 8:644–665. 1929.

Frey-Wyssling, A. *Die Stoffausscheidung der höheren Pflanzen. Monographien aus dem Gesamtgebiet der Physiologie der Pflanzen und der Tiere.* Band 32. Berlin, Julius Springer. 1935.

Frey-Wyssling, A., and K. Mühlethaler. Bau und Funktion der Wurzelhaare. *Schweiz. Landw. Monatsch.* 28:212–219. 1950.

Frohnmeyer, M. Die Entstehung und Ausbildung der Kieselzellen bei den Gramineen. *Biblioth. Bot.* 21(86):1–41. 1914.

Grob, A. Beiträge zur Anatomie der Epidermis der Gramineenblätter. *Biblioth. Bot.* 7(36):1–122. 1896.

Guttenberg, H. von. Die Bewegungsgewebe. In: K. Linsbauer. *Handbuch der Pflanzenanatomie.* Band 5. Lief. 18. 1926.

Guttenberg, H. von. Die Bewegungsgewebe. In: K. Linsbauer. *Handbuch der buch der Pflanzenanatomie.* Band 5. Lief. 42. 1943.

Haberlandt, G. *Physiological plant anatomy.* London, Macmillan and Company. 1914.

Hanstein, J. Über die Organe der Harz- und Schleimabsonderung in den Laubknospen. *Bot. Ztg.* 26:697–713, 721–736, 745–761, 769–787. 1868.

Hayward, H. E., and E. M. Long. The anatomy of the seedling and roots of the Valencia orange. *U. S. Dept. Agr. Tech.* Bul. 786. 1942.

Heath, O. V. S. Studies in stomatal behaviour. II. The role of starch in the light response of stomata. Part 1. Review of literature, and experiments on the relation between aperture and starch content in the stomata of *Pelargonium zonale. New Phytol.* 48:186–211. 1949.

Heinemann, K. Zur Kenntnis der Oberhaut am Maisstengel. *Bot. Centbl. Beihefte* 42:111–159. 1925.

Heintzelmann, C. E., Jr., and R. A. Howard. The comparative morphology of the Icacinaceae. V. The pubescence and the crystals. *Amer. Jour. Bot.* 35:42–52. 1948.

Hoff, A. von. Beitrag zur Kenntnis der mehrzelligen Behaarung von *Rhododendron.* Variabilität, Verwandschaftbeziehungen und phylogenetische Folgerungen. *Deut. Bot. Gesell. Ber.* 63:31–35. 1950.

Kaufman, K. Anatomie und Physiologie der Spaltöffnungsapparate mit verholzten Schliesszellmembranen. *Planta* 3:27–59. 1927.

Kroemer, K. Wurzelhaut, Hypodermis und Endodermis der Angiospermenwurzel. *Biblioth. Bot.* 12(59):1–51. 1903.

Küster, E. *Die Pflanzenzelle.* Jena, Gustav Fischer. 1935.

Leavitt, R. G. Trichomes of the root in vascular cryptogams and angiosperms. *Boston Soc. Nat. Hist. Proc.* 31:273–313. 1904.

Linsbauer, K. Die Epidermis. In: K. Linsbauer. *Handbuch der Pflanzenanatomie.* Band 4. Lief. 27. 1930.

Löv, L. Zur Kenntnis der Entfaltungszellen monokotyler Blätter. *Flora* 20: 283–343. 1926.

Marco, H. F. The anatomy of spruce needles. *Jour. Agr. Res.* 58:357–368. 1939.

Martens, P. Recherches sur la cuticule. IV. Le relief cuticulaire et la différenciation epidermique des organes floraux. *Cellule* 43:289–320. 1934.

Matthews, J. M. *Textile fibers.* 5th ed. Edited by H. R. Mauersberger. New York, John Wiley & Sons. 1947.

Matzke, E. B. The three-dimensional shape of epidermal cells of *Aloe aristata. Amer. Jour. Bot.* 34:182–195. 1947.

Matzke, E. B. The three-dimensional shape of epidermal cells of the apical meristem of *Anacharis densa (Elodea). Amer. Jour. Bot.* 35:323–332. 1948.

McVeigh, I. Regeneration in *Crassula multicava. Amer. Jour. Bot.* 25:7–11. 1938.

Metcalfe, C. R., and L. Chalk. Anatomy of the dicotyledons. Vol. 2. Oxford, Clarendon Press. 1950.

Meyer, B. S., and D. B. Anderson. *Plant physiology.* New York, D. Van Nostrand Company. 1946.

Meyer, F. J. Das trophische Parenchym. A. Assimilationsgewebe. In: K. Linsbauer. *Handbuch der Pflanzenanatomie.* Band 4. Lief. 9. 1923.

Netolitzky, F. Die Pflanzenhaare. In: K. Linsbauer. *Handbuch der Pflanzenanatomie.* Band 4. Lief. 29. 1932.

Olivier, L. Recherches sur l'appareil tégumentaire des racines. *Ann. des Sci. Nat., Bot.* Ser. 6. 11:5–133. 1881.

Pearson, N. L. Observations on seed and seed hair growth in *Asclepias syriaca* L. *Amer. Jour. Bot.* 35:27–36. 1948.

Pfitzer, E. Beiträge zur Kenntnis der Hautgewebe der Pflanzen. III. Über die mehrschichtige Epidermis und das Hypoderma. *Jahrb. f. Wiss. Bot.* 8:16–74. 1872.

Porterfield, W. M. Histogenesis in the bamboo with special reference to the epidermis. *Torrey Bot. Club Bul.* 64:421–432. 1937.

Prat, H. General features of the epidermis in *Zea mays. Mo. Bot. Gard. Ann.* 35:341–351. 1948.

Priestley, J. H. The cuticle in angiosperms. *Bot. Rev.* 9:593–616. 1943.

Priestley, J. H., and L. I. Scott. *An introduction to botany.* London, Longmans, Green & Co. 1938.

Reule, H. Vergleichend-anatomische Untersuchungen in der Gattung *Mesembrianthemum* L. *Flora* 31:400–424. 1937.

Rollins, R. C. Evidence for natural hybridity between guayule (*Parthenium argentatum*) and mariola (*Parthenium incanum*). *Amer. Jour. Bot.* 31:93–99. 1944.

Rosene, H. F. Quantitative measurement of the velocity of water absorption in individual root hairs by a microtechnique. *Plant Physiol.* 18:588–607. 1943.

Rouschal, E., and S. Strugger. Der fluoreszenz-optisch-histochemische Nachweis der kutikulären Rekretion und des Salzweges im Mesophyll. *Deut. Bot. Gesell. Ber.* 58:50–69. 1940.

Sawyer, W. H. Stomatal apparatus of the cultivated cranberry *Vaccinium macrocarpon. Amer. Jour. Bot.* 19:508–513. 1932.

Schwendt, E. Zur Kenntnis der extrafloralen Nektarien. *Bot. Centbl. Beihefte* 22:245–286. 1907.

Sinnott, E. W., and R. Bloch. Cell polarity and the differentiation of root hairs. *Natl. Acad. Sci. Proc.* 25:248–252. 1939.

Skutch, A. F. Unrolling of leaves of *Musa sapientum* and some related plants and their reactions to environmental aridity. *Bot. Gaz.* 90:337–365. 1930.

Stevens, N. E. Thickness of cuticle in cranberry fruits. *Amer. Jour. Bot.* 19: 432–435. 1932.

Strasburger, E. Ein Beitrag zur Entwicklungsgeschichte der Spaltöffnungen. *Jahrb. f. Wiss. Bot.* 5:297–342. 1866–67.

Strugger, S., and F. Weber. Zur Physiologie der Stomata-Nebenzellen. *Deut. Bot. Gesell. Ber.* 44:272–278. 1926.

Tognini, F. Contribuzione allo studio della organogenia comparata degli stomi. *Ist. Bot. della R. Univ. Pavia Atti.* Ser. 2. 4:1–42. 1894.

Turrell, F. M. Citrus leaf stomata: structure, composition, and pore size in relation to penetration of liquids. *Bot. Gaz.* 108:476–483. 1947.

Van Horne, R. L., and L. C. Zopf. A histological study of the glandular hairs of *Lophanthus anisatus* Benth. *Amer. Pharm. Assoc. Jour.* 37:152–156. 1948.

Watson, R. W. The effect of cuticular hardening on the form of epidermal cells. *New Phytol.* 41:223–229. 1942.

Weber, E. Über die Optik und Struktur der Pflanzenwachse. *Schweiz. Bot. Gesell. Ber.* 52:111–175. 1942.

Wilhelm, K. Über eine Eigentümlichkeit der Spaltöffnungen bei Coniferen. *Deut. Bot. Gesell. Ber.* 1:325–330. 1883.

Wilson, C. C. The effect of some environmental factors on the movement of guard cells. *Plant Physiol.* 23:5–37. 1948.

Wylie, R. B. The role of the epidermis in foliar organization and its relation to the minor venation. *Amer. Jour. Bot.* 30:273–280. 1943.

Wylie, R. B. The dominant role of the epidermis in leaves of *Adiantum.* *Amer. Jour. Bot.* 35:465–473. 1948.

Ziegenspeck, H. Vergleichende Untersuchungen der Entwicklung der Spaltöffnungen von Monokotyledonen und Dikotyledonen im Lichte der Polariskopie und Dichroskopie. *Protoplasma* 38:197–224. 1944.

CHAPTER

8

Parenchyma

CONCEPT

The term *parenchyma* refers to a tissue composed of living cells variable in their morphology and physiology, but generally having thin walls and a polyhedral shape (plate 22, *A*), and concerned with vegetative activities of the plant. The individual cells of such a tissue are *parenchyma cells*. The word parenchyma is derived from the Greek *para*, beside, and *en-chein*, to pour, a combination of words that expresses the ancient concept of parenchyma as a semiliquid substance "poured beside" other tissues which are formed earlier and are more solid.

Parenchyma is often spoken of as the fundamental or ground tissue. It fits this definition from morphological as well as physiological aspects. In the plant body as a whole or in its organs parenchyma appears as a ground substance in which other tissues, notably the vascular, are imbedded. It is the foundation of the plant in the sense that the apical meristems and the reproductive cells are parenchymatous in nature. Furthermore, parenchyma cells are involved in phenomena of wound healing and regeneration. Phylogenetically, parenchyma is also the precursor of other tissues, as evidenced by the structure of the most primitive multicellular plants whose bodies consist of parenchyma only.

This tissue is the principal seat of such essential activities of the plant as photosynthesis, assimilation, respiration, storage, secretion, excretion—in short, activities depending on the presence of living protoplasm. Parenchyma cells which occur in the xylem and phloem tissues appear to play an important role in connection with the movement of water in the nonliving tracheary elements and with the transport of food in the sieve elements whose protoplasts lack nuclei.

170

Parenchyma, or its constituent cells, are commonly characterized as primitive, undifferentiated, unspecialized, and simple. As was mentioned in the preceding paragraph, parenchyma cells are phylogenetically more primitive than other types of cells. Developmentally, parenchyma cells also are relatively undifferentiated. They are unspecialized morphologically and physiologically, compared with such cells as sieve elements, tracheids, or fibers, since, in contrast to these three examples of cell categories, parenchyma cells may change functions or combine several different ones. However, parenchyma cells may also be distinctly specialized, for example, with reference to photosynthesis, storage of specific substances, or deposition of materials which are in excess in the plant body. Whether they are specialized or not, parenchyma cells are highly complex physiologically because they possess living protoplasts.

It was pointed out in chapter 4 that living cells are not fixed in their characteristics and that they possess, in varying degrees, the ability to resume meristematic activity. Parenchyma constitutes the principal category of tissue showing such developmental plasticity resulting from its relatively low level of differentiation.

DELIMITATION

Parenchyma cells may occur in extensive continuous masses as parenchyma tissue. They may be also associated with other types of cells in morphologically heterogeneous tissues. The pith and the cortex of stems and roots, the photosynthetic tissue, or mesophyll, of leaves, the flesh of succulent fruits, the endosperm of seeds are all examples of plant parts consisting largely or entirely of parenchyma. As components of heterogeneous tissues parenchyma cells form the vascular rays and the vertical files of living cells in the xylem and the phloem (figs. 11.10, 11.11, 12.7, and 12.8). Sometimes an essentially parenchymatous tissue contains parenchymatous or nonparenchymatous cells or groups of cells, morphologically or physiologically distinct from the main mass of cells in the tissue. Sclereids, for example, may be found in the leaf mesophyll and in the pith and cortical parenchyma (see chapter 10). Laticifers occur in various parenchymatous regions of plants containing latex (see chapter 13). Sieve tubes traverse the cortical parenchyma of certain plants (see chapter 12).

The variable structure of parenchyma tissue and the distribution of parenchyma cells in the plant body clearly illustrate the problems involved in the proper definition and classification of a tissue. On the one hand, parenchyma may fit the most restricted definition of a tissue as a group of cells of common origin, of essentially the same structure, and having the same function (Hayward, 1938, p. 11). On the other hand, the homogeneity of a parenchyma tissue may be disturbed by the presence of varying numbers of nonparenchymatous cells; or parenchyma cells may occur as one of many cell categories in a heterogeneous tissue.

Thus, the spatial delimitation of the parenchyma as a tissue is not precise in the plant body. Furthermore, parenchyma cells may intergrade with cells that are distinctly nonparenchymatous. Parenchyma cells may be more or less elongated and have thick walls, a combination of characters suggesting specialization with regard to support. A certain category of parenchyma cells is so distinctly differentiated as a supporting tissue that it is. designated by the special name of collenchyma (see chapter 9). Parenchyma cells may develop relatively thick lignified walls and assume some of the characteristics of sclerenchyma cells (see chapter 10). Tannin may be found in ordinary parenchyma cells and also in cells basically parenchymatous but of such distinct form (e.g., vesicles, sacs, or tubes) that they are designated as idioblasts (see p. 30). Similarly, certain secretory cells differ from other parenchyma cells mainly in their function; others are so much modified that they are commonly treated as a special category of elements (e.g., laticifers, see chapter 13).

The present chapter is restricted to a consideration of parenchyma concerned with the most ordinary vegetative activities of the plant, excluding the meristematic. The related collenchyma and the highly specialized laticifers are treated in separate chapters. Furthermore, the parenchyma cells of the xylem and the phloem are described in chapters dealing with these two tissues. Finally, the general characteristics of the protoplasts of parenchyma cells are discussed in chapter 2.

STRUCTURE

Cell Contents

The variation in contents of parenchyma cells is intimately related to the activities of these cells (cf. De Bary, 1884; Haberlandt, 1914; Meyer, 1923; Netolitzky, 1935; Sperlich, 1939). The cells of the photosynthetic parenchyma have variable numbers of chloroplasts. At certain times during the day chloroplasts may contain assimilation starch. Because of its high content in chlorophyll the photosynthetic parenchyma is sometimes called *chlorenchyma*. The most distinctly specialized chlorenchyma is represented by leaf mesophyll (plate 61), but chloroplasts occur also in the cortex (plate 20, *A*) and sometimes more deeply in the stem. Cells not concerned with photosynthesis are devoid of chloroplasts but may have leucoplasts. Actively synthesizing cells commonly have conspicuously vacuolated protoplasts.

Many different food substances are synthesized and stored by parenchyma cells. The same protoplast may store one or more kinds of substances. These substances may be dissolved in the vacuolar sap, or they may be discrete solid or fluid bodies in the cytoplasm (fig. 8.1, *C*). Bodies or masses may consist of such ergastic substances as starch grains, granules and crystalloids of protein, and globules of fats and oils. The cell sap may be a depository of sugars and other soluble carbohydrates and of nitrogenous substances in the form of amides and proteins. Some examples of plant organs and their storage products are given in the following discussion (Netolitzky, 1935, p. 8). Amides, proteins, and sugar are dissolved in the cell sap of the fleshy beet root and the bulb scales of the onion. The parenchyma of the potato tuber and of rhizomes of many other plants contains amides and proteins in the cell sap and starch in the cytoplasm. Protein granules and starch grains occur in the cytoplasm of parenchyma cells in the cotyledons of the bean, the pea, and the lentil; protein granules and oil in the endosperm of *Ricinus* and the cotyledons of *Glycine* (soy bean). The most widely distributed storage product is starch. It occurs in parenchyma of the cortex and the pith; in parenchyma of the vascular tissues, that is, xylem and phloem parenchyma and ray parenchyma; in parenchyma of fleshy leaves (bulb scales), rhizomes, tubers, fruits, cotyledons, and the endosperm of seeds (fig. 8.1, *C*).

The physiological activity of protoplasts varies in different kinds of storage parenchyma. In stems and roots of woody species starch accumulation undergoes seasonal fluctuations. It is deposited at one time and is removed at another. Such periodic changes indicate that the storage cells have active protoplasts. The specialized storage organs, such as tubers, bulbs, and rhizomes, may serve for storage only once, their protoplasts dying after the removal of the reserves to the growing organs.

In seeds the living protoplasts are directly concerned with the accumulation of storage products, but their relation to the subsequent mobilization of the storage material is not always clear. Storage cotyledons that, during the growth of the seedling, emerge above the surface of the ground (epigeous germination) and become green evidently have active protoplasts capable of taking part in photosynthesis after the removal of storage products. In contrast, cotyledons that remain below the surface of the ground during germination (hypogeous germination) usually die after they release the food reserves to the growing parts of the seedling. In both types of cotyledons the storage cells themselves probably control the mobilization of the stored food. There is some evidence, however, that the epidermis of cotyledons may be the seat of production of enzymes that digest the food materials (Netolitzky, 1935, p. 11). The protoplasts of the endosperm of some seeds are reported as being actively engaged in the process of dissolution of starch and other reserves. In other seeds the endosperm protoplasts are visibly modified and seem incapable of independent activity after the accumulation of storage material has been completed. In such seeds the digestion of the food reserves is initiated and regulated by the enzymatic activity of the embryo, alone or in conjunction with parts of the endosperm. In the Gramineae, for example, the digestion of starch is brought about by the scutellum of the embryo and by the outermost layer of the endosperm, the aleuron layer (see chapter 20).

Parenchyma may be specialized as a water-storage tissue. Water is abundant in all active vacuolated cells, but in certain plants epidermal or parenchyma cells seem to be particularly adapted for storage of water. Many succulent plants, such as the Cactaceae, *Aloe, Agave,* and *Mesembryanthemum,* contain in their photosynthetic organs chlorophyll-free parenchyma cells full of water. This water tissue consists of living cells of particularly large size and usually with thin walls. The cells are often in rows and may be elongated like palisade cells. Each has a thin layer of parietal cytoplasm, a nucleus, and a large vacuole with watery or somewhat mucilaginous contents. The mucilages seem to increase the capacity of the cells to absorb and to retain water and may occur in the protoplasts and in the walls.

In the underground storage organs there is usually no separate water-storing tissue, but the cells containing starch and other food materials have a high water content. Potato tubers may start shoot growth in air and provide the growing parts with moisture for the initial growth (Netolitzky, 1935, p. 47). A high water content is characteristic not only of underground storage organs, such as tubers and bulbs, but also of fleshy enlargements on aerial stems and of buds. In all these structures the storage of water is combined with that of the ergastic substances serving as food reserves. Many parenchyma cells accumulate phenol derivatives, including tannins. Cells containing tannins may form a connected system in the plant body, or they may occur singly or in groups. In leaves they are often distributed in continuous zones with no relation to the structural characteristics of the cells occuring in these zones. In stems there may be a concentric zonation of tannin cells. Frequently tannin cells are conspicuous in the outermost zone of the pith, the so-called medullary sheath. Tannin cells may accompany the vascular bundles or be included within them. Tannins commonly accumulate in cells located near injuries or infections.

As visible deposits, tannins occur in the vacuoles (plate 2, *A*). The metabolism of carbohydrates and tannins are interrelated, and, according to some studies, starch and tannins mutually exclude each other, except when both are produced in large amounts (Sperlich, 1939, p. 28). Tannin-containing cells may be as readily stimulated to growth and division as cells free of tannins. Cells with tannins, for example, may initiate phellogen and produce tyloses—proliferations of parenchyma cells into lumina of vessels (plate 26; Esau, 1948*a*, *b*).

Parenchyma cells also store mineral substances and form the different kinds of crystal described in chapter 2. Some cells giving rise to crystals retain their protoplasts; others die after the development of crystals.

Cell Walls

Chlorenchyma and many kinds of storage cells commonly have thin primary walls. However, such cells may have also thick primary walls. Some storage parenchyma develops remarkably thick walls (Bailey, 1938) and the carbohydrates deposited in these walls, notably the hemicelluloses, are regarded by some workers as reserve materials (Netolitzky, 1935). Thick walls occur, for example, in the endosperm of date palm (*Phoenix dactylifera*), persimmon (*Diospyros;* fig. 8.1, *D*), *Asparagus*, and *Coffea arabica*. The walls of such endosperm become thinner during germination. Although the thick-walled storage cells appear to have living protoplasts, the removal of the walls is not necessarily an independent activity of such protoplasts but may be regulated by the embryo (Netolitzky, 1935, p. 15).

Relatively thick and often lignified secondary walls also occur in parenchyma cells, particularly in those of the secondary xylem.

Cell Arrangement

Mature parenchyma tissue either is closely packed or is permeated by a more or less prominent air-space system. The storage paren-

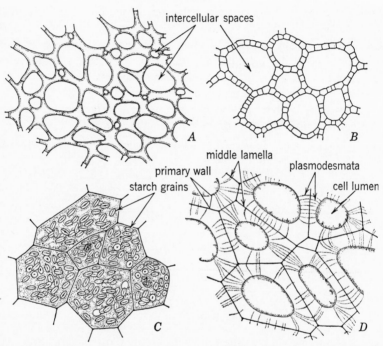

Fig. 8.1. Examples of parenchyma tissue. *A*, tissue of armed parenchyma cells with prominent intercellular spaces from a lacuna in a leaf of *Canna*. (See fig. 16.10, *G*.) *B*, lacunate parenchyma from a transection of petiole of *Zantedeschia*. *C*, endosperm parenchyma of *Secale* (rye). *D*, endosperm parenchyma of *Diospyros* (persimmon). (*A*, ×90; *B*, ×24; *C*, ×180; *D*, ×620.)

chyma of fleshy axial organs or fruits has abundant intercellular spaces. In contrast, the endosperm of most seeds contains none or only small intercellular spaces (fig. 8.1, *C*). However, during germination the cells are gradually separated from each other (Netolitzky, 1935, p. 24). This structural peculiarity seems to support the notion, mentioned previously, that the mobilization of the reserves in the endosperm is stimulated and regulated, not by the activity of the storing cells themselves, but by the embryo and perhaps also by the peripheral layers of the endosperm.

Chlorenchyma is a familiar example of a tissue having a well-developed aerating system. This structural detail is particularly characteristic of the leaf mesophyll, where the proportion of air by volume may be between 77 and 713 parts in 1,000 (Sifton, 1945). Intercellular spaces are abundant in the photosynthetic parenchyma of stems too. In general, they characterize such parenchyma in all groups of land plants from the liverworts and mosses to the angiosperms. Parenchyma which develops in the absence of light, as in the pith and roots, also has more or less prominent intercellular spaces.

Air spaces reach their highest development in the aquatic angiosperms, both in individual size and in combined volume (Sifton, 1945). In these plants the air in the spaces serves not only for aeration but also to give the plants buoyancy and support. The air spaces form an elaborate system that appears to be continuous from the leaf to the root. Oxygen can thus diffuse from its point of highest concentration in the leaves toward the place of scarcity in the tissues lacking chlorophyll.

The intercellular spaces of vascular plants arise either schizogenously or lysigenously (see chapter 3). The schizogenous method may give rise to very large spaces, particularly if the cells divide with reference to these spaces (Hulbary, 1944). In stems and leaves of *Elodea* and other monocotyledons cells divide parallel to the longitudinal axis of the stem or petiole and perpendicular to the surface of the initial air spaces so that these spaces become bounded by an increasingly large number of cells (fig. 8.1, *B*). Other large air spaces may arise lysigenously. For example, cortical cells break down in the roots of certain Gramineae and Cyperaceae, leaving large lacunae arranged radially or tangentially (Klinge, 1879; Sifton, 1945).

Cell Shape

Parenchyma cells are commonly described as having a polyhedral shape, with the various diameters differing relatively little from each other (plate 22, *A*, *C*). Many kinds of parenchyma cells, however, are more or less elongated and merge imperceptibly with the so-called prosenchyma cells (elongated cells with tapering ends) in shape and dimensions. Furthermore, parenchyma cells in the mesophyll and other plant parts may be variously lobed, folded, and armed (figs. 8.1, *A*, and 16.2, *B*; plate 65; Geesteranus, 1941; Lewis, 1925).

Parenchyma cells have served as an object for intensive studies on cell shape, involving special techniques for isolating cells, constructing models of cells, and subjecting the models to statistical analyses (cf. Lewis, 1944; Marvin and Matzke, 1939; Matzke, 1946). These studies show that, in general, parenchyma cells in relatively homogeneous complexes, with small intercellular spaces or none, have the shape of polyhedra with an approximate average of 14 faces (fig. 8.2, *B*). A geometrically perfect, 14-sided polyhedron with 8 hexagonal and 6 quadrilateral faces has been named the orthic tetrakaidecahedron

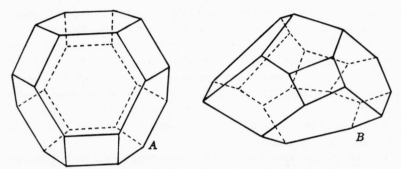

Fig. 8.2. The shape of parenchyma cells. *A*, a diagram of the orthic tetrakaidecahedron, a 14-sided polyhedron with 8 hexagonal and 6 square faces. *B*, diagram of a cell from the pith of *Ailanthus glandulosa*. It has 1 heptagonal, 4 hexagonal, 5 pentagonal, and 4 quadrilateral faces, making a total of 14 faces. An example of a cell form approximating an orthic tetrakaidecahedron. (After Matzke, 1940.)

(fig. 8.2, *A*; Matzke, 1940). This ideal figure is extremely rare among plant cells but is approximated more commonly and more closely than the 12-sided figure with 12 rhombic faces (the rhombic dodecahedron) which the early botanists considered to be the fundamental form of cells in undifferentiated parenchyma (Matzke, 1940). From the beginnings of botany, cells in tissues were regarded as assuming shapes giving the greatest economy of space—minimum surface with maximum volume—and consequently they were interpreted as potential spheres that had a polyhedral shape because of mutual contact and pressure. The rhombic dodecahedron was at first assumed to fit this interpretation best; later, it was found that the orthic tetrakaidecahedron satisfies more conditions in liquid films and also has a greater economy in the surface-to-volume relationship.

The rare occurrence of the ideal tetrakaidecahedron among plant cells is understandable. Even in the most homogeneous tissues cells are not of equal volumes, are not regularly spaced, and do not normally originate as spheres that are subsequently compressed (Matzke, 1940).

The approximation to a 14-sided figure was observed in parenchyma of various vegetative parts in dictoyledons (Duffy, 1951; Hulbary, 1944, 1948; Lewis, 1923; Marvin, 1939*b*, 1944), of the carpel vesicles in citrus (Dodd, 1944), and of petioles of a fern (Higinbotham, 1942). Presence of intercellular spaces, particularly of large ones, reduces the number of contacts (Hulbary, 1944). If a tissue contains large and small cells, the number of faces is correlated with size. The small cells have fewer than 14 facets, the large cells more than 14 (Marvin, 1939*b*, 1944).

By studies of nonliving systems attempts were made to determine some of the possible factors that influence cell shape. In one system —lead shot placed in metal cylinders and subjected to pressure—pressure was the main factor determining the shape (Marvin, 1939*a*; Matzke, 1939). In the other—soap foam bubbles placed in a container and left to adjust themselves—the surface tension played the major role (Matzke, 1946; Matzke and Nestler, 1946). Although, in general, the results obtained with these two systems were similar, the foam exhibited greater regularity than the compressed shot with regard to the number of contacts and the shape of the facets. Plant cells occupied an intermediate position between lead shot and soap bubbles in the characteristics of the three-dimensional configurations. These observations suggest that pressure and surface tension both might play a part in shaping the cells. However, there must be other factors as well.

Quite obscure appear to be the forces operating in the growth of folded cells (arm-palisade cells, fig. 16.2, *B*) or of cells with internal ridges as in *Pinus* mesophyll (plate 65; Küster, 1935, p. 577; Meyer, 1923, p. 23). In the ontogeny of stellately armed parenchyma cells (fig. 8.1, *A*) lateral tension appears to be one of the factors determining the final shape (Geesteranus, 1941; Lewis, 1925). Certain developmental phenomena, such as increase in length of cells and division of cells, violate the principle of least surfaces (Lundegårdh, 1921; Matzke and Nestler, 1946); and in cell division the usual position of a new wall indicates no relation to surface tension phenomena (Sinnott and Bloch, 1941). As Lundegårdh (1921, p. 159) expresses it, the living substance utilizes simple physical laws but is not entirely governed by them.

ORIGIN

The parenchyma tissue of the primary plant body, that is, the parenchyma of the cortex and the pith, of the mesophyll of leaves, and of the flower parts, differentiates from the ground meristem. The parenchyma associated with the primary and secondary vascular tissues is formed by the procambium and the vascular cambium, respectively. Parenchyma may also arise from the phellogen in the form of phelloderm.

REFERENCES

Bailey, I. W. Cell wall structure of higher plants. *Indus. and Engin. Chem.* 30:40–47. 1938.

De Bary, A. *Comparative anatomy of the vegetative organs of the phanerogams and ferns.* Oxford, Clarendon Press. 1884.

Dodd, J. D. Three-dimensional cell shape in the carpel vesicles of *Citrus grandis. Amer. Jour. Bot.* 31:120–127. 1944.

Duffy, R. M. Comparative cellular configurations in the meristematic and mature cortical cells of the primary root of tomato. *Amer. Jour. Bot.* 38:393–408. 1951.

Esau, K. Phloem structure in the grapevine, and its seasonal changes. *Hilgardia* 18:217–297. 1948*a*.

Esau, K. Anatomic effects of the viruses of Pierce's disease and phony peach. *Hilgardia* 18:423–481. 1948*b*.

Geesteranus, R. A. M. On the development of the stellate form of the pith cells of *Juncus* species. *Nederl. Akad. van Wetenschap. Proc.* 44:489–501, 648–653. 1941.

Haberlandt, G. *Physiological plant anatomy.* London, Macmillan and Company. 1914.

Hayward, H. E. *Structure of economic plants.* New York, The Macmillan Company. 1938.

Higinbotham, N. The three-dimensional shapes of undifferentiated cells in the petiole of *Angiopteris evecta. Amer. Jour. Bot.* 29:851–858. 1942.

Hulbary, R. L. The influence of air spaces on the three-dimensional shapes of cells in *Elodea* stems, and a comparison with pith cells of *Ailanthus. Amer. Jour. Bot.* 31:561–580. 1944.

Hulbary, R. L. Three-dimensional cell shape in the tuberous roots of *Asparagus* and in the leaf of *Rhoeo. Amer. Jour. Bot.* 35:558–566. 1948.

Klinge, J. Vergleichend histologische Untersuchung der Gramineen- und Cyperaceen-Wurzeln insbesondere der Wurzel-Leitbündel. *Acad. Imp. des Sci. St. Petersbourg, Mém.* Ser. 7. 26:1–70. 1879.

Küster, E. *Die Pflanzenzelle.* Jena, Gustav Fischer. 1935.

Lewis, F. T. The typical shape of polyhedral cells in vegetable parenchyma and the restoration of that shape following cell division. *Amer. Acad. Arts and Sci. Proc.* 58:537–552. 1923.

Lewis, F. T. A further study of polyhedral shapes of cells. I. The stellate cells of *Juncus effusus;* II. Cells of human adipose tissue; III. Stratified cells of human oral epithelium. *Amer. Acad. Arts and Sci. Proc.* 61:1–34. 1925.

Lewis, F. T. The geometry of growth and cell division in columnar parenchyma. *Amer. Jour. Bot.* 31:619–629. 1944.

Lundergårdh, H. Zelle und Cytoplasma. In: K. Linsbauer. *Handbuch der Pflanzenanatomie.* Band 1. Lief. 1. 1921.

Marvin, J. W. The shape of compressed lead shot and its relation to cell shape. *Amer. Jour. Bot.* 26:280–288. 1939a.

Marvin, J. W. Cell shape studies in the pith of *Eupatorium purpureum. Amer. Jour Bot.* 26:487–504. 1939b.

Marvin, J. W. Cell shape and cell volume relations in the pith of *Eupatorium perfoliatum* L. *Amer. Jour. Bot.* 31:208–218. 1944.

Marvin, J. W., and E. B. Matzke. A new method for the construction of three-dimensional cell models. *Amer. Jour. Bot.* 26:101–103. 1939.

Matzke, E. B. Volume-shape relationships in lead shot and their bearing on cell shapes. *Amer. Jour. Bot.* 26:288–295. 1939.

Matzke, E. B. What shape is a cell? *Teach. Biol.* 10:34–40. 1940.

Matzke, E. B. The three-dimensional shape of bubbles of foam—an analysis of the rôle of surface forces in three-dimensional cell shape determination. *Amer. Jour. Bot.* 33:58–80. 1946.

Matzke, E. B., and J. Nestler. Volume-shape relationships in variant foams. A further study of the rôle of surface forces in three-dimensional cell shape determination. *Amer. Jour. Bot.* 33:130–144. 1946.

Meyer, F. J. Das trophische Parenchym. A. Assimilationsgewebe. In: K. Linsbauer. *Handbuch der Pflanzenanatomie.* Band 4. Lief. 9. 1923.

Netolitzky, F. Das trophische Parenchym. C. Speichergewebe. In: K. Linsbauer. *Handbuch der Pflanzenanatomie.* Band 4. Lief. 31. 1935.

Sifton, H. B. Air-space tissue in plants. *Bot. Rev.* 11:108–143. 1945.

Sinnott, E. W., and R. Bloch. The relative position of cell walls in developing plant tissues. *Amer. Jour. Bot.* 28:607–617. 1941.

Sperlich, A. Das trophische Parenchym. B. Exkretionsgewebe. In: K. Linsbauer. *Handbuch der Pflanzenanatomie.* Band 4. Lief. 38. 1939.

CHAPTER

9
Collenchyma

CONCEPT

Collenchyma is a living tissue composed of more or less elongated cells with thick primary nonlignified walls. The structure and the arrangement of collenchyma cells in the plant body indicate that the primary function of the tissue is support. Morphologically, collenchyma is a simple tissue, for it consists of one type of cell.

The presence of living protoplasts denotes a close physiologic similarity between collenchyma and parenchyma cells. In form and structure the two types of cells also intergrade. Collenchyma cells are commonly longer and narrower than parenchyma cells, but some collenchyma cells are short and, on the other hand, some parenchyma cells are considerably elongated. Where collenchyma and parenchyma lie next to each other, they frequently intergrade through transitional types of cells. The resemblance to parenchyma is further stressed by the common occurrence of chloroplasts in collenchyma and by the ability of this tissue to undergo reversible changes in wall thickness and to engage in meristematic activity. In view of these similarities and in view of the structural and functional variability of parenchyma (see chapter 8), collenchyma is commonly interpreted as a thick-walled kind of parenchyma structurally specialized as a supporting tissue (De Bary, 1884, p. 119; Hayward, 1938, p. 22). The terms parenchyma and collenchyma are also related, but in the latter the first part of the word, derived from the Greek word *colla*, glue, refers to the thick glistening wall characteristic of collenchyma.

POSITION IN PLANT BODY

Collenchyma is the typical supporting tissue, first, of growing organs and, second, of those mature herbaceous organs that are only slightly modified by secondary growth or lack such growth completely. It is the first supporting tissue in stems, leaves, and floral parts, and it is the main supporting tissue in many mature dicotyledonous leaves and some green stems. Collenchyma may occur in root cortex (Guttenberg, 1940, pp. 112 and 163), particularly if the

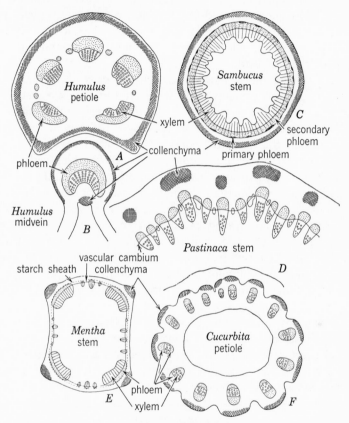

Fig. 9.1. Diagrams showing the distribution of collenchyma (crosshatched) and vascular tissues in various plant parts. All drawings are from transections. (*A, B,* ×19; *C–F,* ×9.5.)

root is exposed to light (Van Fleet, 1950). It is absent in stems and leaves of many of the monocotyledons that early develop sclerenchyma (Falkenberg, 1876; Giltay, 1882).

Collenchyma characteristically occurs in peripheral position in stems and leaves (fig. 9.1). It is present immediately beneath the epidermis, or it may be separated from the epidermis by one or more layers of parenchyma. If it is located next to the epidermis, the inner tangential walls of the epidermis may be thickened like the walls of collenchyma. Sometimes the entire epidermal cells are collenchymatous (Haberlandt, 1914, pp. 202–203). In its subepidermal position, collenchyma occurs in the form of continuous or somewhat discontinuous cylinders (fig. 9.1, *A*, *C*) or in discrete strands (fig. 9.1, *D–F*). In stems and petioles with protruding ribs, collenchyma is particularly well developed in the ribs. In leaves it may differentiate on one or both sides of the veins (fig. 9.1, *B*) and along the margins of the leaf blade.

In many plants the elongated parenchyma cells of the outermost part of the phloem develop thick walls after the sieve elements are obliterated, and the tissue ceases to be concerned with conduction. The resulting structure is commonly called the bundle cap. The parenchyma on the inner periphery of the xylem may be similarly differentiated. If the entire bundle is enclosed by thick-walled elongated cells, it is said to have a bundle sheath. The bundle caps and the bundle sheaths sometimes have thickened primary walls, sometimes lignified secondary walls. The tissues forming these caps and sheaths are often interpreted as collenchyma when they have non-lignified primary walls, sclerenchyma when they have secondary walls. The comparative characteristics of subepidermal collenchyma, on the one hand, and of nonlignified caps and sheaths, on the other, are imperfectly known. In a direct comparison of the strength of collenchyma and of bundle-cap tissue from the same petioles of celery, the collenchyma strands proved to be much stronger (Esau, 1936). This is only an isolated study, however. For the present, if bundle caps and sheaths resemble collenchyma, they may be referred to as *collenchymatous*, an adjective implying similarity to collenchyma, but not necessarily morphologic identity.

STRUCTURE

Cell Shape

Collenchyma cells may be of various lengths, the shortest being like the adjacent cortical parenchyma cells, the longest reaching dimensions comparable to those of fibers. Collenchyma cells of about 2 mm in length have been mentioned in the literature (Haberlandt, 1914, p. 157; Majumdar, 1941; Priestley and Scott, 1939). The short collenchyma cells are prismatic; the long ones are usually tapering. Both kinds of cells are polygonal in transection. Collenchyma cells may vary in shape and size in the same strand. These variations are related to the origin of the cells. A collenchyma strand is formed by a series of longitudinal divisions, which spread from a central point toward the periphery of the future strand. The longitudinal divisions are followed by elongation of the resulting cells, so that the first, that is, the innermost cells, start to elongate earlier than the more peripheral ones and attain a greater length.

The development of collenchyma was studied in considerable detail in the umbellifer *Heracleum* (Majumdar, 1941; Majumdar and Preston, 1941). In this plant the elongation of a collenchyma cell either follows immediately the last longitudinal division of a mother cell or is preceded by one or rarely more transverse divisions. In macerated preparations the products of the latest transverse divisions often remain together, enclosed by the common mother-cell wall. Such cell complexes resemble septate fibers (see chapter 10). When transverse divisions occur before elongation, the shape of the cells is affected. The ends formed by transverse divisions may be slightly oblique or almost transverse. Without such divisions the cells taper at both ends. The cells on the flanks of a collenchyma bundle are short, and their end walls taper little.

Cell Wall

The structure of the cell wall is the most distinctive feature of collenchyma cells. The thickenings are deposited unevenly in a manner somewhat variable in different groups of plants. A common form of collenchyma shows the main deposits of wall material in the angles where several cells are joined together (e.g., *Ficus, Vitis, Ampelopsis, Polygonum, Beta, Rumex, Boehmeria, Morus, Cannabis, Begonia, Pellionia;* fig. 9.2, *B*, and plate 22, *C*). The degree of restriction of wall thickenings to the angles varies in relation to the amount of wall thickening present on other wall parts. If the general wall thickening becomes massive, the thickening in the corners is obscured and the lumen of the cell assumes, in transections, a circular outline, instead of an angular (fig. 9.3). Such developmental modification is observed, for example, in the Umbelliferae (Esau, 1936; Majumdar, 1941). In another form of collenchyma the thickening occurs chiefly on the tangential walls (e.g., *Sambucus, Sanguisorba, Rheum, Eupatorium;* fig. 9.2, *A*). Still another form is characterized by intercellular spaces and the development of the collenchymatous thickenings on the walls facing the intercellular spaces (e.g., Com-

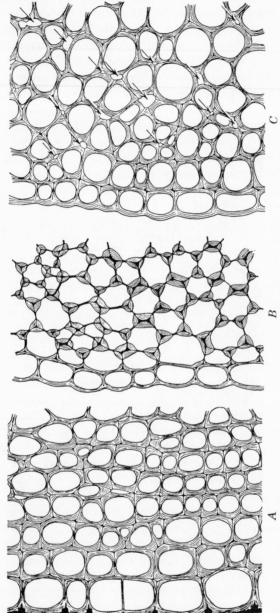

FIG. 9.2. Drawings of different forms of collenchyma in transections. In all drawings the epidermal layer is to the left. *A*, collenchyma of *Sambucus* stem with thickenings mainly on tangential walls (lamellar collenchyma). *B*, collenchyma of *Cucurbita* stem with thickenings in the angles (angular collenchyma). *C*, collenchyma of *Lactuca* stem with numerous intercellular spaces (indicated by arrows) and the most prominent thickenings located next to these spaces (lacunar collenchyma). Note the thick cuticle (shown in black) on the epidermis of the *Sambucus* stem section in *A*. (All, ×320.)

positae, *Salvia, Brunella, Malva, Althaea;* fig. 9.2, *C*). The three forms of collenchyma have been named by Müller (1890) angular (Ecken-collenchym), lamellar (Plattencollenchym), and lacunate (Lücken-collenchym), respectively (Foster, 1949, p. 87). The word lamellar has reference to the plate-like arrangement of the thicken-ings; the lacunate, to the presence of intercellular spaces. In collen-chymatous bundle caps and sheaths the cell-wall thickening is

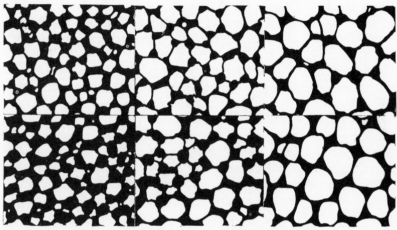

FIG. 9.3. Examples of mature celery collenchyma drawn from transections of petioles. The cells in the different samples vary in diameter and in wall thickness. Although the thickenings are mainly in the angles, this pattern is somewhat ob-scured in the two samples on the left by a spread of the thickenings over a greater part of the walls. The small spaces in the two drawings to the left are not inter-cellular spaces, but lumina in tapering ends of cells. (×210. From Esau, 1936.)

sometimes most emphasized in the corners. More commonly, how-ever, the thickening is either relatively even over the entire wall, or is uneven without being restricted to the corners or the tangential walls.

In longitudinal sections collenchyma shows thin and thick wall portions, depending on the direction of the cut with reference to the thickenings (plate 22, *B*). The nearly transverse end walls are usually thin, whereas the pointed ends may appear solid because of accumulation of wall material (Majumdar, 1941). Primary pit fields occur in collenchyma cells, in both the thinner and the thicker parts of the walls.

The walls of collenchyma consist mainly of cellulose and pectic compounds and contain much water (Anderson, 1927; Cohn, 1892;

Majumdar and Preston, 1941; Preston and Duckworth, 1946). In some species collenchyma walls appear to have an alternation of layers rich in cellulose and poor in pectic compounds with layers that are rich in pectic compounds and poor in cellulose.

Collenchyma walls may contain 67 per cent water, based on fresh weight; 209 per cent, based on dry weight (Cohn, 1892). Heating destroys the ability of walls to absorb water. When collenchyma walls lose their water under the influence of dehydrating agents they shrink visibly. This shrinkage, however, varies if measured in different directions. In a species of *Eupatorium*, for example, the contraction of the walls in radial, tangential, and vertical directions was found to be 27, 10, and ½ to ¾ per cent, respectively (Cohn, 1892). The explanation of the strong radial contraction has been sought both in the distribution of pectic substances and in the structure of cellulose (Anderson, 1927; Preston and Duckworth, 1946).

The characteristic thickening of collenchyma walls begins to develop before the extension of the cell is completed. Apparently the successive layers are formed around the entire cell, but the individual layers are thicker where the wall is most massive in final state (Majumdar and Preston, 1941). The occurrence of a simultaneous increase in thickness and in surface of collenchyma walls is a striking phenomenon, still awaiting a proper explanation in the field of submicroscopic structure (cf. Majumdar and Preston, 1941, and chapter 3).

It has been reported (Venning, 1949) that the degree of wall thickening in collenchyma is increased if during development the plants are exposed to motion by wind. (See also Haberlandt, 1914, pp. 194–197, for other experiments concerning effects of mechanical forces upon cell-wall development.) The wall thickenings of collenchyma are sometimes again removed as, for instance, when a phellogen arises in this tissue, or if collenchyma cells respond to injuries with wound-healing reactions.

If Kerr and Bailey's (1934; Bailey, 1938; and chapter 3) criteria for classifying cell walls are applied to collenchyma walls, the walls must be described as primary. First, these walls thicken before the cell reaches its final size; second, the walls are rich in pectic materials; and third, they are known to undergo reversible changes in thickness.

Collenchyma walls may become modified in older plant parts. In woody species with secondary growth collenchyma follows, at least for a time, the increase in circumference of the axis by active growth with retention of the original characteristics. In some plants (*Tilia,*

Acer, Aesculus) collenchyma cells enlarge and their walls become thinner (De Bary, 1884, pp. 538–539). Apparently it is not known whether this reduction in thickness results from a removal of wall material or from stretching and dehydration. Collenchyma may become lignified and apparently sometimes develops secondary walls. It thus becomes changed into sclerenchyma (Funk, 1912; Mullenders, 1947; Went, 1924).

In many plants collenchyma is a compact tissue lacking intercellular spaces. During the development of such collenchyma, enlargement of cells and the concomitant loosening of connections in the angles is not followed by a development of intercellular spaces. Instead, the potential spaces are filled with intercellular material (Majumdar, 1941). However, not infrequently collenchyma contains intercellular spaces, not only in the lacunate but also in other forms.

Cell Contents

As was stated previously, collenchyma cells have living protoplasts at maturity. Chloroplasts occur in variable numbers. They are most numerous in collenchyma which approaches parenchyma in form. Collenchyma consisting of long narrow cells—the most highly specialized type—contains only a few small chloroplasts or none. Tannins may be present in collenchyma cells.

STRUCTURE IN RELATION TO FUNCTION

Collenchyma appears to be a mechanical tissue particularly adapted for support of growing organs. Thick walls and close packing make it a strong tissue. At the same time, the peculiarities of growth and the structure of its walls permit adjustments to elongation of the organ without loss of strength. As has been previously stressed, collenchyma cells are capable of increasing simultaneously the surface and the thickness of the walls and, therefore, can develop thick walls while the organ is still elongating.

Collenchyma tissue combines considerable tensile strength with flexibility and plasticity. Measurements of the strength of collenchyma have been made by determining the weight necessary to break a strand of the tissue dissected out from the organ (Ambronn, 1881; Curtis, 1938; Esau, 1936). The values thus obtained were in some instances recalculated per unit area of strand and used to express the tensile strength of the tissue. Such values obviously give a measure, not of the tensile strength of the wall proper, but of the tissue as a whole. Nevertheless, they provide useful information about the strength of a tissue, since in the plant body the mechanical effect of a tissue is determined not only by the nature of the walls but also by the shape and arrangement of the cells.

A comparison of collenchyma with fibers is particularly interesting. Collenchyma has been found capable of supporting 10 to 12 kg per mm^2; fiber strands, 15 to 20 kg per mm^2 (Ambronn, 1881). The fiber strands regain their original length even after they have been subjected to a tension of 15 to 20 kg per mm^2, whereas collenchyma remains permanently extended after it has been made to support 1½ to 2 kg per mm^2. In other words, the fibers are elastic, and the collenchyma is plastic. If fibers were to differentiate in growing organs, they would hinder tissue elongation because of their tendency to regain their original length when stretched. Collenchyma, on the other hand, could be expected to respond with a plastic change in length under the same conditions.

The importance of the plasticity of collenchyma walls for the internal adjustment of growing tissues is emphasized by the observation that much of the elongation of the internodes occurs after the collenchyma cells have thickened their walls. In one particular study employing *Heracleum* plants (Majumdar, 1941; Majumdar and Preston, 1941) thick-walled collenchyma cells were found in young internodes that were several times shorter than the extended internodes of the same axes. The individual collenchyma cells in the young internodes were markedly shorter than those in the extended ones.

The plasticity of collenchyma changes with age. Old tissue is harder and more brittle than young (Curtis, 1938). As mentioned previously, in some plants collenchyma may finally become lignified. Hardened collenchyma occurs in plant parts that have ceased to elongate.

ORIGIN

Collenchyma has been variously reported as originating jointly with the vascular tissues from the procambium (Ambronn, 1881; Haberlandt, 1914; Majumdar, 1941) and separately from these tissues in the ground meristem (Ambronn, 1881; Esau, 1936; Haberlandt, 1914; Wisselingh, 1882). This disagreement results from a difference in the interpretation of histogenetic events. Although it is proper to speak of a differentiation of the derivatives of the apical meristems into protoderm, procambium, and ground meristem, these meristems usually become delimited from each other gradually, particularly in shoots. The protoderm may be distinguished close to the initial region and may even have its own initials (see chapter 5), but the procambium of stems and leaves is built up by longitudinal divisions involving an increasingly larger number of cells in the meristem that also gives rise to ground tissues (fig. 15.12). Thus, at first it is impossible to designate a certain part of the meristem as giving rise to the procambium, another to the ground meristem (see chapter 15).

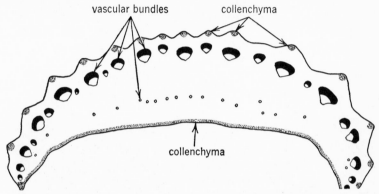

Fɪɢ. 9.4. Transection of celery petiole showing the distribution of collenchyma and vascular bundles. The collenchyma occurs in the form of strands in the ribs on the abaxial side of the petiole, and as a continuous layer on the adaxial side. (×16.)

It may be said, therefore, that the cortical collenchyma and the procambium originate in a common meristem. The final delimitation of the procambium occurs later in some plants than in others, and consequently the ontogenetic relationship between the cortex and the procambium appears close in some plants (Umbelliferae, Piperaceae, Araceae) and distant in others (Labiatae, *Clematis, Aristolochia,* certain Cucurbitaceae, *Chenopodium,* Compositae; Ambronn, 1881).

The development of collenchyma in the Umbelliferae clearly illustrates the lack of separation between cortex and procambium in the early stages of their development (Esau, 1936). In mature petioles of celery, collenchyma strands appear near the periphery in the ribs, separated by cortical parenchyma from the vascular bundles (fig. 9.4). In early ontogeny longitudinal divisions occur in the peripheral part of the petiole. Some of these initiate the procambium, others form the cortex. Subsequently, the procambium becomes distinct from the cortex because its cells are smaller in transverse diameters and greater in length. A secretory duct differentiates outside the procambium. After the appearance of the procambium the cells between it and the protoderm—ground meristem cells—undergo a series of divisions giving rise to the collenchyma (fig. 9.5).

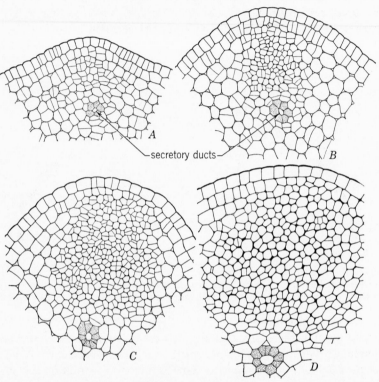

secretory ducts

Fig. 9.5. Development of collenchyma. Transections of celery petioles in different stages of development. *A,* longitudinal divisions initiated between the secretory duct and the epidermis. *B* and *C,* further divisions and appearance of thickenings in the angles, probably resulting from accumulation of intercellular material. *D,* divisions completed and primary wall thickenings developing. (×302. From Esau, 1936.)

The common early growth of procambium and cortex (as exemplified by the Umbelliferae) has probably been taken as evidence that subepidermal collenchyma arises from procambium. If the collenchyma of the Umbelliferae arises from procambium (Ambronn, 1881; Majumdar, 1941), then the cortex, or at least part of it, also arises in this meristem. Such an interpretation would decrease the value of the concept of procambium. In this book the procambium is treated as the meristem giving rise to the primary vascular tissues. It is imperfectly delimited from the ground meristem in its origin. Collenchyma that differentiates early in a given organ becomes highly specialized in its morphology, whereas that formed later is more like parenchyma. This difference is also reflected in the nature of the meristem giving rise to the different kinds of collenchyma. The more specialized collenchyma has its origin in a procambium-like meristem, the less specialized in a parenchymatous ground meristem. Since Haberlandt (1914; pp. 199–202) extended the concept of procambium to include meristems giving rise to all elongated cells of the primary body, he called the collenchyma meristem having elongated cells the procambium. In this book, such meristem is treated as a modification of the ground meristem and is not given a special name.

REFERENCES

Ambronn, H. Über die Entwickelungsgeschichte und die mechanischen Eigenschaften des Collenchyms. Ein Beitrag zur Kenntnis des mechanischen Gewebesystems. *Jahrb. f. Wiss. Bot.* 12:473–541. 1881.

Anderson, D. Über die Struktur der Kollenchymzellwand auf Grund mikrochemischer Untersuchungen. *Akad. der. Wiss. Wien, Math.-Nat. Kl.* 136:429–440. 1927.

Bailey, I. W. Cell wall structure of higher plants. *Indus. and Engin. Chem.* 30:40–47. 1938.

Cohn, J. Beiträge zur Physiologie des Collenchyms. *Jahrb. f. Wiss. Bot.* 24:145–172. 1892.

Curtis, D. S. Determination of stringiness in celery. *Cornell Univ. Agric. Exp. Sta. Mem.* 212. 1938.

De Bary, A. *Comparative anatomy of the vegetative organs of the phanerogams and ferns.* Oxford, Clarendon Press. 1884.

Esau, K. Ontogeny and structure of collenchyma and of vascular tissues in celery petioles. *Hilgardia* 10:431–476. 1936.

Falkenberg, P. *Vergleichende Untersuchungen über den Bau der Vegetationsorgane der Monokotyledonen.* Stuttgart, Ferdinand Enke. 1876.

Foster, A. S. *Practical plant anatomy.* 2nd ed. New York, D. Van Nostrand Company. 1949.

Funk, G. Beiträge zur Kenntnis der mechanischen Gewebesysteme in Stengel und Blatt der Umbelliferen. *Bot. Centbl. Beihefte.* 29:219–297. 1912.

Giltay, E. Sur le collenchyme. *Arch. Néerland. des Sci. Exact. et Nat.* 17:432–459. 1882.

Guttenberg, H. von. Der primäre Bau der Angiospermenwurzel. In: K. Linsbauer. *Handbuch der Pflanzenanatomie.* Band 8. Lief. 39. 1940.

Haberlandt, G. *Physiological plant anatomy.* London, Macmillan and Company. 1914.

Hayward, H. E. *The structure of economic plants.* New York, The Macmillan Company. 1938.

Kerr, T., and I. W. Bailey. The cambium and its derivative tissues. X. Structure, optical properties, and chemical composition of the so-called middle lamella. *Arnold Arboretum Jour.* 15:327–349. 1934.

Majumdar, G. P. The collenchyma of *Heracleum Sphondylium* L. *Leeds Phil. Lit. Soc. Proc.* 4:25–41. 1941.

Majumdar, G. P., and R. D. Preston. The fine structure of collenchyma cells in *Heracleum Sphondylium* L. *Roy. Soc. London, Proc.* Ser. B. 130:201–217. 1941.

Müller, C. Ein Beitrag zur Kenntnis der Formen des Collenchyms. *Deut. Bot. Gesell. Ber.* 8:150–166. 1890.

Mullenders, W. L'origine du phloème interxylémien chez *Stylidium* et *Thunbergia*. Étude anatomique. *Cellule* 51:5–48. 1947.

Preston, R. D., and R. B. Duckworth. The fine structure of the walls of collenchyma cells in *Petasites vulgaris* L. *Leeds Phil. Lit. Soc. Proc.* 4:343–351. 1946.

Priestley, J. H., and L. I. Scott. The formation of a new cell wall at cell division. *Leeds Phil. Lit. Soc. Proc.* 3:532–545. 1939.

Van Fleet, D. S. A comparison of histochemical and anatomical characteristics of the hypodermis with the endodermis in vascular plants. *Amer. Jour. Bot.* 37:721–725. 1950.

Venning, F. D. Stimulation by wind motion of collenchyma formation in celery petioles. *Bot. Gaz.* 110:511–514. 1949.

Went, F. A. F. C. Sur la transformation du collenchyme en sclérenchyme chez les Podostémonacées. *Rec. des. Trav. Bot. Néerland.* 21:513–526. 1924.

Wisselingh, C. van. Contribution à la connaissance du collenchyme. *Arch. Néerland. des Sci. Exact. et Nat.* 17:23–58. 1882.

CHAPTER

10

Sclerenchyma

CONCEPT

The term *sclerenchyma* refers to complexes of thick-walled cells, often lignified, whose principal function is mechanical. These cells are supposed to enable plant organs to withstand various strains, such as may result from stretching, bending, weight, and pressure, without undue damage to the thin-walled softer cells (Haberlandt, 1914, pp. 150–152). The word is derived from the Greek and is a combination of *sclerous*, hard, and *enchyma*, an infusion; it emphasizes the hardness of sclerenchyma walls. The individual cells of sclerenchyma are termed *sclerenchyma cells;* collectively, sclerenchyma cells form sclerenchyma tissue. In terms of the entire mechanical system of a plant, collenchyma and sclerenchyma are combined in the physiological concept of *stereome* (Foster, 1949, p. 93; Haberlandt, 1914, p. 152). The plastic, highly hydrated primary walls of collenchyma, however, distinguish this tissue from sclerenchyma with its hard, elastic secondary walls.

Sclerenchyma cells show much variation in form, structure, origin, and development, and the different types of cells are intergrading. A division of such a graded series of forms into a limited number of categories can be only arbitrary, and the value of such a division depends on the clearness of definition of the criteria upon which it is based. Judged by the variety of systems that have been proposed for the classification of sclerenchyma cells (Foster, 1944; Tobler, 1939), precise criteria for the separation of the forms have not been established.

Most commonly, the sclerenchyma cells are grouped into fibers and sclereids. Fibers are described as long cells, sclereids as relatively short. Sclereids, however, may grade from short to conspicuously elongated cells—not only in different plants, but also in the same individual. The fibers, similarly, may be short or long. Although the pitting is generally more conspicuous in sclereid than in fiber walls, this difference is not constant either. Sometimes the origin of the two categories of cells is considered to be the distinguishing characteristic: sclereids are said to arise through secondary sclerosis of parenchyma cells, fibers from meristematic cells that are early determined as fibers. But there are sclereids that differentiate from cells early individualized as sclereids (e.g., sclereids in *Camellia*, Foster, 1944, and in *Monstera*, Bloch, 1946), and in certain plants phloem parenchyma cells differentiate into fibers when the tissue becomes old and ceases to be concerned with conduction (Esau, 1950).

Sclerenchyma cells frequently possess no living protoplasts at maturity. This characteristic, combined with the presence of secondary walls, distinguishes sclerenchyma from parenchyma and collenchyma. There are, however, many kinds of cells with living protoplasts and lignified secondary walls (*sclerotic parenchyma*, Bailey and Swamy, 1949) which integrade between sclerenchyma and nonsclerified parenchyma cells (De Bary, 1884, p. 115), a circumstance emphasized in chapter 8. Some of these sclerified living cells are classified as parenchyma (e.g., xylem parenchyma cells possessing secondary walls), others as fibers (e.g., the living septate fibers). The distinction between sclerenchyma and parenchyma is further reduced by the occurrence of living protoplasts, at maturity, in some of the extreme types of fibers arising in the primary phloem (Kallen, 1882; Kundu, 1942; Tammes, 1907) and in sclereids (Puchinger, 1922).

FIBERS

Occurrence and Arrangement in the Plant Body

Fibers occur in separate strands or cylinders in the cortex and the phloem, as sheaths or bundle caps associated with the vascular bundles, or in groups or scattered in the xylem and the phloem. In the stems of monocotyledons and dicotyledons the fibers are arranged in several characteristic patterns (De Bary, 1884; Haberlandt, 1914; Schwendener, 1874; Tobler, 1939). In many Gramineae the fibers form a system having the shape of a ribbed hollow cylinder, with the ribs connected to the epidermis (fig. 10.1, *A*; plate 45, *D*). In *Zea, Saccharum, Andropogon, Sorghum*, and other related genera there is no fiber cylinder, but the vascular bundles, particularly the peripheral ones, have prominent sheaths of fibers that are sometimes irregularly fused with each other; and the hypodermal parenchyma may be strongly sclerified (fig. 10.1, *B*; plate 53, *B*; Magee, 1948). Still other patterns are cited in the literature (Majumdar, 1941; Schwendener, 1874). Fibers may be prominent in the leaves of monocotyledons (fig. 10.1, *E*). Here they form sheaths enclosing the vascular bundles, or strands extending between the epidermis and the vascular bundles (plate 59, *C*), or subepidermal strands not connected with the vascular bundles.

In stems of dictoyledons, fibers frequently occur in the outermost part of the primary phloem, forming more or less extensive anastomosing strands or tangential plates (fig. 10.1, *C*, *F*). In some plants no other than the peripheral fibers (primary phloem fibers) occur in the phloem (*Alnus, Betula, Linum, Nerium*). Others develop fibers in the secondary phloem also, few (*Nicotiana, Ulmus, Boehmeria*) or many (*Clematis, Juglans, Magnolia, Quercus, Robinia, Tilia, Vitis;* plate 36, *A*). Some dicotyledons have complete cylinders of fibers, either close to the vascular tissues (*Geranium, Pelargonium, Lonicera,* some Saxifragaceae, Caryophyllaceae, Berberidaceae, Primulaceae) or at a distance from them, but still located to the inside of the innermost layer of the cortex (fig. 10.1, *H*; plate 45, *B*, and 49, *A, B*; *Aristolochia, Cucurbita*). In dicotyledonous stems without secondary growth the isolated vascular bundles may be accompanied by fiber strands on both their inner and outer sides (*Polygonum, Rheum, Senecio*). Plants having phloem internal to the xylem may have fibers associated with this phloem (*Nicotiana*). Finally, a highly characteristic position for fibers in the anigosperms is in the primary and in the secondary xylem where they have varied arrangements. Roots show a distribution of fibers similar to that of the stems and may have fibers in the primary (fig. 10.1, *D*) and in the secondary body. Gymnosperms usually have no fibers in the primary phloem, but many have them in the secondary phloem. Cortical fibers are sometimes present (fig. 10.1, *G*).

Classification

Fibers are divided into two large groups, *xylem fibers* and fibers of the various tissue systems outside the xylem, the *extraxylary fibers*. The developmental and topographical relationships of xylem fibers are usually quite precise. These fibers develop from the same meristematic tissues as the other xylem cells and constitute an integral part of the xylem. The assigning of the extraxylary fibers to their proper tissue systems is much less simple and direct. Some of the

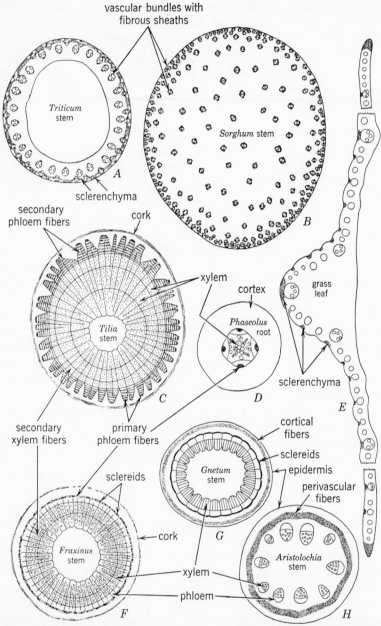

FIG. 10.1. Diagrams of transections of various plant organs showing the distribution of sclerenchyma (stippled), mainly fibers, and of vascular tissues. *A, Triticum* stem with sclerenchyma ensheathing the vascular bundles and forming layers

extraxylary fibers are as definitely related to the phloem as the xylem fibers are to the xylem; in many others the developmental relationship is less clear. The fibers that form continuous cylinders in monocotyledonous stems arise in the ground tissue, at varying distances from the epidermis (fig. 10.1, *A*). They might be classified as cortical fibers except that vascular bundles occur among them and that the limits of the cortex in the monocotyledons are generally vague. The fibers forming sheaths around the vascular bundles in the monocotyledons arise partly from the same procambium as the vascular cells, partly from the ground tissue (cf. Esau, 1943*a*). The fibers of the vine types of stem, such as *Aristolochia* and *Cucurbita*, occur inside the layer of cells characterized by abundant starch accumulation, the starch sheath, which is commonly interpreted as the innermost layer of the cortex (see chapter 15). These fibers are part of the vascular cylinder but do not appear to be related to the phloem on a developmental basis.

The fibers located on the outer periphery of the vascular cylinder, often close to the phloem, are frequently classified as pericyclic fibers. The pericycle is thought to be a tissue separate from the vascular, both topographically and developmentally (see chapter 15). However, in the stems of the majority of dicotyledons investigated ontogenetically the phloem abuts on the cortex and there is no distinct tissue between the cortex and the phloem that could be termed pericycle in the usual sense of this word (Esau, 1950; Ozenda, 1949; fig. 10.2 and plate 23). Nevertheless, in much of the literature of the past half-century the primary phloem fibers have been called pericyclic fibers because the developmental relation of these fibers to the phloem has been ignored or not recognized.

Thus, the extraxylary fibers constitute, developmentally, a heterogeneous group of sclerenchyma cells of uncertain classification. Al-

---

in the peripheral part of the stem. *B, Sorghum* stem with sclerenchyma in the form of fibrous sheaths about the vascular bundles. *C, Tilia* stem with fibers in the primary and the secondary phloem and in the secondary xylem. *D, Phaseolus* root, after completion of primary growth, with fibers in the primary phloem. *E*, grass leaf with sclerenchyma in strands beneath the abaxial (lower) epidermis and along the margins of the blade. *F, Fraxinus* stem with fibers in the primary phloem and the secondary xylem; the phloem fibers occur in strands separated from each other by sclereids derived from the interfascicular parenchyma. *G, Gnetum gnemon* stem with fibers in the cortex and sclereids in the perivascular position. *H, Aristolochia* stem with a cylinder of fibers inside the starch sheath in perivascular position. (*A, G, ×12.5; B, C, F, ×6.2; D, ×8.8; E, ×26; H, ×11.5.*)

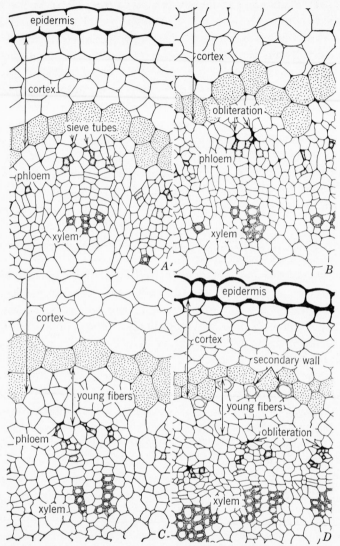

FIG. 10.2. Development of the primary phloem fibers in *Linum perenne* L. *A*, the
first primary sieve tubes are mature. *B* and *C*, new sieve tubes differentiate while
the older ones are obliterated, together with their companion cells. *D*, the cells
remaining after the obliteration of the sieve tubes begin to develop secondary
walls characteristic of flax fibers. (*A–C*, ×620; *D*, ×330. Drawn from photomicrographs in Esau, 1943*b*.)

though it would be desirable to assign all these fibers to the tissue systems to which they belong by origin, such a classification must await further developmental studies and also a proper reevaluation of the concept of the pericycle.

The extraxylary fibers are sometimes combined into a group termed *bast fibers* (Foster, 1949, Exercise IX). The term bast has been criticized in the literature because of its inaccurate botanical meaning (Eames and MacDaniels, 1947, p. 112; Hayward, 1938, p. 23). The word bast was originally applied to fiber strands obtained from the extracambial region of dicotyledonous stems (Haberlandt, 1914, p. 152). In its etymology "bast" is related to the verb "to bind." It was adopted as a name for the fiber strands because they were used for binding. The bast of the extracambial region of dicotyledonous stems is constituted, in most instances, of fibers of the phloem. In its development the concept of bast followed a double course. In one direction it was extended to cover the extraxylary fibers in various other arrangements than those in the dicotyledonous stems; in the other, it became a specific term for the phloem and was widened to include all the cells of this tissue. In the second usage, the nonsclerified conducting and parenchymatous elements of the phloem received the name "soft bast," the fibers, "hard bast" (Haberlandt, 1914, p. 720). Although the application of bast to the phloem as a whole has now become largely obsolete because of the existence of the well-defined and specific term phloem, the designation of all the extraxylary fibers as bast is still employed (Esau, 1943*b*; Foster, 1949, p. 108). The term bast fibers is also used in references dealing with the economic use of plant fibers (Dewey, 1943).

In the present book, the term extraxylary fibers is commonly used for bast fibers, and certain of the extraxylary fibers are classified as follows: *phloic* or *phloem* fibers, fibers originating in primary or secondary phloem; *cortical fibers*, fibers originating in the cortex; *perivascular fibers*, fibers located on the periphery of the vascular cylinder inside the innermost cortical layer but apparently not originating in the phloem. The term perivascular has been used in the literature (Van Fleet, 1948) in somewhat the same descriptive topographic sense as is adopted here.

The xylem or wood fibers have a common origin, but they are morphologically heterogeneous. They intergrade with the imperforate tracheary elements (the tracheids) and with the parenchyma cells, and certain xylem fibers resemble phloem fibers (Bailey, 1936; Forsaith, 1926; Record, 1947). Wood fibers are subdivided into two main categories, the *fiber-tracheids* and the *libriform fibers*. The forms which are transitional between tracheids and the extreme types of fibers are the fiber-tracheids. The extreme types of fibers resemble phloem fibers and are therefore called libriform fibers, from *liber*, a Latin term for "inner bark," that is, phloem. Some of the xylem fibers form transverse partitions late in their development and are spoken of as *septate fibers*. Phloem fibers also may be septate.

Structural Characteristics

Extraxylary Fibers. Although a long spindle-like shape is considered typical of extraxylary fibers (and fibers in general), these elements may vary in length, and their ends are sometimes blunt, rather than tapering, and may be branched. Generally, primary extraxylary fibers are longer than the secondary. The bast fibers of commerce (various extraxylary fibers) vary from a fraction of a millimeter to about ½ meter (Dewey, 1943). The longest fibers (primary phloem fibers) measured (55 cm) were found in ramie, *Boehmeria nivea* (Aldaba, 1927).

The cell walls of the extraxylary fibers are frequently very thick. In the phloem fibers of flax (*Linum usitatissimum*) the secondary thickening may amount to 90 per cent of the area of the cell in cross section (fig. 10.3). The pits are simple or slightly bordered. Some extraxylary fibers have lignified walls, others nonlignified. The flax fiber is typically not lignified, and its secondary wall consists of almost pure cellulose (Anderson, 1927). Some extraxylary fibers, notably those of the monocotyledons, are strongly lignified.

Concentric lamellations may be observed in extraxylary fibers with or without treatment with swelling reagents. In flax fibers the individual lamellae vary in thickness from 0.1 to 0.2 micron (Hock, 1942). In certain types of extraxylary fibers the lamellation appears to result from an alternation of cellulosic and noncellulosic layers (Bailey, 1938). In the flax fiber the cellulosic layers are alternately strongly and weakly birefringent and also vary in density of staining (Hock, 1942). This observation suggests a structure similar to that of the cotton-hair wall (cotton fiber), in which the lamellation is a reflection of varying densities of the cellulosic matrix in the successive lamellae. The orientation of the cellulosic microfibrils has also received attention and has been found to vary in fibers from different plants (Hock, 1942; Preston, 1943).

Xylem Fibers. Wood fibers typically have lignified secondary walls. They vary in size, shape, thickness of wall, and type and abundance of pitting (see chapter 11). The variations in structural details and the corresponding divisions of this group of fibers into categories are best understood if they are considered with reference

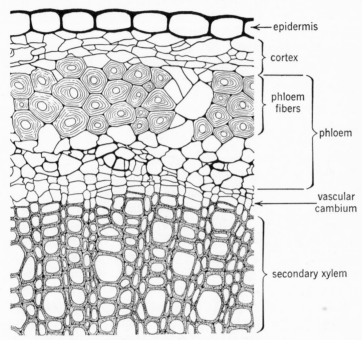

epidermis

cortex

phloem
fibers

phloem

vascular
cambium

secondary xylem

FIG. 10.3. Primary phloem fibers of *Linum usitatissimum* L. Transection of stem showing spatial relation of fibers to other tissues of the stem. The fibers of *L. usitatissimum* have a similar course of development as shown for *L. perenne* in fig. 10.2 and plate 23. (×320. Drawn from photomicrograph in Esau, 1943*b*.)

to the possible evolution of the xylem fibers. Phylogenetically, these fibers are pictured as being derived from an imperforate xylem cell combining the functions of water conduction with that of support, that is, a tracheid. A good indication that fibers and tracheids are phylogenetically related is the occurrence of almost imperceptible gradations between these two cell types in certain angiosperms such as the oak (Forsaith, 1926). The gradations suggest the following principal changes during the evolution of the fiber from a tracheid: increase in wall thickness, decrease in length, and reduction in the size of bordered pits (fig. 11.1). In the extreme condition the pit appears simple or nearly so. Of these characteristics, wall thickness and particularly the nature of pitting are used to differentiate between the two main categories of wood fibers, fiber-tracheids and libriform fibers (Bailey, 1936; Chalk, 1937; Committee on Nomenclature, 1933; Record, 1947). However, even these criteria do not permit the establishment of types for each category that would serve for the identification of elements in different species. The limits of the categories are best decided by comparing the elements of a given species among themselves (Bailey, 1936). First the tracheid is identified by the resemblance of its pitting to that of the vessel members in the same plant. Then the limits for the fiber-tracheids are established by the identification of cells with pits whose borders are reduced as compared with those in the tracheids. Finally the cells with simple pits, or essentially so, are classified as libriform fibers. (Cf. figs. 11.8 and 11.9.)

Commonly, the thickness of wall increases in the sequence of tracheid, fiber-tracheid, libriform fiber. The increase in wall thickness results in an increase in the length of the pit canal. In the fiber-tracheid these canals lead into small but evident pit chambers, and the inner apertures are lenticular to slit-like and usually extended beyond the outlines of the border (fig. 3.5). The libriform fibers also have long slit-like canals, but their pit chambers are much reduced or absent, an expression of the extreme reduction of borders. The inner apertures of the pit-pairs in the fiber-tracheids and libriform fibers are often crossed with each other. (See chapter 3.)

The phylogenetic decrease in length during the development of a fiber from a primitive tracheid is a concomitant of a decrease in length of cambial fusiform initials. In a given sample of wood, however, the tracheids are usually shorter, the fibers longer, with the libriform fibers attaining the greatest length (fig. 11.9). The fibers become longer than the associated tracheids because they undergo a more extensive apical elongation during tissue differentiation.

Fiber-tracheids and libriform fibers may both be septate (Bailey, 1936; Committee on Nomenclature, 1933). The septa are true walls, but they are formed after the deposition of the secondary layers on the longitudinal walls of the element. The formation of septa in the fiber-tracheids of *Hypericum* has been found to involve a regular mitosis followed by cytokinesis (Vestal and Vestal, 1940). In contrast to other wood fibers, the septate forms long retain their protoplasts and serve for storage of starch, oils, and resins, and they may deposit crystals of calcium oxalate in the heartwood (Harrar,

1946; Record, 1947). Similar septate fibers occur in both the xylem and the phloem of some plants (e.g., *Vitis*). Septate fibers are widely distributed in dicotyledons (Spackman and Swamy, 1949).

Parts of the secondary wall of fiber-tracheids and libriform fibers may have a great capacity for absorption of water. In the presence of water such walls swell, sometimes so strongly that cell lumina are occluded. Upon drying, the walls shrink again. Fibers possessing hygroscopic walls are sometimes termed *mucilaginous* or *gelatinous* (Record, 1947; Rendle, 1937). The gelatinous wall layers do not contain excessive amounts of pectinaceous, gummy, or mucilaginous substances, but they show a peculiar physical condition of the cellulose which possibly is responsible for their gelatinous nature (Bailey and Kerr, 1937). Many woods contain gelatinous fibers. Oak (*Quercus*) and black locust (*Robinia*) are noteworthy examples.

Origin and Development

Remarks made in the beginning of the chapter indicate that fibers arise from various meristems. Fibers of the xylem and the phloem are derived from procambium or cambium. In the cambium, the fibers arise from the fusiform initials. Extraxylary fibers other than those of the phloem arise from the ground meristem, but the cells that eventually become fibers early cease to divide transversely and elongate (Meeuse, 1938). In some Gramineae and Cyperaceae fibers originate in the protoderm and become elements of the epidermis (Haberlandt, 1914, p. 203). In plants having fibrous bundle sheaths, part of the fibers may be derived from the procambium and part from the ground meristem (Esau, 1943*a*; Sinnott and Bloch, 1943). In the shoots of some monocotyledons the proportion of bundle-sheath fibers in a vascular bundle may be very high, or the bundles may consist of fibers only (De Bary, 1884, p. 266). Since such fibrous bundles appear to be connected with vascular bundles and since there are bundles with various proportions of fibers and vascular elements, the fibrous bundles probably should be considered as originating from the procambium.

From the developmental standpoint the attainment of great length by fibers is of particular interest. Primary and secondary fibers show pronounced differences in their development. Primary fibers are initiated before the organ has elongated, and they can reach considerable length by elongating while the associated cells are still dividing. To this symplastic growth may be added apical intrusive growth (see chapter 4). In contrast, secondary fibers originate in the part of the organ that has ceased to elongate, and they can increase in length only by intrusive growth (see chapters 4 and 6). This difference in the method of growth possibly explains why in the same stem primary phloem fibers may attain greater lengths than the secondary. In *Cannabis* (hemp), for example, the primary phloem fibers were found to average 12.7 mm, the secondary 2.2 mm (Kundu, 1942).

The occurrence of growth of the primary extraxylary fibers in unison with the rest of the growing organ is suggested by the observation that longer fibers occur in longer organs. For example, the adult length of primary phloem fibers in *Cannabis* is well correlated with the adult length of the internodes (Kundu, 1942). Similarly, the longest phloem fibers in flax occur in the longest stems (Tammes, 1907). In *Sanseviera* and *Agave* the average length of the extraxylary fibers depends upon the length of leaf, and in *Musa* upon that of the leaf sheath (Meeuse, 1938).

The great length attained by some primary extraxylary fibers cannot be readily explained, however, on the basis of elongation by symplastic growth only. In *Sanseviera*, *Agave*, and *Musa* the fibers become 40 to 70 times longer than the meristematic cells from which they arise (Meeuse, 1938). In *Luffa* the elongation of the fibers of the fruit at first keeps pace exactly with the increase in size of the fruit itself, but, after the fibers attain about 200 microns in length, their rate of extension becomes greater than that of the fruit as a whole (Sinnott and Bloch, 1943). Thus, it appears that the fibers may have independent growth in addition to that correlated with the other tissues. Microscopic observations support this assumption (Kundu, 1942; Schoch-Bodmer and Huber, 1945; Sinnott and Bloch, 1943). The apices of the fibers long remain thin walled and rich in cytoplasm. They may be serrated and forked because of adjustments to the outlines of adjacent cells. Furthermore, the number of fibers, as determined in transections of stems, gradually increases although longitudinal divisions do not occur. All these observations support the view that the apices of the fibers elongate and intrude among the associated cells. Since this growth occurs in a stem that is still elongating, intrusive growth is probably followed by symplastic growth of the new three-ply wall system formed by the apposition of the new wall of the fiber apex to that of another cell (Schoch-Bodmer and Huber, 1945). In flax the phloem fibers have been found growing at both apices, upwardly and downwardly, and the length of the stem in which this apical growth of fibers was taking place was estimated to be about 19 mm (Schoch-Bodmer and Huber, 1945). Although the secondary phloem fibers fail to attain the same lengths as the primary, they commonly become longer than the cambial initials by apical intrusive growth (Kundu, 1942; Schoch-Bodmer and Huber, 1949).

Apical elongation is well substantiated with reference to the secondary xylem fibers (Schoch-Bodmer and Huber, 1949; see also chapter 4). Table 10.1 illustrates the result of such growth by comparing the lengths of fiber-tracheids with those of cambial cells in certain woods.

TABLE 10.1

COMPARISON OF LENGTHS OF FIBER-TRACHEIDS AND CAMBIAL CELLS IN CERTAIN DICOTYLEDONOUS TREES

(Based on data from Bailey, 1920, and Forsaith, 1926)

Species of tree	Length in millimeters		Ratio of length of fiber-tracheid to cambial cell × 100
	Cambial cell	Fiber-tracheid	
Liquidambar Styraciflua L. Red gum	0.70	0.96	136
Betula populifolia Marsh. Gray birch	0.94	1.31	140
Quercus alba L. White oak	0.53	1.00	189
Carya ovata (Mill.) C. Koch Hickory	0.52	1.30	250
Fraxinus americana L. White ash	0.29	0.96	330
Ulmus americana L. White elm	0.35	1.53	436
Robinia Pseudo-Acacia L. Black locust	0.17	0.87	510

In the development of extraxylary fibers divisions generally cease when elongation of the cells begins. Nevertheless, the nuclei may continue to divide so that the developing fibers become multinucleate (fig. 10.4). This phenomenon is particularly characteristic of the very long primary phloem fibers (see literature in Esau, 1938*b*, 1943*b*). In the same plants the primary phloem fibers may be multinucleate and the shorter, secondary phloem fibers uninucleate (Esau, 1938*a*; Kundu, 1942).

The prolonged growth in length of the primary bast fibers results in a highly complicated method of secondary wall development. As has been explained in chapter 3, the deposition of secondary walls begins after the primary wall completes its increase in surface. While the primary fibers elongate by symplastic growth in correlation with the surrounding cells, they remain thin walled. Presumably at this stage the entire fiber wall is increasing its surface. Later, during the apical-growth stage, the apices of the cells remain thin, whereas the median portions of the cells, which have completed their elongation, begin to form secondary walls. This secondary thickening of the

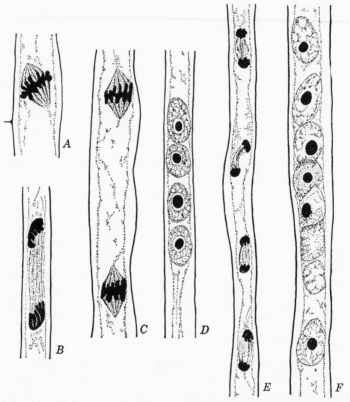

Fɪɢ. 10.4. Nuclear division in the phloem fibers of *Nicotiana tabacum.* The successive mitoses, *A–C* and *E*, are not followed by cytokineses, and a multinucleate condition, *D* and *F*, results. (×780. Drawn from photomicrographs in Esau, 1938*b*.)

primary phloem fibers was studied in particular detail in *Linum* and *Boehmeria* (Aldaba, 1927; Anderson, 1927). In these two plants the secondary wall of the fibers develops in the form of distinct lamellae, each being tubular in shape and growing from the base upward. (Presumably in the earlier stage of the process there is also a downward growth of the tubule while the lower end of the fiber is still elongating. It is conceivable that this end would cease growing first, because it is imbedded in maturing tissues, whereas the upper end is advancing into a still-growing tissue.) Thus, several telescoping hyaline tubules arise successively, each tubule being longer than that immediately following (fig. 10.5). After the cell ceases to grow at the apex, some of the successively formed layers reach the apex, others stop their growth at lower levels, while new layers arise above them and complete the wall thickening in the upper cell parts. This partial interruption of wall growth results in the formation of compartments in the fibers. The compartments may be in communication with each other. Apparently the deposition of secondary walls in primary fibers may continue long past the stage at which the cell completes its elongation. In flax and in hemp the fibers of the phloem in the adult plant parts are reported to possess living protoplasts and to continue depositing secondary wall layers (Kundu, 1942; Tammes, 1907).

One of the striking features observed in the growth of secondary walls in primary phloem fibers is that this wall is not cemented to the primary wall and the successive layers of the secondary wall also appear to be distinct, at least while the cell is not yet mature (Aldaba, 1927; Anderson, 1927; Kundu, 1942). In sectioned material the secondary wall of an immature fiber commonly appears detached from the primary and is often separated into two or more layers which are more or less infolded (plate 24, *A*). This infolding and wrinkling is probably an artifact, but it also is taken as an indication that the secondary wall layers are in a loose and relaxed state during their formation (Anderson, 1927; Kundu, 1942).

Structure in Relation to Economic Utilization

Fiber plants have been utilized economically since ancient times. Flax is known to have been cultivated by man as early as 3,000 years B.C. in Europe and Egypt, and hemp at approximately the same time in China (Ash, 1948; Dewey, 1943). In the technical field, the term fiber usually does not have the strict botanical connotation of individual cells of a certain category of sclerenchyma. In plants in which the commercial fibers originate in the phloem (e.g., flax, hemp, ramie, and jute) the term fiber denotes a fiber strand. The fibers obtained from monocotyledonous leaves commonly represent vascular bundles together with the associated fibers (plate 59, *C*). The epidermal hairs of cotton seed and of the kapok seed pod are also termed fibers. In still other plants the vascular system of the root

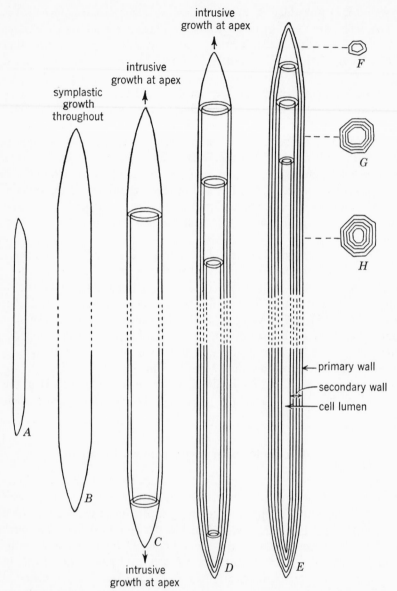

Fig. 10.5. Diagrammatic representation of the growth and differentiation of primary phloem fibers combining the concepts of Aldaba (1927), Anderson (1927), and Schoch-Bodmer and Huber (1945). *A*, young fiber, still narrow and short. *B*, the fiber is increasing in width and is elongating by symplastic growth. *C*, the median part of the fiber has reached its final length and has formed the first layer of secondary wall; the apices are elongating by apical intrusive growth. *D*,

(*Muhlenbergia*) or of the entire plant (*Tillandsia*) are used as fibers. Commercial fibers are separated into hard fibers and soft fibers. The former are monocotyledonous leaf fibers with heavily lignified walls, hard and stiff in texture. Examples of plants yielding such fibers are *Agave* species (henequen and sisal), *Musa textilis* (abaca), *Yucca*, and *Phormium tenax* (plate 59, *C*). The soft fibers may be lignified or free of lignin, but all are soft and flexible. Here are included the phloem fibers of such plants as *Linum usitatissimum* (flax), *Cannabis sativa* (hemp), *Corchorus capsularis* (jute), *Boehmeria nivea* (ramie), *Hibiscus cannabinus* (kenaf), and others (Crane, 1947; Dewey, 1943).

The length of the fiber strand depends on the length of the organ from which the fibers are obtained and on the degree of anastomosing of the strands within the plant. The vascular bundles and fiber strands of the monocotyledonous leaves commonly have a long, straight course with rather small, weak cross anastomoses uniting the bundles with each other. The phloem fiber strands of the dicotyledons, on the other hand, form a network in which the individual strands have no identity as such (Kundu, 1943). It is assumed that the shape and length of the fiber cells, their degree of overlapping, and their connection with each other are factors in development of strength in fiber strands. However, the available data are still too fragmentary to determine the exact relation between the nature and connection of the constituent cells, on one hand, and the characteristics of the commercial fiber and the yarn made from it, on the other (Ott, 1943, p. 1046).

In the preparation of commercial fiber the plants are subjected to a process of partial maceration called *retting* (technical form of the word rotting). In this process the plant material is exposed to a decomposing action by bacteria and fungi. These are allowed to act on the plant parts until the tissues surrounding the fibers are so softened that the fibers can be easily freed mechanically (Ash, 1948). In the early stages of retting only the intercellular material is affected

---

apical growth has been completed at the lower end but continues at the upper; secondary-wall deposition continues, the successive lamellae, tubular in structure, being deposited one upon the other and ever closer to the apices of the cell. *E*, growth in length has been completed at both ends; the four layers of the secondary wall have reached the lower end of the cell, but the upper end is not yet fully mature. *F–H*, transections of the oldest fiber (*E*) taken at several levels and showing the differences in the number of layers of the secondary wall at these levels.

by pectic enzymes (Bonner, 1936; Anderson, 1927). Later the primary wall may be attacked also (Anderson, 1927). An effort is made to discontinue the retting process before the fiber strands are macerated into individual cells. Lignification of cell walls, which usually involves the intercellular substance also, interferes with retting (Anderson, 1927).

SCLEREIDS

Occurrence and Arrangement in the Plant Body

Sclereids are widely distributed in the plant body (De Bary, 1884; Haberlandt, 1914; Puchinger, 1922). The cortex and the pith of gymnosperms and dicotyledons often contain sclereids, arranged singly or in groups. Sclereids are also common components of the xylem and the phloem, where they may intergrade with fibers. In many plants the interfascicular parenchyma cells located between the strands of primary phloem fibers develop lignified secondary walls and differentiate into sclereids which, together with the fibers, form a continuous sclerenchyma cylinder on the outer periphery of the vascular system. The plants in which a continuous sclerenchyma cylinder is present in the primary state may show a disruption of this cylinder when the vascular system surrounded by the sclerenchyma increases in circumference through secondary growth. The breaks in the sclerenchyma cylinder are filled with parenchyma cells which later may differentiate into sclereids (e.g., *Aristolochia*, plate 49, *D*).

Many species of plants, particularly in the tropics, contain sclereids in the leaves (Boas, 1912; Foster, 1944, 1945*a*, 1945*b*, 1946, 1947). The leaf sclereids may be few to abundant. In some leaves the mesophyll is completely permeated by sclereids (plate 24, *B*). In certain species the leaf sclereids occur at the ends of vascular bundles (Foster, 1946, 1947). Sclereids are also common in fruits and seeds. In fruits they sometimes are dispersed in the soft flesh singly or in groups (e.g., *Pyrus*, *Cydonia*, *Vaccinium;* Yarbrough and Morrow, 1947). In solid layers they constitute hard coverings in the form of shells of nuts or of endocarps of stone fruits (see chapter 19). The hardness and strength of the seed coat often result from the presence of abundant sclereids (fig. 10.6; Netolitzky, 1926; Zimmerman, 1936). Solid layers of sclereids occur in the epidermis of some protective scales (fig. 10.7).

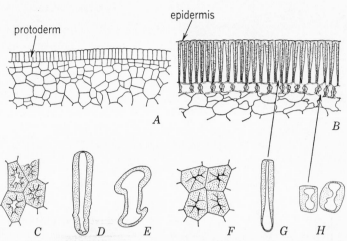

Fɪɢ. 10.6. Sclereids of leguminous seed coats. *A* and *B*, outer parts of *Phaseolus* seed coat from transections of seeds in two stages of development. The epidermis in *B* consists of a solid layer of macrosclereids. Beneath these are the subepidermal sclereids with most of the wall thickenings localized on the anticlinal walls. *C–E*, sclereids from *Pisum* seed coat, *F–H*, from *Phaseolus* seed coat. In *C* and *F* are groups of epidermal sclereids seen from the surface. They show the uneven inner surface of the secondary wall. *D* and *G*, epidermal sclereids; *E* and *H*, subepidermal sclereids. (*A* and *B*, ✕200; *C* and *F*, ✕490; *D*, *E*, *G*, *H*, ✕245.)

Classification

Sclereids vary widely in shape, size, and characteristics of their walls. It was inevitable, therefore, that an extensive terminology was developed in the course of study of these elements (Foster, 1949, p. 95). One of the most comprehensive classifications distinguishes the four following categories of sclereids (Foster, 1949, pp. 95–96; Haberlandt, 1914, pp. 158–161): *brachysclereids*, stone cells, short, roughly isodiametric sclereids, resembling parenchyma cells in shape, widely distributed in cortex, phloem, and pith of stems, and in the flesh of fruits (fig. 3.2, *A*), *macrosclereids*, elongated rod-like cells, exemplified by sclereids forming the palisade-like epidermal layer of leguminous seeds (fig. 10.6, *B*, *C*, *D*, *F*, *G*; Hamly, 1932; Reeve, 1946*a*, *b*); *osteosclereids*, bone-shaped sclereids (that is, columnar cells enlarged at the ends; fig. 10.6, *E*), like those present in leaves of many dicotyledons and in seed coats; and *astrosclereids*, literally star-sclereids, cells ramified to varied degrees and often found in the leaves of dicotyledons (fig. 10.8, *A*). This classification is rather arbitrary and

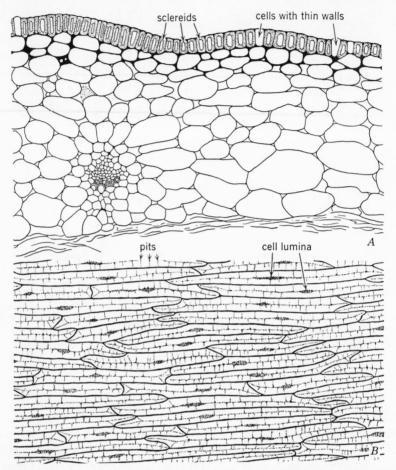

FIG. 10.7. Epidermal sclereids in a protective bulb scale of *Allium sativum* (garlic). *A*, section of scale, with sclereid walls stippled. *B*, surface view of scale showing the solid layer of epidermal sclereids overlapping each other. (Both, ×99. From Mann, 1952.)

does not cover all the forms of sclereids known at present (Foster, 1949, p. 96). Its usefulness is further limited by the polymorphism of each of the established categories (fig. 10.9) and by the existence of transitions among the categories.

Structural Characteristics

The secondary walls of the sclereids vary in thickness and are typically lignified. If the walls are relatively thin, the sclereids can-

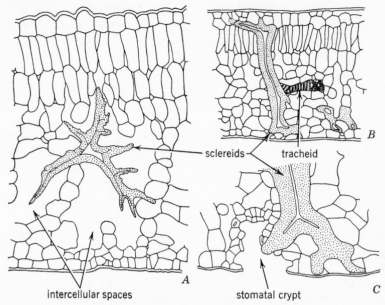

intercellular spaces   stomatal crypt

FIG. 10.8. Foliar sclereids. *A*, branched form from *Trochodendron* leaf blade. *B*, columnar, with horizontal branches above and below, from *Mouriria* leaf; the sclereid is in contact with a terminal tracheid of a small vascular bundle; one of the lower processes touches the cuticle. *C*, portion of similar sclereid as in *B*; it shows processes extending to the cuticle and one penetrating between two guard cells into the stomatal crypt (cavity lined with epidermis having many stomata). (*A*, ×155; *B*, ×115; *C*, ×333. After Foster, 1945*b*, 1947.)

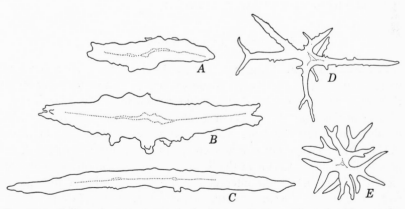

FIG. 10.9. Foliar sclereids of *Trochodendron aralioides*. The sclereids may be described as follows: *A*, short fusiform; *B*, very broad fusiform; *C*, irregular fiber-like; *D*, irregularly branched; *E*, radiately branched. (All, ×103. After Foster, 1945*a*.)

not be definitely separated from sclerotic parenchyma. The thick-walled forms, on the other hand, may contrast with the parenchyma cells to a striking degree. In many sclereids the lumina are almost filled with massive wall deposits, and the secondary wall shows prominent pits, often with ramiform canal-like cavities (Foster, 1944; Puchinger, 1922). The pits are commonly simple, but sometimes the secondary wall slightly overarches a small pit chamber. The secondary wall often appears concentrically lamellated in ordinary and polarized light. The lamellation may be the result of an alternation of isotropic layers with those composed of cellulose (Bailey and Kerr, 1935). Crystals are imbedded in the secondary wall of the sclereids in certain species (Bailey and Nast, 1948).

In some sclereids the deposition of the secondary walls is uneven. In the macrosclereids of the seed coats of the Leguminosae, for example, most of the secondary deposit is localized on the lateral walls in the end of the cell turned toward the surface of the seed (fig. 10.6, *B*). Furthermore, this thickening is laid down in the form of longitudinal ridges arranged vertically or helically and constricting the lumen of the cell in such a way that it appears star shaped in sections cut at right angles to the long axis of the cell (fig. 10.6, *C*, *F*; Hamly, 1932; Netolitzky, 1926; Reeve, 1946*b*).

Regarding the contents of sclereids, the literature indicates that these cells may either retain their protoplasts upon reaching maturity or become dead elements. The degree of activity of the protoplasts in the sclereids is apparently variable (Foster, 1949, p. 99; Puchinger, 1922) and has not been adequately studied.

Origin and Development

Sclereids arise either through a belated sclerosis of apparently ordinary parenchyma cells (secondary sclerosis) or directly from cells that are early individualized as sclereid primordia. The sclerification of cells in the phloem may occur after the tissue ceases to function in conduction. The *Camellia* leaf sclereids begin their development during the final phase of enlargement of the leaf (Foster, 1944). The primordia of the sclereids in the *Mouriria* leaf, on the other hand, are clearly evident before the intercellular spaces appear in the mesophyll and while the small veins are still entirely procambial (Foster, 1947). Similarly, the sclereids of the air roots of *Monstera* develop from cells early set aside by polarized divisions in the rib meristem of the cortex (Bloch, 1946). In one and the same organ, sclereids may arise over an extended period of time, as in *Trochodendron* leaves (Foster, 1945b).

Within the vascular tissues the sclereids develop from derivatives of the procambial and the cambial cells. Stone cells imbedded in the cork originate from the phellogen. Macrosclereids of the seed coats are of protodermal origin (fig. 10.6, *A*, *B*; Reeve, 1946b). Many sclereids differentiate from ground parenchyma cells or, if they are individualized early, from ground-meristem cells. In some leaves these ground-parenchyma cells are part of the spongy mesophyll (Foster, 1945b). The sclereids of *Mouriria*, which are located at the terminations of the vascular bundles in the mesophyll are, from the time of their origin, in contact with procambial cells, and both the sclereids and the procambium arise from the same layer in the ground meristem (Foster, 1947).

If the sclereids resemble parenchyma cells, their development involves no striking changes in shape, compared with that of the adjacent parenchyma cells. The principal change is the development of the secondary wall. The sclereids which assume shapes strikingly different from those of the associated parenchyma cells show considerable independence in their growth. They invade intercellular spaces, intrude among other cells, sometimes penetrating the epidermis (fig. 10.8, *B*, *C*; Foster, 1947), become very much larger than the initial cells, and assume extraordinary, often grotesque shapes.

The causal relationships in the development of the sclereids constitute a challenging problem for a student of histogenesis. In some plants sclereid growth seems to be highly individualistic and uncoordinated with the growth of the other cells (Foster, 1944, 1945b). In others, the origin and the development of sclereids appear to be a part of the growth pattern of the cell complex as a whole (Bloch, 1946; Foster, 1947). In some plants sclereids grow and branch in a relatively compact tissue (e.g., *Mouriria*, Foster, 1947); in others they begin development in a lacunose tissue and grow mainly by sending out protrusions into intercellular spaces (e.g., *Monstera*, Bloch, 1946; *Pseudotsuga*, Sterling, 1947).

The mechanics of growth of the sclereids can best be explained as a combination of symplastic growth in the early stages of their development, when they still grow in unison with the adjacent cells, and apical intrusive growth in the later stages, when they elongate by penetrating into intercellular spaces and intruding among other cells (Foster, 1947).

REFERENCES

Aldaba, V. C. The structure and development of the cell wall in plants. I. Bast fibers of *Boehmeria* and *Linum*. *Amer. Jour. Bot.* 14:16–24. 1927.

Anderson, D. B. A microchemical study of the structure and development of flax fibers. *Amer. Jour. Bot.* 14:187–211. 1927.

Ash, A. L. Hemp—production and utilization. *Econ. Bot.* 2:158–169. 1948.

Bailey, I. W. The cambium and its derivative tissues. II. Size variations of cambial initials in gymnosperms and angiosperms. *Amer. Jour. Bot.* 7:355–367. 1920.

Bailey, I. W. The problem of differentiating and classifying tracheids, fiber-tracheids, and libriform wood fibers. *Trop. Woods* 1936(45):18–23. 1936.

Bailey, I. W. Cell wall structure of higher plants. *Indus. and Engin. Chem.* 30:40–47. 1938.

Bailey, I. W., and T. Kerr. The visible structure of the secondary wall and its significance in physical and chemical investigations of tracheary cells and fibers. *Arnold Arboretum Jour.* 16:273–300. 1935.

Bailey, I. W., and T. Kerr. The structural variability of the secondary wall as revealed by "lignin" residues. *Arnold Arboretum Jour.* 18:261–272. 1937.

Bailey, I. W., and C. G. Nast. Morphology and relationships of *Illicium*, *Schizandra*, and *Kadsura*. I. Stem and leaf. *Arnold Arboretum Jour.* 29:77–89. 1948.

Bailey, I. W., and B. G. L. Swamy. The morphology and relationships of *Austrobaileya*. *Arnold Arboretum Jour.* 30:211–226. 1949.

Bloch, R. Differentiation and pattern in *Monstera deliciosa*. The idioblastic development of the trichosclereids in the air roots. *Amer. Jour. Bot.* 33:544–551. 1946.

Boas, F. Beiträge zur Anatomie und Systematik der Simarubaceen. *Bot. Centbl. Beihefte* 29:303–356. 1912.

Bonner, J. The chemistry and physiology of the pectins. *Bot. Rev.* 2:475–497. 1936.

Chalk, L. The phylogenetic value of certain anatomical features of dicotyledonous woods. *Ann. Bot.* 1:409–428. 1937.

Committee on Nomenclature. International Association of Wood Anatomists. Glossary of terms used in describing woods. *Trop. Woods* 1933(36):1–12. 1933.

Crane, J. C. Kenaf—fiber-plant rival of jute. *Econ. Bot.* 1:334–350. 1947.

De Bary, A. *Comparative anatomy of the vegetative organs of the phanerogams and ferns.* Oxford, Clarendon Press. 1884.

Dewey, L. H. Fiber production in the western hemisphere. *U. S. Dept. Agr. Misc. Publ.* 518. 1943.

Eames, A. J., and L. H. MacDaniels. *An introduction to plant anatomy.* 2nd ed. New York, McGraw-Hill Book Company. 1947.

Esau, K. Ontogeny and structure of the phloem of tobacco. *Hilgardia* 11:343–424. 1938*a*.

Esau, K. The multinucleate condition in fibers of tobacco. *Hilgardia* 11:427–434. 1938*b*.

Esau, K. Ontogeny of the vascular bundle in *Zea Mays*. *Hilgardia* **15**:327–368. 1943*a*.

Esau, K. Vascular differentiation in the vegetative shoot of *Linum*. III. The origin of the bast fibers. *Amer. Jour. Bot.* **30**:579–586. 1943*b*.

Esau, K. Development and structure of the phloem tissue. II. *Bot. Rev.* **16**:67–114. 1950.

Forsaith, C. C. The technology of New York State timbers. *N. Y. State Col. Forestry, Syracuse Univ., Tech. Pub.* 18. Vol. 26. 1926.

Foster, A. S. Structure and development of sclereids in the petiole of *Camellia japonica* L. *Torrey Bot. Club Bul.* **71**:302–326. 1944.

Foster, A. S. The foliar sclereids of *Trochodendron aralioides* Sieb. and Zucc. *Arnold Arboretum Jour.* **26**:155–162. 1945*a*.

Foster, A. S. Origin and development of sclereids in the foliage leaf of *Trochodendron aralioides* Sieb. and Zucc. *Amer. Jour. Bot.* **32**:456–468. 1945*b*.

Foster, A. S. Comparative morphology of the foliar sclereids in the genus *Mouriria* Aubl. *Arnold Arboretum Jour.* **27**:253–271. 1946.

Foster, A. S. Structure and ontogeny of the terminal sclereids in the leaf of *Mouriria Huberi* Cogn. *Amer. Jour. Bot.* **34**:501–514. 1947.

Foster, A. S. *Practical plant anatomy.* 2nd ed. New York, D. Van Nostrand Company. 1949.

Haberlandt, G. *Physiological plant anatomy.* London, Macmillan and Company. 1914.

Hamly, D. C. Softening the seeds of *Melilotus alba*. *Bot. Gaz.* **93**:345–375. 1932.

Harrar, E. S. Note on starch grains in septate fiber-tracheids. *Trop. Woods* **1946**(85):1–9. 1946.

Hayward, H. E. *The structure of economic plants.* New York, The Macmillan Company. 1938.

Hock, C. W. Microscopic structure of flax and related fibers. *U. S. Natl. Bur. Standards Jour. Res.* **29**:41–50. 1942.

Kallen, F. Verhalten des Protoplasmas in den Geweben von *Urtica urens*, entwickelungsgeschichtlich dargestellt. *Flora* **65**:65–80, 81–92, 97–105. 1882.

Kundu, B. C. The anatomy of two Indian fibre plants, *Cannabis* and *Corchorus* with special reference to the fibre distribution and development. *Indian Bot. Soc. Jour.* **21**:93–128. 1942.

Kundu, B. C. Anatomy of the jute stem—formation of network of fibres. *Indian Cent. Jute Com. Bul.* **6**:157–161. 1943.

Magee, J. A. Histological structure of the stem of *Zea mays* in relation to stiffness of stalk. *Iowa State Col. Jour. Sci.* **22**:257–268. 1948.

Majumdar, G. P. A new type of mechanical construction in the stem of *Panicum punctatum* Burm. *Current Sci. (India)* **10**:256–257. 1941.

Mann, L. K. Anatomy of the garlic bulb and factors affecting bulb development. *Hilgardia* **21**:195–251. 1952.

Meeuse, A. D. J. Development and growth of the sclerenchyma fibres and some remarks on the development of tracheids in some monocotyledons. *Rec. des Trav. Bot. Néerland.* **35**:288–321. 1938.

Netolitzky, F. Anatomie der Angiospermensamen. In: K. Linsbauer. *Handbuch der Pflanzenanatomie.* Band 2. Lief. 14. 1926.

Ott, E. *Cellulose and cellulose derivatives.* New York, Interscience Publishers. 1943.

Ozenda, P. *Recherches sur les Dicotylédones apocarpiques. Contribution a l'étude des Angiospermes dites primitives.* Thesis. Paris, École Normale Supérieure. Publ. Ser. Biol. Fasc. II. 1949.

Preston, R. D. The fine structure of the walls of phloem fibres. *Chron. Bot.* 7:414–416. 1943.

Puchinger, . H. Über die Lebensdauer sclerotisierter Zellen. *Akad. der Wiss. Wien, Math.-Nat. Kl. Sitzber.* Abt. 1. 131:47–57. 1922.

Record, S. J. *Identification of the timbers of temperate North America.* New York, John Wiley & Sons. 1947.

Reeve, R. M. Structural composition of the slereids in the integument of *Pisum sativum* L. *Amer. Jour. Bot.* 33:191–204. 1946*a*.

Reeve, R. M. Ontogeny of the slereids in the integument of *Pisum sativum* L. *Amer. Jour. Bot.* 33:806–816. 1946*b*.

Rendle, B. J. Gelatinous wood fibers. *Trop. Woods* 1937(52):11–19. 1937.

Schoch-Bodmer, H., and P. Huber. Das Spitzenwachstum der Fasern bei *Linum perenne* L. *Experientia* 1:327–328. 1945.

Schoch-Bodmer, H., and P. Huber. Spitzenwachstum und Gabelbildung bei secundären Fasern. *Schweiz. Ztschr. f. Forstw.* 100:551–567. 1949.

Schwendener, S. *Das mechanische Princip im anatomischen Bau der Monokotylen mit vergleichenden Ausblicken auf die übrigen Pflanzenklassen.* Leipzig, Wilhelm Engelmann. 1874.

Sinnott, E. W., and R. Bloch. Development of the fibrous net in the fruit of various races of *Luffa cylindrica. Bot. Gaz.* 105:90–99. 1943.

Spackman, W., and B. G. L. Swamy. The nature and occurrence of septate fibers in dicotyledons. Abst. *Amer. Jour. Bot.* 36:804. 1949.

Sterling, C. Sclereid formation in the shoot of *Pseudotsuga taxifolia. Amer. Jour. Bot.* 34:45–52. 1947.

Tammes, T. Der Flachsstengel. Eine statistisch-anatomische Monographie. *Natuurk. Verhand. v. d. Holland Maatsch. d. Wetenschappen t. Haarlem.* Derde Verzameling. Deel VI. Vierde Stuk. 1907.

Tobler, F. Die mechanischen Elemente und das mechanische System. In: K. Linsbauer. *Handbuch der Pflanzenanatomie.* Band 4. Lief. 37. 1939.

Van Fleet, D. S. Cortical patterns and gradients in vascular plants. *Amer. Jour. Bot.* 35:219–227. 1948.

Vestal, P. A., and M. R. Vestal. The formation of septa in the fiber tracheids of *Hypericum Androsemum* L. *Harvard Univ. Bot. Mus. Leaflet* 8:169–188. 1940.

Yarbrough, J. A., and E. B. Morrow. Stone cells in *Vaccinium. Amer. Soc. Hort. Sci. Proc.* 50:224–228. 1947.

Zimmerman, K. Zur physiologischen Anatomie der Leguminosentesta. *Landw. Vers. Sta.* 127:1–56. 1936.

Xylem

CONCEPT

The vascular system of the plant is composed of xylem, the principal water-conducting tissue, and phloem, the food-conducting tissue. As components of the vascular system xylem and phloem are called *vascular tissues*. Sometimes the two together are spoken of as *the vascular tissue*. The term *xylem* was introduced by Nägeli (1858) and is derived from the Greek *xylos*, meaning wood.

The physiologic and phylogenetic importance of the vascular system and its prominence among the structural elements of the plant body led early to a taxonomic segregation of plants having such a system into one group, the so-called *vascular plants* (Jeffrey, 1917; Just, 1945). In some other classifications these plants were variously recombined under different names, but the conspicuousness of the vascular tissues as a structural detail of the plant body has been newly emphasized by the introduction of the term *Tracheophyta* to include all vascular plants (Eames, 1936; Just, 1945). This group consists of the Pteridophyta (Psilophytinae, Lycopodinae, Equisetinae, and Filicinae) and the Spermatophyta (Gymnospermae and Angiospermae) of the older classifications.

The terms vascular plants and Tracheophyta refer to the characteristic elements of the xylem, the vessels and the tracheary elements in general. Because of its enduring rigid walls the xylem is more conspicuous than the phloem, is better preserved in fossils, and may be studied with greater ease. It is this tissue, therefore, rather than the phloem, that serves for the identification of vascular plants.

Structurally, the xylem is a complex tissue, for it consists of many different types of cells, living and nonliving. The most characteristic components are the tracheary elements, which conduct water. Some of the tracheary elements combine the function of conduction with that of support. The xylem also commonly contains specialized

221

supporting elements, the fibers. It is further characterized by the presence of living, or parenchymatous, cells concerned with various vital activities. In certain groups of plants, the xylem includes laticifers. Sclereids derived from sclerified parenchymatous elements may be present in the xylem.

The common association of fibers with other xylem and phloem elements brought about the introduction of the term "fibrovascular tissue" with reference to the xylem and the phloem. This term is rarely employed now (Jeffrey, 1917).

CLASSIFICATION

The xylem of a given plant first appears during its early ontogeny —in the embryo or the post-embryonic stage—and keeps pace with the growing plant organs by continuous development from the derivatives of the apical meristems. As a result of this growth, the primary plant body, which is eventually formed by the activity of the apical meristems, is permeated by a continuous xylem system (together with the accompanying phloem system) whose pattern varies in different kinds of plants. The xylem differentiating in the primary plant body is the *primary xylem*. The immediate precursor of this xylem is the *procambium* (see chapter 4).

If the plant is of such a nature that, after the completion of primary growth, it forms secondary tissues through the activity of the *vascular cambium*, then the xylem produced by this meristem constitutes the *secondary xylem*.

The histologic characteristics of the two kinds of xylem are considered later in this chapter. Depending on the kind of plant, the primary xylem is more or less distinct from the secondary, but in many characteristics the two xylems intergrade with each other (Esau, 1943). Therefore, to be useful the classification into primary and secondary xylem must be conceived broadly, relating the two components of the xylem to the development of the plant as a whole, in a manner outlined in the preceding paragraphs.

ELEMENTS OF THE XYLEM

Tracheary Elements

Tracheids and Vessel Members. The term tracheary element is derived from "trachea," a name originally applied to certain primary xylem elements resembling animal tracheae (Sanio, 1863). Two fundamental types of tracheary elements occur in the xylem, *tracheids* and *vessel members* (or *vessel elements;* figs. 11.1, 11.8, 11.9). In the mature state both are more or less elongated cells (some vessel members may be drum-shaped, fig. 11.9 and plate 25, *A*), with lignified secondary walls and devoid of protoplasts. They differ from each other in that the tracheids are imperforate cells, having only pit-pairs on their common walls, whereas the vessel members are perforated in certain areas of contact with other vessel members. Thus the vessel members are fused into long continuous tubes, the *vessels* (fig. 4.2, *E*; also sometimes called *tracheae*). Sap moving through these structures passes freely from element to element through the perforations, whereas in the tracheids it traverses the walls, particularly the thin pit membranes (Stamm, 1946).

The perforations of vessel members commonly occur on the end walls, but they may be present on the lateral walls too. The wall area bearing the perforation is called the *perforation plate* (Record, 1947). A perforation plate may have a single perforation (*simple perforation*) or multiple perforations (fig. 11.2). Multiple perforations are arranged either in a parallel series (*scalariform perforation plate*, from the Latin *scalaris*, ladder), or in a reticulate manner (*reticulate perforation plate*, from the Latin *rete*, net), or as a group of approximately circular holes (*foraminate perforation plate*, from the Latin *foramen*, hole).

Each vessel (that is, a series of vessel members joined end to end) is limited in length, and the vessels in a series are connected to each other by imperforate walls in the same manner as tracheids. Water and aqueous solutions pass through these imperforate walls, but such substances as mercury and gases fail to do so. The exact length of vessels is difficult to determine. Some data suggest that individual vessels may be 10 ft long in the ash, 2 ft in the maple (Handley, 1936).

Formation of a Vessel. A vessel originates ontogenetically from a longitudinal series of meristematic cells. These are procambial cells in the primary xylem, cambial derivatives in the secondary. The primordial vessel members may or may not elongate before they develop secondary walls, but they usually expand laterally (fig. 11.3, *A*, and plate 25, *A*). After this growth is completed, secondary wall layers are deposited in a pattern characteristic for the given type of vessel elements. The portions of the primary wall that later are transformed into perforations are not covered by secondary

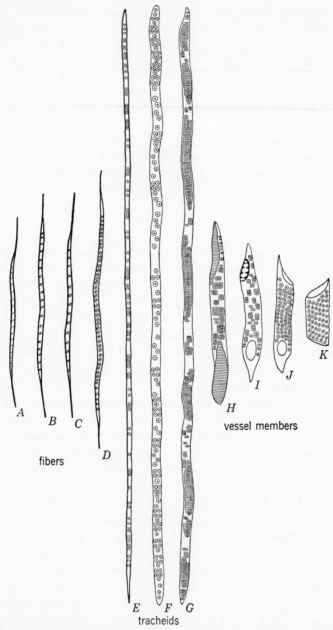

F IG . 11.1. Illustration of the main lines of specialization of the tracheary elements and fibers. *E–G*, long tracheids from primitive woods. *E* and *F* have circular bordered pits; *G* has elongated bordered pits in scalariform arrangement.

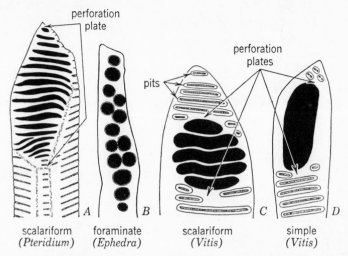

perforation
plate

perforation
plates

pits

A	*B*	*C*	*D*
scalariform	foraminate	scalariform	simple
(Pteridium)	*(Ephedra)*	*(Vitis)*	*(Vitis)*

Fig. 11.2. End walls of vessel members showing three different types of perforation plates: *A* and *C*, scalariform; *B*, foraminate (ephedroid); and *D*, simple. *A*, *C*, and *D* show, in addition to the perforations, some bordered pits arranged in scalariform manner. The entire view in *B* is a perforation plate. (*A*, *B*, ×255; *C*, *D*, ×480.)

wall material (Esau and Hewitt, 1940). Nevertheless, they commonly become thickened, as compared with the rest of the primary wall (fig. 11.3, and plate 25, *C*). This thickening appears to result, not from a deposition of additional wall substance, but from swelling of the intercellular substance. In such walls the cellulose layers remain very thin, whereas the intercellular pectic lamella increases in thickness. After the secondary walls, where they occur, are fully formed and lignified, the swollen parts of the primary wall break down (fig. 11.3, *F*, and plate 25, *D*; they are probably dissolved by the protoplast) and, finally, the protoplasts die and disappear.

Not all workers agree with the interpretation of vessel formation given above. Some assume that the primordial vessel members expand very suddenly and that the end walls do not keep pace with this expansion but are torn in the process. The evidence given in

(The tracheid in *G* has been reduced in scale.) *D–A*, principal trends in evolution of fibers: decrease in total length, reduction in the size of pit borders, and change in the shape and size of pit apertures. *H–K*, principal trends in evolution of vessel members: decrease in total length, reduction in inclination of end walls, change from scalariform to simple perforation plates, and change from an opposite to an alternate pit arrangement. (After Bailey and Tupper, 1918.)

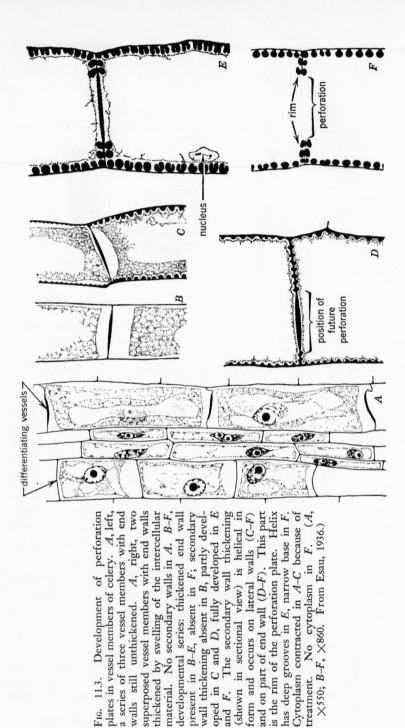

Fig. 11.3. Development of perforation plates in vessel members of celery. *A*, left, a series of three vessel members with end walls still unthickened. *A*, right, two superposed vessel members with end walls thickened by swelling of the intercellular material. No secondary walls in *A*. *B–F*, developmental series: thickened end wall present in *B–E*, absent in *F*; secondary wall thickening absent in *B*, partly developed in *C* and *D*, fully developed in *E* and *F*. The secondary wall thickening (shown in sectional view) is helical in form and occurs on lateral walls (*C–F*) and on part of end wall (*D–F*). This part is the rim of the perforation plate. Helix has deep grooves in *E*, narrow base in *F*. Cytoplasm contracted in *A–C* because of treatment. No cytoplasm in *F*. (*A*, ×550; *B–F*, ×860. From Esau, 1936.)

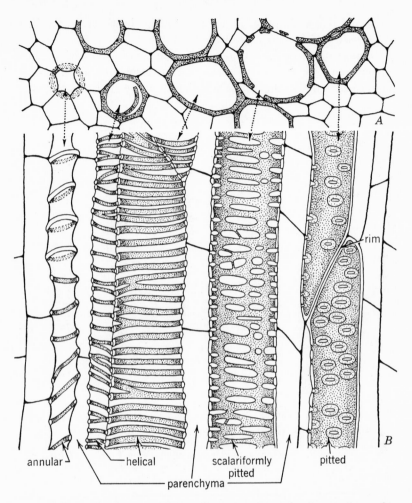

annular ⌐ ⌐helical   scalariformly   pitted
                              pitted
              └──────── parenchyma ────────┘

Fig. 11.4. Parts of primary tracheary elements and associated parenchyma from a young stem of *Aristolochia*, as seen in transverse (*A*) and longitudinal (*B*) sections. In both sections the earliest part of the xylem appears to the left. The element with the annular thickenings is partly extended as compared with its state when it first matured, and the adjacent parenchyma cells are bulging slightly into its lumen. The helically thickened elements have a few interconnections among the coils of the helix, suggesting a transition to the scalariform type of thickening. The wide element with helical thickenings in *B* shows a junction between two superposed elements, above in the picture. At the junction the coils of the helices of the two elements oppose each other. The junction between the two vessel members with bordered pits, to the right in *B*, was cut through the rim of the perforation plate. (×512.)

227

support of this assumption is not convincing, however. (See literature in Esau and Hewitt, 1940.)

Structure of Secondary Walls. The secondary walls of tracheary elements develop in a wide variety of patterns. Generally, in the first-formed part of the primary xylem a more limited area of the

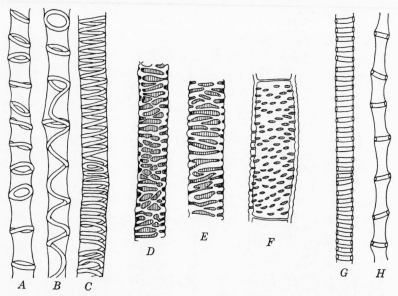

Fig. 11.5. Secondary wall structure in primary tracheary elements. The secondary thickenings are as follows: *A*, annular; *B*, partly annular, partly helical; *C*, helical; *D*, reticulate; *E*, scalariform-reticulate; *F*, pitted; *G* and *H*, annular in an unstretched element (*G*), and in a stretched element (*H*). *A–F*, from an *Avena* seedling; *G* and *H*, from a *Zea* seedling. (*A–F*, ×450; *G*, *H*, ×420. *A–F*, drawn from photomicrographs in Goodwin, 1942.)

primary wall is covered by secondary wall layers than in the later-formed primary xylem and in the secondary xylem. Beginning with the earliest primary xylem, the secondary thickenings are deposited in the successive elements as rings, continuous spirals (more exactly, helices), then as helices, with the individual coils of a helix here and there interconnected with each other, giving the wall a ladder-like appearance (figs. 11.4 and 11.5). Such secondary thickenings are called, respectively, *annular, spiral* or *helical,* and *scalariform.* In a still later ontogenetic type of tracheary elements, the *reticulate* tracheary element, the secondary wall appears like a net. When the meshes of the net are rather distinctly elongated transversely, the thickening is sometimes called *scalariform-reticulate* (fig. 11.5, *E*). Tracheary elements with a still more extensive secondary wall constitute pitted elements (figs. 11.4 and 11.5, *F*). In these, the secondary wall is interrupted only in the pit areas (and in the perforation plates of the vessel members). Pitted elements are characteristic of the latest primary xylem and of the secondary xylem.

The details of the secondary wall sculpture in elements with annular, helical, scalariform, and reticulate thickenings vary in different species of plants, and not all four patterns are necessarily present in a given plant. Furthermore, there may be gradual transitions among the different types, or combinations of more than one type of thickening in the same longitudinal series of elements or even in the same individual element (fig. 11.5, *B*). Rings and helices vary in thickness. Some helices are grooved on their inner surface, occasionally so deeply that the helix appears double (fig. 11.3, *E*). Sometimes more than one helix is present in one element. The rings and the helices appear to be firmly attached to the primary wall. In many plants the thickening is connected with the primary wall by means of a narrow band (Majumdar, 1941; Moog, 1925). In sectional views the portion of the ring or the helix projecting over the narrow base appears like a border of a bordered pit (fig. 11.3, *F*).

The different types of pitting encountered in tracheary cells have been described in detail in chapter 3. Briefly, most of the pits are bordered. The pit membranes characteristically have a torus in certain gymnosperms. If the bordered pits are elongated transversely and arranged in vertical series, the pitting is called scalariform (fig. 11.1, *G*, and 11.2, *A*). (Such wall thickening is often difficult to distinguish from the scalariform-reticulate; Bailey, 1925, 1944*b*.) The circular or oval bordered pits are arranged in horizontal (opposite pitting) or oblique (alternate pitting) series (fig. 3.6). Helical thickening bands may develop on the surface of the more continuous pitted part of the secondary wall.

The pits on the wall of a given tracheary element are rarely all exactly alike (fig. 11.6). Large bordered pit-pairs commonly occur on walls between two tracheary elements (intervascular pitting). There may be no pit-pairs or only few small ones between a tracheary element and a fiber. Pit-pairs between tracheary elements and parenchyma cells are simple, half-bordered (with the border on the tracheary side, plate 9), or bordered (Frost, 1929).

The ontogenetic series of primary tracheary elements, beginning with the elements having annular thickenings and ending with those

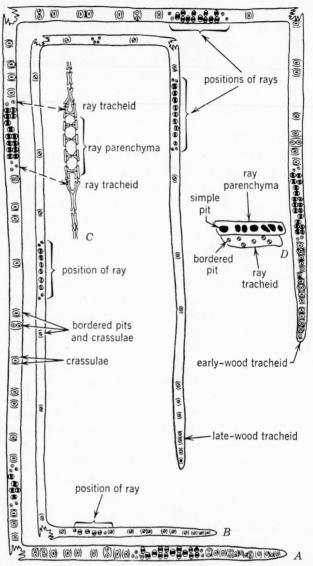

Fig. 11.6. Elements from the secondary xylem of *Pinus*. *A*, early-wood and, *B*, late-wood tracheids. Both are shown exposing their radial walls. *C*, ray in transverse section as seen in tangential section of the wood. *D*, two ray cells as seen in a radial section of the wood. The tracheids in *A* and *B* show, respectively, five and three contact areas with rays. The small pits in these areas are those connecting the vertical-system tracheids with ray tracheids. The large pits with partial borders occur where ray parenchyma cells were connected with the vertical-system tracheids. Elsewhere the tracheids show pits with full borders

having pitted walls (sometimes with the omission of one or another type), occurs among vascular plants from the lowest (*Psilotum;* Moore and Andrews, 1936) to the highest levels on the phylogenetic scale. However, the higher gymnosperms, the Ginkgoales, the Coniferales, and the Gnetales (and possibly the fern group Ophioglos-

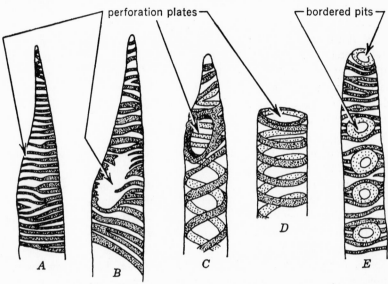

Fig. 11.7. Structural details of primary xylem elements with helical secondary thickenings. *A–D*, ends of dicotyledonous vessel members with the following variations in the perforation plates: *A*, scalariform; *B*, simple in transition from scalariform; *C*, simple, with rim; *D*, simple, with rim, on a truncated end. The views in *A–C* may be used to illustrate the evolutionary sequence in the development of a simple perforation plate in helically thickened primary tracheary elements. *E*, end of tracheary element of *Gnetum* showing a combination of helical secondary thickenings with bordered pits. (After Bailey, 1944*b*.)

sales) have a peculiar primary xylem unlike that of the other known vascular plants (Bailey, 1925, 1944*b*, 1949). In these groups, the helical and reticulate thickenings are combined with circular bordered pits of the type characteristic of the secondary tracheary elements of these plants (fig. 11.7, *E*); and scalariformly pitted elements are completely omitted.

Phylogenetic Specialization. The xylem occupies a unique position among plant tissues in that the study of its anatomy has come

and are associated with crassulae. (All, ×100. *A*, *B*, *D*, adapted from Forsaith, 1926, courtesy New York State College of Forestry.)

to play such an important role with reference to taxonomy and phylogeny. The lines of specialization of the various structural features have been better established for the xylem than for any other single tissue (Bailey, 1944*b*; Bailey and Tupper, 1918; Chalk, 1937; Tippo, 1946). Many examples may be cited of the use that has been made of xylem anatomy to clarify taxonomic affinities (e.g., papers by Bailey and associates; Heimsch, 1942; Metcalfe and Chalk, 1950; Tippo, 1938; Vestal, 1937; and others). Among the individual features of the xylem the structure of the tracheary elements has been investigated especially thoroughly. Extensive comparative studies employing statistical methods and conducted with notable consistency have properly evaluated the variations in the morphology of the tracheary elements and explained their significance (see papers by Bailey and associates; also Cheadle, 1942, 1943*a*, *b*, 1944; Frost, 1930*a*, *b*, 1931; Tippo, 1946).

The tracheid is a more primitive element than the vessel member. The tracheid is the only kind of element found in the fossil seed plants, the pteridosperms (Andrews, 1940; Arnold, 1947), and in most of the living lower vascular plants and gymnosperms (Jeffrey, 1917). Vessel members have evolved from tracheids and occur in the following groups: (1) the highest gymnosperms, the Gnetales; (2) the dicotyledons, except representatives of the lowest taxonomic groups (Bailey, 1944*a*; Bailey and Nast, 1945*a*; Bailey and Swamy, 1948; Swamy and Bailey, 1950); (3) the monocotyledons (Cheadle, 1942–1944); (4) the fern *Pteridium* (Bliss, 1939; Duerden, 1940), and (5) the genus *Selaginella* of the Lycopodiaceae (Duerden, 1934).

Vessels arose independently, through parallel evolution, in the five groups of plants named above. In the dicotyledons specialization of tracheids into vessel members occurred first in the secondary xylem and then gradually proceeded into the primary xylem, beginning with the latest part of this tissue (Bailey, 1944*b*). In monocotyledons (Cheadle, 1942–1944) vessels do not occur in the secondary xylem (few monocotyledons develop such tissue), and in the primary xylem they evolved first in the ontogenetically latest part, then in the earlier parts of this tissue. Monocotyledonous vessels appeared first in the root and later extended into stems, inflorescence axes, and leaves.

In the Gnetales (fig. 11.8) the vessel members originated from tracheids that had circular bordered pits of the coniferous type (Bailey, 1944*b*, 1949). The perforation of the end wall evolved by modifications and fusion of pits.

In *Pteridium*, in *Selaginella*, and in the secondary xylem of the angiosperms the vessel members arose from tracheids with scalariform bordered pitting (fig. 11.1, *G*; Bailey, 1944*b*, 1949). The vessel members of the primary xylem of angiosperms evolved not only from scalariform pitted tracheids but also from tracheids with reticulate and helical secondary thickenings (fig. 11.7; Bailey, 1944*b*; Cheadle, 1942–1944). (The evolution of tracheary elements with annular thickenings has not been sufficiently investigated.) The perforation plate in vessel members derived from scalariformly pitted tracheids evolved in steps from a part of a wall bearing several bordered pits. At first only the pit membranes disappeared, then the borders ceased to develop, and finally there was a loss of the bars between individual openings. Thus, a pitted wall part became a scalariform perforation plate, which changed into a simple perforation plate bearing a single opening. Concomitantly with these changes the vessel members gradually evolved definite end walls of decreasing degree of inclination, in contrast to the tapering ends of tracheids (fig. 11.1).

Structures representing the successive stages in the evolution of vessels of secondary xylem of dicotyledons are preserved in the existing representatives of this group of plants. Thus they are readily accessible for study and are well understood (Bailey, 1944*b*; Tippo, 1946). Surveys of vessel members in a broad and representative sampling of dicotyledons reveal that specialization has proceeded from long, narrow elements with tapering ends to short, wide ones having slightly inclined and transverse end walls which are almost completely eliminated by perforation (fig. 11.1). The phylogenetic shortening of vessel members is a particularly constant characteristic and has occurred in all Tracheophyta that have developed vessels (Bailey, 1944*b*).

The pitting on the longitudinal walls of the vessel members has also undergone evolutionary changes (Bailey, 1944*b*). In intervessel pitting, bordered pit-pairs in scalariform series have been replaced by circular bordered pit-pairs, first in opposite and ultimately in alternate series (fig. 11.1). The pit-pairs in walls between vessels and parenchyma have changed from fully bordered, to half-bordered, and finally to entirely simple (Frost, 1931).

Although vessels evolved in the higher vascular plants, imperforate tracheary elements have also been retained, and they too have undergone phylogenetic modifications (fig. 11.1). The tracheids became

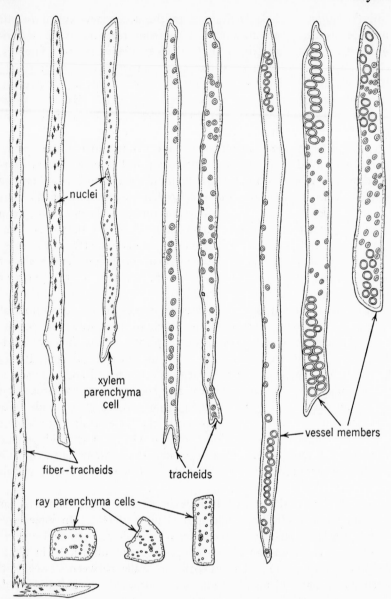

FIG. 11.8. Isolated elements from the secondary xylem of *Ephedra californica* (Gymnospermae, Gnetales). An example of a primitive wood with relatively little morphologic differentiation among the elements of the vertical system. Typical fibers, as purely mechanical elements lacking protoplasts, are absent. The xylem parenchyma cells are elongated and have secondary walls with simple pits. The fiber-tracheids have pits with reduced borders and retain living contents at

shorter and developed a pitting essentially similar (the pits may be somewhat reduced) to that in the associated vessel members. However, the tracheids shortened much less than did the vessel members, and they generally did not increase in width. The different trends of specialization of tracheary elements discussed in the preceding paragraphs are not necessarily closely correlated within specific groups of plants (Bailey, 1944*b*, 1949). Some of these trends may be accelerated, others retarded, so that the more and the less highly specialized characters occur in combinations. Despite these inconsistencies, however, the main trends of vessel specialization in angiosperms are so reliably established that they are playing a significant role in the determination of specialization of other structures in the xylem. Furthermore, they are used in the classification and identification of angiosperms, as well as in considerations of their origin (Bailey, 1944*b*, 1949; Tippo, 1946).

Fibers

The xylem fibers are treated in detail in chapter 10. To repeat briefly, fibers have thicker walls and reduced pit borders as compared with tracheids from which they have evolved (fig. 11.1). The two main types of xylem fiber, the fiber-tracheids and the libriform fibers, intergrade with each other and also with the tracheids. Because of this lack of clear separation between fibers and tracheids, the two kinds of elements are sometimes grouped together under the term "imperforate tracheary elements" (Bailey and Tupper, 1918; Committee on Nomenclature, 1933). Like tracheids, fibers have undergone a phylogenetic shortening with increase of specialization of the xylem (fig. 11.1), although they are usually longer than the tracheids of the same plant (see chapter 10). Length is not a sure criterion for separating the various imperforate xylem elements. Wood anatomists rely mainly on the nature of pits. Fiber tracheids have bordered pits with less developed borders than tracheids, whereas libriform fibers have simple or almost simple pits (Bailey, 1936; Chalk, 1937). Fibers are most highly specialized as supporting elements in those woods that have the most specialized vessel members (fig. 11.9).

maturity. The tracheids show pits with large borders. The vessel members are slender, elongated, and have much inclined end walls bearing foraminate perforation plates. The ray parenchyma cells have secondary walls with simple pits. ($\times$170.)

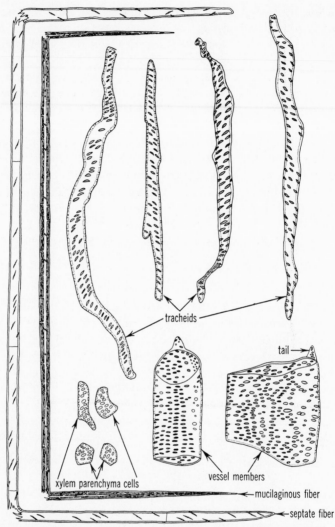

FIG. 11.9. Isolated elements from the secondary xylem of *Aristolochia brasiliensis,* a dicotyledonous vine. An example of a specialized wood with the elements of the vertical system diverse in form. The fibers are of the libriform type with much reduced pit borders. Some are thin-walled and septate; others are thick-walled and mucilaginous. The tracheids are elongated and irregular in shape, with slightly bordered elongated pits. The vessel members are short and have slightly inclined or transverse end walls with simple perforations. The pits connecting the vessel members with other tracheary elements are slightly bordered; others are simple. The xylem parenchyma cells are irregular in shape and have simple pits. Ray parenchyma cells are not shown. They are relatively large, with thin primary walls. (×130.)

On the contrary, where the vessel members are tracheid-like, extreme types of fibers are lacking (fig. 11.8; Bailey, 1936).

Parenchyma Cells

Living parenchyma cells occur in both the primary and the secondary xylem. In the latter they are commonly present in two forms: *xylem, or wood, parenchyma*, derived, together with the tracheary elements and fibers, from the fusiform cambial initials, and *ray parenchyma*, formed by the ray initials of the cambium (fig. 11.11). The xylem parenchyma cells may be as long as the fusiform initials (*fusiform wood parenchyma cells*, fig. 11.8), or they may be several times shorter, if a fusiform derivative divides transversely before differentiating into parenchyma (*wood parenchyma strand*, fig. 11.11). The shorter type of xylem parenchyma cells is the more common (Record, 1947).

The ray parenchyma cells vary in shape but permit the distinction of two fundamental forms (plate 28, *B*), cells with their longest axes oriented radially (*procumbent ray cells*) and cells with their longest axes oriented vertically (*upright ray cells*) (Committee on Nomenclature, 1933; Record, 1947). The phylogenetic origin of the various types of parenchyma cells in the secondary xylem has not been adequately investigated.

The ray and the xylem parenchyma cells of the secondary xylem may or may not have secondary walls. If a secondary wall is present, the pit-pairs between the parenchyma cells and the tracheary elements may be bordered, half-bordered, or simple. Only simple pit-pairs occur between parenchyma cells.

The parenchyma cells of the xylem have a variety of contents. They are particularly noted for storage of food reserves in the form of starch or fat (Sinnott, 1918). Generally, the starch reserves accumulate toward the end of a growth season and are again depleted, not necessarily completely, during the cambial activity of the following season. Tannins, crystals, and various other substances (see chapters 2 and 8) may occur in these cells.

Tyloses. In many plants the xylem and the ray parenchyma cells develop protrusions that enter tracheary cells when these become inactive or the xylem tissue is injured (plate 26; Esau, 1948; Gerry, 1914; Gertz, 1916). Such outgrowths from parenchyma cells are called *tyloses* (singular *tylose* or *tylosis*). Tylose development occurs through the pit-pairs connecting the parenchyma cells with the tracheary elements. The development of the tylose is probably an instance of localized growth of the cell wall in surface, namely, of the cell wall that forms the part of the pit membrane on the parenchyma side. (The possibility that only the protoplast enters the tracheary cell after a perforation of the pit membrane seems to be implied in the definition of the tylose as a "proliferation of the protoplast," given by the wood anatomists, Committee on Nomenclature, 1933.)

Tyloses are sometimes so numerous that they completely fill the lumen of the tracheid or vessel element (plates 26, *A*, and 29). The nucleus of the originating parenchyma cell and part of the cytoplasm appear in the tylose. In the mature state the tyloses may remain thin walled or develop secondary walls. Sometimes they develop into sclereids (Record, 1947). Tyloses may become subdivided (Gertz, 1916).

PRIMARY XYLEM

Protoxylem and Metaxylem

When the primary xylem is studied in detail, some developmental and structural differences usually may be observed between the earlier and the later formed parts of this tissue. These two parts have been named *protoxylem* and *metaxylem* (*proto* and *meta* are derived from the Greek and mean first and beyond, respectively). Originally, the distinction between the protoxylem and the metaxylem was made with regard to the relative time of appearance of the two tissues, later the consideration of the morphologic differences was superimposed over the initial concept (cf. Bugnon, 1925; Esau, 1943; Frey-Wyssling, 1940). When the terms protoxylem and metaxylem are used in this book, they are defined on the basis of the ontogenetic relation of the tissue parts of the primary xylem to the organ as a whole.

Protoxylem is the tissue which appears at the beginning of vascular differentiation and occupies a characteristic position in the primary vascular system of a given plant organ (see chapters 15–17). Ordinarily a plant organ passes through a definite period of elongation soon after its initiation. The protoxylem usually matures before the organ completes its elongation. The metaxylem, which appears after the protoxylem, is in the process of differentiation while the organ is elongating and matures after this elongation is finished. The protoxylem, as just characterized, commonly has annular and helical thickenings in its tracheary elements, whereas the metaxylem may have helical, scalariform, reticulate, and pitted secondary thickenings (figs. 11.4 and 11.5). Thus, morphologically, the two parts of the xylem may intergrade.

The nonliving tracheary elements of the protoxylem are unable to keep pace with the extension of the adjacent cells and are, therefore, stretched and frequently completely destroyed. During this stretching the primary wall is presumably torn, whereas the secondary wall is distorted. The rings are separated from one another and tilted, and the helices are extended (fig. 11.5, *A, B, H*). Since the metaxylem matures after the organ completes its growth in length, its elements are not destroyed by stretching. In plants having no secondary growth, the metaxylem constitutes the only water-conducting tissue of the mature plant. In the presence of large amounts of secondary growth the metaxylem usually becomes non-functioning, although its tracheary elements appear to remain intact. Sometimes they are filled with tyloses.

The protoxylem usually contains relatively few tracheary elements (tracheids or vessel elements) and a considerable proportion of parenchyma cells. The latter either remain thin walled after the obliteration of the tracheary elements or become lignified, with or without the development of secondary walls (Raimann, 1890). The metaxylem is, as a rule, a more complex tissue than the protoxylem, and its tracheary elements are generally wider (plates 52 and 53). These elements may be differentiated into tracheids or vessel members, and they are accompanied by parenchyma and frequently also by fibers. The relatively high proportion of cells with lignified secondary walls makes the metaxylem appear more compact than the protoxylem.

Secondary Wall Structure in Relation to the Development of the Xylem

Considerable evidence is available that the wall character of the primary xylem elements is influenced by the amount of elongation of the organ. The normal proportion of the easily extensible elements with annular and helical thickenings in the primary xylem may be affected by changes in the rate of elongation of the plant. Thus, if the elongation of a plant organ is retarded or inhibited (e.g., by regulation of light or use of X-rays), pitted elements instead of the extensible types appear close to the apical meristem (Goodwin, 1942; Koernike, 1905; Smith and Kersten, 1942). Among naturally growing roots those that elongate much have a larger proportion of extensible forms of xylem cells than roots showing little elongation (Scherer, 1904).

The causal relationships between the cessation of elongation and the development of pitted elements are still obscure (Goodwin, 1942; Stafford, 1948). Judging from the details of development of secondary walls, the pattern of such walls is foreshadowed in the cytoplasm. Before the secondary wall thickening is actually present, its pattern can be recognized in the variable density of the parietal cytoplasm (Barkley, 1927; Sinnott and Bloch, 1945). The cytoplasm becomes denser along the parts of the wall that later are covered by the secondary thickenings. If such cells are plasmolyzed and the protoplast withdraws from the wall, the pattern is seen to be located in the outer part of the protoplast, rather than on the wall (Crüger, 1855). These observations do not support the concept that the secondary thickening of the extensible primary xylem elements is laid down as a continuous layer that is later pulled apart into rings, helices, or reticulae (Smith and Kersten, 1942; Stover, 1951, p. 70).

The observations on the relation between the secondary wall structure in the primary xylem and the elongation of the plant parts clearly show that, in distinguishing between protoxylem and metaxylem, too much emphasis upon wall sculpture would detract from the value of these terms. The relative time of maturation gives the only consistent basis for classification of the primary xylem into protoxylem and metaxylem (Esau, 1943; Frey-Wyssling, 1940; Goodwin, 1942).

SECONDARY XYLEM

Distinction from the Primary Xylem

Like the classification of the primary xylem into the protoxylem and the metaxylem, the distinction between the primary and the secondary xylem cannot be sharply drawn. In this instance, too, the classification is of little value unless it is conceived in relation to the growth of the plant or of a plant organ as a whole (see chapters 1 and 4). Briefly, the primary xylem is the xylem differentiating in conjunction with the growth of the primary plant body and derived from the procambium. The secondary xylem is a part of the accessory secondary body superimposed over the primary and formed by the vascular cambium.

The secondary xylem is formed by a relatively complex meristem, the cambium, consisting of fusiform and ray initials, and is, therefore, composed of two systems, the vertical and the horizontal (rays), an architecture not characteristic of the primary xylem (figs. 11.10 and 11.11). In the dicotyledons the secondary xylem is commonly more complex than the primary in having a wider variety of component cells. The sculpture of the secondary walls of the primary and secondary tracheary elements has been considered earlier in this chapter. The elements of the late part of the metaxylem often intergrade with the secondary elements, since both may be similarly pitted.

Frequently the arrangement of cells, as seen in transverse sections, is stressed as a criterion for distinguishing the primary from the secondary xylem. The procambium and the primary xylem are said to have a haphazard cell arrangement; the cambium and the secondary xylem, an orderly arrangement, with the cells aligned parallel with the radii of the secondary body. This distinction is highly unreliable, for in many plants the primary xylem shows just as definite radial seriation of cells as the secondary (cf. Esau, 1943, and chapter 15).

The most reliable feature separating the primary and secondary xylems of a given angiospermous plant has been found to be the length of the tracheary cells (Bailey, 1944b). Although the helically thickened tracheary elements are generally longer than the pitted elements of the same primary xylem, these pitted elements are still considerably longer than the first secondary tracheary elements. Indeed, this difference is so conspicuous that one can speak of a nonconformity between the two xylems (Bailey, 1944b). This apparent break in the continuity of development may be caused, not only by the elongation of the metaxylem cells and lack of a comparable elongation of the cambial derivatives, but also by possible transverse divisions of the procambial cells just before the initiation of cambial activity. In the gymnosperms, too, the last primary xylem elements are longer than the first secondary elements (Bailey, 1920).

In a discussion of the relative lengths of procambial and cambial derivatives it is important to remember that the possible elongation of the secondary elements occurs in a plant body that has ceased to elongate. All the elongation in the cambial zone occurs by apical intrusive growth. In the procambium symplastic growth probably predominates, but apical intrusive growth is not necessarily absent. It is present in the development of primary phloem fibers (see chapter 10) and could be expected to occur in the formation of the long primary tracheary cells.

Basic Structural Characteristics

Vertical and Horizontal Systems. The arrangement of cells into the vertical, or longitudinal, system, on the one hand, and the transverse, horizontal, or ray system, on the other, constitutes one of the conspicuous characteristics of the secondary wood (figs. 11.10 and 11.11). The rays and the vertical system form two interpenetrating systems closely integrated with each other in origin, structure, and function. In an active xylem the rays most commonly consist of living cells. The vertical system contains, depending on the species of plant, one or more of the different kinds of nonliving tracheary element, fiber, and parenchyma cell. The living cells of the rays and those of the vertical system are interconnected with each other, so that one can speak of a continuous system of living cells permeating the wood. Moreover, this system often is connected, through the rays, with the living cells of the pith, the phloem, and the cortex.

The longitudinal axis of the vertical system is parallel with the longitudinal axis of the organ in which the xylem occurs. Therefore, transverse and longitudinal sections of an organ coincide with the same kind of sections of the vertical system. The rays, on the contrary, have their longitudinal axes parallel with the radii of the approximately cylindrical bodies of stem and root and their branches. Consequently, transverse and radial longitudinal sections of an organ show the rays in longitudinal section, whereas tangential longitudinal sections expose the rays in their transverse section. If statements are made that xylem is sectioned transversely and longitudinally (radially or tangentially), the plane of sectioning is referred to the organ as a whole and, therefore, also to the vertical system of the xylem.

The rays are characterized as having length, width, and height. The length is measured between the cambium and the innermost end of the ray. The width of the ray corresponds to its tangential extent and is commonly expressed in the number of cells in this direction. The height of a ray is its extent in the direction parallel with the longitudinal axis of the stem or root.

The rays vary much in their dimensions in different plants and may be of more than one size in the same plant. If a ray is one cell wide, it is termed *uniseriate* (plates 27 and 28). The contrasting type is the *multiseriate* ray (plate 30, *C*), which may be a few cells to many cells wide (if the ray is two cells in width, it is called *biseriate*). A multiseriate ray, as seen in a tangential section of the xylem, tapers toward

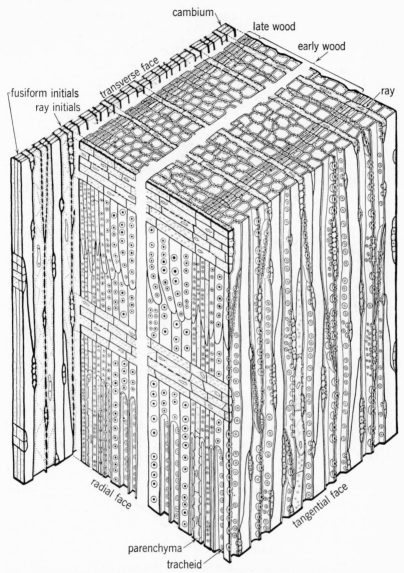

FIG. 11.10. Block diagram of the cambium and secondary xylem of *Thuja occidentalis* L. (White Cedar). Example of gymnosperm (conifer) wood. The vertical system is composed of tracheids and a small amount of parenchyma. The horizontal system consists of low, uniseriate rays composed of parenchyma cells. (Courtesy of I. W. Bailey. Drawn by Mrs. J. P. Rogerson under the supervision of L. G. Livingston. Redrawn.)

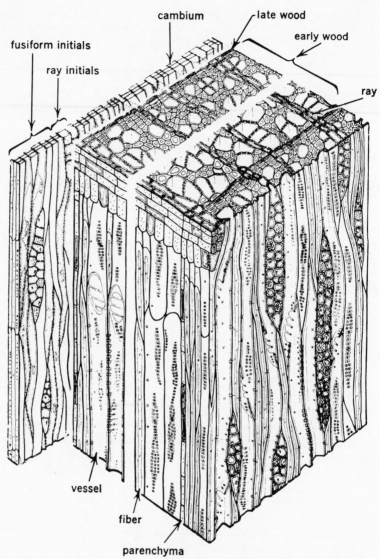

FIG. 11.11. Block diagram of the cambium and secondary xylem of *Liriodendron tulipifera* L. (Tulip Tree). An example of angiosperm (dicotyledon) wood. The vertical system consists of vessel members with bordered pits in opposite arrangement and inclined end walls bearing scalariform perforation plates; fiber tracheids with slightly bordered pits; and xylem parenchyma strands in terminal arrangement. The horizontal system contains heterogeneous rays (the marginal cells are upright, the others procumbent), uniseriate and biseriate, of various heights. (Courtesy of I. W. Bailey. Drawn by Mrs. J. P. Rogerson under the supervision of L. G. Livingston.)

the upper and lower margins, where it is commonly uniseriate. Thus a wide ray appears lenticular or fusiform in its transectional outline. Both kinds of ray may be low or high. Although the height and width of rays often undergo considerable change through the successive layers of secondary xylem (Bailey and Howard, 1941*c*; Bannan, 1937, 1950, 1951; Barghoorn, 1940*a*, 1941*a*), the kind and extent of change induced are characteristic of a given species. The length of a ray, on the other hand, is an indefinite characteristic for three reasons: first, new rays are constantly initiated as the axis increases in circumference; second, some rays are discontinued after having been formed for a while; and, third, the length of the ray is affected by the vigor of growth.

Storied and Nonstoried Woods. In chapter 6 a distinction was made between storied and nonstoried cambia, with reference to the arrangement of the fusiform initials in tangential sections. Nonstoried cambia produce nonstoried woods (figs. 11.10, 11.11; plates 27–29). The xylem derived from a storied cambium may be storied (plate 30) or only partly so, if the original stratification is obscured by changes during the differentiation of the xylem. One of the most common of such changes is the elongation of the elements in the vertical system. Tracheids, fiber-tracheids, and libriform fibers generally become longer than the fusiform cambial cells from which they were derived. The apices of these elements extend by intrusive growth beyond the limits of their own horizontal tier and thus partly efface its demarcation from the tiers above and below. A relatively indistinct stratification may be carried over by the xylem also from the cambium itself, since cambia show varied degrees of stratification. The degree of stratification may change during the development of the successive increments of xylem. Phylogenetically the storied condition is more highly specialized than the nonstoried, and the storied is associated with short vessel members (plate 30, *B*).

Growth layers. The activity of the cambium is commonly periodic, and the xylem produced during one growth period constitutes a *growth layer* (figs. 11.10, 11.11; plates 27–29, 31). In transverse sections of stems and roots such layers are referred to as *growth rings*. If the growth is definitely seasonal and occurs once during a season, the growth layer and the growth ring may be called the *annual layer* and the *annual ring*, respectively. If, however, the seasonal growth is interrupted by adverse climatic conditions, diseases, or other agents, and is later again resumed, a second growth layer will be visible in the wood added during one season. Such an additional layer is sometimes called a *false annual ring*.

The growth rings are of varied degrees of distinctness, depending upon the species of wood and also upon growing conditions (Record, 1947; Record and Hess, 1943). The cause of the visibility of the growth layers in a section of wood is the structural difference between the xylem produced in the early and the late parts of the growth season. The *early wood* is less dense than the *late wood* and has generally larger cells and, proportionally, a smaller amount of wall substance per unit volume. In the temperate zone the early wood and the late wood are commonly called "spring wood" and "summer wood," respectively. The early wood of a given season merges more or less gradually with the late wood of the same season, but the division line between the late wood of one season and the early wood of the following season is ordinarily sharp.

Growth rings occur in deciduous and evergreen trees. Furthermore, they are not confined to the temperate zone, with its striking contrast between the season of growth and the season of dormancy or rest, but may be present in subtropical and tropical woods. In the tropical species growth rings are often formed only under certain environmental conditions, whereas in many plants of the northern hemisphere zonation is produced under all conditions of growth (Bailey, 1944*a*). The width of rings is easily influenced by the external environment and is, therefore, variable. In straight parts of a tree growing under uniform conditions, the rings show orderly concentric arrangement. However, many agencies of mechanical, chemical, and physiochemical nature may cause eccentric growth, sometimes of such a pronounced degree that part of the growth layers do not continue around the circumference of the axis (Forsaith, 1926; Jaccard, 1938).

Sapwood and Heartwood. The elements of the secondary xylem are variously specialized in relation to their function. The tracheary elements and the fibers that are concerned, respectively, with movement of water and support typically become devoid of protoplasts before their principal contribution to the physiological activity of the plant begins. The living cells, which store and translocate food, are alive at the height of xylem activity. Eventually, the parenchyma cells die. This stage is preceded by numerous changes in the wood that visibly differentiate the active *sapwood* from the inactive *heartwood* (Record, 1947).

Many of the differences between sapwood and heartwood are chemical. With increasing age, the wood loses water and stored food materials and becomes infiltrated with various organic substances, such as oils, gums, resins, tannins, and aromatic and coloring materials. Some of these substances impregnate the walls; others enter the cell lumina also. In many woods tyloses develop in the tracheary cells. In gymnosperm xylem the pit membranes having tori become fixed so that the tori are appressed to the borders and close the apertures. These various changes do not affect the strength of the wood but make it more durable than the sapwood, less easily attacked by decay organisms, and less penetrable to various liquids (including artificial preservatives). The infiltration of the coloring matter makes the heartwood particularly distinct from the sapwood.

The proportion of sapwood and heartwood and the degree of visible and actual differences between the two is highly variable in different species and in different conditions of growth. Some trees have no clearly differentiated heartwood (e.g., *Populus, Salix, Picea, Abies*), others have thin sapwood (e.g., *Robinia, Morus, Taxus*), and still others a thick sapwood (e.g., *Acer, Fraxinus, Fagus*). In some species the sapwood is early converted into heartwood; in others it shows greater longevity. The development of heartwood sometimes results from a pathological state.

Gymnosperm Wood

The xylem of gymnosperms is generally simpler and more homogeneous than that of angiosperms (compare figs. 11.10 and 11.11; plates 27 and 29). The chief distinction between the two kinds of wood is the absence of vessels in the gymnosperms (except in Gnetales; fig. 11.8) and their presence in most angiosperms. A further outstanding peculiarity of gymnosperm wood is the relatively small amount of parenchyma, particularly vertical parenchyma (Huber and Prütz, 1938; Phillips, 1941).

The xylem of the Coniferales has been extensively studied, beginning with the classical investigations of Sanio (1872–74) and continuing into the modern times (e.g., Bailey, 1909, 1910; Bailey and Faull, 1934; Bannan, 1934-1951; Barghoorn, 1940a; Strasburger, 1891).

The Vertical System. In gymnosperm xylem, the vertical system consists mostly or entirely of tracheids. The late-wood tracheids develop relatively thick walls and pits with reduced borders, so that they may be classified as fiber-tracheids (Record, 1947), but libriform fibers do not occur. The tracheids are long cells—they vary in length from 0.5 to 11 mm (Bailey and Tupper, 1918)—with their ends overlapping those of other tracheids (figs. 11.6, 11.10, and plate 27). The individual cells are regarded as having basically 14 sides with frequent increases in the number of faces to 18 and even 22 because of the in-curved tips (Lewis, 1935). Although the fusiform initials from which these cells arise are wedge shaped at their ends, showing their pointed faces in tangential sections and their blunt ends in the radial sections, the tracheid ends are more or less modified because the cells undergo apical growth and adjust the shape of their ends to that of the spaces that they invade. These ends may even be forked (fig. 11.8).

The tracheids of extant gymnosperms are interconnected by circular or oval bordered pit-pairs in single, opposite, or alternate arrangement (figs. 11.6 and 11.10). Some studies have shown that the number of pits on each tracheid may vary from approximately 50 to 300 (Stamm, 1946). The pit-pairs are most abundant on the ends where the tracheids overlap each other. In general, the pits are confined to the radial facets of the cells. Only the late-wood tracheids are pitted on their tangential walls. Tori are present on the pit membranes in *Ginkgo*, Gnetales, and most Coniferales.

The tracheids characteristically show thickenings of intercellular material and primary walls along the upper and lower margins of the pit-pairs (fig. 11.6 and plate 8, *A*). These thickenings are called *crassulae* (from the Latin, little thickenings; Committee on Nomenclature, 1933; Record, 1947). Still another not uncommon wall sculpture is represented by the *trabeculae*, small bars extending across the lumina of the tracheids from one tangential wall to the other (Record, 1947). Tracheids with trabeculae commonly occur in long radial series of cells. Helical thickenings on pitted walls have been observed in the tracheids of some conifers (Bailey, 1909).

Each tracheid is in contact with one or more rays. The proportion of the length of the tracheid wall that is joined to ray cells has been calculated as varying from 0.072 to 0.288 in different conifers (Stamm, 1931).

Where present, the vertical xylem parenchyma of the Coniferales is commonly distributed throughout the growth ring and occurs in long strands derived from transverse divisions of the mostly long fusiform cambial cells. Some conifers, like *Taxus*, *Torreya*, and *Araucaria*, have no parenchyma in the vertical system. In *Pinus*, vertical parenchyma occurs only in the epithelium of the resin ducts (plate 27).

Structure of Rays. The rays of gymnosperms are composed either of parenchyma cells alone (fig. 11.10), or of parenchyma cells and tracheids (plate 8, *B*). Ray tracheids are distinguished from ray parenchyma cells chiefly by their bordered pits and lack of protoplasts. The distribution of ray tracheids is highly variable in a given plant and is not constant even in the same ray (Bannan, 1934a, 1937; Barghoorn, 1940a). Ray tracheids have lignified secondary walls. In some conifers these walls are thick and sculptured, with projections in the form of teeth or bands extending across the lumen of the cell. The ray-parenchyma cells have living protoplasts in the sapwood and often darkly colored resinous deposits in the heartwood. They have only primary walls in the Taxodiaceae, the Araucariaceae, the Taxaceae, the Podocarpaceae, the Cupressaceae, and the Cephalotaxaceae; secondary walls in the Abietoideae of the Pinaceae (Bailey and Faull, 1934).

The rays of conifers are for the most part only one cell wide and from 1 to 20, sometimes up to 50 cells high. Ray tracheids may occur singly or in series, at the margins of a ray or interspersed among the layers of parenchyma cells. The presence of a resin duct in a ray makes the ray more than one cell wide except at the upper and lower limits (plate 27, *A*).

The ray cells having secondary walls are pitted with each other and also with the tracheids of the vertical system. The pit-pairs between the parenchyma cells and the vertical tracheids are particularly distinctive. They are usually half-bordered, with the border being on the side of the tracheid (plate 9). The shape of these pit-pairs, their number, and their distribution on the rectangular facets of a wall, where a ray cell is in contact with a vertical tracheid (the so-called cross field) are important features from the standpoint of phylogeny and classification within smaller groups (Bailey, 1910; Matzke and Hulbary, 1942; Peirce, 1936; Record, 1947).

Resin Ducts. Certain gymnosperms develop resin ducts in the vertical system or in both the vertical and horizontal systems. Typically, resin ducts arise as schizogenous intercellular spaces by separation of resin producing parenchyma cells from each other (Bannan, 1936; Frank, 1923; Thomson and Sifton, 1925; see also chapter 3). These cells constitute the lining, that is, the *epithelium*, of the resin duct and excrete the resin (Record, 1947). Eventually a resin duct may become closed by the enlarging epithelial cells. These tylosis-like intrusions are called *tylosoids* (Record, 1947, p. 76). They differ from tyloses in that they do not grow through pits.

The literature on the secondary xylem of conifers contains much evidence that resin ducts develop in response to injury; in other words, they are traumatic structures (from the Greek *trauma*, a wound). Their association with injuries has been observed in natural conditions and in controlled experiments (Bailey and Faull, 1934; Bannan, 1934*b*, 1936; Thomson and Sifton, 1925). The phenomena that induce the development of resin ducts are numerous. Some of these are formation of open and pressure wounds and injuries by frost and wind. Different groups of conifers are not alike in their response to injuries. In the Abieteae the resin ducts are cyst-like and develop in tangential series near wounds. Those of the Pineae are long, scattered, and dispersed far from the center of injury (a damage done to the crown may induce duct formation in the trunk). In *Abies* and *Tsuga* the epithelial cells are thick walled and lignified, and most of them die during the year of origin. These genera, therefore, produce a comparatively small amount of resin. In *Pinus*, on the other hand, the epithelial cells are thin walled, remain active for several years, and produce abundant resin. Transitional types of behavior are observed in some other Coniferae. The variations in development and activity of the resin ducts suggest a phylogenetic series of increasing sensitivity to injury from the subtribe Abieteae to the subtribe Pineae (Bannan, 1936). The distribution and the longevity of the resin ducts in the Pineae explain why these structures give the impression of being constant formations in the secondary xylem of this group of conifers.

Angiosperm Wood

The expression angiosperm wood commonly refers to the secondary xylem of the dicotyledons. The woody monocotyledons having secondary growth do not form a solid and homogeneous body of secondary xylem and are not a commercial source of wood (Record, 1947).

The secondary xylem of the dicotyledons is generally more complex than the wood of most gymnosperms since its elements are more varied in kind, size, form, and arrangement. The most complex dicotyledonous woods, such as that of oak, may contain vessel members, tracheids, fiber-tracheids, libriform fibers, vertical xylem parenchyma, and rays of different sizes. Certain dicotyledonous woods are, however, less complicated in structure. Many Juglandaceae, for example, contain only fiber-tracheids among the imperforate nonliving cells (Heimsch and Wetmore, 1939). In the absence of vessels, the xylem of certain primitive dicotyledons appears so similar to the gymnosperm wood that it has been erroneously interpreted as being of the coniferous type (see critique in Bailey, 1944*a*).

Distribution of Vessels. The arrangement of vessels in dicotyledonous woods shows characteristic patterns that are utilized in the classification of these woods (Record, 1947). When the vessels have essentially equal diameters and are uniformly distributed through a growth ring, the wood is called *diffuse porous* (fig. 11.11 and plate 28; *Acer, Betula, Liriodendron*). (The word porous refers to the appearance of the vessels in transections. They seem like holes or pores in the section of the wood.) Woods with vessels of unequal diameters and with the largest vessels localized in the early wood are called *ring porous* because of the ring-like arrangement of the large vessels in transections of the xylem cylinder (plates 29, *C*, and 31, *B*; *Castanea, Fraxinus, Robinia*, and certain species of *Quercus*). Between these two extremes, various intergrades occur (e.g., plate 31, *A*). Moreover, in a given species, the distribution of vessels may vary in relation to environmental conditions and may change even with increasing age of a tree. The ring-porous condition appears to be highly specialized and occurs only in comparatively few woods, nearly all being species of the north temperate zone (Gilbert, 1940; Record, 1947).

Within the major types of distributional patterns, the individual vessels, as seen in transverse sections, may be isolated from each other, or they may occur in clusters of various sizes and shapes. The isolated vessels are circular or oval in outline; the clustered ones are flattened along the lines of contact with other vessels (plate 28, *C*).

Studies on ring-porosity in the dicotyledons have revealed some interesting physiologic relationships. Ring-porous xylem contains longer vessels than diffuse-porous xylem (Handley, 1936). It conducts water almost entirely in the outermost growth increment and has a flow of water that is about ten times faster than that of diffuse-porous wood (Huber, 1935). Trees with ring-porous wood appear to produce their early-wood vessel system rapidly, whereas species with diffuse-porous wood form their new xylem slowly (Priestley and Scott, 1936). A frequent accompaniment of the ring-porous condition is an early development of tyloses in the large early-wood vessels. It indicates that these highly specialized vessels are conducting for a short time only (Huber, 1935).

Distribution of Xylem Parenchyma. The amount of xylem parenchyma in dicotyledonous woods varies from very small or none to very large and shows diverse but intergrading patterns of distribution. These patterns have been the object of many thorough studies, but a general agreement on the classification of parenchyma distribution has not yet been reached (Hess, 1950; Metcalfe and Chalk, 1950, p. XXIII).

There are two basic types of parenchyma distribution. In one the position of the parenchyma is independent of that of the vessels (although the two may be touching each other); in the other the two kinds of element are definitely associated with one another topographically. Parenchyma showing the first kind of arrangement is called *apotracheal* (plate 31, *D*; *apo* means from in Greek and expresses, in this instance, independence from); the second, *paratracheal* (plate 31, *C*; *para* means beside in Greek). In each distributional type subordinate variations are recognized (Bailey and Howard, 1941*a*). Apotracheal parenchyma may be dispersed throughout the growth ring (*diffuse* parenchyma), or appear in bands (*banded* parenchyma), or be restricted to the end of a seasonal increment (*terminal* parenchyma). (Some workers distinguish also *initial* parenchyma, which is said to be restricted to the beginning of a growth increment. See Metcalfe and Chalk, 1950, p. XXIII.) Paratracheal parenchyma may be *scanty* or *abundant, abaxial* (in contact with the abaxial surfaces of the vessels, that is, surfaces away from the center of the axis), or *vasicentric* (surrounding the vessels). Recent studies have shown that septate fibers (which commonly retain protoplasts and store starch) show apotracheal and paratracheal distributional patterns similar to those of the parenchyma and that, where septate fibers are abundant, parenchyma is small in amount (Spackman and Swamy, 1949). The phylogenetic sequence among the distributional types of wood parenchyma is from the diffuse arrangement to the other apotracheal and the paratracheal types (Kribs, 1937; Tippo, 1946), although there is no clear evidence concerning the transitional forms.

Structure of Rays. The dicotyledons typically contain only parenchyma cells in the rays. The two main types of ray parenchyma cells, the procumbent and the upright, occur in various combinations. According to a widely used classification, the ray is termed *homogeneous* if it consists of only procumbent or only upright cells, *heterogeneous* if it contains both morphological cell types (fig. 11.11, and plate 28; Record, 1947). (Certain wood anatomists propose to substitute the terms *homocellular* and *heterocellular*, respectively, and to use the homogeneous and heterogeneous to indicate certain other structural differences; cf. Reinders-Gouwentak, 1950.) Uniseriate and multiseriate rays both may be either homogeneous or heterogeneous. The most common heterogeneous type of ray has a multiseriate middle part of procumbent cells and uniseriate vertical extensions of upright cells (fig. 11.11; Record, 1947).

The variation in ray structure in different plant species is most understandable if it is presented from the phylogenetic point of view (Bailey and Howard, 1941*b*; Barghoorn, 1940*b*, 1941*a*, *b*; Kribs, 1935;

Tippo, 1946). Plants with primitive xylem have a combination of two kinds of ray, conspicuously high-celled (i.e., with cells vertically elongated) uniseriate rays and heterogeneous multiseriate rays. This primitive ray structure has been variously modified during evolution. Multiseriate rays have been either increased or decreased in size and number. Uniseriate rays have undergone a reduction in height and number. One or the other or both kinds of ray have been eliminated in certain evolutionary lines. Thus, examples of specialized ray structure might be a combination of large multiseriate rays with small uniseriate (e.g., *Quercus*, plate 29); or the presence of only one kind of ray, either multiseriate or uniseriate (plate 28); or the complete absence of rays (Barghoorn, 1941*b*). Specialization also affected the cellular composition of the rays and resulted in the development of homogeneous rays from heterogeneous.

The more advanced ray structure often appears only in the later increments of the xylem, with the earlier formed secondary xylem having a primitive structure. In such instances the process of phylogenetic modification may be determined by comparing successive tangential sections through the wood and noting the changes that a particular ray underwent after its inception and during its continued growth within the consecutive growth layers. In this way the progressive modification in the ontogeny of a given ray may be revealed (Barghoorn, 1940*b*, 1941*a*). The significant implication of such changes in ray structure is that the ontogenetic stages in the xylem of the same individual plant represent different levels of phylogenetic specialization (Barghoorn, 1941*a*).

The reduction in the size of rays, which may occur during specialization, results from several kinds of modifications in the cambium (Barghoorn, 1941*a*, *b*; Chattaway, 1937). First, there may be a loss of ray initials from the cambium, either within the group of initials or on its margins. Fusiform initials take the place of the lost ray initials. If such displacement occurs within a group of ray initials, the ray appears to be split by the fusiform initials into two or more parts. Second, an actual separation of a ray into parts may occur through intrusion of a fusiform initial, by apical intrusive growth, into a group of ray initials. Third, the ray may be broken up into parts by the change of some of the ray initials into fusiform initials (plate 30, *D*). The third method often modifies large multiseriate rays into structures resembling aggregations of small multiseriate rays. Rays may also increase in size, for example, by fusion with one another or by radial divisions of ray initials. Fusions of rays are brought about by elimination from the cambium of fusiform initials intervening between groups of ray initials (Barghoorn, 1940*b*; cf. also chapter 6).

These are but few examples of cellular changes that occur in the ontogenetic and phylogenetic modifications of the ray system in the dicotyledons. Similarly complex modifications have been observed in the development of rays in the gymnosperms (Bannan, 1950, 1951; Barghoorn, 1940*a*). The examples listed suffice, however, to emphasize the high degree of plasticity of the cambium, the interchangeability between fusiform and ray initials, and the importance of a thorough knowledge of ontogeny for a proper interpretation of the phylogeny of plant structures.

Gum Ducts. Intercellular canals similar to the resin ducts of the gymnosperms occur in dicotyledonous woods (Record, 1947). These are called *gum ducts*, although they may contain various substances, such as resins, oils, gums, and mucilages. The gum ducts occur in the vertical and horizontal systems and originate by schizogeny or lysigeny or by a combination of the two methods. Frequently they have no differentiated epithelium. Instead of long canals, relatively small cavities may develop. These are the gum cysts, comparable to the resin cysts of the gymnosperms.

Many of the gum ducts are undoubtedly traumatic in origin, and the agents inducing their formation are as varied as those responsible for the development of the resin ducts in the gymnosperms. Gum ducts often develop in association with *gummosis*, a degeneration of cells resulting in the formation of complex and variable substances commonly referred to as gum. Most investigators agree that gum is derived from decomposition of carbohydrates, particularly starch, but also of those occurring in the cell walls. Hence gummosis results in depletion of starch in cells, but it may also bring about a breakdown of the cell walls. The gum may collect in the gum ducts or in various xylem cells, including vessel members. Plants frequently respond with gummosis to disease infection, to injury by insects, and to physiological disturbances. (Cf. Esau, 1948.)

Differentiation in the Secondary Xylem

The derivatives that arise on the inner face of the cambium through tangential divisions of the cambial initials undergo complex changes during their development into the various elements of the xylem (figs. 11.10 and 11.11). The basic distinction in form and orientation between the elements of the vertical and the horizontal systems is determined by the structure of the cambium itself, since the cambium is composed of fusiform and ray initials. Also, all the changes in the relative proportions between these two systems—for example, the addition or elimination of rays—originate in the cambium.

The derivatives of the ray initials undergo relatively little change during differentiation. Generally, the ray cells remain parenchymatous —some with primary walls, others with secondary walls—and their contents may not change much, since the ray initials themselves often contain such substances as starch and tannins. Ray cells enlarge radially as they emerge from the cambium, but the distinction between the upright and the procumbent cells is apparent in the cambium. The most profound change occurs in the ray tracheids of gymnosperms, for these cells develop secondary walls with bordered pits and become devoid of protoplasts.

The ontogenetic changes in the vertical system vary with the type of cell and may result in striking contrasts between the cambial cells and their derivatives. The cells developing into vessel members elongate slightly, if at all (fig. 4.2, *E*), but they expand laterally, often so strongly that their ultimate width exceeds their height. Short, wide vessel members are characteristic of highly specialized xylem. In many species of dicotyledons the vessel members expand in their median parts but not at the ends, which overlap those of the vertically adjacent elements. These ends are ultimately not occupied by the perforation and appear like elongated wall processes with or without pits (fig. 11.9). These processes are called tails (Chalk and Chattaway, 1934, 1935).

Expansion of the vessel members affects the arrangement and the shape of adjacent cells. These cells become crowded out of their original position and cease to reflect the radial seriation present in the cambial zone. The rays, too, may be deflected from their original positions. The cells in the immediate vicinity of an expanding vessel enlarge parallel with the surface of the vessel and assume a flattened appearance. But often these cells do not keep pace with the increase of the circumference of the vessel and become partly or completely separated from each other. As a result, the expanding vessel element comes in contact with new cells. The expansion of a vessel member can be pictured as a phenomenon involving both symplastic and intrusive growth (Preston, 1939; Schoch-Bodmer and Huber, 1947). As long as the cells next to the vessel element expand in unison with the vessel element, the common walls of the various cells undergo symplastic growth. During separation of adjacent cells, the vessel-member wall intrudes between the walls of the other cells, somewhat like a growing tip of a tracheid or a fiber intrudes between the cells located above or below it.

The separation of the cells located next to an expanding vessel causes the development of cells having odd, irregular shapes. Some remain partially attached to each other—presumably in places where plasmodesmata are particularly abundant—and, as the vessel member continues to enlarge, these connections extend into long tubular structures (plate 25, *B*). The parenchyma cells and the tracheids that are thus affected by developmental adjustments have received the names disjunctive parenchyma and disjunctive tracheids, respectively (Record, 1947). These cells are modified growth forms of the xylem parenchyma and the tracheids of the vertical system.

In contrast to the vessel members, the tracheids and the fibers show relatively little increase in width but often elongate much during their differentiation. The degree of elongation of these elements in the different groups of plants varies widely. In the conifers, for example, the cambial initials themselves are very long, and their derivatives elongate only slightly. In the dicotyledons, on the contrary, the tracheids and the fibers become considerably longer than the meristematic cells (fig. 4.2, *D*, *E*; Bailey, 1920; Forsaith, 1926). If the xylem contains tracheids, fiber-tracheids, and fibers, the fibers elongate most, although the tracheids attain the largest volume because of their greater width (Bailey, 1936). The elongation occurs through apical intrusive growth. In the extreme storied woods, there may be little or no elongation of any kind of element (plate 30, *B*; Record, 1947).

Woods containing no vessels retain a rather symmetric arrangement of cells, because in the absence of strongly expanding cells the original radial seriation characteristic of the cambial region is not much disturbed. There is some change in alignment resulting from apical intrusive growth of the vertical tracheids.

Vessel elements, tracheids, fiber-tracheids, and libriform fibers develop secondary walls after they reach their final length and width. At the same time the end walls of the vessel members become perforated. Ultimately the protoplasts disintegrate in those cells that are nonliving in the mature state.

The fusiform meristematic cells that differentiate into the vertical parenchyma typically do not elongate. If a parenchyma strand is formed, the fusiform cell divides transversely. No such divisions occur during the development of a fusiform parenchyma cell. In some plants the parenchyma cells develop secondary walls but do not die until the heartwood is formed. The parenchyma cells associated with resin and gum ducts in the vertical system arise like xylem parenchyma cells by transverse divisions of fusiform cambial cells.

Strength of Wood in Relation to Structure

The composition of the xylem tissue and the structure and the arrangement of the component elements determine the physical properties of woods and their suitability for commercial uses (Eames and MacDaniels, 1947; Forsaith, 1926; Record, 1947; Stone, 1921). A consideration of the effect of structure upon one of the most important characteristics, strength, enhances the understanding of xylem histology. The word strength is used here in a broad sense, referring collectively to properties enabling the wood to resist different forces or loads. These properties are manifold and are not necessarily closely correlated, so that a given wood may be strong with reference to one kind of force and weak with reference to another.

Probably the most important single characteristic that gives an indication of the strength of wood is its specific gravity. In an absolutely dry wood specific gravity depends on the volume of the wall material and its chemistry. The specific gravity of the wall substance as such has been calculated to be between 1.40 and 1.62, but because of variable proportions of walls in the different woods their specific gravity may be as low at 0.04 and as high as 1.46 (Record, 1947). The strength that might be predicted from specific gravity, however, is often considerably modified by histologic structure.

It is particularly instructive to compare the effects of the different types of xylem elements upon the strength of the wood. Because of their length, thickness of walls, and sparse pits, libriform fibers and fiber-tracheids are chiefly responsible for the strength of the dicotyledonous woods. (The weakening effect of pits upon the walls has been demonstrated experimentally, Forsaith, 1926.) These types of cells are particularly influential when aggregated in dense masses. The importance of fibers as mechanical cells is clearly indicated by the close correlation often observed between fiber volume, specific gravity, and strength of woods (Forsaith, 1926).

Along with the strong fibers, dicotyledonous woods also contain elements that are relatively weak. Among these the vessels are particularly notable because their diameters are large and their walls thin. Obviously, their number and distribution influence their weakening effect. For example, ring-porous woods with their aggregation of very large vessels in a localized region are less resistant to certain stresses than woods with more evenly distributed vessels.

Vertical xylem parenchyma may influence the strength of a wood if it is abundant. In some dicotyledons it may occupy as much as 23 per cent of the total volume of the xylem (Forsaith, 1926). Apparently the distribution of parenchyma is of as much importance as its total volume, and it might be expected to reduce the resistance to certain forces, if it occurs in wide bands in recurring zonations.

The relation of rays to the strength of woods is complicated by the circumstance that woods with a greater volume of ray tissue often are highly specialized and have a large volume of heavy-walled fibers giving them a high specific gravity. If two species of woods are of the same specific gravity but have a different volume of ray tissue, the wood with the larger amount of this tissue is weaker (Forsaith, 1926).

Gymnosperm woods do not have such weak elements as the vessels of angiosperms and possess only a relatively small volume of parenchyma cells. On the other hand, they do not have such strong elements as the fibers of dicotyledonous woods. In general, gymnosperm woods vary in strength and hardness. (The terms softwood for gymnosperm wood and hardwood for angiosperm wood are misnomers, Record, 1947). The homogeneous structure of gymnosperm woods, with the predominance of long elements, makes them easily workable and particularly suitable for paper making.

The change of sapwood to heartwood does not increase the strength of the wood, but there is a strength difference between the early wood and the late wood of a given growth increment. The late wood is generally stronger because of the larger volume of wall material. Variation in the width of the growth rings affects the strength of different woods in different ways. Reduction in the width of a ring of a conifer lowers the proportion of the thin-walled, large-celled early-wood type. Within certain limits, therefore, coniferous wood with narrow rings is stronger than wood with wide rings. In dicotyledons, on the contrary, reduction in width of rings occurs mainly at the expense of the late wood. Therefore, hardwoods with wider rings are stronger. These relations hold, of course, as long as no uncommon reduction of wall thickness accompanies the development of wide rings.

REFERENCES

Andrews, H. N., Jr. On the stelar anatomy of the pteridosperms, with particular reference to the secondary wood. *Mo. Bot. Gard. Ann.* 27:51–118. 1940.

Arnold, C. A. *An introduction to paleobotany.* New York, McGraw-Hill Book Company. 1947.

Bailey, I. W. The structure of the wood in the Pineae. *Bot. Gaz.* 48:47–55. 1909.

Bailey, I. W. Anatomical characters in the evolution of *Pinus. Amer. Nat.* 44: 284–293. 1910.

Bailey, I. W. The cambium and its derivative tissues. II. Size variations of cambial initials in gymnosperms and angiosperms. *Amer. Jour. Bot.* 7:355–367. 1920.

Bailey, I. W. Some salient lines of specialization in tracheary pitting. I. Gymnospermae. *Ann. Bot.* 39:587–598. 1925.

Bailey, I. W. The problem of differentiating and classifying tracheids, fiber-tracheids, and libriform wood fibers. *Trop. Woods* 1936(45):18–23. 1936.

Bailey, I. W. The comparative morphology of the Winteraceae. III. Wood. *Arnold Arboretum Jour.* 25:97–103. 1944a.

Bailey, I. W. The development of vessels in angiosperms and its significance in morphological research. *Amer. Jour. Bot.* 31:421–428. 1944b.

Bailey, I. W. Origin of the angiosperms: need for a broadened outlook. *Arnold Arboretum Jour.* 30:64–70. 1949.

Bailey, I. W., and A. F. Faull. The cambium and its derivative tissues. IX. Structural variability in the redwood *Sequoia sempervirens,* and its significance in the identification of the fossil woods. *Arnold Arboretum Jour.* 15:233–254. 1934.

Bailey, I. W., and R. A. Howard. The comparative morphology of the Icacinaceae. II. Vessels. *Arnold Arboretum Jour.* 22:171–187. 1941a.

Bailey, I. W., and R. A. Howard. The comparative morphology of the Icacinaceae. III. Imperforate tracheary elements and xylem parenchyma. *Arnold Arboretum Jour.* 22:432–442. 1941b.

Bailey, I. W., and R. A. Howard. The comparative morphology of the Icacinaceae. IV. Rays of the secondary xylem. *Arnold Arboretum Jour.* 22:556–568. 1941c.

Bailey, I. W., and C. G. Nast. Morphology and relationships of *Trochodendron* and *Tetracentron.* I. Stem, root, and leaf. *Arnold Arboretum Jour.* 26:143–154. 1945a.

Bailey, I. W., and C. G. Nast. The comparative morphology of the Winteraceae. VII. Summary and conclusions. *Arnold Arboretum Jour.* 26:37–47. 1945b.

Bailey, I. W., and B. G. L. Swamy. *Amborella trichopoda* Baill., a new type of vesselless dicotyledon. *Arnold Arboretum Jour.* 29:245–254. 1948.

Bailey, I. W., and B. G. L. Swamy. The morphology and relationships of *Austrobaileya. Arnold Arboretum Jour.* 30:211–226. 1949.

Bailey, I. W., and W. W. Tupper. Size variation in tracheary cells. I. A comparison between the secondary xylems of vascular cryptogams, gymnosperms and angiosperms. *Amer. Acad. Arts and Sci. Proc.* 54:149–204. 1918.

Bannan, M. W. Origin and cellular character of xylem rays in gymnosperms. *Bot. Gaz.* 96:260–281. 1934a.

Bannan, M. W. Seasonal wounding and resin cyst production in the hemlock, *Tsuga canadensis* (L.) Carr. *Ann. Bot.* 18:857–868. 1934*b*.

Bannan, M. W. Vertical resin ducts in the secondary wood of the Abietineae. *New Phytol.* 35:11–46. 1936.

Bannan, M. W. Observations on the distribution of xylem-ray tissue in conifers. *Ann. Bot.* 1:717–726. 1937.

Bannan, M. W. Variability in wood structure in root of native Ontario conifers. *Torrey Bot. Club Bul.* 68:173–194. 1941*a*.

Bannan, M. W. Wood structure of *Thuja occidentalis*. *Bot. Gaz.* 103:295–309. 1941*b*.

Bannan, M. W. Wood structure of the native Ontario species of *Juniperus*. *Amer. Jour. Bot.* 29:245–252. 1942.

Bannan, M. W. Wood structure of *Libocedrus decurrens*. *Amer. Jour. Bot.* 31:346–351. 1944.

Bannan, M. W. The frequency of anticlinal divisions in fusiform cambial cells in *Chamaecyparis*. *Amer. Jour. Bot.* 37:511–519. 1950.

Bannan, M. W. The reduction of fusiform cambial cells in *Chamaecyparis* and *Thuja*. *Canad. Jour. Bot.* 29:57–67. 1951.

Barghoorn, E. S., Jr. Origin and development of the uniseriate ray in the Coniferae. *Torrey Bot. Club Bul.* 67:303–328. 1940*a*.

Barghoorn, E. S., Jr. The ontogenetic development and phylogenetic specialization of rays in the xylem of dicotyledons. I. The primitive ray structure. *Amer. Jour. Bot.* 27:918–928. 1940*b*.

Barghoorn, E. S., Jr. The ontogenetic development and phylogenetic specialization of rays in the xylem of dicotyledons. II. Modification of the multiseriate and uniseriate rays. *Amer. Jour. Bot.* 28:273–282. 1941*a*.

Barghoorn, E. S., Jr. The ontogenetic development and phylogenetic specialization of rays in the xylem of dicotyledons. III. The elimination of rays. *Torrey Bot. Club Bul.* 68:317–325. 1941*b*.

Barkley, G. Differentiation of vascular bundle of *Trichosanthes anguina*. *Bot. Gaz.* 83:173–184. 1927.

Bliss, M. C. The tracheal elements in the ferns. *Amer. Jour. Bot.* 26:620–624. 1939.

Bugnon, P. Origine, évolution et valeur des concepts de protoxylème et de metaxylème. *Soc. Linn. de Normandie, Bul.* Ser. 7. 7:123–151. 1925.

Chalk, L. The phylogenetic value of certain anatomical features of dicotyledonous woods. *Ann. Bot.* 1:409–428. 1937.

Chalk, L., and M. M. Chattaway. Measuring the length of vessel members. *Trop. Woods* 1934(40):19–26. 1934.

Chalk, L., and M. M. Chattaway. Factors affecting dimensional variations of vessel members. *Trop. Woods* 1935(41):17–37. 1935.

Chattaway, M. M. The wood anatomy of the family Sterculiaceae. *Roy. Soc. London, Phil. Trans.* Ser. B. 228:313–365. 1937.

Cheadle, V. I. The occurrence and types of vessels in the various organs of the plant in the Monocotyledoneae. *Amer. Jour. Bot.* 29:441–450. 1942.

Cheadle, V. I. The origin and certain trends of specialization of the vessel in the Monocotyledoneae. *Amer. Jour. Bot.* 30:11–17. 1943*a*.

Cheadle, V. I. Vessel specialization in the late metaxylem of the various organs in the Monocotyledoneae. *Amer. Jour. Bot.* 30:484–490. 1943*b*.

Cheadle, V. I. Specialization of vessels within the xylem of each organ in the Monocotyledoneae. *Amer. Jour. Bot.* 31:81–92. 1944.

Committee on Nomenclature, International Association of Wood Anatomists. Glossary of terms used in describing woods. *Trop. Woods* 1933(36):1–12. 1933.

Crüger, H. Zur Entwickelungsgeschichte der Zellenwand. *Bot. Ztg.* 13:601–613, 617–629. 1855.

Duerden, H. On the occurrence of vessels in *Selaginella*. *Ann. Bot.* 48:459–465. 1934.

Duerden, H. On the xylem elements of certain ferns. *Ann. Bot.* 4:523–531. 1940.

Eames, A. J. *Morphology of vascular plants.* New York, McGraw-Hill Book Company. 1936.

Eames, A. J., and L. H. MacDaniels. *An introduction to plant anatomy.* 2nd ed. New York, McGraw-Hill Book Company. 1947.

Esau, K. Vessel development in celery. *Hilgardia* 10:479–488. 1936.

Esau, K. Origin and development of primary vascular tissues in seed plants. *Bot. Rev.* 9:125–206. 1943.

Esau, K. Anatomic effects of the viruses of Pierce's disease and phony peach. *Hilgardia* 18:423–482. 1948.

Esau, K., and W. B. Hewitt. Structure of end walls in differentiating vessels. *Hilgardia* 13:229–244. 1940.

Forsaith, C. C. The technology of New York State timbers. *N. Y. State Col. Forestry, Syracuse Univ., Tech. Pub.* 18. Vol. 26. 1926.

Frank, A. Über die Harzbildung in Holz und Rinde der Koniferen. *Bot. Arch.* 3:173–184. 1923.

Frey-Wyssling, A. Zur Ontogenie des Xylems in Stengeln mit sekundärem Dickenwachstum. *Deut. Bot. Gesell. Ber.* 58:166–181. 1940.

Frost, F. H. Histology of the wood of angiosperms. I. The nature of pitting between tracheary and parenchymatous elements. *Torrey Bot. Club Bul.* 56: 259–264. 1929.

Frost, F. H. Specialization in secondary xylem of dicotyledons. I. Origin of vessel. *Bot. Gaz.* 89:67–94. 1930*a*.

Frost, F. H. Specialization in secondary xylem of dicotyledons. II. Evolution of end walls of vessel segment. *Bot. Gaz.* 90:198–212. 1930*b*.

Frost, F. H. Specialization in secondary xylem of dicotyledons. III. Specialization of lateral wall of vessel segment. *Bot. Gaz.* 91:88–96. 1931.

Gerry, E. Tyloses: their occurrence and practical significance in some American woods. *Jour. Agr. Res.* 1:445–469. 1914.

Gertz, O. Untersuchungen über septierte Thyllen nebst anderen Beiträgen zu einer Monographie der Thyllenfrage. *Lunds Univ. Arsskr. N. F. Avd. 2.* Vol. 12. No. 12. 1916.

Gilbert, S. G. Evolutionary significance of ring porosity in woody angiosperms. *Bot. Gaz.* 102:105–120. 1940.

Goodwin, R. H. On the development of xylary elements in the first internode of *Avena* in dark and light. *Amer. Jour. Bot.* 29:818–828. 1942.

Handley, W. R. C. Some observations on the problem of vessel length determination in woody dicotyledons. *New Phytol.* 35:456–471. 1936.

Heimsch, C., Jr. Comparative anatomy of the secondary xylem of the "Gruniales" and "Terebinthales" of Wettstein with reference to taxonomic grouping. *Lilloa* 8:83–198. 1942.

Heimsch, C., Jr., and R. H. Wetmore. The significance of wood anatomy in the taxonomy of the Juglandaceae. *Amer. Jour. Bot.* 26:651–660. 1939.

Hess, R. W. Classification of wood parenchyma in dicotyledons. *Trop. Woods* 1950(96):1–20. 1950.

Huber, B. Die physiologische Bedeutung der Ring- und Zerstreutporigkeit. *Deut. Bot. Gesell. Ber.* 53:711–719. 1935.

Huber, B., and G. Prütz. Über den Anteil von Fasern, Gefässen und Parenchym am Aufbau verschiedener Hölzer. *Holz als Roh- und Werkstoff* 1:377–381. 1938.

Jaccard, P. Exzentrisches Dickenwachstum und anatomisch-histologische Differenzierung des Holzes. *Schweiz. Bot. Gesell. Ber.* 48:491–537. 1938.

Jeffrey, E. C. *The anatomy of woody plants.* Chicago, University of Chicago Press. 1917.

Just, T. The proper designation of vascular plants. *Bot. Rev.* 11:299–309. 1945.

Koernike, M. Über die Wirkung von Röntgen- und Radiumstrahlen auf die Pflanzen. *Deut. Bot. Gesell. Ber.* 23:404–415. 1905.

Kribs, D. A. Salient lines of structural specialization in the wood rays of dicotyledons. *Bot. Gaz.* 96:547–557. 1935.

Kribs, D. A. Salient lines of structural specialization in the wood parenchyma of dicotyledons. *Torrey Bot. Club. Bul.* 64:177–184. 1937.

Lewis, F. T. The shape of the tracheids in the pine. *Amer. Jour. Bot.* 22:741–762. 1935.

Majumdar, G. P. The origin and nature of the bases of the secondary thickenings of xylem vessels in *Heracleum Sphondylium* L. *Current Sci. (India)* 10:82–83. 1941.

Matzke, E. B., and R. L. Hulbary. An analysis of the wood of the three commercial species of white pine. *Torrey Bot. Club. Bul.* 69:573–582. 1942.

Metcalfe, C. R., and L. Chalk. *Anatomy of the dicotyledons.* 2 vols. Oxford, Clarendon Press. 1950.

Moog, H. Über die spiraligen Verdickungsleisten der Tracheen und Tracheiden unter besonderer Berücksichtigung ihrer Ausziehbarkeit. *Bot. Centbl. Beihefte* 42:186–228. 1925.

Moore, J. A., and H. N. Andrews, Jr. Transitional pittings in tracheids of *Psilotum. Mo. Bot. Gard. Ann.* 23:151–158. 1936.

Nägeli, C. W. Das Wachsthum des Stammes und der Wurzel bei den Gefässpflanzen und die Anordnung der Gefässstränge im Stengel. *Beiträge z. wiss Bot.* Heft. 1:1–156. 1858.

Peirce, A. S. Anatomical interrelationships of the Taxodiaceae. *Trop. Woods* 1936(46):1–15. 1936.

Phillips, E. W. J. The identification of coniferous woods by their microscopic structure. *Linn. Soc. London, Jour., Bot.* 52:259–320. 1941.

Preston, R. D. Wall structure and growth. I. Spring vessels in some ring-porous dicotyledons. *Ann. Bot.* 3:507–530. 1939.

Priestley, J. H., and L. I. Scott. A note upon summer wood production in the tree. *Leeds Phil. Lit. Soc. Proc.* 3:235–248. 1936.

Raimann, R. Über unverholzte Elemente in der innersten Xylemzone der Dicotyledonen. *Akad. der Wiss. Wien, Math.-Nat. Cl. Sitzber.* Abt. 1. **1889**(98): 40–75. 1890.

Record, S. J. *Identification of the timbers of temperate North America.* New York, John Wiley & Sons. 1947.

Record, S. J., and R. W. Hess. *Timbers of the New World.* New Haven, Yale University Press. 1943.

Reinders-Gouwentak, C. A. Ray terminology in wood anatomy. *K. Akad. van Wetensch. te Amsterdam, Proc., Sect. Sci.* 53:1265–1275. 1950.

Sanio, C. Vergleichende Untersuchungen über die Elementarorgane des Holzkörpers. *Bot. Ztg.* 21:85–91, 93–98, 101–111, 113–118, 121–128, 357–363, 369–375, 377–385, 389–399, 401–412. 1863.

Sanio, K. Über die Grösse der Holzzellen bei der gemeinen Kiefer (*Pinus silvestris*). *Jahrb. f. Wiss. Bot.* 8:401–420. 1872.

Sanio, K. Anatomie der gemeinen Kiefer (*Pinus silvestris* L.) II. *Jahrb. f. Wiss. Bot.* 9:50–126. 1873–74.

Scherer, P. E. Studien über Gefässbündeltypen und Gefässformen. *Bot. Centbl. Beihefte* 16:67–110. 1904.

Schoch-Bodmer, H., and P. Huber. Wachstumstypen plastischer Pflanzenmembranen. *Naturf. Gesell. Schaffhausen, Mitt.* 21:29–43. 1947.

Sinnott, E. W. Factors determining character and distribution of food reserve in woody plants. *Bot. Gaz.* 66:162–175. 1918.

Sinnott, E. W., and R. Bloch. The cytoplasmic basis of intercellular patterns in vascular differentiation. *Amer. Jour. Bot.* 32:151–156. 1945.

Smith, G. F., and H. Kersten. The relation between xylem thickenings in primary roots of *Vicia faba* seedlings and elongation, as shown by soft X-ray irradiation. *Torrey Bot. Club Bul.* 69:221–234. 1942.

Spackman, W., and B. G. L. Swamy. The nature and occurrence of septate fibers in dicotyledons. Abst. *Amer. Jour. Bot.* 36:804. 1949.

Stafford, H. A. Studies on the growth and xylary development of *Phleum pratense* seedlings in darkness and in light. *Amer. Jour. Bot.* 35:706–715. 1948.

Stamm, A. J. A new method for determining the proportion of the length of a tracheid that is in contact with rays. *Bot. Gaz.* 92:101–107. 1931.

Stamm, A. J. Passage of liquids, vapors, and dissolved materials through softwoods. *U. S. Dept. Agric. Tech. Bul.* 929. 1946.

Stone, H. *A textbook of wood.* London, William Rider and Son. 1921.

Stover, E. L. *An introduction to the anatomy of seed plants.* Boston, D. C. Heath and Company. 1951.

Strasburger, E. *Über den Bau und die Verrichtungen der Leitungsbahnen in den Pflanzen. Histologische Beiträge.* Band 3. Jena, Gustav Fischer. 1891.

Swamy, B. G. L., and I. W. Bailey. *Sarcandra,* a vesselless genus of the Chloranthaceae. *Arnold Arboretum Jour.* 31:117–129. 1950.

Thomson, R. G., and H. B. Sifton. Resin canals in the Canadian spruce (*Picea canadensis* (Mill.) B. S. P.)—an anatomical study, especially in relation to traumatic effects and their bearing on phylogeny. *Roy. Soc. London, Phil. Trans.* Ser. B. 214:63–111. 1925.

Tippo, O. Comparative anatomy of the Moraceae and their presumed allies. *Bot. Gaz.* 100:1–99. 1938.

Tippo, O. The role of wood anatomy in phylogeny. *Amer. Midland Nat.* 36: 362–372. 1946.

Vestal, P. A. The significance of comparative anatomy in establishing the relationship of the Hypericaceae to the Guttiferae and their allies. *Philippine Jour. Sci.* 64:199–256. 1937.

CHAPTER

12

Phloem

CONCEPT

The phloem is the principal food-conducting tissue of the vascular plants. The phloem and the xylem are, as a rule, spatially associated with each other (fig. 12.1 and plate 45, *B*) and together constitute the vascular system of the plant body. Like the xylem, the phloem is composed of several different kinds of cells, concerned with different functions, and therefore it, too, exemplifies a morphologically and physiologically complex tissue.

The basic components of the phloem are the sieve elements, several kinds of parenchyma cells, fibers, and sclereids. In plants possessing a laticiferous system, elements of this system may be found in the phloem also. Various idioblasts, specialized morphologically and physiologically, are encountered in the phloem. In this chapter, only the principal components of the phloem are considered in detail.

Information on the structure of the phloem is relatively incomplete, and knowledge on the phylogeny of this tissue quite fragmentary, in comparison with the relatively unified large body of data in the corresponding fields of study of the xylem. Various circumstances are responsible for this difference in our understanding of the two tissues. The phloem shows unique cytologic characteristics which require exacting techniques for investigation. The phloem cells, other than the fibers and the sclereids, do not develop such rigid, persisting walls as the xylem elements, and, after the phloem ceases to act as a conducting tissue, it becomes much modified, functionally and structurally. The most pronounced changes occur in the conducting elements themselves, for they become disorganized to various degrees. Thus, in contrast to the xylem, the phloem early loses its original nature and appearance, and in such a state it cannot be properly studied with regard to its structural details. The lack of firmness is also related to the generally poor preservation of phloem

265

in fossils (Jeffrey, 1917). In much of the commercial utilization of xylem this tissue is not separated into its individual components, and the proper evaluation of its economic qualities requires the knowledge of its structure as a tissue (see chapter 11). The commercial

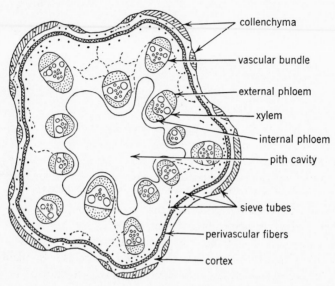

collenchyma

vascular bundle

external phloem

xylem

internal phloem

pith cavity

sieve tubes

perivascular fibers

cortex

Fig. 12.1. Diagram of transection of *Cucurbita* stem, showing distribution of tissues. *Cucurbita* is an herbaceous vine with discrete vascular bundles, each having external and internal phloem (bicollateral bundles). The vascular region is delimited on the outside by a cylinder of sclerenchyma (perivascular fibers). Outside these is the cortex composed of parenchyma and collenchyma. An epidermis covers the cortex. On the inside, the vascular region borders on a cavity which resulted from breakdown of the pith. Small strands of sieve tubes and companion cells traverse the parenchyma of the vascular region and the tissues of the cortex. (×8.)

importance of the phloem, on the other hand, is determined largely by its content of fibers and such organic substances as tannins, spices, latex, and drugs, all products that are separated or extracted from the tissue. Thus the commercial utilization of the products of the phloem is not a strong stimulus for the study of the phloem as a tissue.

Historically, too, the significance of the xylem as a conducting tissue was recognized earlier than that of the phloem. In the phloem, the fibers attracted the first attention and, as was outlined in chapter 10, the tissue received the name of *bast*—a word related to the verb to bind—because the fibers formed in it were used for binding. After the discovery of the sieve element by Hartig in 1837, the true nature of the tissue was gradually revealed. In 1858 Nägeli gave it the name of *phloem* (derived from the Greek word for bark), thus eliminating the emphasis upon the presence of fibers in this tissue. In time phloem became the generally accepted term for the food-conducting tissue of vascular plants. Nevertheless, substitute terms are still being used, particularly in the German (Leptom, Siebteil, Cribralteil) and French (liber, tissu criblé) literatures (cf. Esau, 1939). The term *leptom* deserves special mention. It refers, since Haberlandt (1914, p. 347), to the soft-walled part of the phloem, including sieve elements, companion cells, and parenchyma cells, but excluding fibers. The parallel term for the xylem is *hadrom*, which refers to the tracheary and parenchymatous elements of the xylem but excludes the fibers.

Sometimes it is convenient to treat as a unit the phloem of stems and roots and all the tissues located outside it. The term *bark* is frequently employed for this purpose. Bark is a nontechnical term that should be clearly distinguished from the technical terms cortex and periderm (Eames and MacDaniels, 1947, p. 254). In stems and roots possessing only primary tissues bark most commonly refers to the primary phloem and the cortex. In axes in secondary state of growth it may include primary and secondary phloem, various amounts of cortex, and periderm (see chapter 14).

From the researches on phloem conducted since the discovery of the sieve element and periodically reviewed from different points of view by various authors (De Bary, 1884; Strasburger, 1891; Perrot, 1899; Schmidt, 1917; Huber, 1937; Esau, 1939, 1950; Crafts, 1951; Holdheide, 1951) the concept gradually emerged that the main, single characteristic of the phloem is the presence of highly specialized cells, the sieve elements, which together with the accompanying parenchymatous members of the tissue are concerned with the translocation of elaborated food materials, and that the structural peculiarities of the sieve elements are related to their function. Furthermore, the libers, if present, came to be regarded as a part of the phloem, just as wood fibers are part of the xylem.

CLASSIFICATION

Like the xylem, the phloem is classified as primary or secondary on the basis of its time of appearance in relation to the development of the plant or the organ as a whole. The primary phloem is initiated in the embryo (Esau, 1943a), is constantly added to during the development of the primary plant body, and completes its differentiation when the primary plant body is fully formed. Like the primary xylem, the primary phloem differentiates from procambium. If the plant shows secondary growth, the vascular cambium that forms secondary xylem toward the interior of the stem or root produces secondary phloem in the opposite direction, that is, toward the periphery of the stem or root.

Although most commonly the phloem occupies an external position with reference to the xylem in stems, or abaxial in leaves and leaf-like organs, certain ferns and many dicotyledonous families (e.g., Apocynaceae, Asclepiadaceae, Convolvulaceae, Cucurbitaceae, Myrtaceae, Solanaceae, Compositae) have a part of the phloem located on the opposite side of the xylem as well (figs. 12.1, 15.1, *B*, and plate 32, *A*). The two parts of the phloem are called *external* and *internal* phloem, respectively. They may be termed, respectively, *abaxial* (that is, away from the axis) and *adaxial* (that is, toward the axis) phloem as well. In the leaves these terms refer the position of the phloem to the stem, or axis, to which the leaf is attached. In the stems and roots the axis of reference would be an imaginary one, passing longitudinally through the center of the organ.

The term internal phloem replaces that of the *intraxylary phloem* (Committee on Nomenclature, 1933). The latter term is sometimes confused with *interxylary phloem* (Eames and MacDaniels, 1947, p. 311), referring to phloem strands or layers included in the secondary xylem of certain dicotyledons, that is, to the *included phloem* (Committee on Nomenclature, 1933).

In angiosperms the internal phloem is initiated somewhat later than the external. Nevertheless it constitutes a part of the primary phloem system. It resembles the external primary phloem in development, composition, and structure and arrangement of cells (Esau, 1938a, 1939). Generally, it is not increased in amount by cambial activity.

ELEMENTS OF THE PHLOEM

Sieve Elements

Parallel with the classification of the tracheary elements into the phylogenetically primitive tracheids and the more advanced vessel members, the conducting elements of the phloem, here called collectively *sieve elements,* may be segregated into the less specialized *sieve cells* (fig. 12.7) and the more specialized *sieve-tube members* (or *sieve-tube elements;* fig. 12.8). The tracheids and the sieve cells are rather individualized as components of the tissues in which they occur, whereas the vessel members and the sieve-tube members are combined into longitudinal series, the vessels and the *sieve tubes,* respectively.

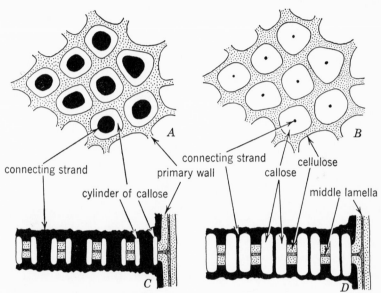

FIG. 12.2. Diagrams interpreting the structure of a sieve area in an angiosperm sieve tube. Each drawing represents a part of a sieve area with several connecting strands. Surface views in *A* and *B*, sectional views in *C* and *D*. The protoplasmic contents of the sieve elements covering the sieve areas in *C* and *D* are shown in black; so are also the strands connecting these contents across the sieve areas. *A* and *C* illustrate younger sieve areas; *B* and *D* older sieve areas. In *B* and *D* the amount of callose lining the pores is larger and the connecting strands thinner than in *A* and *C.*

In both classifications the characteristics of the wall structures—pits and perforation plates in the tracheary elements, *sieve areas* and *sieve plates* in the sieve elements—serve to distinguish the elements of the two kinds of categories.

Sieve Areas and Sieve Plates. The morphologic specialization of the sieve elements is expressed in the development of the sieve areas on their walls and in the peculiar modifications of their protoplasts. The sieve areas (the term implies a resemblance to a sieve) are depressed wall areas with clusters of perforations or pores, through which the protoplasts of the adjacent sieve elements are interconnected by *connecting strands* (figs. 12.2, 12.3; plates 32, *C, D,* 33, and 34, *C, D*).

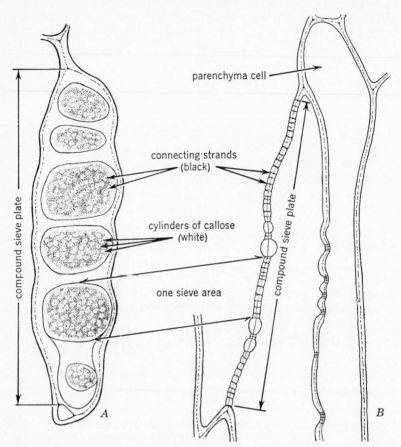

parenchyma cell

connecting·strands
(black)

cylinders of callose
(white)

one sieve area

compound sieve plate

compound sieve plate

A

B

Fig. 12.3. Structure of sieve areas. *A*, compound sieve plate of *Nicotiana* in surface view. It consists of six sieve areas. In each there are numerous connecting strands (black dots), each surrounded by callose (white rings around the black dots). The sieve areas occur in depressions of the sieve plate wall. *B*, parts of sieve-tube members (left) and of a phloem parenchyma cell (right) showing wall details. The compound sieve plate to the left occurred between two sieve elements. It consists of five sieve areas shown in sectional view. The sieve plate is a double structure in the sense that half of it belongs to one element, the other to another, adjacent element. Depressions with plasmodesmata occur in the wall between the sieve element and the parenchyma cell. These depressions are paired structures composed of sieve areas in the sieve-tube wall and primary pit fields in the parenchyma wall. (*A*, ×1,070; *B*, ×930. After Esau, 1938*a*.)

Thus the sieve areas are comparable to primary pit fields with plasmodesmata that occur in primary walls of living parenchyma cells. In fact, the sieve areas are, morphologically, specialized primary pit fields. However, the connecting strands between protoplasts in a sieve area are more prominent than the plasmodesmata in an unmodified pit field. Furthermore, in a sieve area each connecting strand is encased in a tubule or cylinder of substance called *callose* (fig. 12.2 and plate 32, *C*, *D*). This substance is recognized by means of its staining reactions, particularly with anilin blue and resorcin blue. Both dyes give the callose a clear blue color (Esau, 1948). The chemical nature of callose and its source and manner of deposition in the sieve area are imperfectly known (Rawlins, 1933, p. 50; Schmidt, 1917). It seems that callose replaces cellulose around each connecting strand and also impregnates the cellulose in the immediate vicinity of the callose cylinder (Esau, 1939, 1948).

The term *callose* (Mangin, 1890) was preceded by *callus,* a word first used by Hanstein (1864) with reference to the massive accumulations of callose on sieve areas of old sieve elements. These terms are not synonymous, since callose refers to a certain wall substance, callus to accumulations of this substance. The relation between the terms callose and callus may be compared to that existing between the terms cutin and cuticle. Callus as found on sieve areas is, of course, not related to callus tissue developing at the base of cuttings or below wounds. These two unrelated formations bear the same name because both constitute thickened masses, a concept implied by the word callus.

The wall in a sieve area is obviously a double structure in the sense that it consists of two layers of primary wall, one belonging to one cell and the other to another, cemented together by intercellular substance (fig. 12.3, *B*). With reference to the secondary walls the term pit-pair is employed to designate a combination of two pits opposing each other in a wall between two cells (see chapter 3). No similar precision in terminology has been introduced with reference to the sieve areas in the sieve elements. Therefore, the term sieve area sometimes indicates a paired structure, sometimes one half of a paired structure. This usage corresponds to the similarly flexible application of the term wall either to the wall of a given cell or to the paired walls of two connected cells.

In surface view, a sieve area appears like a depression in a wall with a number of dots—the transections of the connecting strands— each surrounded with a ring of callose (figs. 12.2, 12.3, *A*; plates 32,

C, D, and 33, *A*). In sectional views also the sieve areas (pairs of sieve areas) are recognized as thin places in the wall with the connecting strands and associated callose traversing the wall from one cell lumen to the other (figs. 12.2, *C, D*, and 12.3, *B*; plate 33, *B*).

The sieve areas as characterized above are found in sieve elements at the height of their activity. Preceding this state, while a cell is not yet differentiated as a sieve element, a sieve area is an ordinary primary pit field with plasmodesmata. During the differentiation of such a primary pit field into a sieve area, callose appears in the immediate vicinity of each plasmodesma, and the plasmodesmata are modified into connecting strands. Plasmodesmata differ from the connecting strands in differentiated sieve areas in that the connecting strands are more conspicuous and less easily ruptured. The increase in conspicuousness of the strands results partly from their becoming thicker, partly from their increased avidity for various stains. It is possible that, in plants having particularly large connecting strands in the sieve areas, plasmodesmata fuse in groups to form these strands (cf. Esau, 1939, 1950). On the other hand, in sieve areas of low degree of specialization the connecting strands are so thin that it is difficult to judge whether they differ from plasmodesmata (plate 34, *C, D*).

As the sieve element ages, the amount of callose in the sieve area is augmented (figs. 12.2, *B, D*, and 12.4). Its mass increases within the pores and constricts the connecting strands. Callose is also deposited on the surface of the sieve area, among the callose cylinders. The sieve area ceases to appear as a depression in the wall. Instead, it assumes the appearance of a thickened area, for the callose eventually projects above the surface of the adjacent wall parts (fig. 12.4, *E–G*). When the element reaches the end of its activity, the sieve areas are covered with prominent masses of callose traversed by tenuous connecting strands (Crafts, 1939*a*). If there are several sieve areas close together, the callose masses of the adjacent areas may fuse. Since such extensive accumulation of callose usually indicates cessation of activity of the sieve element, the mass of callose at this stage of development of a sieve area has received the name of *definitive callus* (Lecomte, 1889).

When the protoplast of the inactive sieve element completely disorganizes, the connecting strands disappear from the definitive callus. The callus commonly separates from the sieve area and also disappears (fig. 12.4, *H*). The sieve area freed of callose represents a thin portion of cellulose wall with numerous open perforations.

Thus, the sieve-like structure of the sieve area becomes clearly evident only after the element ceases to function.

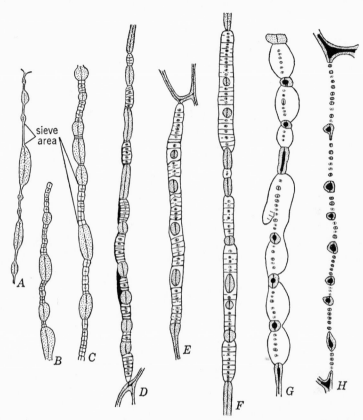

Fig. 12.4. Development of compound sieve plate of *Nicotiana*. *A*, sieve areas still in the stage of primary pit fields in a cambial wall (presumably traversed by plasmodesmata in living state). *B–D*, development of callose (white) and the resulting thickening of the sieve areas until they no longer appear as depressions. The connecting strands also become readily visible during this development (black lines traversing the sieve areas). *E* and *F*, increase in the amount of callose and the resulting stretching of the connecting strands. *G*, most massive callose accumulations (definitive callus). The connecting strands have disappeared with the death of the protoplasts. *H*, old sieve plate with no callose and with open pores from a nonfunctional sieve tube. (All, ✕860. After Esau, 1938*a*.)

Like the pits in the tracheary elements, the sieve areas occur in various numbers and are variously distributed in sieve elements of different plants. They also show unequal degrees of specialization;

that is, they vary in the size of connecting strands and callose cylinders. In some, the sieve areas of a given cell are all alike in the degree of specialization (fig. 12.7); in others, part of these structures possess distinctly larger strands and more prominent callose cylinders than the rest. The sieve areas with the more markedly developed parts are commonly localized on certain walls of the sieve elements, most often on the end walls. The wall parts bearing the highly specialized sieve areas are called *sieve plates* (cf. Cheadle and Whitford, 1941; Esau, 1950). If a sieve plate consists of a single sieve area, it is a *simple sieve plate* (plate 32, *C, D*). Many sieve areas, arranged in scalariform, reticulate, or any other manner, constitute a *compound sieve plate* (fig. 12.3; plates 33, *A–C*, and 34, *A*). Sieve elements having sieve plates on their end walls usually bear less differentiated sieve areas—some with strands so small that they might be no larger than plasmodesmata—on their lateral walls (fig. 12.8). However, just as vessel members may have perforation plates in their side walls, sieve-tube members may have sieve plates in their lateral walls. In some plant species the sieve areas of the sieve plates and those on the lateral walls are sharply differentiated from each other with reference to the size of their parts; in others, the two intergrade with one another through intermediate forms (Esau, 1948, 1950).

Sieve Cells and Sieve Tubes. The two types of sieve elements, the sieve cells and the sieve-tube members (or sieve-tube elements), differ in the degree of differentiation of their sieve areas and in the distribution of these areas on the walls (Cheadle and Whitford, 1941). A *sieve cell* is an element with relatively unspecialized sieve areas, not strikingly differentiated from one another and consequently with no wall parts that can be conveniently distinguished from others as sieve plates (fig. 12.7). Sieve cells are commonly long and slender, and they taper at their ends or have steeply inclined end walls. In the tissue they overlap each other, and the sieve areas are usually particularly numerous on these ends.

Sieve-tube members are sieve elements in which some of the sieve areas are more highly specialized than others and are localized in the form of sieve plates (fig. 12.8). The sieve plates occur mainly on end walls which vary from much inclined to transverse. Sieve-tube members are usually disposed end to end in long series, the common wall parts bearing the sieve plates. These series of sieve-tube members are *sieve tubes*. The walls of laterally adjacent sieve-tubes bear sieve areas of a lower degree of specialization than those of the sieve plates. Sometimes sieve plates also occur on these walls.

Phylogenetic Specialization. The lack of comprehensive data on the comparative anatomy of the phloem of vascular plants makes it impossible to present a precise picture of evolution of the phloem elements comparable to that given with reference to the xylem elements in chapter 11.

Judging from the literature (cf. Esau, 1950) the lower vascular plants and the gymnosperms generally have sieve cells as defined in this book, whereas most angiosperms have sieve-tube members. The evolutionary changes of sieve-tube members have been studied most comprehensively in the late primary phloem (metaphloem, see p. 287) of the monocotyledons (Cheadle, 1948; Cheadle and Uhl, 1948; Cheadle and Whitford, 1941). These sieve-tube members show the following trends in evolutionary specialization: a progressive localization of highly specialized sieve areas on the end walls; a gradual change in the orientation of these end walls from very oblique to transverse; a gradual change from compound to simple sieve plates; and a progressive decrease in conspicuousness of the sieve areas on the side walls. The specialization of sieve-tube members in the secondary phloem of dicotyledons appears to have progressed along similar lines (cf. Esau, 1950).

The phylogenetic specialization of sieve elements, as far as it has been established, shows some parallelism with the evolutionary modification of tracheary elements. The sieve cells with their overlapping ends and lack of sieve plates (fig. 12.7) may be placed beside the tracheids that are connected with each other through bordered pits. In the sieve elements specialization has resulted in an enlargement of the connecting strands and, consequently, also in the increase in diameter of the pores and of the callose cylinders encasing the connecting strands. In the tracheary elements specialization has led to the removal of parts of wall and the establishment of direct continuity between lumina of the individual cells. The application of the term perforation plate to the most specialized wall parts in the vessel members parallels the use of the term sieve plate with reference to the wall parts of the sieve-tube members bearing the highly differentiated sieve areas. In both kinds of elements there has been a change in the orientation of the end walls from oblique to transverse, and, whereas in the vessel member multiperforate end walls were replaced by those with simple perforations, in the sieve-tube member the compound sieve plate gave rise to the simple sieve plate. The phylogenetic decrease in length, so well established for vessel members, has not been sufficiently investigated with reference to sieve elements.

As was mentioned in chapter 11, the specialization of vessels in the monocotyledons occurred first in the root and then progressed toward the aerial parts of the plant. In contrast, the evolution of sieve tubes appears to have progressed from the leaves to the aerial stems, and finally to the roots (Cheadle, 1948; Cheadle and Uhl, 1948; Cheadle and Whitford, 1941). Thus the specialization of xylem and phloem elements is not necessarily closely correlated in any one plant or organ.

Morphology of the Walls. The sieve elements generally possess primary walls, chiefly of cellulose. Only a subfamily of the Coniferae, the Abietineae, are reported to have secondary but unlignified walls in the sieve cells (plate 34, *C*; Abbe and Crafts, 1939).

A widely observed characteristic of the primary walls of sieve elements is their relative thickness (fig. 12.5; cf. Esau, 1950). The thickening of the wall usually becomes evident during the late stages of differentiation of the element. In many plants it is reduced as the element ages. In some plants this wall is exceptionally thick and has a crenulated inner surface. The wall appears to be highly hydrated, and therefore its thickness may be easily underestimated in dehydrated sections. The thick sieve-element wall is usually called the *nacré* wall. (Nacré is a French word meaning "having a pearly luster.")

Protoplast. Of the individual parts of the sieve element the protoplast has received the major attention from phloem investigators, for the interpretation of the function of this element depends on the proper understanding of the nature of its contents. Physiological literature reveals much evidence that organic solutes move largely in the phloem, but the proof that the sieve element is the main conduit of this movement is limited. The most significant results in this direction were obtained in an experiment on movement of certain materials through bridges of tissue of varied composition. These bridges were prepared by operational procedures that left leaf blades of *Pelargonium* partially connected to the plant (Schumacher, 1930). In one trial the bridge consisted of phloem, in another of xylem, in the third of ground parenchyma. When the blade was darkened, nitrogen and other substances were translocated from it only if the bridge consisted of phloem. If, however, the phloem in such a bridge was so treated that its sieve tubes were rendered nonfunctioning (by introducing eosin solution through the leaf and thus inducing the development of masses of callose on the sieve plates), the movement out of the blade was interrupted.

Even without the evidence just reviewed the sieve elements have been generally regarded, since their discovery, as the principal conducting elements in the phloem. This assumption was arrived at partly through studies of morphologic characteristics of these elements, partly through the discovery of the occurrence of exudation of a liquid from the sieve elements when the phloem is cut open in an otherwise intact plant. Workers also came to agree that materials move rapidly through the sieve elements. However, the particular features of the protoplast that make this rapid flow possible are variously interpreted (cf. Crafts, 1951; Esau, 1950).

The most outstanding characteristic of the sieve-element protoplast is that it lacks a nucleus when the cell completes its development and becomes functional; and that, despite the lack of such an essential component, the protoplast continues to exhibit certain vital characteristics (Esau, 1950). The loss of the nucleus occurs during the differentiation of the element (fig. 12.5). In the meristematic state the sieve element resembles other procambial or cambial cells in having a more or less vacuolated protoplast with a conspicuous nucleus. Later the nucleus disorganizes and disappears as a discrete body. In some plants, scattered among unrelated families, the nucleolus (or nucleoli, if more than one are present) is extruded from the nucleus before the latter finally disorganizes (plate 35, *A*, *B*). Such nucleoli persist in the sieve elements while the sieve elements exist as intact cells (fig. 12.6, *H–J*; Esau, 1947).

A common property of the sieve-tube member protoplast in the dicotyledons is its content of variable amounts of a relatively viscous substance, the so-called *slime*, usually interpreted as being proteinaceous in nature (Schmidt, 1917; cf. also Esau, 1947, 1950). This material appears to be located mainly in the vacuole, together with the vacuolar sap and its various organic and inorganic ingredients. The slime is readily displaced when the phloem is sectioned for microscopic observation and accumulates most commonly on the sieve plates (plate 32, *B*).

The slime originates in the cytoplasm in the form of discrete bodies, the *slime bodies* (fig. 12.5 and plate 35, *B*, *D*). These may be spheroidal, or spindle shaped, or variously twisted and coiled. They occur singly or in multiples in one element. They absorb cytoplasmic stains and are, therefore, easily demonstrated under the microscope. Their apparent proteinaceous nature and often odd,

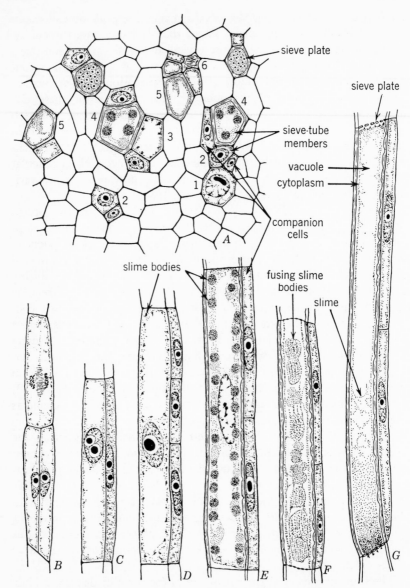

Fig. 12.5. Differentiation of sieve-tube members in *Cucurbita*. *A*, transection of primary phloem with the different stages numbered as follows. (1) meristematic phloem cell just before division; (2) after the division into sieve-tube member and companion cell; (3) slime bodies have just begun to develop in the sieve-element protoplast; (4) slime bodies are of maximal size and the thick (nacré) wall is present in the sieve element; (5) the slime bodies have dispersed; (6) sieve element is partly obliterated. Similar stages are depicted in the longi-

flagellate-like appearance has been the cause of their being erroneously interpreted as causal agents of virus diseases (cf. Esau, 1938*b*). During the differentiation of the sieve-tube member, the slime bodies lose their sharp outlines, become more fluid, sometimes fuse with one another, and eventually become incorporated in the vacuole as amorphous sieve-tube slime (fig. 12.5, *G*). The slime bodies spread out and disperse at the same time as the nucleus breaks down. In some Leguminosae (e.g., *Robinia*) structures interpreted as slime bodies do not disperse.

Not all dicotyledons have equally large amounts of slime. In many arborescent species the sieve-tube protoplasts are thin in consistency. The monocotyledons, the gymnosperms, and the still lower vascular plants, in which no slime bodies have been recorded, show watery vacuolar contents, with only small amounts of slime.

Sieve elements of many plant species contain small plastids that elaborate a carbohydrate referred to as starch but commonly giving a red staining reaction when treated with iodine. In sectioned material the starch grains are as readily displaced as the slime and appear with the slime near the sieve areas (fig. 12.6, *F*, *G*). The plastids often have the shape of discs with a lightly stained center (plate 35, *C*).

The condition of the cytoplasm of the sieve elements after the disorganization of the nucleus is the main subject of controversy in the literature on the sieve-element protoplast (cf. Esau, 1950). The proponents of the mass-flow or pressure-flow concept of movement of materials in the phloem characterize the sieve-element cytoplasm as denatured, passive, and highly permeable to assimilates in solution (Crafts, 1939*a*, *b*, 1948, 1951; Huber, 1941). The denatured cytoplasm is reported to differ from the normal cytoplasm by being unable to accumulate neutral-red stain or to respond with plasmolysis

tudinal sections in *B–G*. *B*, meristematic phloem cells in division (above) and just after division (below) into a sieve-tube member and precursor of companion cells. *C*, young sieve element and precursor of companion cells. *D*, sieve-tube member with slime bodies beginning to develop; precursor of companion cells has divided into three companion cells. *E*, slime bodies of maximal size, nucleus highly vacuolated, thick walls in the sieve element. *F*, slime bodies partly fused into amorphous masses and nucleus absent. *G*, mature sieve element with thin parietal cytoplasm, large vacuole containing vacuolar sap and slime (mostly in the lower end of element). In *G*, the protoplast is connected with the lower sieve plate but is partly withdrawn from the upper. Note the depressions (sieve areas) in the sieve-element walls facing the companion cells in *E–G*. (All, ×740.)

to treatment with hypertonic solutions. It is also described as lacking a tonoplast, that is, a delimitation between the cytoplasm and the vacuole. On the other hand, the advocates of a diffusional movement in the phloem interpret the sieve-element protoplast as possessing the normal property of differential permeability and as being actively concerned with the transport of assimilates (Curtis, 1935; Mason and Phillis, 1937; Schumacher, 1933, 1937, 1939). They report that the sieve element can be plasmolyzed (plate 35, E) and deplasmolyzed but that to prove such reactivity the material must be handled very carefully, since the enucleate protoplast is highly sensitive to manipulations and is easily disrupted (Rouschal, 1941; Schumacher, 1939).

It is, in fact, common knowledge that the true picture of the structure of the mature sieve-element protoplast is difficult to obtain in sectioned material because the cell contents of such elements become so thoroughly displaced. The most direct cause of such displacement is the positive pressure which exists in the mature sieve element and forces their contents in the direction of the cut as soon as it is made. Some of these contents appear on the surface of the cut in the form of phloem exudate. The unilateral flow in response to cutting causes the slimy vacuolar contents to accumulate on the sieve areas near the cut, giving the impression that they are filtered out from the sap flowing through the sieve areas. If cuts are made at two ends of a phloem strand, the slime accumulations face one way (plate 32, B) at one end of the section, and another way at the opposite end, and may appear at both ends of the elements in the median part of the section. The accumulations on the sieve plates are called "slime plugs."

To eliminate the action of the internal pressure, workers devised methods of pretreating the material before severing it from the plants, either by killing portions of the plant with boiling water or by withdrawing some water and reducing the turgor of the tissues (Rouschal, 1941; cf. also Esau, 1950). Using such specialized techniques and extreme care in handling the material during all stages of preparation, investigators eventually developed the now rather generally held concept that the sieve elements have a thin layer of parietal cytoplasm around a large central vacuole containing the usual cell sap and, in addition, varying amounts of slime (fig. 12.5, G). This enucleate protoplast is firmly attached to the sieve areas, particularly to those of the sieve plates, by means of the connecting strands traversing the pores in the sieve areas.

The nature of the connecting strands in the sieve areas is not yet properly understood (Esau, 1950). Some workers are of the opinion that they are cytoplasmic structures like the plasmodesmata and that, if slime is present in the pores, it is forced into them by the steepening of the pressure gradient caused by the cutting (Crafts, 1939*a*, *b*; Schmidt, 1917). Other workers assume that the vacuolar contents are normally interconnected across the sieve areas (Hill, 1908; Mühldorf, 1937). The problem cannot be resolved without further studies on the relation of slime to the cytoplasm, but there is considerable evidence that the slime is in some manner associated with the cytoplasm in the connecting strands (plate 33, *D*; Esau, 1948, 1950).

Companion Cells

The sieve-tube members of monocotyledons and dicotyledons are commonly associated with apparently highly specialized parenchyma cells called *companion cells* (Esau, 1950; Wilhelm, 1880). These cells arise from the same meristematic cell as the associated sieve-tube member, so that the two kinds of elements are closely related in their ontogeny (fig. 12.5). In the formation of the companion cells the meristematic precursor of the sieve-tube member divides longitudinally one or more times. One of the resulting cells, usually distinguished by its relatively large size, differentiates into a sieve-tube member. The others become companion cells, with or without some transverse or other divisions preceding their differentiation. The number of companion cells associated with a given sieve-tube member varies from one to several in different species and may be also somewhat variable in the same plant (fig. 12.6, *A–C*). Companion cells also vary in size. Some are as long as the sieve-tube member with which they are related; others are shorter than the sieve-tube members. The companion cells of a given sieve-tube element may occur on various sides of this element, or they may form continuous longitudinal series on one side of it (fig. 12.6, *J*). In some herbaceous dicotyledons and in many monocotyledons having little or no phloem parenchyma, the companion cells of the superposed series of sieve-tube members form continuous longitudinal series (Strasburger, 1891), but in other plants the companion cells of different elements are commonly not in contact with each other.

The companion cell appears to be intimately connected with the sieve element (Esau, 1948, 1950). The wall between the two is either thin or has many obviously depressed areas (fig. 12.6, *D, E*).

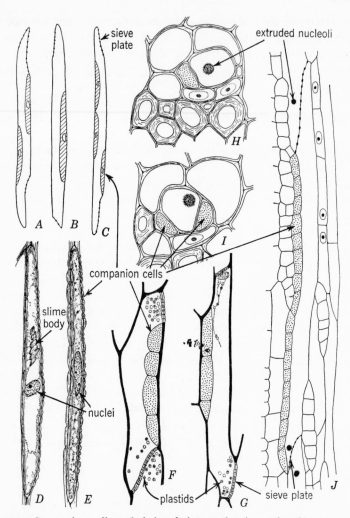

Fɪɢ. 12.6. Companion cells and their relation to the sieve-tube elements. *A–C*,
sieve-tube elements of *Vitis* with the associated companion cells (hatched). *D*
and *E*, enlarged views of *Vitis* companion cells, one still young and containing
a discrete slime body (*D*), the other mature, with the slime body dispersed in
the cytoplasm (*E*). Each companion cell is oriented so that in the section the
sieve-tube member would have been to the right. *F* and *G*, sieve-tube elements
of *Daucus* (carrot), each with several companion cells (stippled). The small
bodies near the sieve plates are plastids with starch. *H–J*, phloem sections of
Eucalyptus, transverse (*H* and *I*) and longitudinal (*J*). The companion cells
are stippled. The sieve elements show extruded nucleoli in their lumina. (*A–C*,
×90; *D, E*, ×700; *F, G*, ×385; *H, I*, ×710; *J*, ×250. From Esau: *A–E*, 1948*a*;
F and *G*, 1940; *H–J*, 1947.)

These are, presumably, primary pit fields on the side of the companion cells, sieve areas on the side of the sieve tube. There is some evidence that plasmodesmata are present in the depressed areas. In macerated material the companion cells commonly remain attached to the sieve-tube element.

In contrast to the sieve element, the companion cell retains its nucleus upon completing its development (fig. 12.5). At the height of activity its protoplast commonly stains more heavily than that of ordinary parenchyma cells, and it is noteworthy that this chromaticity increases after the companion cell develops beyond the meristematic state. The material that stains deeply in the companion cells might be a substance similar to the sieve-tube slime. The evidence for this assumption is found in the genus *Vitis*, in which the companion cells develop the same kind of slime bodies as the sieve tubes (fig. 12.6, *D*) and the chromaticity of the companion-cell protoplast increases after the dispersal of these bodies (Esau, 1947, 1948). The companion cells apparently form no starch.

The sieve-tube elements and their companion cells are thought to be closely associated not only ontogenetically and morphologically but also physiologically. The main evidence of functional association is the concurrence in the activity of the two kinds of cells. The companion cell is formed shortly before the sieve-tube member differentiates as such, and, when the sieve-tube protoplasts are disorganized at the end of its activity, the associated companion cells, according to many observations, die also.

Although the companion cells are considered to be characteristic components of the angiospermous phloem, no comprehensive comparative studies have been made on their distribution in this group of plants. There is evidence that they may be absent in the primitive woody dicotyledons (Bailey and Swamy, 1949). Furthermore, companion cells are frequently lacking in the earliest part of the primary phloem (protophloem, p. 286) of the angiosperms which functions for only a short time (Esau, 1939, 1943*c*).

The sieve cells of the gymnosperms (fig. 12.7 and plate 37) and vascular cryptogams have no companion cells. Certain ray and phloem parenchyma cells of the conifers are apparently closely associated morphologically and physiologically with the sieve cells (Chrysler, 1913; cf. Esau, 1939, 1950). These parenchyma cells have received the name *albuminous cells*, because in sections they frequently stain deeply with cytoplasmic stains, as though they were particularly rich in proteinaceous materials (Strasburger, 1891). When albuminous cells occur in rays, they are usually located at the margins of rays and constitute the erect ray cells which are taller and of smaller transverse diameters than the procumbent ray cells. Albuminous cells included among phloem parenchyma cells do not differ from the latter in shape. The walls of the sieve cells facing the albuminous cells have conspicuous sieve areas. During the height of seasonal activity albuminous cells contain no starch, but they may do so during the winter (Strasburger, 1891). Albuminous cells appear to die when the sieve cells are disorganized (Strasburger, 1891). Thus the relation between albuminous cells and sieve cells seems to resemble that between companion cells and sieve-tube members of the angiosperms, except that there is no direct ontogenetic relation between albuminous cells and sieve cells.

Parenchyma Cells

The phloem contains variable amounts of parenchyma cells other than companion and albuminous cells. These are concerned with many of the activities characteristic of living parenchyma cells, such as storage of starch, fat, and other organic food materials, and accumulations of tannins and resins.

The parenchyma cells of the primary phloem are elongated and are oriented, like the sieve elements, with their long axes parallel with the longitudinal extent of the vascular tissue. In the secondary phloem, parenchyma occurs in two systems, the vertical and the horizontal (figs. 12.7–12.11). The parenchyma of the vertical system is called *phloem parenchyma*, a term corresponding to the term xylem parenchyma for the vertical parenchyma in the secondary xylem (see chapter 11). The horizontal parenchyma constitutes the *phloem rays*.

The secondary phloem parenchyma occurs mainly in two basic forms. The cells may be either comparable to the fusiform cambial cells in length or considerably shorter because of transverse divisions in the fusiform derivatives that give rise to them. In conformity with the terminology used for the xylem, the long parenchyma cells may be called *fusiform phloem parenchyma cells*, and a series of short ones derived from one fusiform cell may be called a *phloem parenchyma strand*. The ray cells are elongated in the radial direction (fig. 12.7; *procumbent cells*). In some species the marginal cells are elongated vertically (fig. 12.8; *erect cells;* Barghoorn, 1940; Strasburger, 1891).

In the active phloem, the phloem parenchyma and the ray cells apparently have only primary unlignified walls. After the tissue ceases to conduct, the parenchyma cells may remain relatively unchanged, or they may become sclerified. In many plants phellogen eventually arises in the phloem (see chapter 14). It is formed by the phloem parenchyma and the ray parenchyma.

The walls of both kinds of parenchyma cells have numerous primary pit fields. Such structures occur also between companion cells and the other parenchymatous members of the phloem. In walls between the sieve elements and the parenchyma (or companion) cells, the primary pit field in the parenchyma wall is complemented by a sieve area on the side of the sieve element (Esau, 1948; Hill, 1901, 1908; Strasburger, 1891).

Fibers

The fundamental structure of phloem fibers, their origin, and their development were considered in detail in chapter 10 (cf. also Esau, 1950). Fibers occur in both primary and secondary phloem. Those of the primary tissue commonly develop in organs that are still elongating. By a combination of symplastic and apical intrusive growth, the primary fibers may become very long. The secondary phloem fibers arise from fusiform cambial cells as components of the vertical system. These fibers may elongate by apical intrusive growth, but, as a rule, they remain conspicuously shorter than the primary fibers of the same plant. The primary and the secondary phloem fibers develop secondary walls after they complete their elongation. In some plants the fibers are typically lignified; in others they are not. The pits in their walls are usually simple, but they may be slightly bordered. Septate and mucilaginous fibers also occur in the phloem. In some plant species the secondary phloem fibers mature early and appear to be highly specialized as mechanical elements (e.g., *Tilia;* see chapter 15). In other species they have primary walls and active protoplasts in the functioning phloem and mature as fibers only after the sieve elements cease to function (e.g., *Prunus,* plate 36, *B; Parthenium*). Some workers consider such fibers to be sclerotic phloem parenchyma cells (Holdheide, 1951). Septate fibers mature together with the sieve elements but retain active protoplasts and are concerned with starch storage (e.g., *Vitis,* plate 36, *A*).

PRIMARY PHLOEM

In conformity with the classification of the primary xylem into protoxylem and metaxylem, the primary phloem may be divided into *protophloem* and *metaphloem*. The protophloem shows mature elements before the plant organ completes elongation. The metaphloem matures after this growth has taken place, although it may be differentiating during the elongation. The terms protophloem and metaphloem evolved in relation to the development of the parallel xylem terminology (cf. Esau, 1943*a*).

Protophloem

The protophloem constitutes the conducting tissue of the actively growing parts of the plant and is known to contain sieve elements possessing the usual specialized characteristics of such elements, that is, highly vacuolate, enucleate protoplasts and walls bearing sieve areas. There is some doubt regarding the morphologic nature of the first phloem elements in the gymnosperms, since no sieve areas have been recognized in them. Furthermore, their protoplasmic characteristics are poorly known (Esau, 1950). In the angiosperms, sieve elements have been observed in the protophloem of roots, stems, and leaves in woody and herbaceous species (Esau, 1939, 1950). These elements appear to be sieve-tube members, but they often lack companion cells. They are elongated but have narrow transverse diameters, and their sieve areas are revealed only in good preparations and at high magnifications. The recognition of these elements is facilitated by their somewhat thickened walls, which readily absorb cellulose stains (plate 38, *A*), and by the scarcity of stainable contents in their lumina (Esau, 1942, 1943*c*, 1948). The light staining of contents often makes the sieve elements particularly conspicuous among the adjacent protophloem cells still possessing dense protoplasts (plate 76, *A*).

The sieve tubes of the protophloem apparently function for a brief period only. In rapidly elongating organs they are destroyed (fig. 10.2, *B*, and plate 38, *B*), soon after maturation, by the effects of elongation of the surrounding cells. Being enucleate cells they are unable to keep pace with this growth by active elongation and are passively stretched. Often the surrounding cells crush both the partly stretched elements and their companion cells, if such are present. The remnants of the crushed cells may later disappear completely. This phenomenon of effacement of the sieve elements is commonly called obliteration. In many dicotyledons the cells remaining in the protophloem after the sieve tubes are obliterated differentiate into fibers (Esau, 1943*b*, 1950; Léger, 1897; see also chapter 10). Certain vine types of stems, which possess a sclerenchyma cylinder outside the vascular strands (e.g., *Aristolochia* and *Cucurbita*, figs. 10.1, *H*, and 12.1), form no fibers in the protophloem. In the leaf blades and the petioles of dicotyledons the protophloem cells remaining after the destruction of the sieve tubes often differentiate into long, collenchymatously thickened cells remaining unlignified (see chapter 9). The strands of these cells appear, in transverse sections, like bundle caps delimiting the vascular bundles on their abaxial sides (Esau, 1936). This type of transformation of the protophloem in leaves is widely distributed and occurs also in those species that have protophloem fibers in the stems (cf. Esau, 1950). As was pointed out in chapter 10, the profound change that the protophloem undergoes during the early stages of development of an organ obscures the original nature of the tissue and may lead to the erroneous assumption that this tissue is distinct from the rest of the phloem and constitutes part of the so-called pericycle.

Metaphloem

Since the metaphloem matures after the growth in length of the surrounding tissues is completed, it is retained as a conducting tissue longer than the protophloem. Some herbaceous dicotyledons, most monocotyledons, and many lower vascular plants produce no secondary tissues and depend entirely on the metaphloem for food conduction after their primary bodies are fully expanded. In woody and herbaceous species having secondary growth the metaphloem sieve elements become inactive after the secondary conducting elements differentiate. In such plants the metaphloem sieve elements may be partly crushed or completely obliterated.

The absence of secondary growth in persisting plants such as ferns, bamboo, and palms raises the question whether these plants have sieve elements which, despite their enucleate protoplasts, remain functional for many years. The scanty references to this subject (cf. Esau, 1939, p. 423) suggest that such longer longevity might occur.

The sieve elements of the metaphloem (plate 38, *C*) are commonly longer and wider than those of the protophloem, and their sieve areas are more distinct. In the angiosperms investigated thus far, these elements are sieve-tube members. Companion cells and phloem parenchyma are typically present in the metaphloem of the dicotyledons. In the monocotyledons, the sieve tubes and companion cells often form strands containing no phloem parenchyma among them, although such cells may be present on the periphery of the strands (Cheadle and Uhl, 1948; Esau, 1943*c*). A monocotyledonous type of metaphloem, without phloem parenchyma cells among the sieve tubes, may be found in herbaceous dicotyledons (e.g., Ranunculaceae, fig. 15.8).

According to the literature, the metaphloem of dicotyledons usually lacks fibers (Esau, 1950). If primary phloem fibers occur in dicotyledons, they arise in the protophloem, but not in the metaphloem, even if such elements are later formed in the secondary phloem. In herbaceous species the old metaphloem may become strongly sclerified (Léger, 1895; Wilson, 1922). Whether the cells undergoing such sclerification should be classified as fibers or as sclerotic phloem parenchyma has not been determined. In monocotyledons sclerenchyma encloses vascular bundles as bundle sheaths and may also be present in the metaphloem (Cheadle and Uhl, 1948).

The delimitation between protophloem and metaphloem is sometimes rather clear, as, for example, in the aerial parts of monocotyledons having only sieve tubes in the protophloem and distinct companion cells associated with the sieve tubes in the metaphloem (Esau, 1943*c*; plate 53, *B*). (There is no such clear distinction in the roots of the same plants.) In dicotyledons the two tissues usually merge gradually, and their delimitation must be based on a developmental study.

In plants having secondary phloem the distinction between this tissue and the metaphloem may be quite uncertain (Esau, 1943*a*, 1948; Strasburger, 1891). The delimitation of the two tissues is particularly difficult if radial seriation of cells occurs in both tissues. An exception has been found in the genus *Prunus*, in which the last cells initiated on the phloem side by the procambium mature as large parenchyma cells and sharply delimit the primary from the secondary phloem (figs. 15.17 and 15.18; Schneider, 1945). In general, the developmental relations between the two parts of the phloem have not been sufficiently investigated. No data are available on the relative lengths of primary and secondary sieve elements comparable to those assembled for the tracheary elements which prove that the last metaxylem cells are distinctly longer than the first secondary elements (see chaper 11).

SECONDARY PHLOEM

Basic Structural Characteristics

The arrangement of cells in the secondary phloem parallels that in the secondary xylem. A vertical or longitudinal system of cells, derived from the fusiform initials of the cambium, is interpenetrated by the horizontal or transverse ray system derived from the ray initials (figs. 12.7–12.9). The principal components of the vertical system are sieve elements (either sieve cells or sieve-tube members, the latter usually with companion cells), phloem parenchyma, and phloem fibers. Those of the horizontal system are ray-parenchyma cells.

Storied, nonstoried, and intermediate types of arrangement of phloem cells may be found in different species of plants. As in the xylem, the type of arrangement is determined, first, by the nature of the cambium (that is, whether it is stratified or not) and, second, by the degree of elongation of the various elements of the vertical system during tissue differentiation.

Many woody species of dicotyledons show a division of the secondary phloem into seasonal growth increments (Holdheide, 1951), although this division is less clear than in the secondary xylem. The growth layers in the phloem are distinguishable if the cells of the early phloem strongly expand in the radial direction, whereas those of the late phloem remain narrow (fig. 12.10 and plate 36, *A*; Artschwager, 1950; Esau, 1948; Holdheide, 1951; Huber, 1949). The collapse of the sieve elements in the nonfunctioning part of the phloem and the concomitant modifications in some other cells—notably the enlargement of the parenchyma cells—contribute toward obscuring the structural differences that might exist in the different parts of a growth layer at its inception (plate 36, *B*). Many gymnosperms and angiosperms form fibers in tangential bands in the secondary phloem (figs. 12.7 and 12.8). The number of these fiber bands is not necessarily constant from season to season and cannot be safely used to determine the age of the phloem tissue (Esau, 1948; Huber, 1949; Strasburger, 1891).

The phloem rays are continuous with the xylem rays since both arise from a common group of ray initials in the cambium. (Compare figs. 12.7 and 12.8 with figs. 11.10 and 11.11.) The phloem ray and the xylem ray together constitute the vascular ray. Near the cambium the phloem and xylem rays having common origin are usually the same in height and width. However, the older part of the phloem ray, which is displaced outwardly by the expansion of the secondary body, may increase in width, sometimes very considerably (Holdheide, 1951; plate 49, *C*). By means of this dilation of rays the phloem is adjusted to the increase in the circumference of the axis resulting from secondary growth. Sometimes the ray cells merely extend tangentially, but more commonly the number of ray cells is increased in the tangential direction by radial divisions. Often such growth is restricted to some rays, and the others retain their original width. No comparable increase in tangential extent occurs in the vertical system. The increase in width of the phloem rays is interrupted when a phellogen arises in the phloem and cuts off the outer part of this tissue by interpolating cork between it and the inner tissue.

Before the phloem rays become dilated in the older parts of the tissue their variations in form and size are similar to those of xylem rays in the same species. There are uniseriate, biseriate, and multiseriate phloem rays; some are high, and others low; and small and large rays may be present in the same species. The rays may be composed of one kind of cell (fig. 12.7), or they may contain both kinds of cell, procumbent and erect (fig. 12.8). Phloem rays do not attain the same lengths as xylem rays, because the vascular cambium produces less phloem than xylem and also because so often the outer portions of the phloem are sloughed off through the activity of the phellogen.

Conifer Phloem

In conifers phloem parallels xylem in the relative simplicity of its structure (fig. 12.7). The vertical system contains sieve cells, parenchyma cells, and frequently fibers. The rays are mostly uniseriate and contain parenchyma only or parenchyma and albuminous cells. The cell arrangement is nonstoried. The expansion of cells during differentiation is uniform, the apical elongation slight, and, therefore, the radial seriation of cells, which originates in the cambium, is retained in the mature tissue (plate 37, *A*). In general, conifer phloem seems to show relatively little developmental disturbance in the cell arrangement which it inherits from the cambium (Barghoorn, 1940; Klinken, 1914).

The sieve cells of conifers are slender, elongated elements comparable to the fusiform initials from which they are derived. They overlap each other at their ends, and each is in contact with several rays. The sieve areas are particularly abundant on the ends which overlap those of other sieve cells. Elsewhere the sieve areas appear to be regu-

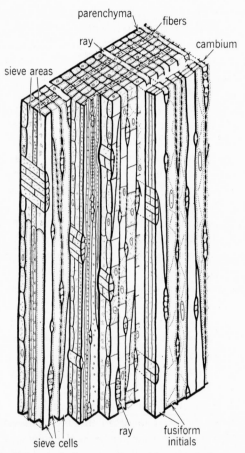

Fig. 12.7. Block diagram of the secondary phloem and the cambium of *Thuja occidentalis* (White Cedar), a conifer. (Courtesy of I. W. Bailey. Drawn by Mrs. J. P. Rogerson under the supervision of L. G. Livingston. Redrawn.)

larly restricted to the radial walls (Abbe and Crafts, 1939; Strasburger, 1891). The connecting strands in the sieve areas are probably only a little larger than plasmodesmata (Abbe and Crafts, 1939), but they show the usual chromaticity characteristic of these structures and the firm connection with the sieve areas (plate 34, *C, D*). Within a given sieve area the connecting strands are aggregated into groups, and the callose associated with the strands in one group appears to fuse into one structure. In other words, several connecting strands seemingly traverse one common callose cylinder (cf. Esau, 1939, 1950).

The phloem parenchyma cells commonly occur in longitudinal strands (fig. 12.7). They store starch at certain times of the year but are particularly conspicuous when they contain resinous and tanniferous inclusions (plate 37, *A*). Crystals also are commonly deposited in the parenchyma. In the Abietineae, phloem parenchyma cells occur, often in tangential bands, among the sieve cells (plate 37). In representatives of the Taxaceae, the Taxodiaceae, and the Cupressaceae, phloem parenchyma cells alternate, in tangential bands, with the sieve cells and fibers (fig. 12.7). In several genera an orderly sequence (with some variations) of fibers, sieve cells, phloem parenchyma, sieve cells, fibers has been described (Abbe and Crafts, 1939; Huber, 1939; Isenberg, 1943). The Abietineae have no fibers but apparently develop secondary walls in the sieve cells, whereas the Taxaceae, the Taxodiaceae, and the Cupressaceae have fibers and only primary walls in the sieve cells (Abbe and Crafts, 1939). Large ramified sclereids may develop in the old parts of secondary phloem in *Abies* (Holdheide, 1951).

A characteristic feature of the conifer phloem is the previously mentioned absence of companion cells and the presence of albuminous cells. In the phloem of trees advanced in age, albuminous cells have been reported to occur only in the rays in certain conifers, in the rays and among the phloem parenchyma cells (that is, in the vertical system) in others, and only among the phloem parenchyma cells in still others (Strasburger, 1891).

The secondary phloem of conifers may contain resin canals. These structures have been studied in detail in *Picea canadensis* (Thomson and Sifton, 1925), in which they occur in the rays and are characterized by having series of cyst-like bulbous expansions. With the increase in width of the rays in the outer part of the stem, these resin canals enlarge too, by divisions of epithelial cells. Moreover, the number of layers of the epithelial cells is increased by divisions periclinal with respect to the periphery of the duct. As a result of this activity, the resin duct appears as though surrounded by a cambial zone. As in the xylem, the resin canals in the secondary phloem of *Picea* appear to arise in response to injury.

Dicotyledon Phloem

The secondary phloem of the dicotyledons has been studied much less comprehensively and not so systematically as the secondary xylem of the same group of plants, and mostly without regard to the phylogenetic aspects of its structure (see literature in Esau, 1939, 1950). The phloem in dicotyledons shows a wider diversity of patterns of cell arrangement and more variations in the component cells than the phloem in conifers. Storied, intermediate, and nonstoried arrangements of cells are encountered, and the rays may be uniseriate, biseriate, and multiseriate. The elements of the vertical system are sieve-tube members usually with companion cells, phloem parenchyma cells, and fibers; those of the transverse system, ray parenchyma cells (fig. 12.8). Both systems may contain sclereids, secretory elements of schizogenous and lysigenous origins, laticifers, and various idioblasts with specialized contents. Crystal formation is common and occurs in phloem parenchyma cells—some subdivided into small cells (chambered) each with one crystal—in sclerenchyma cells, and in the rays.

One of the most conspicuous differences in the appearance of the phloem of different species results from the distribution of the fibers (MacDaniels, 1918; Möller, 1882; Strasburger, 1891). In certain dicotyledons the fibers occur in tangential bands, more or less regularly alternating with bands containing the sieve tubes and the parenchymatous components of the vertical system (figs. 12.8–12.11; plate 36, *A*; *Tilia, Vitis, Liriodendron, Magnolia, Corchorus*). The fibers may be only supporting cells (*Tilia, Corchorus*), or they may be septate and store starch (*Vitis*). Sometimes there are few fibers, scattered among other cells of the vertical system (*Tecoma, Nicotiana, Cephalanthus, Laurus*), or they may be absent (*Aristolochia*). The fibers may be very abundant, with sieve tubes and parenchyma cells scattered among them in small strands (*Carya;* Artschwager, 1950). In some plants the functioning phloem contains no sclerified elements, but, after the sieve tubes cease to function, fibers and sclereids differentiate (plate 36, *B*; *Prunus*).

The sieve tubes and the parenchyma cells show varied spatial interrelationships. Sometimes the sieve tubes occur in long, continuous radial series (*Prunus*), or, on the contrary, they may form tangential bands alternating with similar bands of parenchyma (*Robinia, Aristolochia*). In phloem having tangential bands of fibers alternating

with similarly disposed bands of sieve elements and associated parenchymatous elements, the sieve tubes are commonly separated by
phloem parenchyma cells from the fibers and the rays.

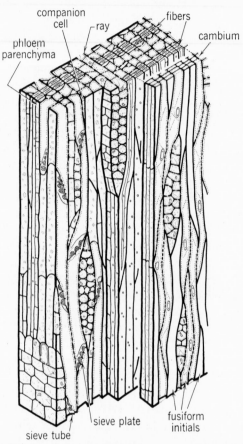

Fɪɢ. 12.8. Block diagram of the secondary phloem and the cambium of *Liriodendron tulipifera* (Tulip Tree), a dicotyledon. (Courtesy of I. W. Bailey. Drawn
by Mrs. J. P. Rogerson under the supervision of L. G. Livingston. Redrawn.)

Many woody dicotyledons have nonstratified phloem with elongated sieve-tube members bearing mostly compound sieve plates on
the inclined end walls (*Betula, Quercus, Populus, Aesculus, Tilia, Liriodendron, Juglans*). In these genera the sieve areas of the sieve plates
are distinctly more differentiated than the lateral sieve areas. In some
dicotyledons, as in the Pomoideae, there is less distinction between
the two kinds of sieve areas, and the long slender sieve elements, with

their very much inclined end walls, approach the sieve cells of conifers in their seemingly primitive structure (Huber, 1939). The sieve
elements of the Pomoideae, however, have companion cells. Slightly
inclined (*Fagus, Acer*) and transverse (*Fraxinus, Ulmus, Robinia*) end
walls usually bear simple sieve plates. The individual sieve-tube mem-

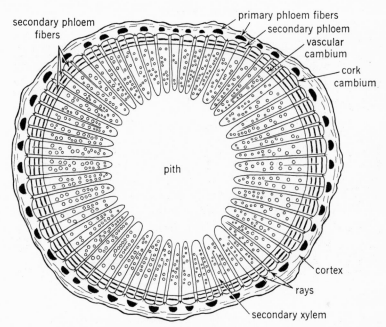

secondary phloem
fibers

primary phloem fibers

secondary phloem

vascular
cambium

cork
cambium

pith

cortex

rays

secondary xylem

Fig. 12.9. Transection of a grapevine cane (one-year-old branch), showing
arrangement of the vascular tissues. The epidermis, the cortex, and the primary
phloem were cut off by the activity of the phellogen which interpolated a layer
of cork between the primary and the secondary phloem (see plate 43, *A, B*).
The latter shows tangential bands of fibers in the vertical system (see plate
36, *A*). (×6½.)

bers in such plants are relatively short, and the phloem may be more
or less distinctly storied (*Robinia*).

If the sieve-tube members possess inclined end walls, the ends of the
cells are roughly wedge shaped and are so oriented that the wide side
of the wedge is exposed in the radial section, the narrow in the tangential. The compound sieve plates are bòrne on the wide sides of the
wedge-like ends and are therefore seen in face views in the radial
sections (fig. 12.11, *A*, and plate 33, *A*), in sectional views in the tangential (fig. 12.11, *B*, and plate 33, *B*).

As previously mentioned, the secondary phloem rays are comparable to the xylem rays of the same species but may become dilated in the older parts of the tissue. The degree of this dilation is highly variable. The extreme dilation of certain of the rays is one of the most con-

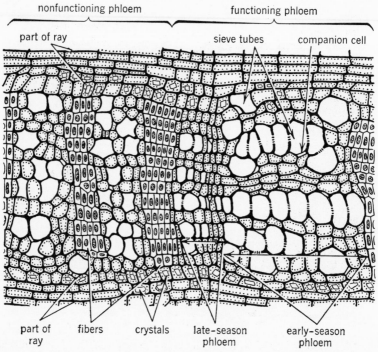

FIG. 12.10. Transection of the secondary phloem of the grapevine (*Vitis vinifera*). The sieve tubes were left unstippled to distinguish them from the various parenchyma cells. The septate fibers with secondary walls occur in tangential bands. The cells along the margins of the rays (phloem parenchyma and ray parenchyma) contain crystals. The functioning phloem has prominent connecting strands in the sieve areas (left white). The sieve tubes in the nonfunctioning phloem have partly infolded walls. The rays are shown in part. (Compare with fig. 12.9.) (×155.)

spicuous characteristics of the phloem of *Tilia* (plate 49, *C*; cf. Foster, 1949, p. 170). The wide rays separate the vertical system together with the undilated rays into blocks narrowed down toward the periphery of the stem.

Herbaceous dicotyledons possessing secondary growth may have secondary phloem resembling that of the woody species (*Nicotiana*, *Gossypium*). Some herbaceous species, like the vine *Cucurbita*, have a secondary phloem scarcely distinguishable from the primary except in having larger cells (plate 32, *A*). The secondary phloem of *Cucurbita* has repeatedly served, in the history of phloem research, for the study of morphology and physiology of the sieve elements (cf. Esau,

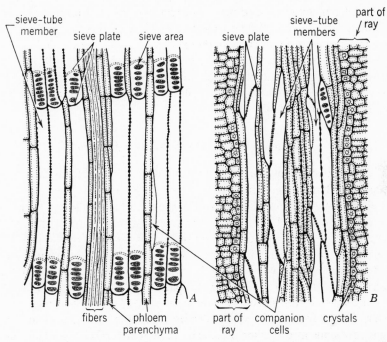

FIG. 12.11. Longitudinal sections of the secondary phloem of the grapevine (*Vitis vinifera*), radial (*A*) and tangential (*B*). The compound sieve plates appear in surface view in the radial section, in sectional view in the tangential section. The beaded effect of the lateral walls between adjacent sieve-tube members results from the presence of small sieve areas in these walls. The parenchyma walls having a similar appearance have primary pit fields. Note the crystals in the cells along the margins of the rays. The rays are shown only in part. (Compare with fig. 12.9.) (Both, ×103.)

1939, 1950). *Cucurbita* has external and internal phloem, and only the external phloem is augmented by secondary growth. The secondary phloem consists of wide sieve tubes, narrow companion cells, and phloem parenchyma cells of intermediate size. There are no fibers and no rays. The sieve plates are simple and have exceptionally large pores and connecting strands. It is commonly assumed that each of these connecting strands results from a fusion of a group of plasmodesmata (cf. Esau, 1939). The lateral walls bear sieve areas that are much less specialized than the single sieve areas of the simple sieve plates. In transections the small companion cells often appear as though cut out of the sides of the sieve tubes. Longitudinally, companion cells usually extend from one end of a sieve-tube member to the other. Sometimes only one companion cell occurs alongside a sieve-tube member, sometimes a vertical row of two or more.

Secondary phloem of relatively simple structure is found in dicotyledonous storage organs, such as those of the carrot, the dandelion, and the beet (Artschwager, 1926; Artschwager and McGuire, 1943; Esau, 1940). Storage parenchyma predominates in this kind of phloem, and the sieve tubes and companion cells appear as strands anastomosing within the parenchyma.

Differentiation in the Secondary Phloem

The derivatives of the vascular cambium on the phloem side commonly undergo some divisions before the various phloem elements begin to differentiate. There may be simply a few tangential divisions increasing the number of derivatives, or a given fusiform derivative may undergo certain specialized divisions. In the conifers the fusiform derivative differentiates into a sieve cell, usually without being subdivided into smaller cells (fig. 12.7). In the dicotyledons there are at least the longitudinal divisions that separate the future companion cells from the associated sieve-tube members (fig. 12.8). Sometimes, however, the fusiform initial subdivides by transverse, oblique, or longitudinal divisions into smaller cells, each of which further subdivides into a companion cell (or cells) and a sieve-tube member. After the completion of all these divisions the sieve-tube members pass through the complex cytologic changes characteristic of these cells, and their primary pit fields become modified into sieve areas.

The fusiform cells that give rise to phloem parenchyma are often subdivided into smaller cells by transverse or oblique divisions (parenchyma strand formation), or they differentiate into long fusiform parenchyma cells. The fibers differentiate from fusiform derivatives by first undergoing apical intrusive growth and later forming secondary walls.

The phloem cells expand transversely to varied degrees as they diverge from the cambium. Frequently, sieve-tube members show the greatest increase in diameter, whereas fibers may expand only slightly. Ray cells commonly change little during differentiation, except that they expand somewhat. In certain species some of the ray and phloem parenchyma cells eventually develop secondary walls and differentiate into sclereids with or without some intrusive growth preceding the sclerification.

Nonfunctioning Phloem

In most dicotyledons a given secondary phloem increment appears to function as a conducting tissue only one season, as a rule. Some time before the beginning of a new growth season most or all of the sieve tubes become inactive. *Tilia* and *Vitis* seemingly deviate from this rule. In *Tilia* the sieve tubes are reported as remaining active for several years without any noticeable changes in their appearance during the winter. In *Vitis* large masses of callose (dormancy callus) appear on the sieve areas with the onset of winter but are removed in the spring, before the cambium is reactivated (plate 33, *C*, *D*). After the disappearance of dormancy callus, the sieve tubes assume characteristics similar to those of newly differentiated elements and function for another season (Esau, 1948). In the conifers, too, the sieve cells are not long lived, although in some Abietineae they appear to function for two seasons (Huber, 1939).

The part of the phloem in which the sieve elements have ceased to function may be referred to as *nonfunctioning* or *inactive phloem* (Esau, 1939, 1948, 1950). This phloem commonly retains living parenchyma cells that continue to store starch and tannins until the tissue is severed from living parts of the plant by the activity of the phellogen. Thus the distinction between functioning and nonfunctioning phloem as defined in this book is determined by the condition of the sieve elements.

The various signs of the inactive state of the sieve elements are readily detected. The sieve areas are either covered with a mass of callose (definitive callus) or entirely free of this substance, for callose eventually disappears in old nonfunctioning sieve elements (fig. 12.4, *G*, *H*). The contents of the sieve elements may be completely disorganized, or they may be absent and the cells filled with gas. The determination of the nonfunctioning state of the phloem is particularly certain if the sieve elements are more or less collapsed or crushed.

The sieve elements are not the only structures that become disorganized in the old phloem. As was mentioned previously, the companion cells of dicotyledons and the albuminous cells of conifers cease to function at the same time as the associated sieve elements do. In certain plants, some of the phloem and ray parenchyma cells collapse also (cf. Esau, 1939). The characteristics of the inactive phloem as a whole are somewhat varied in different plants. In certain dicotyledons, like *Tilia*, *Populus*, and *Juglans*, the functionless sieve tubes suffer relatively little change in shape. In others, like *Aristolochia* and *Robinia*, the sieve elements and associated cells collapse completely, and, since they occur in tangential bands, the crushed cells alternate more or less regularly with the tangential bands of turgid parenchyma cells. In still others the collapse of the sieve tubes is accompanied by a conspicuous shrinkage of the tissue and bending of the rays (plate 36, *B*). In conifers the collapse of the old sieve cells is very marked. The nonfunctioning phloem of the Abietineae shows dense masses of collapsed sieve cells interspersed with intact phloem parenchyma cells, and the rays are bent and folded in such a tissue (plate 37, *A*). In the groups of Coniferae having fibers in the phloem, the sieve cells are crushed between the fibers and the enlarging phloem parenchyma cells (Abbe and Crafts, 1939). In *Vitis vinifera* the nonfunctioning sieve tubes become filled with tyloses-like proliferations from the phloem parenchyma cells (Esau, 1948).

The amount of the nonfunctioning phloem that accumulates in a given plant depends on the activity of the phellogen. If the phellogen is superficial and is not replaced by deeper-lying phellogens for many years, the plant may have a broad zone of nonfunctioning phloem (e.g., *Prunus*, Schneider, 1945). If, on the contrary, the phellogen forms year after year in successively deeper layers of the axis, it prevents the accumulation of inactive phloem (e.g., *Vitis*, Esau, 1948).

REFERENCES

Abbe, L. B., and A. S. Crafts. Phloem of white pine and other coniferous species. *Bot. Gaz.* 100:695–722. 1939.

Artschwager, E. Anatomy of the vegetative organs of the sugar beet. *Jour. Agr. Res.* 33:143–176. 1926.

Artschwager, E. The time factor in the differentiation of the secondary xylem and phloem in pecan. *Amer. Jour. Bot.* 37:15–24. 1950.

Artschwager, E., and R. C. McGuire. Contribution to the morphology and anatomy of the Russian dandelion (*Taraxacum kok-saghyz*). *U. S. Dept. Agr. Tech. Bul.* 843. 1943.

Bailey, I. W., and B. G. L. Swamy. The morphology and relationships of *Austrobaileya*. *Arnold Arboretum Jour.* 30:211–226. 1949.

Barghoorn, E. S., Jr. Origin and development of the uniseriate ray in the Coniferae. *Torrey Bot. Club Bul.* 67:303–328. 1940.

Cheadle, V. I. Observations on the phloem in the Monocotyledoneae. II. Additional data on the occurrence and phylogenetic specialization in structure of the sieve tubes in the metaphloem. *Amer. Jour. Bot.* 35:129–131. 1948.

Cheadle, V. I., and N. W. Uhl. The relation of metaphloem to the types of vascular bundles in the Monocotyledoneae. *Amer. Jour. Bot.* 35:578–583. 1948.

Cheadle, V. I., and N. B. Whitford. Observations on the phloem in the Monocotyledoneae. I. The occurrence and phylogenetic specialization in structure of the sieve tubes in the metaphloem. *Amer. Jour. Bot.* 28:623–627. 1941.

Chrysler, M. A. The origin of the erect cells in the phloem of the Abietineae. *Bot. Gaz.* 56:36–50. 1913.

Committee on Nomenclature, International Association of Wood Anatomists. Glossary of terms used in describing woods. *Trop. Woods* 1933(36):1–12. 1933.

Crafts, A. S. The relation between structure and function of the phloem. *Amer. Jour. Bot.* 26:172–177. 1939*a*.

Crafts, A. S. The protoplasmic properties of sieve tubes. *Protoplasma* 33:389–398. 1939*b*.

Crafts, A. S. Movement of materials in phloem as influenced by the porous nature of the tissues. In: Interaction of water and porous materials. *Faraday Soc. Disc. No.* 3:153–159. 1948.

Crafts, A. S. Movement of assimilates, viruses, growth regulators, and chemical indicators in plants. *Bot. Rev.* 17:203–284. 1951.

Curtis, O. F. *The translocation of solutes in plants.* New York, McGraw-Hill Book Company. 1935.

De Bary, A. *Comparative anatomy of the vegetative organs of the phanerogams and ferns.* Oxford, Clarendon Press. 1884.

Eames, A. J., and L. H. MacDaniels. *An introduction to plant anatomy.* 2nd ed. New York, McGraw-Hill Book Company. 1947.

Esau, K. Ontogeny and structure of collenchyma and of vascular tissues in celery petioles. *Hilgardia* 10:431–476. 1936.

Esau, K. Ontogeny and structure of the phloem of tobacco. *Hilgardia* 11:343–424. 1938*a*.

Esau, K. Some anatomical aspects of plant virus disease problems. *Bot. Rev.* 4:548–579. 1938*b*.

Esau, K. Development and structure of the phloem tissue. *Bot. Rev.* 5:373–432. 1939.

Esau, K. Developmental anatomy of the fleshy storage organ of *Daucus carota.* *Hilgardia* 13:175–226. 1940.

Esau, K. Vascular differentiation in the vegetative shoot of *Linum.* I. The procambium. *Amer. Jour. Bot.* 29:738–747. 1942.

Esau, K. Origin and development of primary vascular tissues in seed plants. *Bot. Rev.* 9:125–206. 1943*a*.

Esau, K. Vascular differentiation in the vegetative shoot of *Linum.* III. The origin of bast fibers. *Amer. Jour. Bot.* 30:579–586. 1943*b*.

Esau, K. Ontogeny of the vascular bundle in *Zea Mays.* *Hilgardia* 15:327–368. 1943*c*.

Esau, K. A study of some sieve-tube inclusions. *Amer. Jour. Bot.* 34:224–233. 1947.

Esau, K. Phloem structure in the grapevine, and its seasonal changes. *Hilgardia* 18:217–296. 1948.

Esau, K. Development and structure of the phloem tissue. II. *Bot. Rev.* 16:67–114. 1950.

Foster, A. S. *Practical plant anatomy.* 2nd ed. New York, D. Van Nostrand Company. 1949.

Haberlandt, G. *Physiological plant anatomy.* London, Macmillan and Company. 1914.

Hanstein, J. *Die Milchsaftgefässe und die verwandten Organe der Rinde.* Berlin, Wiegandt und Hempel. 1864.

Hartig, T. Vergleichende Untersuchungen über die Organisation des Stammes der einheimischen Waldbäume. *Jahresber. Forsch. Forstwissensch. und Forstl. Naturkunde* 1:125–168. 1837.

Hill, A. W. The histology of the sieve tubes of *Pinus. Ann. Bot.* 15:575–611. 1901.

Hill, A. W. The histology of the sieve tubes of angiosperms. *Ann. Bot.* 22:245–290. 1908.

Holdheide, W. Anatomie mitteleuropäischer Gehölzrinden (mit mikrophotographischem Atlas). In: H. Freund. *Handbuch der Mikroskopie in der Technik.* Band 5. Heft 1. Pp. 193–367. Frankfurt am Main, Umschau Verlag. 1951.

Huber, B. Hundert Jahre Siebröhren-Forschung. *Protoplasma* 29:132–148. 1937.

Huber, B. Das Siebröhrensystem unserer Bäume und seine jahreszeitlichen Veränderungen. *Jahrb. f. Wiss. Bot.* 88:176–242. 1939.

Huber, B. Gesichertes und Problematisches in der Wanderung der Assimilate. *Deut. Bot. Gesell. Ber.* 59:181–194. 1941.

Huber, B. Zur Phylogenie des Jahrringbaues der Rinde. *Svensk Bot. Tidskr.* 43:376–382. 1949.

Huber, B., and E. Rouschal. Anatomische und zellphysiologische Beobachtungen am Siebröhrensystem der Bäume. *Deut. Bot. Gesell. Ber.* 56:380–391. 1938.

Isenberg, I. H. The anatomy of redwood bark. *Madroño* 7:85–91. 1943.

Jeffrey, E. C. *The anatomy of woody plants.* Chicago, University of Chicago Press. 1917.

Klinken, J. Über das gleitende Wachstum der Initialen im Kambium der Koniferen und den Markstrahlenverlauf in ihrer secundären Rinde. *Biblioth. Bot.* 19(84):1–41. 1914.

Lecomte, H. Contribution a l'étude du liber des angiospermes. *Ann. des Sci. Nat., Bot.* Ser. 7. 10:193–324. 1889.

Léger, L. J. Recherches sur l'appareil végétatif des Papavéracées. *Soc. Linn. de Normandie, Mém.* 18:193–624. 1895.

Léger, L. J. Recherches sur l'origine et les transformations des éléments libériens. *Soc. Linn. de Normandie, Mém.* 19:49–182. 1897.

MacDaniels, L. H. The histology of the phloem in certain woody angiosperms. *Amer. Jour. Bot.* 5:347–378. 1918.

Mangin, L. Sur la callose, nouvelle substance fondamentale existant dans la membrane. *Acad. des Sci. Compt. Rend.* 110:644–647. 1890.

Mason, T. G., and E. Phillis. The migration of solutes. *Bot. Rev.* 3:47–71. 1937.

Möller, J. *Anatomie der Baumrinden.* Berlin, Julius Springer. 1882.

Mühldorf, A. Das plasmatische Wesen der pflanzlichen Zellbrücken. *Bot. Centbl. Beihefte.* 56:171–364. 1937.

Nägeli, C. W. Das Wachsthum des Stammes und der Wurzel bei den Gefässpflanzen und die Anordnung der Gefässstränge im Stengel. *Beitr. z. Wiss. Bot.* Heft 1:1–156. 1858.

Perrot, E. *Le tissu criblé.* Paris, Librairie Lechevallier. 1899.

Rawlins, T. E. *Phytopathological and botanical research methods.* New York, John Wiley & Sons. 1933.

Rouschal, E. Untersuchungen über die Protoplasmatik und Funktion der Siebröhren. *Flora* 35:135–200. 1941.

Schmidt, E. W. *Bau und Funktion der Siebröhre der Angiospermen.* Jena, Gustav Fischer. 1917.

Schneider, H. The anatomy of peach and cherry phloem. *Torrey Bot. Club Bul.* 72:137–156. 1945.

Schumacher, W. Untersuchungen über die Lokalisation der Stoffwanderung in den Leitbündeln höherer Pflanzen. *Jahrb. f. Wiss. Bot.* 73:770–823. 1930.

Schumacher, W. Untersuchungen über die Wanderung des Fluoreszeïns in den Siebröhren. *Jahrb. f. Wiss. Bot.* 77:685–732. 1933.

Schumacher, W. Weitere Untersuchungen über die Wanderung von Farbstoffen in den Siebröhren. *Jahrb. f. Wiss. Bot.* 85:422–449. 1937.

Schumacher, W. Über die Plasmolysierbarkeit der Siebröhren. *Jahrb. f. Wiss. Bot.* 88:545–553. 1939.

Strasburger, E. *Über den Bau und die Verrichtungen der Leitungsbahnen in den Pflanzen. Histologische Beiträge.* Band 3. Jena, Gustav Fischer. 1891.

Thomson, R. B., and H. B. Sifton. Resin canals in the Canadian spruce (*Picea canadensis* (Mill.) B. S. P.)—an anatomical study, especially in relation to traumatic effects and their bearing on phylogeny. *Roy. Soc. London, Phil. Trans.* Ser. B. 214:63–111. 1925.

Wilhelm, K. *Beiträge zur Kenntnis des Siebröhrenapparates dicotyler Pflanzen.* Leipzig, Wilhelm Engelmann. 1880.

Wilson, C. L. Lignification of mature phloem in herbaceous types. *Amer. Jour. Bot.* 9:239–244. 1922.

CHAPTER

13

Laticifers

CONCEPT

Laticifers are cells or series of fused cells containing a fluid called *latex* (plural, *latices*) and forming systems that permeate various tissues of the plant body. The word *laticifer* and its adjectival form *laticiferous* are derived from the word latex, meaning juice in Latin. The latex is often milky or even white in appearance, and therefore the laticifers are sometimes called lactiferous cells or vessels (Jackson, 1928). The term lactiferous is derived from the Latin word for milk, *lac*. Since the latex is highly variable in its physical and chemical composition and is not necessarily milky, the less specific terms laticifer and laticiferous are more appropriate than lactiferous. It is also preferable to employ *laticifer* as a general term (Jackson, 1928) instead of laticiferous ducts or tubes because of the simplicity and wide applicability of this term.

Although the structures bearing the latex may be single cells or series of fused cells, both kinds often produce complex systems of tube-like growth form in which recognition of the limits of individual cells is highly problematical. The term laticifer, therefore, appears most useful if applied to either a single cell or a structure resulting from fusion of cells. A single-cell laticifer can be qualified, on the basis of origin, as a *simple laticifer,* and the structure derived from union of cells as a *compound laticifer.*

The laticifers vary widely in their structure, and the latex in its composition. Latex may be present in ordinary parenchyma cells, as in guayule (*Parthenium argentatum;* Bonner and Galston, 1947), or it may be formed in complex branching (*Euphorbia*) or anastomosing (*Hevea*) systems of tubes. The ordinary parenchyma cells with latex and the elaborate laticiferous systems intergrade with each other through intermediate types of structures of various degrees of morphologic specialization. Laticifers also intergrade with certain idioblasts which contain no latex and, therefore, are not included among the laticifers (e.g., tannin sacs of Leguminosae or *Sambucus*). The situation is further complicated by the use of the term laticiferous ducts or canals with reference to certain kinds of secretory intercellular canals (Blaser, 1945; Venning, 1948). The contents of laticifers, the latex, also cannot be clearly distinguished from the inclusions of certain other specialized cells such as various so-called mucilage, tannin, or protein sacs (Sperlich, 1939).

In view of the wide variation in the morphology and contents of laticifers, the delimitation of these structures is not the same in the various texts, reviews, and comparative studies (De Bary, 1884; Foster, 1949; Haberlandt, 1914; Hayward, 1938; Léger, 1895; Sperlich, 1939). No attempt is made in this book to circumscribe laticifers with any degree of precision, but the structures that are rather generally interpreted as laticifers are reviewed in detail, and some of the related elements are briefly mentioned for comparison. The intercellular canals, whatever may be their contents, are not considered.

Laticifers have been described only in the angiosperms and only in relatively few scattered families of dicotyledons and monocotyledons. The plants containing latex range from such small herbaceous annuals as the spurges (*Euphorbia*) to large trees like the rubber-yielding *Hevea*. They occur in all parts of the world, but arborescent types are most common in the tropical floras.

CLASSIFICATION

Laticifers are grouped in two major classes on the basis of their structure: the *articulated* (that is, jointed; plate 40) and the *nonarticulated* (plate 39, *A–C*). The former are compound in origin and consist of longitudinal chains of cells in which the walls separating the individual cells either remain intact, or become perforated, or are completely removed. The perforation or resorption of the end walls gives rise to laticifers that are tube-like in form and resemble xylem vessels in origin. This type of laticifer is often called laticiferous vessel. The nonarticulated laticifers originate from single cells which through continued growth develop into tube-like structures, often much branched, but typically they undergo no fusions with other similar cells. This type of laticifer is simple in origin and is often called a laticiferous cell.

The variations in structure of the two types of laticifers permit the establishment of subdivisions under each. Some of the articulated

laticifers consist of long cell chains or compound tubes not connected with each other laterally; others form lateral anastomoses with

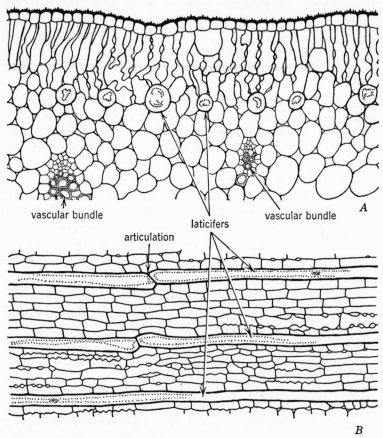

FIG. 13.1. Articulated laticifers of *Allium sativum*. *A*, transverse and, *B*, tangential
(parallel with the epidermis) sections of leaves showing the laticifers in relation
to other tissues. In *A* the mesophyll beneath the epidermis is differentiated as
palisade parenchyma. The laticifers occur in the third layer of the mesophyll
and are not in contact with the vascular bundles. Their contracted contents are
shown by stippling. In *B* the laticifers appear like continuous tubes except in
places where the end wall (articulation) between superposed cells is visible.
The end wall is not perforated. (Compare with fig. 13.3, *A*.) (Both, ×79.
Drawn from photomicrographs by L. K. Mann.)

similar cell chains or tubes, all combined into a net-like structure or
reticulum. These two forms of laticifers can be called *articulated
nonanastomosing* laticifers (fig. 13.1) and *articulated anastomosing*
(plate 39, *D*) laticifers, respectively.

The nonarticulated laticifers also vary in degree of complexity in their structure. Some develop into long, more or less straight tubes; others branch repeatedly, each cell thus forming an immense system of tubes. The appropriate names for these two types of structures are *nonarticulated unbranched* laticifers and *nonarticulated branched* (plate 39, *A–C*) laticifers, respectively.

Examples of the various types of laticifers are found in the following families and genera. Articulated anastomosing: Compositae, tribe Cichorieae (*Cichorium, Lactuca, Scorzonera, Sonchus, Taraxacum, Tragopogon*); Campanulaceae, including the Lobelioideae; Caricaceae (*Carica papaya*); Papaveraceae (*Papaver, Argemone*); Euphorbiaceae (*Hevea, Manihot*). Articulated nonanastomosing: Convolvulaceae (*Ipomoea, Convolvulus, Dichondra*); Papaveraceae (*Chelidonium*); Sapotaceae (*Achras sapota*); Liliaceae (*Allium*); Musaceae (*Musa*). Nonarticulated branched: Euphorbiaceae (*Euphorbia*); Asclepiadaceae (*Asclepias, Cryptostegia*); Apocynaceae (*Nerium oleander*); Moraceae (*Ficus, Broussonetia, Maclura*). Nonarticulated unbranched: Apocynaceae (*Vinca*); Urticaceae (*Urtica*); Moraceae (*Cannabis*).

The list given above clearly shows that the type of laticiferous element is not constant in a given family. One of the best-known examples of variations is the presence of nonarticulated laticifers in *Euphorbia* and of articulated laticifers in *Hevea*, both plants belonging to the same family, the Euphorbiaceae. It is also reported (Schaffstein, 1932) that certain Asclepiadaceae develop two kinds of laticifers, articulated and nonarticulated, in the same plant body and that the parenchyma cells, which lie near the articulated elements, assume some of the characteristics of laticiferous cells and appear to be transitional between typical laticifers and ordinary parenchyma cells. Another evidence of a lack of sharp distinction between articulated and nonarticulated laticifers is the combination of a union of cells with a development of short branches, or protuberances, observed in the formation of laticifers of some plants (Calvert, 1887; De Bary, 1884, p. 436; Parkin, 1900; Scott, 1884).

Systematic comparative studies on the laticifers are scarce, and the possible phylogenetic significance of the variations in the degree of their specialization has not yet been revealed. Sometimes, however, a comparison of the laticifers in the representatives of the same family or of closely related families suggests possible series of increasing specialization.

In the Aroideae (De Bary, 1884, p. 436), for example, certain species appear to lack laticifers or any related structures. Others have longitudinal rows of elongated, cylindrical sac-like cells, with no perforations in their end walls and no lateral anastomoses. Still others contain anastomosing tubes, with open communications established among the individual cells. A similar series is recognizable in the Papaveraceae and the closely allied Fumariaceae (Léger, 1895). Some workers consider that the Fumariaceae have no laticifers (Sperlich, 1939). Its representatives, however, possess certain idioblasts that appear to intergrade with the laticifers of the Papaveraceae. Some of these idioblasts are indistinguishable from other parenchyma cells, except by their peculiar colored contents, rich in alkaloids; others are larger and occur singly or in chains. In the Papaveraceae similar files of cells are transformed into tubes by perforation of the end walls (*Chelidonium*) or by a partial or complete resorption of the transverse walls and a development of lateral anastomoses joining the tubes with each other (*Papaver*). The contents of these tubes in the Papaveraceae are interpreted as latex. This latex is milky granular in appearance, sometimes highly colored, and rich in alkaloids. The Cruciferae, which are farther removed from the Papaveraceae than the Fumariaceae, also have idioblastic cells resembling laticifers (Sperlich, 1939). These cells contain the enzyme myrosin. They are often long and branched but are not classified as laticifers because their contents cannot be properly called latex.

COMPOSITION AND PHYSICAL STATE OF LATEX

Latex is a substance consisting of a liquid matrix with minute organic particles in suspension. The matrix may be regarded as the cell sap of the laticifer (Frey-Wyssling, 1935). Like cell sap it contains various substances in solution and in colloidal suspension: carbohydrates, organic acids, salts, alkaloids, sterols, fats, tannins, and mucilages. The dispersed particles commonly belong to the hydrocarbon family of terpenes, which includes such substances as essential oils, balsams, resins, camphors, carotenoids, and rubber (Bonner and Galston, 1947). Among these substances the resins and particularly rubber, with the empirical formula of $(C_5H_8)_n$, are characteristic components of the latex in many plants. The terpenes occur in different amounts, depending on the kind of plant, and the rubber, specifically, is sometimes entirely lacking. Latex may contain a large amount of protein (*Ficus callosa*), sugar (Compositae), or tannins (*Musa*, Aroideae). The latex of some Papaveraceae is well known for its content in alkaloids (*Papaver somniferum*), that of *Carica papaya* for the occurrence of the proteolytic enzyme papain. Crystals of oxalates and malates may be abundant in latex. Certain plants contain starch grains in the laticifers, often together with the enzyme diastase. The starch grains of the genus *Euphorbia* may attain very large size and assume various, sometimes peculiar, shapes —spheroids, rods, dumbbells, and bones.

The best-known latex is that of the various rubber-yielding plants (Bonner and Galston, 1947; Moyer, 1937; Moyle, 1942; Sperlich, 1939; Whaley, 1948). The rubber content varies widely in different species. Of the 1791 dicotyledonous species of plants reported to contain rubber, only 554 have been used as rubber producers, and only few of these yield enough pure rubber to make them commercially valuable. In *Hevea*, rubber may constitute 40 to 50 per cent of the latex. The rubber particles suspended in latex vary in size and shape. When the latex is released from the plant, the particles clump together; that is, the latex coagulates. This property is utilized in the commercial separation of rubber from latex.

The latex of various plants may be clear (*Morus*, *Nerium oleander*) or milky (*Asclepias*, *Euphorbia*, *Ficus*, *Lactuca*). It is yellow-brown in *Cannabis* and yellow or orange in the Papaveraceae. The turbidity and milkiness of latex does not depend directly on its composition but results from the difference between the refractive indices of the particles and the dispersion medium.

Students of laticiferous plants have made the curious observation that latex often harbors flagellates. Their presence induces no visible external symptoms in the plants but is suspected of reducing their vigor (Harvey and Lee, 1943).

Laticifers release the latex when they are cut open. The flow of latex is a pressure flow (Bonner and Galston, 1947; Frey-Wyssling, 1933). In the intact plant the laticifers are under turgor and at the same time are in osmotic equilibrium with the surrounding parenchyma cells. When the laticifer is opened, a turgor gradient is established and the flow occurs toward the cut where the turgor has been reduced to zero (Frey-Wyssling, 1933; Spencer, 1939c). This flow eventually ceases, and subsequently the turgor is restored (Spencer, 1939a).

CYTOLOGY OF LATICIFERS

The nature of the protoplast of laticifers has been imperfectly investigated. Its study is as difficult as that of the sieve-element protoplast. The common concept is that the laticifers maintain a living protoplast, that the nuclei remain in this protoplast upon maturation of the elements, and that the cytoplasm occurs as a parietal layer enclosing a vacuole composed of the latex. In nonarticulated laticifers of many plants the nuclei are known to undergo divisions resulting in a multinucleate condition (plate 39, *C*). Because of this characteristic the nonarticulated laticifers are interpreted as coenocytes (Foster, 1949, p. 145). Articulated laticifers, in which communications are established between the individual cells, are also multinucleate but apparently only because the protoplasts fuse and not because of a subsequent multiplication of nuclei (Sperlich, 1939). In young laticifers the nuclei are readily distinguished; later the dense latex obscures their visibility (fig. 13.3, *B, C*; Frey-Wyssling, 1935). According to studies on *Hevea* and *Manihot*, nuclei degenerate in laticifers, with an extrusion of nucleoli (Milanez, 1946, 1949).

The proof of the presence of parietal cytoplasm is difficult to obtain. As in sieve elements, there is no clear demarcation between the cytoplasm and the vacuole in mature laticifers (Bonner and Galston, 1947; Sperlich, 1939), and in sectioned material the contents suffer considerable displacement. Nevertheless, some workers report having recognized the shrunken cytoplasm in the center of laticifers from which latex has ceased to flow (Frey-Wyssling, 1935; Moyer, 1937). The most significant studies have been performed with the articulated laticifers of *Carica papaya* (Moyer, 1937). In ripe fruits of this plant the loose ground parenchyma was washed away and the laticifers were isolated without too much injury to them. Placed on a 1.5 per cent agar preparation, they remained alive for 3 to 4 days and were subjected to plasmolytic tests. These tests strongly indicated the presence of a protoplasmic sheath lining the wall. A contrasting interpretation of the relation between cytoplasm and vacuole is presented with regard to *Hevea* and *Manihot* (Milanez, 1946, 1949). The small vacuoles of the young laticifers are described as being absorbed by the cytoplasm instead of fusing into a single large vacuole. Such development implies that, in the mature laticifers, the cytoplasm is highly hydrated and the latex is part of this cytoplasm.

Most evidence suggests that the latex particles are formed in the laticifers themselves, either in the cytoplasm or in plastids (Bonner and Galston, 1947; Frey-Wyssling, 1935; Milanez, 1946, 1949). If the laticifers have a distinct vacuole, then one must assume the subsequent escape of the latex particles into the vacuolar sap which becomes part of the latex. This interpretation strikingly parallels that given for the relation between the slime and the protoplast in the sieve elements (see chapter 12).

STRUCTURE OF WALLS

The walls of the laticifers are primary, soft, and apparently plastic (Milanez, 1946; Sperlich, 1939). They may be no thicker than the walls of the adjacent parenchyma cells, or they may be noticeably thicker. The walls often increase in thickness with the age of the element. The thick walls have been described as rich in pectic substances, and they seem to be hydrated. The thickening may be uneven, but primary pit fields are rarely observed. There is a report in the early literature on laticifers that plasmodesmata occur between these structures and the adjacent parenchyma cells (Sperlich, 1939).

Presence of callose has been recorded in laticifers. In *Hevea* pluglike masses of callose have been found in the laticifers at the bases of aged leaves (Spencer, 1939*b*). When such leaves are severed from the plant, no latex issues either from the leaf or from the part of the severed petiole remaining on the stem. The early report on callose in laticifers of *Allium* (Rendle, 1889) has not been confirmed by later studies (Mann, 1952).

DEVELOPMENT OF LATICIFERS

Nonarticulated Laticifers

The branched nonarticulated laticifers of the Euphorbiaceae, the Asclepiadaceae, and the Apocynaceae are reported as arising during the development of the embryo in the form of relatively few primordia, then growing concomitantly with the plant into branched systems permeating the whole plant body (Cameron, 1936; Schaffstein, 1932; Sperlich, 1939; and others). The differentiation of such laticifers has been studied intensively in the genus *Euphorbia*. In this plant the primordial laticifers appear in the embryo when the cotyledons are initiated. The laticifers become distinct because of their large size and refringent contents. They are located in the plane of the embryo that later represents the cotyledonary node. As seen in transverse sections, the laticifer primordia occur in various numbers in the peripheral part of the vascular cylinder. In some species only four primordia were recognized; in others eight, arranged in four pairs; and in still others, many primordia, distributed

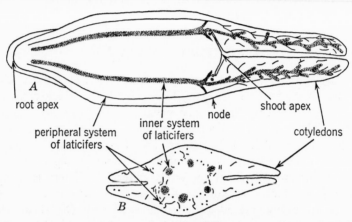

Fɪɢ. 13.2. Arrangement of nonarticulated laticifers in an embryo of *Euphorbia marginata* in longitudinal section of the entire embryo (*A*) and transection of the cotyledonary node (*B*). The stippled laticifers constitute the main system of tubes located, in the hypocotyl, on the periphery of the vascular cylinder (inner system of laticifers). The thin solid lines and dots indicate the system of tubes which occur, in the hypocotyl, near the periphery of the axis (peripheral system of laticifers). Both systems are prolonged into the cotyledons where they branch profusely. At the cotyledonary node in *A*, small branches extend toward the apical meristem of the epicotyl. (Adapted from Cameron, 1936.)

in arcs or in a complete circle around the vascular cylinder. The primordial laticifers form protrusions in various directions, and the apices of these protrusions push their way among the surrounding cells by intrusive growth.

When the seed of *Euphorbia* is mature, the embryo has a system of tubes arranged in a characteristic manner (fig. 13.2). One set of tubes extends from the cotyledonary node downward, following the periphery of the vascular cylinder of the hypocotyl. Another set passes downward within the cortex, usually near its periphery. The two sets of tubes end near the root meristem at the base of the hypocotylary axis. A third set is prolonged into the cotyledons where the tubes branch, sometimes profusely. A fourth set of tubes extends inwardly and upwardly from the nodal primordia toward the shoot apex of the epicotyl where the tubes form a ring-like network. The terminations of this network reach into the third or fourth layers beneath the surface of the apical meristem. Thus, there are laticifer terminations in the immediate vicinity of both apical meristems, those of the shoot and those of the root. When the seed germinates and the embryo develops into a plant, the laticifers keep pace with this growth by continuously penetrating the meristematic tissues formed by the active apical meristems. When axillary buds or lateral roots arise, they also are penetrated by the growing tips of the laticifers. Most workers agree that the nonarticulated laticifers do not fuse with each other.

During the development of nonarticulated laticifers their nuclei repeatedly divide so that each actively growing tip is provided with cytoplasm and nuclei. Since these tips penetrate the tissues close to the apical meristems, the tube portions below the tips occur for a time in growing tissues. Presumably the laticifers extend in unison with the growing tissues; otherwise they would be torn and obliterated like the protophloem sieve elements. Thus, one may picture the laticifers as elongating at their apices by intrusive growth and subsequently extending with the surrounding tissues by symplastic growth.

The question has been raised in the literature whether the laticifers are indefinitely capable of growth and, specifically, whether the tubes in the older portions of the plant retain the ability to invade tissues (Schaffstein, 1932; Schmalhausen, 1877). Laticifer branches penetrating into the pith, the cortex, and the primary phloem of woody species are known to become nonfunctional and die when the surrounding tissues die. In live tissues, however, they seem to retain the capacity for further growth (Schaffstein, 1932). In some experiments, laticifers of *Euphorbia* were observed penetrating from hypocotyl into adventitious shoots that arose on decapitated seedlings. Similarly, laticifers grew into adventitious roots that originated on cuttings. They were also found growing into the dividing tissue beneath a callus formed in grafting. All these observations suggest that laticifers of the nonarticulated branched type may be stimulated to resumption of growth, if they are brought in contact with actively growing tissue. In the absence of such tissue in their vicinity they reach a certain maximum of development and then cease to grow. In dormant meristematic tissues laticifers appear to be quiescent (Schaffstein, 1932).

The retention of potentiality for growth in branched nonarticulated laticifers helps to explain some of the observations on the relation of such laticifers to secondary tissues in *Cryptostegia* (Artschwager, 1946; Blaser, 1945). In the primary body of this plant, laticifers branch in the pith, the cortex, and the primary phloem. When secondary growth takes place, no new laticifers are formed but the secondary phloem is penetrated by prolongations from the cortical and primary phloem laticifers. In the primary state a given laticifer (that is, a structure derived from one cell) may be represented by branches in all three parts of the stem. The connections between the inner and the outer branches of the laticifer are located in the interfascicular areas of the vascular system. These connections are seemingly not ruptured by the activity of the vascular cambium during secondary growth. Instead, the parts of the laticifer located in the interfascicular cambium appear to extend by localized growth (intercalary growth) and eventually become imbedded in secondary phloem and xylem (Blaser, 1945).

Nonarticulated unbranched laticifers show a simpler pattern of growth than the branched type (Schaffstein, 1932; Sperlich, 1939; Varossieau, 1943; Zander, 1928). The primordia of these laticifers have been recognized, not in the embryo, but in the developing shoot (*Vinca, Cannabis*) or in the shoot and root (*Eucommia*). New primordia arise repeatedly beneath the apical meristems, and each elongates into an unbranched tube, apparently by a combination of intrusive and symplastic growth. In the shoot the tubes may extend for some distance in the stem and also diverge into the leaves (*Vinca*). Laticifers may arise in the leaves also, independently of those formed in the stem (*Cannabis, Eucommia*). In some species the unbranched laticifers become multinucleate during development.

Articulated Laticifers

The articulated laticifers develop into extensive tube-like structures, not by the growth of individual cells, but by the constant addition of new primordia to the existing ones. The development of articulated laticifers has been studied most intensively in the Cichorieae (Sperlich, 1939). The laticifers in *Hevea* and *Manihot* (Euphorbiaceae) develop rather similarly to those of the Cichorieae (Milanez, 1946, 1949; Scott, 1884, 1886). The primordial laticifers of the Cichorieae are visible in the hypocotyl and the cotyledons of the embryo in the mature seed (Baranova, 1935; Schmalhausen, 1877; Scott, 1882). These primordia are arranged in longitudinal rows, but their end walls are intact. During the first stages of germination the end walls break down and the cell rows are converted into vessels. As the plant develops from the embryo, the vessels are extended by differentiation of further meristematic cells into laticiferous elements. Thus, the laticifers differentiate acropetally (that is, in a succession toward the apex) into the newly formed plant parts, and they are prolonged not only within the axis but also into the leaves and, later, into the flowers and fruits. The direction of differentiation is basically the same as in the nonarticulated branched laticifers, but it occurs by successive conversion of cells into laticiferous elements instead of by apical intrusive growth. Where the vessels lie side by side, parts of the common wall become resorbed (plate 40, *B*). If they are farther apart, the intervening cells may become changed into laticiferous cells with resorption of common walls, or the existing vessels may send out lateral protuberances that fuse with those from another vessel. Thus an anastomosing network of laticifers is formed. Some of the lateral protuberances may end blindly in the tissue.

The Cichorieae produce laticifers during secondary growth also, in the secondary phloem. This development has been followed in some detail in the fleshy roots of *Tragopogon* (Scott, 1882), *Scorzonera* (Baranova, 1935), and *Taraxacum* (Artschwager and McGuire, 1943). Longitudinal rows of derivatives from fusiform cambial initials fuse into tubes through resorption of the end walls. Lateral connections are established—directly or by means of protuberances—among the tubes differentiating in the same tangential plane. The development of articulated laticifers of the nonanastomosing kind is similar to that of the anastomosing laticifers, except that no lateral connections are established among the various tubes (fig. 13.3, *B–H*; Karling, 1929).

In grafts performed with *Hevea* (Bonner and Galston, 1947) and *Taraxacum* (Prokofiev, 1945) the establishment of connection between the laticiferous systems of stock and scion was indicated by the evidence of transport of latex from one member of the graft to the other. Both of these genera have anastomosing articulated laticifers and the interconnection of the laticifers across the graft union is probably a result of their pronounced ability to unite with similar elements.

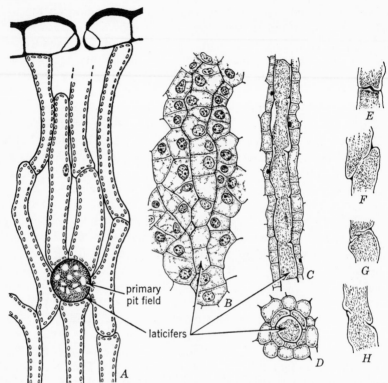

FIG. 13.3. Articulated laticifers. *A*, transection through a fleshy scale of *Allium cepa*, showing, beneath the epidermis, a few mesophyll cells and a laticifer with the end wall seen in surface view. This end wall bears prominent primary pit fields. *B–H*, details of laticifer development in *Achras sapota* in longitudinal (*B, C, E–H*) and transverse (*D*) sections. *B* shows a vertical file of young laticifer cells (the series of cells from the arrow upward) with the end walls still intact. *C*, the file of cells has been converted into a part of a laticiferous vessel by partial dissolution of end walls. Remnants of end walls indicate the articulations between the members of the laticifer. The transverse view in *D* shows flattened cells ensheathing the laticfer. These cells show no cytologic specialization. *E–H*, developmental series showing stages in the perforation of the end wall. The wall to be perforated first becomes swollen (*E*) and then breaks down (*F–H*). (Compare with fig. 11.3.) (*A*, ×300. *B–H*, adapted from Karling, 1929.)

ARRANGEMENT IN THE PLANT BODY

Laticifers are frequently distributed rather generally through the plant (fig. 13.4, *B*), but sometimes they are more or less restricted to certain tissues (De Bary, 1884; Sperlich, 1939). Most commonly they are associated with the phloem (fig. 13.4, *A*, and plate 40, *A*). There

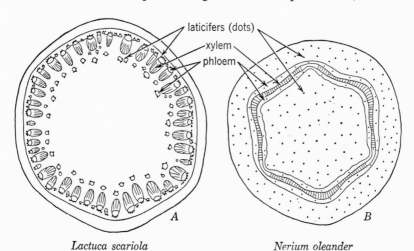

Lactuca scariola   *Nerium oleander*

Fig. 13.4. Diagrams showing the distribution of the laticifers in transections of stems of *Lactuca scariola* (Prickly Lettuce) (*A*) and *Nerium oleander* (*B*). In *A* the laticifers are articulated and are associated with the external and the internal phloem. In *B* they are nonarticulated and are dispersed throughout all the tissues, including the xylem. (Both, ×13.)

is much information on the arrangement of the laticifers in the aerial parts of plants. However, laticifers occur in roots also, and those of the fleshy roots of certain Cichorieae have been investigated in detail (e.g., Artschwager and McGuire, 1943).

Nonarticulated Laticifers

In the genus *Euphorbia* the main tubes of the branched nonarticulated laticifers commonly are located in the outer part of the vascular cylinder. From here, branches extend into the cortex and sometimes also into the pith by growing through the interfascicular areas. The cortical branches spread to the epidermis. The minor branches are narrower than the main tubes, and the ultimate ramifications end blindly. In some of the Apocynaceae, the Asclepiadaceae, and the

Moraceae laticifers appear rather generally dispersed in various tissues, including the vascular. In others the main tubes traverse only the pith and form branches at the nodes, some of which penetrate the parenchyma above the leaf insertion (leaf gap) and enter the leaves. Branched nonarticulated laticifers commonly occur in leaves. Here they follow the vascular bundles, ramify in the mesophyll, and often reach the epidermis. In some Euphorbiaceae laticifers intrude among the epidermal cells, reach the cuticle, and even continue along the surface of the epidermal cells beneath the cuticle (Sperlich, 1939).

The unbranched nonarticulated laticifers of *Vinca* and *Cannabis* occur in the primary phloem but are apparently absent in the secondary tissues (Schaffstein, 1932; Zander, 1928).

Articulated Laticifers

Articulated laticifers also show various arrangements and a frequent association with the phloem. In the primary body of the Cichorieae, laticifers appear on the outer periphery of the phloem (plate 40, *A*) and within the phloem itself. In species with internal phloem, laticifers are associated with this tissue also (fig. 13.4, *A*). The internal and the external laticifers are interconnected across the interfascicular areas. The arrangement of laticifers in the secondary body of the Cichorieae may be exemplified by the use of *Taraxacum kok-saghyz*, a species utilized commercially for its rubber content (Artschwager and McGuire, 1943; Krotkov, 1945). The laticifers are within the secondary phloem. This tissue is formed by the cambium as a series of concentric layers of parenchyma cells and of layers containing the sieve tubes and the laticifers. The two kinds of layer alternate with each other radially. Rays of parenchyma traverse the whole tissue in the radial direction. Sieve tubes, companion cells, some phloem parenchyma, and the laticifers are combined into bundles which anastomose and form a network (plate 39, *D*). Within the network the sieve tubes and the laticifers are not connected with each other, but only with elements of their own kind. The laticifers of one growth zone are rarely joined with the laticifers of another growth zone.

In leaves the articulated laticifers of the Cichorieae accompany the vascular bundles, ramify more or less profusely in the mesophyll, and reach the epidermis. The epidermal hairs of the floral involucres of the Cichorieae become directly connected with laticifers by a breakdown of the separating walls and, as a result, the latex readily issues from these hairs when they are broken (Sperlich, 1939).

In several other families articulated laticifers have patterns of distribution in the plant body similar to those of the Cichorieae. In the Caricaceae, however, laticifers apparently occur not only in the

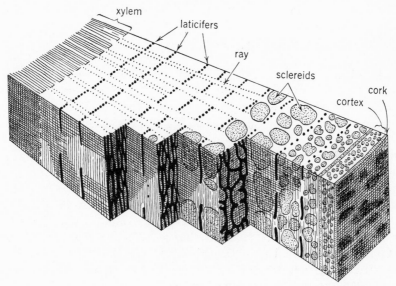

Fig. 13.5. Block diagram of the phloem and adjacent tissues of *Hevea brasiliensis*, depicting the arrangement of the articulated laticifers in the secondary phloem. The secondary phloem shows an alternation of layers containing sieve tubes and associated parenchyma cells with those in which the laticifers (shown in solid black) differentiate. Parenchymatous secondary phloem rays traverse the tissue radially. As seen in tangential sections the laticifers of a given growth zone are thoroughly interconnected into a reticulum. Sclereids occur in the part of the phloem where the sieve tubes and laticifers are nonfunctional. (Adapted from Vischer, 1923.)

phloem but also in the xylem (De Bary, 1884, p. 434). The laticiferous system that makes *Hevea* (Euphorbiaceae) such an outstanding rubber producer is the secondary system that develops in the secondary phloem (fig. 13.5; Sperlich, 1939; Vischer, 1923).

In the monocotyledons the laticifers of *Musa* are associated with the vascular tissues and also occur in the cortex (Skutch, 1932). In *Allium* the laticifers are entirely separated from the vascular tissue. They lie near the abaxial surface of the leaves or scales (fig. 13.1, *A*), between the second and third layers of parenchyma. The

Allium laticifers have the form of longitudinal chains of cells arranged parallel in the upper parts of the foliar organs and converging toward their bases. The individual cells of the compound laticifers are considerably elongated (fig. 13.1, *B*). The end walls are not perforated but have conspicuous primary pit areas (fig. 13.3, *A*; De Bary, 1884, p. 147). Although *Allium* laticifers are classified as nonanastomosing, they form some interconnections at the bases of the leaves or scales.

POSSIBLE FUNCTION

The laticifers have been the object of intensive study since the early days of plant anatomy (De Bary, 1884; Sperlich, 1939). Because of their distribution in the plant body and their liquid, often milky contents that flow out readily when the plant is cut, the laticiferous system was compared by the early botanists with the circulatory system of animals. The laticifers were called vital sap vessels (Lebenssaftgefässe) and were assumed to have the same function as the blood vessels of animals. Later, they were thought to be related to the vascular elements, particularly the sieve tubes. Still later, the laticifers were interpreted as elements morphologically distinct from the sieve tubes, but related to secretory structures. Views on the function of the laticifers changed in accordance with the various interpretations of their morphological nature. Conclusive information on their role in the life of the plant is still lacking (Bonner and Galston, 1947; Whaley, 1948).

One of the common views advanced was that the laticifers were concerned with food conduction. The evidence for such a role was seen in their high content in food material and in their arrangement in the plant body. However, no actual movement of materials has been observed in the laticifers, only a local and spasmodic one, and no experiments have as yet been designed to test the assumption that food is conducted by the laticifers.

The laticifers have been described also as elements storing food materials. The results of experiments conducted to test this view are contradictory but generally indicate that food materials present in the latex are not readily mobilized when plants are deprived of means to form carbohydrates.

Since latex readily absorbs water from adjacent tissues, it has been thought to be involved with regulation of water balance in the plant. It has also been described as an agency for transport of oxygen, or as material utilized by the plant for protection against animals.

The most widely accepted interpretation of the role of the laticifers is that they form an excretory system. Laticifers accumulate many substances that are commonly recognized as excretory, and such substances are more abundant than food materials in the latex. The terpenes, some of which (rubber and resin) are commonly present in the latices of various plants, appear to be nonfunctional by-products of cellular metabolism, particularly of that characteristic of young growing tissues. When once deposited in the cells, the terpenes are not known to be utilized again by the plant (Benedict, 1949; Bonner and Galston, 1947; Haan and van Aggelen-Bot, 1948).

The highly polymerized terpenes, like rubber, are incapable of passing across cell walls and remain in the cells in which they are formed. It seems significant, therefore, that the formation of high-molecular-weight terpenes by plants commonly coincides with the occurence of laticifers, which appear to be adapted as repositories for this type of excreted substance. Resin, on the other hand, is frequently excreted into specialized intercellular passages, the resin ducts, or to the surface of the plant through excretory trichomes. In the Compositae some groups have laticiferous systems, others have resin ducts, and the two kinds of structures do not occur together (Frey-Wyssling, 1935).

The laticifers are often placed in one class with the secretory structures (Eames and MacDaniels, 1947; Hayward, 1938). Such a classification emphasizes the common properties of the secreted and excreted substances—their separation from the protoplasts—but not their differences. If the secreta are interpreted as substances having a special physiologic function after they are secreted (enzymes, hormones, nectar) and the excreta as end products of a dissimilatory metabolism, not further utilized by the plant (resins, oils, rubber) (Frey-Wyssling, 1935), then the laticifers would appear to fit best in the class of excretory structures. At the same time, the variety of substances present in the latex and the variations in its composition in different plants suggest the possibility that the laticifers may have more than one function.

REFERENCES

Artschwager, E. Contribution to the morphology and anatomy of *Cryptostegia* (*Cryptostegia grandiflora*). *U. S. Dept. Agric. Tech. Bul.* 915. 1946.

Artschwager, E., and R. C. McGuire. Contribution to the morphology and anatomy of the Russian dandelion (*Taraxacum kok-saghyz*). *U. S. Dept. Agric. Tech. Bul.* 843. 1943.

Baranova, E. A.   Ontogenez mlechnoĭ systemy tau-sagyza (*Scorzonera tau-saghyz* Lipsch. et Bosse).   [Ontogeny of the laticiferous system of tau-saghyz (*Scorzonera tau-saghyz* Lipsch. et Bosse).]   *Jour. Bot. de l'URSS.* 20:600–616.   1935.

Benedict, H. M.   A further study on the nonutilization of rubber as a food reserve by guayule.   *Bot. Gaz.* 111:36–43.   1949.

Blaser, H. W.   Anatomy of *Cryptostegia grandiflora* with special reference to the latex.   *Amer. Jour. Bot.* 32:135–141.   1945.

Bonner, J., and A. W. Galston.   The physiology and biochemistry of rubber formation in plants.   *Bot. Rev.* 13:543–596.   1947.

Calvert, A.   The laticiferous tissue in the stem of *Hevea brasiliensis*.   *Ann. Bot.* 1:75–77.   1887.

Cameron, D.   An investigation of the latex systems in *Euphorbia marginata*, with particular attention to the distribution of latex in the embryo.   *Bot. Soc. Edinb. Trans. and Proc.* 32(I):187–194.   1936.

De Bary, A.   *Comparative anatomy of the vegetative organs of the phanerogams and ferns.*   Oxford, Clarendon Press.   1884.

Eames, A. J., and L. H. MacDaniels.   *An introduction to plant anatomy.*   2nd ed.   New York, McGraw-Hlil Book Company.   1947.

Foster, A. S.   *Practical plant anatomy.*   2nd ed.   New York, D. Van Nostrand Company.   1949.

Frey-Wyssling, A.   Der Milchsafterguss von *Hevea brasiliensis* als Blutungserscheinung.   Ein Beitrag zur Druckstromtheorie.   *Jahrb. f. Wiss. Bot.* 77:560–626.   1933.

Frey-Wyssling, A.   *Die Stoffausscheidung der höheren Pflanzen. Monographien aus dem Gesamtgebiet der Physiologie der Pflanzen und der Tiere.* Band 32.   Berlin, Julius Springer.   1935.

Haan, I. de, and G. M. van Aggelen-Bot.   De vorming van rubber bij *Hevea brasiliensis*.   *Arch. v. Rubbercult. Nederland. Indië* 26:121–180.   1948.

Haberlandt, G.   *Physiological plant anatomy.*   London, Macmillan and Company.   1914.

Harvey, R. B., and S. B. Lee.   Flagellates of laticiferous plants.   *Plant Physiol.* 18:633–655.   1943.

Hayward, H. E.   *The structure of economic plants.*   New York, The Macmillan Company.   1938.

Jackson, B. D.   *A glossary of botanic terms.*   4th ed.   London, Duckworth.   1928.

Karling, J. S.   The laticiferous system of *Achras zapota* L.   *Amer. Jour. Bot.* 16:803–824.   1929.

Krotkov, G. A.   A review of literature on *Taraxacum kok-saghyz* Rod.   *Bot. Rev.* 11:417–461.   1945.

Léger, L. J.   Recherches sur l'appareil végétatif des Papavéracées.   (Papavéracées et Fumariacées D. C.)   *Soc. Linn. de Normandie, Mém.* 18:193–624.   1895.

Mann, L. K.   Anatomy of the garlic bulb and factors affecting bulb development.   *Hilgardia* 21:195–251.   1952.

Milanez, F. R.   Nota prévia sôbre os laticíferos de *Hevea brasiliensis*.   *Arqu. do Serv. Florestal* 2:39–65.   1946.

Milanez, F. R.   Segunda nota sôbre os laticíferos.   *Lilloa* 16:193–211.   1949.

Moyer, L. S. Recent advances in the physiology of latex. *Bot. Rev.* 3:522–544. 1937.

Moyle, A. E. Bibliography and collected abstracts on rubber-producing plants. *Tex. Agr. Expt. Sta. Cir.* 99. 1942.

Parkin, J. Observations on latex and its functions. *Ann. Bot.* 14:193–214. 1900.

Prokofiev, A. A. On the synthesis of rubber in plants—filling of laticiferous vessels with foreign latex. *Acad. Sci. URSS, Compt. Rend. (Doklady)* 48: 520–523. 1945.

Rendle, A. B. On the vesicular vessels of the onion. *Ann. Bot.* 3:169–177. 1889.

Schaffstein, G. Untersuchungen an ungegliederten Milchröhren. *Bot. Centbl. Beihefte.* 49:197–220. 1932.

Schmalhausen, J. Beiträge zur Kenntnis der Milchsaftbehälter der Pflanzen. *Acad. Imp. des Sci. St. Pétersbourg, Mém.* Ser. 7. 24(2):1–27. 1877.

Scott, D. H. The development of articulated laticiferous vessels. *Quart. Jour. Micros. Sci.* 22:136–153. 1882.

Scott, D. H. On the laticiferous tissue of *Manihot Glaziovii* (the Ceàra rubber). *Quart. Jour. Micros. Sci.* 24:194–204. 1884.

Scott, D. H. On the occurrence of articulated laticiferous vessels in *Hevea*. *Linn. Soc. London, Jour., Bot.* 21:566–573. 1886.

Skutch, A. F. Anatomy of the axis of the banana. *Bot. Gaz.* 93:233–258. 1932.

Spencer, H. J. The effect of puncturing individual latex tubes of *Euphorbia Wulfenii*. *Ann. Bot.* 3:227–229. 1939a.

Spencer, H. J. On the nature of the blocking of the laticiferous system at the leaf-base of *Hevea brasiliensis*. *Ann. Bot.* 3:231–235. 1939b.

Spencer, H. J. Latex outflow and water uptake in the leaf of *Ficus elastica*. *Ann. Bot.* 3:237–241. 1939c.

Sperlich, A. Das trophische Parenchym. B. Exkretionsgewebe. In: K. Linsbauer. *Handbuch der Pflanzenanatomie.* Band 4. Lief. 38. 1939.

Szuleta, J. Les cellules a tannin dans la moelle de sureau (*Sambucus nigra*). *Acad. des Sci. Compt. Rend.* 204:711–713. 1937.

Varossieau, W. W. Waarnemingen over de melksaphoudende elementen van *Eucommia ulmoides* Oliv. *Nederland Akad. van Wetenschap. Verslagen. Afd. Natuurk.* 52:105–115. 1943.

Venning, F. D. The ontogeny of the laticiferous canals in the Anacardiaceae. *Amer. Jour. Bot.* 35:637–644. 1948.

Vischer, W. Über die Konstanz anatomischer und physiologischer Eigenschaften von *Hevea brasiliensis* Müller Arg. (Euphorbiaceae). *Naturf. Gesell. in Basel, Verhandl.* 35:174–185. 1923.

Whaley, W. G. Rubber—the primary sources for American production. *Econ. Bot.* 2:198–216. 1948.

Zander, A. Über Verlauf und Enstehung der Milchröhren des Hanfes (*Cannabis sativa*). *Flora* 23:191–218. 1928.

CHAPTER

14

The Periderm

CONCEPT

Periderm is the protective tissue replacing the epidermis when the epidermis is killed and sloughed away. Periderm formation is a common phenomenon in stems and roots of dicotyledons and gymnosperms that increase in thickness by secondary growth. Structurally, the periderm consists of three parts: (1) the meristem *phellogen;* (2) the *phellem* or cork, produced by the phellogen toward the outside; and (3) the *phelloderm*, a tissue that resembles cortical parenchyma and consists of the inner derivatives of the phellogen. The term periderm and terms referring to its parts are derived from Greek words among which *phellem* means cork, *gen*, to produce, *derma*, skin, and *peri*, about.

The term periderm should be clearly distinguished from the non-technical term *bark* (see chapter 12). Bark has various meanings but is applied most commonly to all tissues outside the vascular cambium of the axis, in either primary or secondary state of growth. In this usage bark includes primary phloem and cortex in axes with primary tissues only, and primary and secondary phloem, various amounts of cortex, and periderm in axes with secondary tissues. The term bark is used also more specifically to designate the tissue that accumulates on the surface of the plant axis as a result of phellogen activity. As the periderm develops, it separates, by means of a non-living layer of cork cells, variable amounts of primary and secondary tissues of the axis from the subjacent living tissues. The tissue layers thus separated die. The term bark in its restricted meaning refers to these dead tissues together with the layers of cork. The use of the term bark in its wider sense, that is, with reference to all the tissues outside the vascular cambium, is frequently convenient and practical. If it is so used, the cork and the tissues of the axis isolated by it may be combined under the designation of *outer bark*. The technical term for the outer bark is *rhytidome* (De Bary, 1884, p. 545). This term is derived from the Greek word meaning wrinkle and refers to the appearance of the outer bark when it consists of layers of cork alternating with layers of tissue cut off by the cork.

The structure and the development of periderm are better known in stems than in roots. Therefore, most of the information on periderm given in this chapter pertains to stems, unless roots are mentioned specifically. Additional data on root periderm appear in chapter 17.

OCCURRENCE

Periderm characteristically appears on the surface of those plant parts that possess a continuous and pronounced increase in thickness by secondary growth. Roots and stems and their branches in gymnosperms and woody dicotyledons are best examples of such parts. Periderm occurs in herbaceous dicotyledons, sometimes limited to the oldest parts of stem or root. Monocotyledons rarely develop a protective tissue comparable to the periderm of dicotyledons (see p. 334). Foliar organs normally produce no cork. Scales of winter buds in some gymnosperms and dicotyledons may be cited as an exception. In stems of extant vascular cryptogams, which as a rule lack secondary growth, no periderm is formed even in species that eventually slough away the epidermis and part of the cortex (Ogura, 1938). In underground stems of some vascular cryptogams the epidermis or the outer cortical layers become suberized.

Periderm formation in stems of woody plants may be considerably delayed, as compared with the onset of secondary growth of the vascular tissues, or it may never occur, despite the obvious increase in thickness of the stem. In such instances the tissues outside the vascular cambium, including the epidermis, keep pace with the increase in axis circumference by growth and divisions of cells (e.g., species of *Viscum, Menispermum, Ilex, Acer, Citrus, Laurus, Eucalyptus, Acacia*).

Periderm differentiates on surfaces exposed after abscission of plant parts, such as leaves or branches (see chapter 16). Cork frequently develops around diseased or dead tissue complexes within the plant body and also beneath the surface of wounds (wound periderm or wound cork; plate 57).

CHARACTERISTICS OF THE COMPONENTS

In contrast to the vascular cambium, the phellogen is relatively simple in structure, being composed of one type of cell. The phellogen cells are rectangular in transections, somewhat flattened radially. In longitudinal views they may be rectangular or somewhat irregular in shape. Their protoplasts are vacuolated to varying degrees and may contain tannins and chloroplasts.

The cork cells are approximately prismatic in shape, often somewhat elongated parallel with the long axis of the stem, and having the radial diameters shorter than the tangential. Some exact determinations of their shape showed that the cork cells are, like parenchyma cells (see chapter 8), basically tetrakaidecahedral in form, with an average of 13.59 contact faces to one cell (Lewis, 1928). They are usually arranged compactly, without intercellular spaces, and in radial rows, clearly showing their origin from a tangentially dividing meristem (plates 41, *C, D,* and 42, *A*). Cork cells may or may not be compressed radially.

The phellem owes its protective characteristics to the presence of suberin in its walls. Cork cells may contain 35 per cent fatty acids, along with 20 to 30 per cent lignin, some cellulose, polyterpenes, and tannins (Cooke, 1948). The suberization of cork cells begins before they attain their full size (De Bary, 1884, p. 113; Sifton, 1945). Commonly the suberin occurs within a distinct lamella deposited over a cellulose wall layer, which may be lignified. In thick-walled kinds of cork, additional lignified cellulose layers are formed toward the cell lumen, that is, on the inside of the suberin lamella (Eames and MacDaniels, 1947, p. 252). This lamella and the lignified layer inside it probably are secondary wall layers in the sense of the term used in this book. These layers are usually devoid of pits (Haberlandt, 1914, p. 135).

Some plants contain within the cork tissue cells that are free of suberin, although otherwise resembling cork cells. These nonsuberized cells are called *phelloids,* that is, phellem-like. They occur in various proportions and various arrangements in the phellem (Mühldorf, 1925; Mylius, 1913; Pfeiffer, 1928). Sclerified cells occur in the phellem of some plants. The cork cell walls may be brown or yellow, or they may remain colorless, but these characteristics are not related to suberization. Often the color of the cork cells depends on the presence of colored resinous and tanniferous compounds in their lumina. Cork cells become devoid of protoplasts after differentiation and are then filled either with air or with the just-mentioned highly colored organic substances. The type of phellem used for bottle cork consists of thin-walled, air-filled cells. The mature cork is a compressible, resilient tissue. It is highly impervious to water and resistant to oil. Because of air-filled lumina, it is light and has thermal insulating qualities (Cooke, 1948).

The phelloderm cells resemble cortical cells in wall structure and contents. Their shape is similar to that of the phellogen cells. They may be distinguished from cortical cells by their arrangement in radial series resulting from their origin from the tangentially dividing phellogen.

PLACE OF ORIGIN OF PHELLOGEN

In considering the place of origin of the meristem forming the periderm, it is necessary to distinguish between the first periderm (plates 43, C, and 49) and the subsequent periderms, which arise beneath the first and replace it as the axis continues to increase in circumference (fig. 14.2 and plate 43, D). In the stem, meristematic activity resulting in the formation of the first periderm may be initiated at different depths outside the vascular cambium (De Bary, 1884, chapter 15; Douliot, 1889; Möller, 1882; Sanio, 1860). In most stems the first phellogen arises in the subepidermal layer (plate 41, A, B). In a few plants epidermal cells give rise to the phellogen (e.g., *Nerium oleander, Pyrus*). Sometimes only a part of the phellogen is formed from epidermis, while the other part arises in subepidermal cells (fig. 14.1, A). In some stems the second or third cortical layer initiates the development of periderm (*Robinia pseudacacia, Gleditschia triacanthos,* and other Leguminosae; species of *Aristolochia, Pinus,* and *Larix*). In still others this tissue arises near the vascular region or directly within the phloem (Caryophyllaceae, Cupressineae, Ericaceae, *Berberis, Camellia, Punica, Vitis;* plate 43, A, B). If the first periderm is followed by others, these are formed repeatedly, sometimes each season, in successively deeper layers of the cortex or phloem. Cork development within the xylem (interxylary cork) may be associated with anomalous (see p. 384) secondary growth (Diettert, 1938; Metcalfe and Chalk, 1950, pp. 667, 795).

A superficial periderm is commonly initiated parallel to the surface of the stem. If, however, the stem is angled in outline or is ridged, the periderm arises beneath the angles or ridges somewhat deeper than elsewhere. Thus, the prominent parts of the stem are removed, and the outline of the stem becomes less uneven (Möller, 1882; Sanio, 1860). The deeper-lying initial periderms are also formed completely around the circumference of the axis.

The subsequent periderms show two typical methods of origin. Those that follow deep-seated initial periderms commonly replicate the disposition of such periderms; that is, they encircle the axis like the first periderm (e.g., *Vitis*). In contrast, sequent periderms that follow a superficial type of initial periderm usually arise in discontinuous layers located in various parts of the axis circumference. The layers have the shape of shells or scales curved toward the outside, and the successively deeper layers overlap the more peripheral ones (fig. 14.2).

Secondary growth of vascular tissues and formation of periderm are common in roots of dicotyledons and conifers. In most of these roots the first periderm originates deeply in the axis, namely in the pericycle (fig. 17.9 and plate 75, *C*, *D*). Some dicotyledonous roots having secondary growth of short duration form only a superficial periderm (see chapter 17). Like stems, the roots also may produce periderm layers at successively greater depths in the axis.

INITIATION AND ACTIVITY OF PHELLOGEN

The cells of the epidermis, the collenchyma, or the parenchyma that initiate periderm are living cells, and their change into phellogen is simply an expression of their ability to resume meristematic activity under appropriate conditions. These cells are usually indistinguishable from neighboring cells. Sometimes, however, the subepidermal layer, where the phellogen arises most frequently, is morphologically distinct from the adjacent cortical cells in that it develops no collenchymatous thickenings and shows an orderly compact arrangement of cells.

The phellogen is initiated by periclinal divisions (plate 41, *A*). There is usually no obvious cytologic change in preparation for the first divisions. If the cells concerned have starch and tannins, these disappear gradually during the successive divisions (Esau, 1948*a*). The first periclinal division in a given cell forms two apparently similar cells. Frequently the inner of these two cells divides no further and is then regarded as a phelloderm cell, while the outer divides and constitutes the phellogen cell (fig. 14.1, *C*). The outer of the two products of the second division matures into the first cork

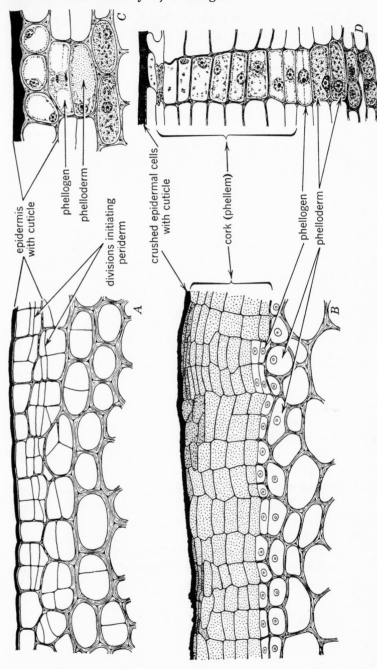

FIG. 14.1. Origin of periderm, partly in epidermis, partly beneath it, in *Pyrus* (*A, B*) and beneath epidermis in *Prunus* (*C, D;* see also fig. 15.18). Nuclei indicate phellogen and phelloderm in *B*. (*A, B,* ×440; *C, D,* ×630.)

cell, while the inner functions as the phellogen cell by dividing again. Sometimes the first division results in the formation of a cork cell and a phellogen cell. Although most of the successive divisions are periclinal, occasional anticlinal divisions in the phellogen increase the number of radial rows of cork cells and enable the periderm to keep pace with the increase in circumference of the axis (fig. 14.1, *B*).

The meristematic activity initiating the periderm begins either around the entire circumference at approximately the same time, or in localized areas. In the latter instance, the first divisions are frequently those concerned with the formation of lenticels (see below). From the margins of these structures the divisions spread around the stem circumference.

The number of divisions resulting in the formation of cork cells usually exceeds those that give rise to phelloderm cells (fig. 14.1, *B*, *D*; Sanio, 1860). Some plants have no phelloderm at all; in others this tissue is one to three cells in depth, but there may be as many as six phelloderm cells in one radial row. The number of phelloderm cells in the same layer of periderm changes somewhat as the stem ages. In *Tilia*, for example, the phelloderm may be one cell deep in the first year, two in the second, three or four later. The amount of phelloderm formed varies not only with the species but also within the same plant. The subsequent periderms formed beneath the first, in later years, contain as much phelloderm as the first or less (Kuhla, 1897).

The number of phellem cells in one radial file produced during one year varies from 2 to 20, depending on the plant species. If the initial periderm of a stem is retained for many years, the outer cork layers crack and commonly peel off, so that on the stem itself the cork maintains approximately the same thickness. In some stems, however, large amounts of cork accumulate on the surface (*Quercus suber, Aristolochia*, plate 49, *D*). The initial periderms that are soon replaced by deeper ones, and also the sequent periderms, usually produce only small numbers of cork layers. The phellem is commonly thin in roots, especially in the fleshy kinds. Apparently environmental conditions in the soil promote a rapid decay and sloughing away of the outermost cork layers.

TIME OF ORIGIN OF PHELLOGEN

The time of appearance of the first and subsequent periderms varies in relation to species or larger taxonomic groupings or, sometimes, among individuals of the same species (De Bary, 1884, chapter 15; Douliot, 1889; Möller, 1882; Sanio, 1860). It is affected also by environmental conditions.

Most dicotyledons and gymnosperms develop the initial periderm —whether superficial or deeper lying—during the first year of growth, usually after the primary elongation is completed (fig. 15.16; De Bary, 1884, p. 558). Such early periderm frequently arises almost at once around the circumference of the stem. If the periderm appears late in the life of the axis, the divisions leading to its initiation start in localized areas and spread slowly around the circumference. In such instances, several years may pass before the periderm is continuous at a given level of the stem.

The first superficial periderm may be retained for life or for many years (species of *Fagus, Abies, Carpinus, Quercus*). The phellogen cells then undergo periodic anticlinal divisions that increase the circumference of the meristem and of the resulting periderm. An initial periderm formed in deeper parts of the axis may also persist for a long time (*Ribes, Berberis, Punica*). More commonly, however, the first periderms, whether superficial or deep seated, are soon replaced by subsequent periderms in successively deeper regions of the axis. Diseases and other external agents may upset the normal pattern of periderm development, either delaying (Esau, 1948*b*) or hastening its appearance, or inducing the formation of deeper periderms when the plant normally develops only superficial periderm (Kauffert, 1937). The ability of the plant to produce phellogen in deeper layers when the superficial periderm is removed is utilized in the production of commercial cork from the cork oak, *Quercus suber* (Metcalf, 1947). The first superficial cork is removed to the phellogen. The exposed tissue dries out to about ⅛ in. in depth. A new phellogen is established beneath the dry layer and rapidly produces a massive cork of a better quality than the first.

PHYSIOLOGICAL ASPECTS OF CORK FORMATION

The differentiation of the derivatives of the phellogen into cork is affected by environmental conditions. The physiological aspects of cork development have been studied, particularly with reference to wound healing (e.g., Artschwager and Starrett, 1933; Bloch, 1941; Priestley and Swingle, 1929; Wylie, 1930, 1931). It seems, however, that the formation of cork beneath wounds, or in the scar left after leaf fall, or in stems and roots growing in thickness follows the same fundamental sequence. The exposed surface is sealed with fatty substances, cutin and suberin, in the presence of air. This blocking creates internal conditions favorable for meristematic activity that results in cork formation. The process of blocking requires certain external conditions, mainly appropriate amounts of moisture and adequate aeration. Their absence inhibits the blocking and indirectly also the formation of cork. Excessive moisture prevents the maturation of cork, as has been observed in potato tubers grown in too moist soil (Mylius, 1913). Moisture may suppress suberization entirely and induce a development of callus tissue instead of cork (Küster, 1925).

MORPHOLOGY OF PERIDERM AND RHYTIDOME

The external appearance of axes bearing periderm is highly variable. This variation depends partly on the characteristics and manner of growth of the periderm itself and partly on the amount and kind of tissue separated by the periderm from the axis. As was explained on p. 325, the periderm and the tissues cut off by its development together constitute the rhytidome or outer bark.

If the plant has only a superficial periderm, a relatively small amount of primary tissue is cut off, involving either a part of or the entire epidermis or possibly one or two cortical layers. This tissue is eventually sloughed away, and the phellem is exposed. The stem in this instance would be considered to have no rhytidome. If the exposed cork tissue is thin, it commonly has a smooth surface (plate 49, *C*). If it is thick, the surface is cracked and fissured (plate 49, *D*). Massive cork usually shows layers that seem to represent annual increments.

The deeper periderms cut off larger amounts of the original stem tissues and usually form a rhytidome. In some rhytidomes parenchyma and soft cork cells predominate; others contain large amounts of fibers usually derived from the phloem. The manner of origin of the successive layers of periderm has a characteristic effect upon the appearance of the rhytidome. If the sequent periderms are formed as overlapping scale-like layers (fig. 14.2), the outer tissue breaks up into units related to the layers of the periderm, and the resulting outer bark is referred to as scalebark (e.g., *Pinus, Pyrus, Malus*). If, on the contrary, the phellogen arises around the entire circumference of the stem, a ringbark is formed, which is characterized by the separation of hollow cylinders (rings) of tissue from the stem. This type of outer bark is common in plants in which the first periderm originates in deep layers of the axis and the subsequent periderms arise more or less concentrically with the first (e.g., Cupressaceae, *Lonicera, Clematis, Vitis*). A scalebark with very large individual scales (e.g., *Platanus*) may be regarded as an intermediate in type between the scalebark and the ringbark.

The manner in which the dead tissues separate from the stem is determined also by the nature of the periderm (De Bary, 1884, p.

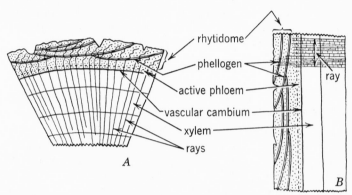

A

B

Fig. 14.2. Diagrams illustrating structure of rhytidome and its location with reference to the vascular tissues. *A*, transverse and, *B*, longitudinal sections of part of stem. The rhytidome in this example is composed of periderm, derived from phellogen, and of inactive phloem.

555; Mühldorf, 1925; Pfeiffer, 1928). In some plants the separation occurs through thin-walled cork cells. In *Platanus* and *Arbutus*, for example, the dead tissue separates from the periderm in the form of large thin scales through the outer thin-walled layer of cork, while the subjacent thick-walled cork tissue remains on the stem and has a smooth surface. The thick-walled cork is removed with the new scales during the subsequent period of scaling off. The sloughing of the outer bark sometimes occurs through a break along thin-walled nonsuberized cells in the cork (phelloids) or within the parenchyma of the stem parts that have been isolated by the development of periderm (Pfeiffer, 1928).

In many plants the periderm cells show considerable cohesion and the succeeding layers of rhytidome adhere closely to one another. The outer bark then becomes thick, is more or less deeply cracked externally, and gradually wears away. Examples of trees with this kind of outer bark are the redwood, *Sequoia sempervirens* (Isenberg,

1943), and certain species of *Quercus, Betula, Salix, Robinia* (plate 43, *C, D*), and *Pinus* (De Bary, 1884, p. 556).

PROTECTIVE TISSUES IN MONOCOTYLEDONS

The monocotyledons rarely form the type of periderm found in the dicotyledons (Eames and MacDaniels, 1947, p. 260; Philipp, 1923; Solereder and Meyer, 1928). In many, the epidermis remains intact, sometimes becoming extremely hard (*Calamus*). There may be a modification of the ground parenchyma into a protective tissue by suberization (species of *Livistonia, Typha, Phoenix,* Gramineae) or thickening and sclerification of walls (*Washingtonia filifera*). Such changes occur in spots and spread toward the interior. Some cell division may occur before the suberization.

In monocotyledons with pronounced secondary growth, a special type of protective tissue is formed by repeated divisions of parenchyma cells and subsequent suberization of the products of division. The divisions are periclinal and are repeated several times in the derivatives of the same cell until a linear series of about four to eight cells is formed. The cells then differentiate into cork cells, while other, deeper-lying parenchyma cells undergo similar divisions and suberization. Thus, the cork arises without the formation of an initial layer, or phellogen, and is referred to as *storied cork* because the linear files of cells form tangential bands as seen in transections. As the formation of cork progresses inwardly, nonsuberized cells may become imbedded among the cork cells. Thus a tissue analogous to the rhytidome of the dicotyledons is formed (*Dracaena, Cordyline, Yucca*). Some of the monocotyledons with secondary growth (e.g., species of *Aloë;* the palms *Cocos* and *Roystonia*) form a periderm resembling that of the dicotyledons.

LENTICELS

Lenticels are structurally differentiated portions of the periderm characterized by a relatively loose arrangement of cells and more or less complete lack of suberization (plate 42, *B*; De Bary, 1884, pp. 560–566; Eames and MacDaniels, 1947, pp. 262–266). The presence of intercellular spaces in the tissue of the lenticels and the continuity of these spaces with those in the interior of the stem has given rise to the interpretation that lenticels, like the stomata, are concerned with gaseous exchange (Haberlandt, 1914, p. 477). Lenticels are generally present on stems and roots. Exceptions are found among stems with a regular formation of complete periderms around the entire circumference (species of *Vitis, Lonicera, Tecoma, Clematis, Rubus*).

Lenticels have received their name because of the lenticular shape they commonly assume. As seen from the surface they appear as lenticular masses of loose cells, usually protruding above the surface through a fissure in the periderm. Depending on the orientation of the fissure, transverse and longitudinal lenticels are recognized (Wetmore, 1926*a, b*). The size of lenticels varies from structures that can be scarcely distinguished with the unaided eye to those that are 1 cm and more in length. The large lenticels usually become so with age, since they enlarge in keeping with the increase in the circumference of the stem (*Betula, Abies pectinata, Tamarix indica, Prunus avium*). In some plants, lenticels do not enlarge but become broken up into smaller ones by differentiation of ordinary periderm within the original lenticels (*Pyrus malus, Rhamnus frangula*). Still other lenticels do not perceptibly change in size and form (*Quercus suber, Fraxinus excelsior, Ailanthus*).

The first lenticels usually arise beneath stomata. They may appear before the stem ceases its primary growth and before the periderm is initiated, or lenticels and periderm may arise simultaneously at the termination of primary growth. The parenchyma cells about the substomatal chamber divide in various planes, chlorophyll disappears, and a colorless loose tissue is formed. The divisions successively occur deeper and deeper in the cortical parenchyma and become oriented periclinally. Thus a periclinally dividing meristem, the lenticel phellogen, is established. The cells resulting from the initial divisions of the parenchyma beneath the stomata and those produced outwardly by the lenticel phellogen constitute the *complementary cells,* so called because they complement the periderm. As the complementary tissue increases in amount, it ruptures the epidermis and protrudes above the surface. The exposed cells die and weather away but are replaced by others developing from the phellogen. By divisions producing cells toward the interior, the phellogen beneath the lenticels forms some phelloderm. The lenticel phellogen is in complete continuity with that formed elsewhere in the stem. Since the number of cells produced in the lenticel region is larger, in both directions, than in regions where cork is formed, the lenticel protrudes above the surface of the periderm and also projects farther inward (plate 42, *B*).

Only in plants with massive cork may the lenticels occur below the surface of the cork (species of *Ulmus, Liquidambar, Quercus*).

Some lenticels arise independently of stomata, either at the same time as the lenticels below the stomata, or later. Lenticels may be formed in the part of periderm that produced cork for a while. In such instances the phellogen ceases to produce cork and forms complementary cells which break through the layer of cork above them. Lenticels formed in the initial but deeply seated periderms and in all the sequent periderms arise with no reference to the stomata. In their eventual distribution in stems of dicotyledons the lenticels may be regularly confronting the vascular rays (Wetmore, 1926*a, b*). In barks separating in the form of scales, lenticels develop on the newly exposed surface of periderm (*Platanus, Pyrus*). If the bark is adherent and fissured, as in *Robinia* and *Prunus domestica*, the lenticels occur at the bottom of the furrows. If the cork tissue is massive, the lenticels are continued through the whole thickness of the tissue, a feature well illustrated by the commercial cork (*Quercus suber*), in which the lenticels are visible as brown powdery streaks in transverse and radial sections.

The complementary cells remain thin walled and nonsuberized. They readily absorb moisture, and therefore in wet weather they enlarge and puff up. In some species the complementary cells are radially flattened and relatively firmly attached to each other (plate 42, *B; Sambucus*). In others, the cells round off and retain very slight connection with other cells (*Prunus, Pyrus, Robinia, Betula, Gleditschia*). In lenticels with loose complementary tissue, firmer and more compact layers, the *closing layers*, are formed from time to time. Often a closing layer is formed at the end of a season. The closing layers are ruptured during the growth of the complementary tissue.

REFERENCES

Artschwager, E. F., and R. C. Starrett. Suberization and wound-cork formation in the sugar beet as affected by temperature and relative humidity. *Jour. Agr. Res.* 47:669–674. 1933.

Bloch, R. Wound healing in higher plants. *Bot. Rev.* 7:110–146. 1941.

Cooke, G. B. Cork and cork products. *Econ. Bot.* 2:393–402. 1948.

De Bary, A. *Comparative anatomy of the vegetative organs of phanerogams and ferns.* Oxford, Clarendon Press. 1884.

Diettert, R. A. The morphology of *Artemisia tridentata* Nutt. *Lloydia* 1:3–74. 1938.

Douliot, H. Recherches sur le périderme. *Ann. des Sci. Nat., Bot.* Ser. 7. 10: 325–395. 1889.

Eames, A. J., and L. H. MacDaniels. *An introduction to plant anatomy.* 2nd ed. New York, McGraw-Hill Book Company. 1947.

Esau, K. Phloem structure in the grapevine, and its seasonal changes. *Hilgardia* 18:217–296. 1948*a*.

Esau, K. Anatomic effects of the viruses of Pierce's disease and phony peach. *Hilgardia* 18:423–482. 1948*b*.

Haberlandt, G. *Physiological plant anatomy.* London, Macmillan and Company. 1914.

Isenberg, I. H. The anatomy of redwood bark. *Madroño* 7:85–91. 1943.

Kauffert, F. Factors influencing the formation of periderm in aspen. *Amer. Jour. Bot.* 24:24–30. 1937.

Küster, E. *Pathologische Pflanzenanatomie.* 3rd ed. Jena, Gustav Fischer. 1925.

Kuhla, F. Über Enstehung und Verbreitung des Phelloderms. *Bot. Centbl.* 71: 81–87, 112–121, 161–170, 193–200, 225–230. 1897.

Lewis, F. T. The shape of cork cells: a simple demonstration that they are tetrakaidecahedral. *Science* 68:625–626. 1928.

Metcalf, W. The cork oak tree in California. *Econ. Bot.* 1:26–46. 1947.

Metcalfe, C. R., and L. Chalk. *Anatomy of the dicotyledons.* 2 vols. Oxford, Clarendon Press. 1950.

Möller, J. *Anatomie der Baumrinden.* Berlin, Julius Springer. 1882.

Mühldorf, A. Über den Ablösungsmodus der Gallen von ihren Wirtspflanzen nebst einer kritischen Übersicht über die Trennungserscheinungen im Pflanzenreiche. *Bot. Centbl. Beihefte* 42:1–110. 1925.

Mylius, G. Das Polyderm. Eine vergleichende Untersuchung über die physiologischen Scheiden: Polyderm, Periderm und Endodermis. *Biblioth. Bot.* 18(79):1–119. 1913.

Ogura, Y. Anatomie der Vegetationsorgane der Pteridophyten. In: K. Linsbauer. *Handbuch der Pflanzenanatomie.* Band 7. Lief. 36. 1938.

Pfeiffer, H. Die pflanzlichen Trennungsgewebe. In: K. Linsbauer. *Handbuch der Pflanzenanatomie.* Band 5. Lief. 22. 1928.

Philipp, M. Über die verkorkten Abschlussgewebe der Monokotylen. *Biblioth. Bot.* 23(92):1–28. 1923.

Priestley, J. H., and C. F. Swingle. Vegetative propagation from the standpoint of plant anatomy. *U. S. Dept. Agric. Tech. Bul.* 151. 1929.

Sanio, C. Vergleichende Untersuchungen über den Bau und die Entwickelung des Korkes. *Jahrb. f. Wiss. Bot.* 2:39–108. 1860.

Sifton, H. B. Air-space tissue in plants. *Bot. Rev.* 11:108–143. 1945.

Solereder, H., and F. J. Meyer. *Systematische Anatomie der Monokotyledonen.* Heft III. Berlin, Gebrüder Borntraeger. 1928.

Wetmore, R. H. Organization and significance of lenticels in dicotyledons. I. Lenticels in relation to aggregate and compound storage rays in woody stems. *Bot. Gaz.* 82:71–88. 1926*a*.

Wetmore, R. H. Organization and significance of lenticels in dicotyledons. II. Lenticels in relation to diffuse storage rays of woody stems. *Bot. Gaz.* 82:113–131. 1926*b*.

Wylie, R. B. Cicatrization of foliage leaves. *Bot. Gaz.* 90:260–278. 1930.

Wylie, R. B. Cicatrization of foliage leaves. II. Wound responses of certain broad-leaved evergreens. *Bot. Gaz.* 92:279–295. 1931.

15

The Stem

CONCEPT

The vegetative body of the sporophyte of the vascular plant is customarily divided into the three so-called organs: stem, leaf, and root. As was discussed in chapter 1, this division is largely a matter of convenience, for the plant is a unit on the basis of its development, evolution, and structure. The boundary between the stem and the leaf is particularly uncertain, and some workers therefore prefer to include the stem and its appendages, the leaves, under the broader concept of the shoot (Arber, 1950; Foster, 1949).

The intrinsic unity of the shoot has been recognized since the early days of botany, but the morphologic value of leaf and stem and their relation to each other have been interpreted in many ways, and there is no agreement on the matter today. The theories that have been advanced to explain the basic structure of the shoot are reviewed in numerous works (e.g., Arber, 1950; Eames, 1936; Majumdar, 1947; Philipson, 1949; Schoute, 1931; Schüepp, 1938; Wetmore, 1943; Zimmermann, 1930). Briefly, three main concepts are used to interpret the morphologic nature of the shoot. (1) The leaf and the stem are ultimate and discrete units of the plant body (e.g., Troll, 1937, p. 176). (2) The shoot consists of growth units (phytons), each comprising a leaf and the subjacent part of stem (e.g., Majumdar, 1947). (3) The leaf itself is shoot-like in nature, its flat dorsiventral structure being a secondary development (cf. Arber, 1950). Regardless of the merits of the various theories, they have served to emphasize the intimate relation between the stem and the leaf. The proper recognition of this unity is essential for the understanding of the primary structure of the stem.

ORIGIN OF THE STEM

The stem, as a part of the shoot, is organized during the development of the embryo (see chapter 20). The differentiation of the characteristic organization of the embryo is attained gradually, and its degree varies in different groups of plants. The fully developed embryo commonly consists of an axis, the *hypocotyl-root axis*, bearing, at the upper end, one or more cotyledons and the primordium of the shoot and, at the lower end, the primordium of the root covered with a rootcap (fig. 1.1). The shoot and root primordia may be no more than meristems (apical meristems), or there may be an embryonic root, the *radicle*, at the lower end of the hypocotyl and an embryonic shoot above the insertion of the cotyledons (seemingly lateral to the single cotyledon in the monocotyledons, chapter 20). The embryonic shoot consists of an axis with unextended internodes and one or more leaf primordia. This shoot, the first bud, is commonly termed the *plumule* (in Latin, little feather), and its stem part is called the *epicotyl*. The terms plumule and epicotyl are here used synonymously to designate the entire shoot primordium present in the embryo (cf. also Darwin, 1892).

The structural relation between the hypocotyl and the cotyledons is comparable to that between a stem and its leaves (cf. Spurr, 1949, and chapter 17). Thus, the beginning of shoot organization is found in the hypocotyl-cotyledon system in which the hypocotyl is the first stem unit of the plant and the cotyledons are the first leaves. The hypocotyl could hardly be called an internode. It is located below a node (the cotyledonary node), but not between nodes.

During the germination of the seed, the root meristem forms the first root, while the shoot meristem continues the development of the first shoot by adding new leaves, nodes, and internodes to the shoot system formed in the embryo. In plants with branching axes, axillary buds arise in the axils of the leaves on the first shoot and develop into lateral branches.

EXTERNAL MORPHOLOGY OF THE SHOOT

A common feature of the stem in the primary state of development is its division into nodes and internodes. As may be learned from chapter 5, this division results from the manner of origin of the leaves at the shoot apex and the subsequent growth of the axis bearing these leaves. The shoot apex gives rise to the leaf primordia in such a close succession that the young shoot may be pictured as composed of a series of superposed shallow discs, each bearing one leaf or more, depending on the arrangement of leaves in a given plant. Later, growth occurs at the bases of these discs, and the leaf insertions become separated from each other. In other words, internodes develop between the nodes by intercalary growth. The duration of this growth may be short or long, depending on the plant species, the environmental conditions, and the type of stem. Sometimes the internodes are practically undeveloped, and the leaves remain crowded on the axis. For example, no internodes can be distinguished in plants bearing their leaves in a rosette. The rosette stage, however, may be followed by an extension of the internodes in the later-formed part of the axis, usually in preparation for flower developement. Bulbs consist of axes with unextended internodes and closely approximated scale leaves. In many rhizomes and in the spurs of fruit trees the internodes remain quite short. In arborescent plants secondary growth eventually obscures the division of the stem into nodes and internodes, and the external evidence of the relation between this organ and the leaves disappears.

The pattern formed in the stem by the alternation of nodes and internodes is affected by the *phyllotaxis* (or *phyllotaxy;* from the Greek *phyllon*, leaf, and *taxis*, arrangement) and by the manner of attachment of the leaves to the stem. Since these features of the shoot have a bearing upon the structure of the primary vascular system and its development in the stem, they are briefly considered in the following paragraphs.

Some leaves have narrow, others have wide, insertions, and still others partly or completely encircle the stem. Each node may bear one, two, or several leaves, the arrangements being called alternate, opposite (or decussate), and whorled, respectively. Students of leaf arrangement have attempted to give mathematical expressions to the orderly sequences in which leaves arise at shoot apices. One of the most notable features of shoot organization is the helical leaf arrangement. By connecting the leaf insertions at successive levels of the axis by imaginary continuous lines, two or more helices may be visualized. One such helix may be constructed by connecting the leaves in the order of their origin at the shoot apex. The early morphologists considered this helix (which they called the genetic spiral) to be of particular significance, for they discovered that the leaves were arranged along such a helix with a characteristic angle of divergence between two successive leaves (cf. Plantefol, 1948). This divergence is frequently expressed in the smallest fractions of the

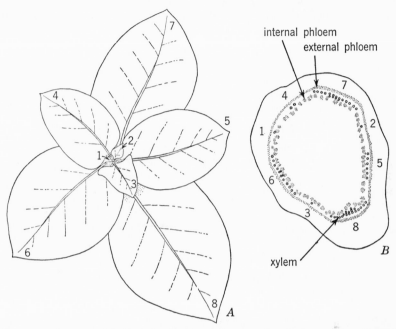

internal phloem
external phloem
xylem

Fig. 15.1. Structure of the primary vascular system in relation to the arrangement of leaves in the shoot of *Nicotiana tabacum*. *A*, young tobacco plant seen from above. *B*, transection of the stem of the same plant. The numbers 1–8 in *B* correspond with the same numbers in *A* and indicate the parts of the vascular system, the leaf traces, which constitute the prolongations of the vascular bundles of the leaves in *A*. While the external and the internal phloem tissues are uniformly distributed around the circumference of the stem, the xylem is localized in such a way that it permits the identification of the leaf traces. Each of the traces of leaves 1–3 has only one tracheary element as seen in transection. The others have two to many, depending on the age of the leaf. The plant has a ⅖ phyllotaxis. (*B*, ×12. From Esau, 1941.)

circumference of the axis intervening between two successive leaves. The most frequent fractions belong to the arithmetic series of Fibonacci: ½, ⅓, ⅖, ⅜, ⁵⁄₁₃, ⁸⁄₂₁, etc., in which each value of the numerator and denominator is a sum of the two values that precede it.

The phyllotactic fractions give information about the distribution of leaves on the mature axis. For example, in a shoot having a ⅖ phyllotaxis one must pass 5 leaves along a continuous helix and encircle the stem twice before coming to a leaf inserted approximately on the same vertical line as the one with which the count was started. If the count is made from the top downward, leaf 1 would occur over leaf 6, leaf 6 over leaf 11, and so on (fig. 15.1). Leaves 1, 6, 11, 16 ··· may appear as a vertical row in mature stems, but at the origin they form a helix, a steeper one than the helix connecting the leaves in the order of their appearance. Still other helices may be projected onto the

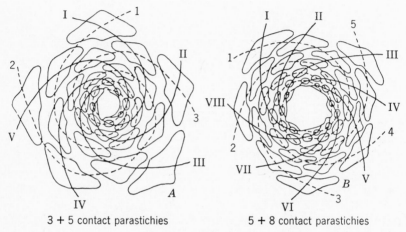

3 + 5 contact parastichies   5 + 8 contact parastichies

FIG. 15.2. Transections of shoots of *Linum perenne* taken near the apices and showing leaf arrangement. In each shoot the curved lines connect the leaves in series which are called parastichies. These particular series are contact parastichies, for they connect the leaves that were in contact with each other when they emerged at the apex. Other parastichies may be constructed in the same shoots (see fig. 15.15). (Both, ×59.)

shoot, some flatter, others steeper, some curving in a clockwise, others in a counterclockwise direction. All these helices are termed *parastichies* (singular *parastichy;* from the Greek *para,* beside, and *stichos,* series).

The fractional classification of the phyllotaxis has been much criticized in the literature because it may not properly express the arrangement of leaves at their origin (Church, 1920; Plantefol, 1948; Snow and Snow, 1934). One of the substitute classifications uses the number of contact parastichies (Church, 1920) to characterize the spatial interrelationship of the leaves at their origin at the apex. The contact parastichies are helical series of leaves in which the successive members of a series approximate each other most closely when seen in surface views of the apices (fig. 15.2).

The phyllotaxis of a given plant is not necessarily constant, and often, during development, the leaf arrangement changes so that the divergence between the successive leaves, as expressed in fractions of the circumference, is decreasing (Priestley and Scott, 1936). Furthermore, different shoots of the same plant may differ from each other in their phyllotactic patterns (fig. 15.2; Esau, 1943a; Sterling, 1945).

THE TISSUE SYSTEMS OF THE STEM

The primary structure of the stem may be described most conveniently by utilizing the classification introduced in chapter 1, which distinguishes three tissue systems: the dermal, the fundamental (or ground tissue system), and the vascular. The principal variations in the structure of stems depend upon the relative amounts and the spatial arrangement of vascular and ground tissues.

In some of the lower vascular plants (plate 44, *A*) and in certain aquatics among the angiosperms, the vascular tissue forms a solid cylinder in the center of the axis. Mostly, however, the vascular tissue of stems is variously interpenetrated by ground tissue. The vascular tissue may be arranged, within the fundamental tissue, as a more or less continuous hollow cylinder (fig. 15.10), or as a cylindrical complex of interconnected strands (fig. 15.3, *A*, and plate 46, *A*), or as anastomosing strands dispersed through all or most of the axis (fig. 15.3, *B*, and plate 54, *A*). In transections of internodes such vascular systems appear, respectively, as a ring of vascular tissue (plate 48, *A*), as a ring of bundles (plate 44, *B*), and as bundles scattered individually (plate 54, *C*). In stems having the vascular system in the form of a solid cylinder, the ground tissue located between the epidermis and the vascular system constitutes the *cortex* (from the Latin word for bark or rind). If the vascular system has the shape of a hollow cylinder, it encloses a part of the fundamental tissue, the *pith*. If this cylinder is divided into strands, called the vascular bundles or *fascicles* (from the Latin *fascis*, bundle), the spaces among the strands, the *interfascicular areas*, are occupied by parenchymatous ground tissue. These plates of tissue can be designated as pith rays or medullary rays (from the Latin *medulla*, pith).

The delimitation of the ground tissue into pith and cortex does not exist if the vascular tissue is dispersed as bundles throughout the circumference of the axis (plate 54, *C*). Still other deviations from a pattern with a distinct separation into cortex, pith, and vascular system occur among plants. The internal phloem of some groups of

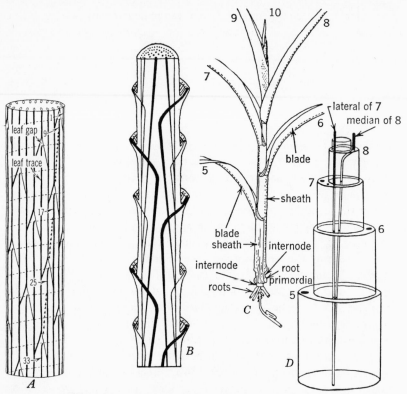

Fig. 15.3. Primary vascular system of angiosperms. *A*, dicotyledon (*Linum perenne*) with the vascular system in the form of a network of leaf traces. In front of each leaf gap a leaf trace diverges into a leaf. Arrows indicate the parastichy of leaves 1–9–17–25–33, etc. The traces of these leaves are connected with each other and also with those of the leaves in the parastichy 6–14–22–30–38, etc. (cf. fig. 15.15, *A*). *B*, monocotyledonous (palm) type of a vascular system. One median (thick) and one small lateral (thin) leaf traces are shown for each leaf. The leaves are in a two-ranked arrangement, and, therefore, the median traces of the successive leaves diverge into the leaves at opposite sides of the stem. Note the difference in the course of median and lateral traces and the interconnections between the two kinds of trace. *C*, young *Zea mays* plant showing the two-ranked arrangement of leaves and the relation between blade, sheath, internode, and roots for the 5th and 6th leaves. The shoot apex is still enclosed by the sheath of the 5th leaf. *D*, diagram of part of plant in *C* showing the course of the median trace of leaf 8 and its connection with the lateral trace of leaf 7. The successive units in *D* represent parts of leaf sheaths shown to be completely closed around the stem for the sake of simplicity. (*A*, adapted from Esau, 1943*a*;
  B, adapted from Linsbauer, 1917; *C* and *D*, adapted from Sharman, 1942.)

plants is somewhat removed from the rest of the vascular tissues and may be said to be located within the pith (Esau, 1938). Certain families have complete vascular bundles scattered within a well-defined pith. Such bundles are called medullary bundles (De Bary, 1884, p. 248). Vascular bundles may occur on the outer side of the main mass of the vascular system, that is, in the cortex. Such bundles are called cortical bundles (De Bary, 1884, p. 256). Finally, individual files of vascular elements may differentiate within the fundamental tissue, as, for example, the sieve tubes that occur throughout the ground tissue between the vascular strands and the epidermis in the Cucurbitaceae (fig. 12.1).

The structure of the epidermal system, its variations, and its functions have been considered in chapter 7. The cortex of stems typically contains much parenchyma with prominent intercellular spaces. Some or all of the cortical cells may have chloroplasts, at least in young stems; and starch, tannins, and crystals are some of the common inclusions. Collenchyma tissue is very often present in the cortex, arranged as a cylinder or in the form of strands near the epidermis or immediately beneath it (fig. 9.1). Sclereids and fibers also occur in the cortex (see chapter 10). The cortex of gymnosperms may develop resin ducts (plate 47), and that of *Citrus*, lysigenous oil cavities. Cortical laticifers occur in some of the latex-forming plants (fig. 13.4, *B*).

The pith of stems is largely parenchymatous. It is typically devoid of chlorophyll in the mature state but has starch-forming leucoplasts. Intercellular spaces are common in the mature pith. Since the pith is often initiated as a rib meristem, its cells may be arranged in longitudinal files (Rouffa and Gunckel, 1951). The pith of many plants is partially destroyed during the growth of the stem. In such instances the internodes are frequently hollow, while the nodes retain their pith (nodal diaphragms). Sometimes, series of horizontal plates of pith are left in the internodes also (*Juglans, Pterocarya*).

The parenchyma cells of the pith—if the latter is retained at maturity—may show varied degrees of differentiation among themselves (Gris, 1872). Frequently, certain pith cells are specialized as depositories of crystals or tannins. Some may develop rather thick walls or differentiate into sclereids. Sometimes the sclereids occur in layers traversing the pith horizontally (*Liriodendron;* Millington and Gunckel, 1950). Either thick- or thin-walled cells may become lignified. Fibers occur rarely (e.g., cycads). In many plants some or all of the pith cells become devoid of contents. Specialized structures like laticifers or secretory canals occur in the pith. The outer part of the pith may be somewhat distinct from the bulk of the pith in having, for example, smaller cells and thicker walls. Such a morphologically distinct outer pith region is sometimes called the perimedullary zone or medullary sheath (Eames and MacDaniels, 1947, p. 156). Although the pith is in general less highly differentiated than the vascular tissues and even less so than the cortex, some workers consider this stem region of considerable diagnostic value in systematics (Doyle and Doyle, 1948; Metcalfe and Chalk, 1950).

The nodes of stems differ from the internodes, first of all, in the arrangement of vascular tissues. The nodal vascular system is complicated by the divergence of some vascular tissue into the leaves (fig. 15.4) and the branches. Furthermore, in some herbaceous plants the main interconnections among the vertically oriented bundles occur by means of horizontally oriented strands in the nodal region (plate 54, *A*). The detailed histology of the vascular bundles may be different at the node (a feature partly determined by the lack of elongation), the cortical and the pith cells may be shorter, and there is less sclerenchyma and more collenchyma than in the internodes (Prunet, 1891). It seems that the degree of differentiation between the nodes and the internodes is influenced by the relative development of the leaves attached to the nodes (Prunet, 1891). If the leaves are rudimentary, as in underground stems, nodes and internodes differ little from each other.

In woody plants, the primary stem structure becomes more or less modified by the formation of secondary tissues. The vascular tissues are augmented by the vascular cambium. Frequently the epidermis alone, or the epidermis and varying amounts of cortex and phloem, become detached from the plant body by the development of periderm. Since eventually the secondary tissues are formed uniformly in the nodal and the internodal regions, the distinctions between the two are not perpetuated in the secondary body.

THE PRIMARY VASCULAR SYSTEM

Relation between the Vascular Tissues of Stem and Leaf

If the vascular system of a leaf-bearing shoot of a seed plant is considered as a whole, the intimate connection between the vascular tissues of stem and leaf is clearly apparent. At each node, portions of the vascular system are deflected into the leaf, which is attached at this node (plate 46, *A*). Within the leaf, the foliar vascular system has a form characteristic of the given species. If the vascular bundles diverging into a leaf are traced backwards into the stem, they may be found to be discrete for variable distances within the stem, and then ultimately to merge with other parts of the vascular system of the stem (fig. 15.3, *A*). A vascular bundle located in the stem but directly related to a leaf, in the sense that it represents the lower part of the vascular supply of this leaf, is termed a *leaf trace* (Hanstein, 1858). A trace may be pictured as extending between the base of a leaf and the point where it is completely merged with other parts of the vascular system in the axis. One or more leaf traces may be associated with each leaf.

The concept of leaf traces implies that at least a part of the axial vascular system develops in direct relation to the leaves. It is an old question in botanical literature how much of the vascular system of the stem belongs by origin (ontogenetic and phylogenetic) to the leaf and how much of it is *cauline* (from the Latin *caulis*, the stem), that is, pertains to the stem proper. This question is related to the broader problem of interpreting the nature of the leaf (see chapter 16; cf. also Arnold, 1947; Eames, 1936; Wetmore, 1943). In some vascular plants, such as the Lycopsida (*Selaginella* and *Lycopodium*), the leaves are small and simple, and their weak traces are peripherally connected to a prominent cauline vascular cylinder (fig. 15.10, *A*; Bower, 1935; Wetmore, 1943). In the Pteropsida (ferns, gymnosperms, and angiosperms), on the contrary, the leaf traces are large in relation to the vascular system of the axis and appear to play an important part in the constitution of the axial system. Some workers consider that at least in certain ferns all vascular tissue in the stem is foliar in origin (Verdoorn, 1938; Wetmore, 1943); others regard the axial system in this group of plants as a composite structure containing both foliar and cauline vascular components, with the contributions from the leaf traces probably varying in amount in different groups (Wardlaw, 1946*a*, *b*; cf. also Wetmore and Wardlaw, 1951). In gymnosperms and angiosperms the primary vascular system of the stem is clearly associated with the leaves and is often described as a system of interconnected leaf traces (e.g., Barthelmess, 1935; De Bary, 1884; Esau, 1943*a*; Gunckel and Wetmore, 1946*b*; Schüepp, 1938; Sterling, 1945). Some workers distinguish between stem bundles and leaf-trace bundles without necessarily implying that the two types of bundles are separate morphological categories (Eames and MacDaniels, 1947, p. 152).

Developmental studies involving removal of leaves suggest that the vascular system of the stem in Pteropsida is not absolutely dependent on the presence of leaves (Philipson, 1949; Wardlaw, 1950*b*; Wetmore, 1943; Wetmore and Wardlaw, 1951). Therefore, the reference to the vascular system of the axis as a system of leaf traces should be used judiciously, perhaps only as a convenient expression of the topographic relation between the vascular tissues of leaf and stem.

Leaf Traces and Leaf Gaps

The leaf trace was defined in the preceding part of this chapter. Briefly, the leaf trace is a vascular bundle connecting the vascular system of the leaf with that of the stem. It extends between the leaf base and the point in the stem where it merges with the vascular system of the stem. If more than one vascular strand diverges into a leaf, each constitutes a leaf trace. (In some references all bundles constituting the vascular supply of one leaf are collectively designated as the leaf trace. The single bundle in such a trace is a leaf-trace bundle.)

Where the leaf trace diverges into a leaf, in the shoot of a pteropsid plant, it appears as though a section of the vascular cylinder of the stem is deflected to one side. Immediately above such a diverging trace, parenchyma instead of vascular tissue differentiates in the vascular region of the stem, but only for a limited distance. Higher up, vascular tissue is present in direct line above the deflected leaf trace. The parenchymatous regions in the vascular system of the stem, located adaxially from the diverging leaf traces, are called *leaf gaps* or *lacunae* (figs. 15.4, 15.10). These gaps do not constitute breaks in the continuity of the axial vascular system. Lateral connections occur between the tissues above and below the gap. In transections of a stem cut at the level of a leaf gap, the gap resembles an interfascicular area.

The gaps are particularly conspicuous in those ferns and angiosperms in which the vascular system in the internodal parts of the axis forms a more or less continuous cylinder (fig. 15.5, *B*). In some ferns the gaps are so high or the leaves so crowded that the gaps formed at the successive nodes overlap one another and the vascular cylinder appears as though dissected into strand-like portions. The transections of such stems show a circle of vascular bundles with parenchymatous areas, the leaf gaps, among them (Ogura, 1938).

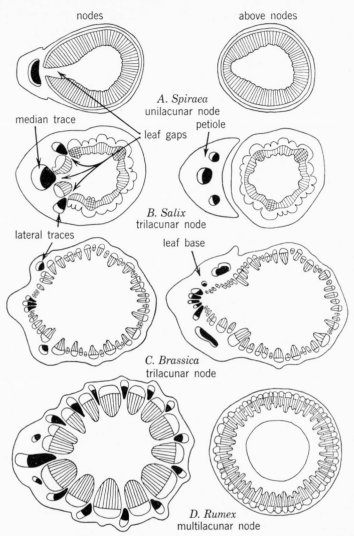

nodes

above nodes

A. *Spiraea*
unilacunar node

median trace

petiole

leaf gaps

lateral traces

B. *Salix*
trilacunar node

leaf base

C. *Brassica*
trilacunar node

D. *Rumex*
multilacunar node

Fig. 15.4. Diagrams illustrating, in transections, the nodal anatomy of dicotyledons. The leaf traces (and the petiolar bundles in *B*) are indicated by blackened xylem areas. In *B* the traces of the leaf attached at the next higher node are marked by crosshatching. All the plants illustrated have alternate leaf arrangement and each leaf has one (*A*), three (*B*, *C*), or many (*D*) leaf traces. The nodes show the same numbers of gaps, or lacunae, as there are leaf traces. In *C* the median leaf trace consists of several bundles. The stem in *A* has some secondary vascular tissue. The internode in *D* is hollow. (*A*, *B*, ×26; *C*, *D*, ×6.)

In plants with the vascular system composed of anastomosing
strands (certain ferns, the gymnosperms, most angiosperms) the recognition of leaf gaps is rather uncertain because in these plants the
parenchyma that occurs above the diverging leaf trace is confluent
with the interfascicular areas (fig. 15.3, *A*; Bailey and Nast, 1944;
Barthelmess, 1935; Nast, 1944; Posthumus, 1924). In such stems the

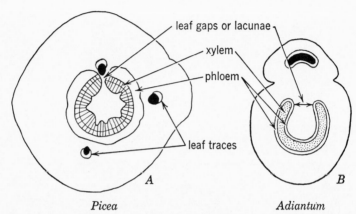

Picea   *Adiantum*

Fig. 15.5. Diagrams illustrating, in transections, the nodal anatomy of *Picea* (a
conifer) and *Adiantum* (a fern). Both have alternate leaf arrangement, single
traces to leaves, and single gaps at the nodes. The stem in *A* has some secondary
vascular tissue. In *B* the phloem appears on both sides of the xylem. The leaf
traces are indicated by blackened xylem region in *A* and *B*. (*A*, ✕33; *B*, ✕16.)

gaps become delimited only after the addition of some secondary
vascular tissues. The secondary xylem covers over the ordinary interfascicular areas closer to the pith than the gaps. The gaps, therefore, project for a greater distance into the secondary xylem cylinder
than the interfascicular areas (plate 47, *B*). In plants with the vascular bundles dispersed within the ground tissue the delimitation of
gaps is even more hypothetical.

Despite the difficulties encountered in the application of the concept of leaf gaps with reference to many vascular plants, this concept
is commonly utilized in the characterization of the nodes. The trace
relationships at the nodes are considered to be of phylogenetic importance, and therefore nodal anatomy is receiving attention in studies
concerned with systematics and phylogeny of angiosperms (Bailey
and Howard, 1941; Bailey and Swamy, 1949; Ozenda, 1949; Sinnott,
1914; Sinnott and Bailey, 1915; Swamy and Bailey, 1950).

Three common types of nodes in the dicotyledons are the *unilacunar*, with a single gap and a single trace to a leaf (fig. 15.4, *A*); the *trilacunar*, with three gaps and three traces to a leaf, one median and two lateral (fig. 15.4, *B*, *C*); and the *multilacunar*, with several

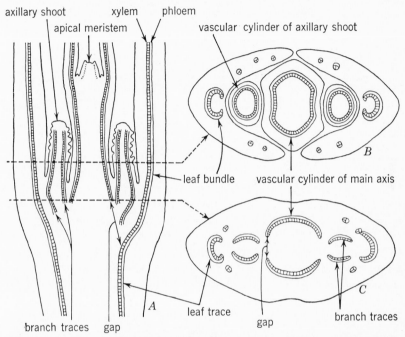

axillary shoot xylem phloem
 apical meristem   vascular cylinder of axillary shoot

B

      leaf bundle vascular cylinder of main axis

C

A leaf trace
branch traces gap   gap   branch traces

Fig. 15.6. Diagrams illustrating the primary vascular system of a plant with a decussate (opposite) leaf arrangement in longitudinal (*A*) and transverse (*B* and *C*) sections. The branches in the axils of the leaves are inflorescences. The leaf trace and the traces of the branch in its axil are associated with one common gap. The two branch traces of level *C* are united into a tubular vascular cylinder of the branch in *B*. Below *C* and outside the plane of *A* the branch traces are connected with the vascular cylinder of the main axis. (Compare with fig. 15.10, *B*.) The xylem is indicated by hatching; the phloem has been left blank. The small bundles in *B* and *C* are branches from the leaf traces. (*A*, ×14; *B*, *C*, ×18.)

to many gaps and traces to a leaf (fig. 15.4, *D*). (If the leaves are opposite or whorled, the node is classified on the basis of the number of gaps to each leaf, fig. 15.6) Sometimes two or three traces are associated with a single gap in a unilacunar node (Bailey and Swamy, 1949; Swamy and Bailey, 1949). The prevailing concept is that the trilacunar condition is primitive in the dicotyledons and that the unilacunar and the multilacunar have been derived from it by a reduction and by an amplification in the number of traces, respectively (cf. Sinnott, 1914). Many monocotyledons have leaves with sheathing bases and nodes with a large number of leaf traces separately inserted around the circumference of the stem (fig. 15.23).

In ferns the number of traces to a leaf varies from one (fig. 15.5, *B*) to many, but regardless of their number they are associated with a single gap (Ogura, 1938). In gymnosperms a unilacunar node is common. In conifers a single gap confronts a single trace (fig. 15.5, *A*); in *Ginkgo*, two traces (Gunckel and Wetmore, 1946*b*).

Plants having similar nodal structure do not necessarily have the same relationship of traces to the other bundles within the vascular system of the stem (fig. 15.15). The traces may differ in the numbers of internodes traversed and in the manner of connection with other bundles (De Bary, 1884; Eames and MacDaniels, 1947). Trace associations are affected by the phyllotaxis of the shoot (Esau, 1943*a*). Some trace systems may be described as anastomosing networks (fig. 15.3, *A*), others as series of sympodia (plate 46, *A*).

In monocotyledons the best-known vascular system is the so-called palm type (fig. 15.3, *B*), which is found not only in the palms but also in many other representatives of this group (De Bary, 1884, p. 262; Branner, 1884). In this system the numerous leaf traces of a single leaf can be roughly divided into small and large. The small traces have an entirely peripheral course in the stem. The large traces approach the center of the stem in their upper parts but are reoriented toward the periphery in their lower parts. Here they are united with other peripheral bundles (fig. 15.3, *D*). Certain other bundle arrangements also occur in monocotyledons (De Bary, 1884; Plowman, 1906; Sharman, 1942; Skutch, 1932), but they are all multi-stranded systems intimately related to the leaves borne on the stem.

Branch Traces and Branch Gaps

Branches developing from axillary buds have vascular connections with the main axis. Dicotyledons and gymnosperms generally have two strands, the two *branch traces*, connecting the vascular system of the branch to that of the main stem (fig. 15.6). Some plants apparently have only one branch trace; others have more than two (Dormer, 1950; Eames and MacDaniels, 1947, p. 144). In monocotyledons the connection of the axillary shoot with the main stem has been described as consisting of many strands (De Bary, 1884, pp. 311–312). Like the leaf traces, the branch traces are prolonged within the main axis and merge with the vascular system of the axis (De Bary, 1884, pp. 307–315). The branch traces form a more or less conspicuous part of the primary vascular cylinder of the main axis, depending on the plant species and the relative time of development of the lateral branch. At the node, branch traces are often closely approximated to the single or the median trace of the leaf subtending the branch, and the two kinds of trace are usually confronted by a common gap in the vascular system of the main axis (fig. 15.6). Ap-

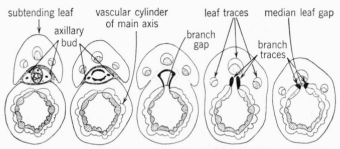

subtending leaf   vascular cylinder   leaf traces   median leaf gap

axillary bud   of main axis   branch gap   branch traces

Fig. 15.7. Diagrams illustrating vascular connection between an axillary branch (still in bud stage) and the main axis in *Salix*. The vascular system of the bud is indicated in black. Note the arrangement of the first two leaves (prophylls) of the bud and the spatial relation of the two branch traces to these leaves. The branch gap and the median gap of the subtending leaf are confluent. (Compare with fig. 15.10, *B*.) (All, ✕9.3.)

parently, branch traces may be associated with a separate gap located above that of the axillant leaf (Eames and MacDaniels, 1947, p. 143).

The occurrence of two branch traces in gymnosperms and dicotyledons is related to the position of the first two foliar structures, the prophylls (see chapter 16), of the axillary shoot (fig. 15.7). These prophylls occur approximately opposite each other, and their median planes cut that of the axillant leaf at right angles (Foster, 1932; Troll, 1937, pp. 333 and 447). The two branch traces are initiated as leaf traces of the two prophylls. Later, they may increase in size through the development of the vascular supply to one or more of the higher leaves on the branch (Garrison, 1949*a*, *b*). In monocotyledons the axillary shoot usually has a single prophyll, sometimes interpreted as a double structure (Arber, 1950, p. 48; Bugnon, 1924; Troll, 1937, p. 447; Veh, 1930). It occurs on the adaxial side of the axillary shoot, and two of its veins constitute in their downward prolongation the first two traces of the axillary shoot.

Types of Vascular Bundles

A strand-like portion of the primary vascular system of the stem or leaf constitutes a vascular strand or vascular bundle. The vascular bundles merit separate attention because they reflect many details of the histology of the system as a whole and are readily accessible for study.

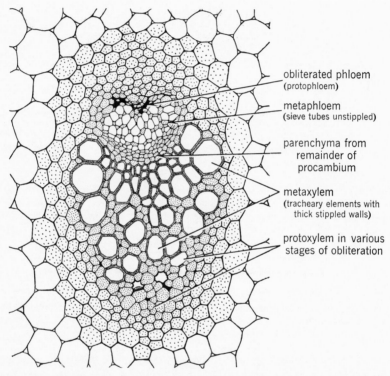

obliterated phloem
(protophloem)

metaphloem
(sieve tubes unstippled)

parenchyma from
remainder of
procambium

metaxylem
(tracheary elements with
thick stippled walls)

protoxylem in various
stages of obliteration

Fig. 15.8. Transection of a vascular bundle of *Ranunculus*, an example of a collateral bundle from an extreme herbaceous dicotyledon lacking secondary growth. (×172.)

The phloem and the xylem are associated with each other not only within the system as a whole but usually also within its parts, the vascular bundles. Variations in the arrangement of the vascular tissues in the bundles have led to the establishment of bundle types (De Bary, 1884). One of the most common bundles in gymnosperms and angiosperms is the *collateral*, in which the phloem occurs on one side of the xylem strand (figs. 15.8, 15.9). The presence of phloem on both sides of the xylem makes the bundle *bicollateral* (plate 32, *A*). Such bundles occur in the dicotyledons having internal phloem. However, in some of these plants the internal phloem of stems forms seemingly independent strands in the peripheral part of the pith, and the term bicollateral bundle is not readily applicable, except perhaps

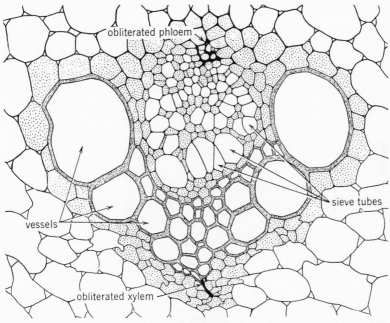

Fig. 15.9. Transection of a vascular bundle of *Asparagus*, an example of a collateral bundle from a herbaceous monocotyledon lacking secondary growth. The obliterated elements indicate the position of the protophloem and protoxylem. The intact tissues are metaphloem and metaxylem. (×316.)

with reference to the strands in the foliar organs where the internal phloem is more closely associated with the other vascular parts (Esau, 1938).

The third type of vascular bundle is called *concentric* because one kind of vascular tissue completely surrounds the other. Concentric bundles are *amphivasal* (from the Greek words for around and vessel), if the xylem surrounds the phloem (plate 44, *D*), or *amphicribral* (*cribrum*, Latin for sieve), if the phloem surrounds the xylem (plate 44, *C*). Examples of amphivasal bundles are found in both the monocotyledons and the dicotyledons (Möbius, 1887). In the latter, the medullary bundles are commonly amphivasal. In monocotyledons, amphivasal bundles may occur in the internode, or they may be restricted to the nodal regions. Transitional forms between collateral and amphivasal bundles have often been observed, and the amphivasal arrangement is interpreted as more specialized (Cheadle and Uhl, 1948; Hall, 1947).

Amphicribral vascular bundles are frequently encountered in ferns. In transections these bundles are circular or oval in outline, or they may be variously curved or lobed (Russow, 1872). In dicotyledons the amphicribral condition occurs in small bundles of the flowers, fruits, ovules, and certain leaves (Eames and MacDaniels, 1947, p. 140) and in the pith bundles of some families (De Bary, 1884, p. 339).

A given bundle type may show many variations in detailed structure and may intergrade with another type by transitional forms. Collateral monocotyledonous bundles furnish a good example of such variability (Cheadle and Uhl, 1948). In some grass bundles the xylem and the phloem meet along a curve, and two large metaxylem vessels appear on the flanks (plate 53, *B*). In another distinctive form the xylem forms, in transections, a V-shaped figure, with the phloem enclosed between the two arms of the V (fig. 15.9). The same bundle usually differs in the arrangement of the xylem and the phloem in the various parts of its course. Thus, it may be collateral at one level, amphivasal at another, and transitional in structure between the two levels.

In most of the lower vascular plants, the monocotyledons, and the extreme herbaceous dicotyledons, the vascular bundles retain no procambium after the primary vascular tissues mature. They therefore lose their potentiality for further growth (figs. 15.8, 15.9, and plate 44, *C*, *D*). In most of the dicotyledons and in the gymnosperms the vascular bundles, in contrast, have a persisting vascular meristem between the xylem and the phloem. This is the cambium which develops from the procambium at the end of the extension growth of the primary body.

THE CONCEPT OF STELE

The early plant anatomists regarded the individual vascular strand as a unit of primary vascular construction (De Bary, 1884). Later, the continuity of the vascular system in the plant body came to be emphasized. This attitude was reflected in Sachs' (1875) classification of the plant tissues into three systems, the dermal, the fundamental, and the vascular, but it was formulated most emphatically by

Van Tieghem and Douliot (1886) when they interpreted the vascular system, whether compact and simple or loose and complex, as a unit combining the vascular tissues and the associated fundamental tissue. This unit was named the *stele*, a term derived from the Greek word meaning column. The stelar concept became the basis of the stelar theory, which postulated that the primary bodies of the stem and the root were basically alike because each consisted of a central core, the stele, enclosed within the cortex. The core was interpreted as including the vascular system with all the interfascicular areas, the pith (if present), and some fundamental tissue on the outer periphery of the vascular system, the pericycle. In relation to the structural variations of the primary vascular system, different types of steles were recognized.

The concept of stele was quickly accepted by many morphologists and was extended to apply to all vascular plants. However, the interpretation of the phylogeny of the stele and the classification of its types has subsequently undergone many changes, and there is still no general agreement on the subject (cf. Bower, 1930; Campbell, 1921; Jeffrey, 1898–99, 1903, 1917; Nast, 1944; Ogura, 1938; Posthumus, 1924; Schoute, 1903; Tansley, 1907–08; Wardlaw, 1944*a*). Some authors even doubt the usefulness of the whole concept (Brebner, 1902; Bugnon, 1924; Hasselberg, 1937; Meyer, 1916). Furthermore, many contributors to physiological anatomy make little or no use of the stelar concept (e.g., Haberlandt, 1914, and contributors to K. Linsbauer, *Handbuch der Pflanzenanatomie*). Nevertheless, the stelar theory has been of unmistakable value in emphasizing the unity of structure of the vascular system and in stimulating extensive comparative research. As a result of this research the literature on the stele has become voluminous and rich in terms. In the following discussion a few of the terms concerning the stele, as referring to primary vascular organization, are reviewed.

The simplest type of stele, and also the most primitive phylogenetically, contains a solid column of vascular tissue enclosing no pith. This is the *protostele* (*protos*, first, in Greek; Jeffrey, 1903). In the simplest protostele the xylem forms the core and the phloem surrounds it as a relatively uniform layer (plate 44, *A*). In more complex types the xylem and the phloem intermingle in the form of strands or plates of variable shape (e.g., species of *Lycopodium* and *Selaginella*). Protosteles are most frequent in the lower vascular plants, but they occur also in the earliest part of the shoot of ferns and in the stems of some water plants among the angiosperms. The pithless central core characteristic of many angiospermous roots is commonly interpreted as protostele.

Presence of pith differentiates the second form of stele, the *siphonostele* (Jeffrey, 1903), that is tubular stele (fig. 15.10). The siphonostele and its variations are most characteristic of the plants above the Lycopsida. The phloem and the xylem show two main distributional patterns in the siphonostele. In the *ectophloic siphonostele* the phloem occurs only on the outer side of the xylem cylinder; in the *amphiphloic siphonostele* or *solenostele* (*solen* and *siphon* from Greek words, both meaning tube) it also differentiates on the inner side of the xylem (internal phloem). In its simplest form the siphonostele has no leaf gaps (fig. 15.10, *A*). Relatively small leaf gaps, not overlapping each other in the internodes, are found in some other siphonosteles (fig. 15.10, *B*, *C*). The transections of such steles in the internodes show a continuous ring of vascular tissue. In many ferns the leaf gaps are large and overlap to the extent that the vascular system appears dissected into a net-like structure, with each segment constituting a concentric vascular bundle (Ogura, 1938). Such vascular structure distinguishes the siphonostelic type called the *dictyostele* (*dictyo*, net, in Greek; Brebner, 1902).

Another modification of the siphonostele is the *eustele* (true stele, from the Greek), in which the vascular system consists of collateral or bicollateral strands, with the leaf gaps and the interfascicular areas not clearly delimited from one another (fig. 15.3, *A*, and plate 46, *A*). The designation of such a stele as eustele was originally chosen because it is the stele type of the highly evolved vascular plants, the gymnosperms and dicotyledons (Brebner, 1902). The most complex stele containing a system of dispersed strands, as in monocotyledons, is called *atactostele* (plate 54; from the Greek *atactos*, without order; Brebner, 1902).

The stelar theory, with its emphasis on the unity of the vascular system, appears to be in conflict with the previously reviewed concept that the vascular system of many plants, especially the higher, is essentially a system of leaf traces. If the leaf traces are assumed to be units of structure, then, obviously, the vascular system of the stem would be a composite structure. However, it is also possible to regard the stem and the leaf as two interdependent parts of a unit, the shoot, in which the elaboration of the vascular system in the cauline portion is more or less influenced by the development of the leaves. In some of the lower vascular plants the development of the vascular tissue of the leaves constitutes a rather insignificant fac-

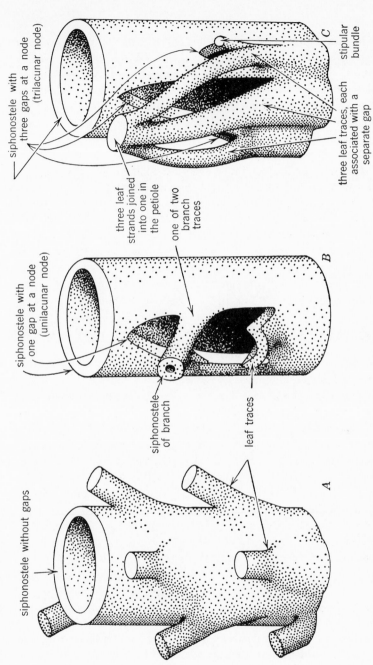

siphonostele with
three gaps at a node
(trilacunar node)

three leaf traces, each
associated with a
separate gap

stipular
bundle

three leaf
strands joined
into one in
the petiole

one of two
branch
traces

siphonostele with
one gap at a node
(unilacunar node)

siphonostele
of branch

leaf traces

siphonostele without gaps

C

B

A

Fig. 15.10. Three-dimensional diagrams of primary vascular systems of *Selaginella* (*A*), *Nicotiana* (*B*), and *Salix* (*C*). *A*, siphonostelic type without leaf gaps. *B* and *C*, siphonostelic types with leaf gaps. Unilacunar node in *B*; trilacunar in *C*. *B* shows also the connection of a branch stele to the main stele, with the branch traces and the single leaf trace associated with a common gap. (Drawn by F. V. Ranzoni from clay models by Guido Girolami. Model for *A* based on Ogura, 1938.)

tor in the development of the system as a whole (microphyllous plants, e.g., *Selaginella, Lycopodium*). In the Pteropsida (macrophyllous plants), on the other hand, the vascular system of the stem is profoundly influenced in its form by the development of the leaves. The different forms of steles could perhaps be looked upon as expressions of the different relations between the leaves and the stem. The one extreme is the protostelic form, which is least influenced by leaf development; the other is the eustele, in which the primary vascular system differentiates almost entirely in relation to the leaves.

The essential unity of leaf and stem is well expressed in the simple concept of a connected system of vascular tissues, on the one hand, and the nonvascular tissues, on the other (Brebner, 1902). From the standpoint of descriptive anatomy and physiology, such a concept may be used successfully in the place of that of the stele, especially with reference to the seed plants. If it is necessary to refer to the vascular region, as distinguished from cortex and pith, the term *vascular cylinder* (Foster, 1949, p. 155) may be employed.

THE LIMITING LAYERS BETWEEN THE CORTEX AND THE VASCULAR CYLINDER

The three primary tissue systems forming the stem—the epidermal, the fundamental, and the vascular—are variously delimited from each other. Commonly the epidermis is clearly set off from the subjacent ground tissue. The demarcation between the ground tissue and the vascular is sometimes plainly indicated, but sometimes it is indefinite. This boundary is more certain in the axes of the lower vascular plants and in the roots of seed plants than in the stems of the latter. The development of the views on the morphologic nature of the limiting layers between the vascular and the fundamental systems has been profoundly affected by the stelar theory, because a morphologic delimitation of the stele was considered an important evidence for the support of the stelar theory (Schoute, 1903).

Endodermis and Starch Sheath

According to the stelar concept, two limiting layers are associated with the primary vascular system: the pericycle, located outside the vascular tissues, and the endodermis surrounding the pericycle. The endodermis is regarded sometimes as the innermost layer of the cortex, sometimes as the outermost layer of the stele (Eames and MacDaniels,

1947, p. 161; Guttenberg, 1943). In the original concept of the stele, the term endodermis was applied to the inner layer of the cortex, regardless of whether this layer had any distinctive morphologic characteristics or not. The more common usage now is to speak of an endodermis when the layer shows a morphologic specialization.

The assigning of the endodermis to one or another part of the axis is made on the basis of ontogeny. As has been emphasized in chapter 5, there is no evidence that the delimitation of vascular and other tissue systems is predetermined in the apical meristems. The developmental segregation of the tissues occurs through differentiation among the derivatives of apical meristems, and the timing and precision of this process are variable in different plants and in the different organs of the same plant. One might, therefore, expect the endodermis to be more or less closely related to the vascular system, depending on the plant material. The seed plants, especially their roots, show a clear relation between the endodermis and the cortex, as far as the two can be traced back into the meristematic region (see chapter 17). In the lower vascular plants the origin of the endodermis appears to be variable (Bartoo, 1930; Johnson, 1933; Ogura, 1938).

The morphologically specialized endodermis forms a single layer of compactly arranged cells, parenchymatous in appearance, but with distinctive wall characteristics. The most outstanding of these is the presence of a band of wall material in the radial and transverse walls, which is chemically different from the rest of the wall (fig. 17.1, *A*, and plate 58, *A*). This band was first recognized as a wall structure by Caspary (1865–66) and is therefore known as the *Casparian strip* or *band*. The Casparian strip shows lignin reactions. Most workers agree that it is also suberized (see chapter 17). In older axes the endodermal cells may become modified by a deposition of a suberin lamella over the entire inner surface of the wall. Still later, a secondary layer of cellulose, sometimes lignified, may cover the suberin lamella (Guttenberg, 1943). The cellulose layer is often most massive on the inner tangential wall (fig. 17.3).

The endodermis is commonly clearly differentiated in the stems of the lower vascular plants and is found here with Casparian strips and with the additional suberin lamella, but apparently not with the secondary cellulose layer (Guttenberg, 1943; Ogura, 1938). It occurs in these plants around the periphery of the vascular cylinder, sometimes also between the pith and the vascular tissues. In some ferns it encloses individual vascular bundles. In seed plants the endodermis is best known in the roots, but there are a number of angiospermous plants, mostly herbaceous, the stems of which develop an endodermis with Casparian strips, and also with somewhat thickened walls (Bond, 1931; Guttenberg, 1943, pp. 122–123; Schoute, 1903; Van Fleet, 1942*a*; Wilton and Roberts, 1936). Underground rhizomes develop an endodermis more frequently than aerial axes (Guttenberg, 1943). Sometimes the endodermis develops in a herbaceous stem when the plant attains flowering state, as in *Senecio* and *Leonurus* (Datta, 1945; Warden, 1935), or it may be restricted to the bases of the stems (Mylius, 1913). The woody dicotyledons and the gymnosperms typically are devoid of an endodermis in the aerial axes (Plaut, 1910).

In young angiospermous stems the innermost layer of the cortex often contains abundant and large starch grains. This layer is called the *starch sheath* (Guttenberg, 1943; Haberlandt, 1914; Schoute, 1903). Since it occupies the position where the endodermis would occur if it developed, the starch sheath is considered homologous with the endodermis (Guttenberg, 1943).

The starch sheath usually extends from a few millimeters to a few centimeters below the apical meristem (Fischer, 1900). It is more conspicuous during the summer than at other times of the year (Schoute, 1903). In older stem regions this layer either assumes the aspect of ordinary cortical parenchyma or, in some plants, differentiates into an endodermis with Casparian strips (Bond, 1931; Datta, 1945; Warden, 1935). The starch sheath sometimes appears as a regular continuous layer (plate 40, *A*); sometimes as interrupted arcs outside the individual vascular strands; and sometimes it is more than one cell layer in depth and has a diffuse outer boundary. No starch sheath commonly occurs in the stems of gymnosperms, although the innermost cortical layers may have somewhat more starch than the outer (Plaut, 1910; Schoute, 1903).

Studies on the histochemical aspects of endodermal differentiation suggest that the endodermis has no special morphologic significance but arises as a result of reaction between substances originating in the vascular system and in the cortex. They suggest, further, that the formation of an endodermis with specialized walls, or of a starch sheath, or of no structurally distinct layer, along the same kind of boundary, is related to the nature of the organ and to environmental conditions (Van Fleet, 1942*a*, *b*, 1950*a*, *b*). The influence of the environment upon the morphological and cytological differentiation of the layer on the periphery of the vascular zone is well illustrated by the development of an endodermis with Casparian strips in the place of a starch sheath in stems of etiolated plants (Priestley, 1926; Priestley and Ewing, 1923). Studies on experimentally induced alterations in the configuration of the vascular system indicate, furthermore, that the differentiation of the endodermis is not restricted to one certain tissue region but appears at the boundary of the vascular system and the ground parenchyma regardless of the origin of cells at this boundary (Wardlaw, 1947).

In view of the variability in morphologic differentiation of cells located in the boundary between the vascular tissue and the ground parenchyma, the term endodermis requires a proper definition. At present, it seems best to restrict the term to a cell layer constituting a boundary between vascular and nonvascular tissues and having Casparian strips or other types of suberized wall layers. Cells in similar position, lacking such wall modifications, but showing some other structural or histochemical resemblance to the true endodermis (cf. Van Fleet, 1950*a*, *b*) may be called *endodermoid cells*. Starch sheath cells lacking Casparian strips are an example of endodermoid cells.

Pericycle

The pericycle was early defined as part of the fundamental tissue of the stele (the conjunctive tissue). The other parts of this tissue are the pith and the medullary rays (Van Tieghem, 1882; Van Tieghem and Douliot, 1886). As has been stated previously in this chapter, the stems and roots of many lower vascular plants and the roots of higher vascular plants typically show an endodermis and a layer or more of parenchyma—the pericycle—between the vascular tissues and the endodermis. In the stems of gymnosperms and angiosperms, however, the endodermis is usually absent, and commonly there is no layer separating the cortex from the vascular tissues, for the protophloem differentiates next to the innermost cortical layer. The sieve elements of the protophloem are soon obliterated, and the remaining cells often differentiate into fibers (see chapters 10 and 12). In these plants, then, the outer boundary of the vascular system consists of tissue which is part of the phloem.

The recognition of the phloic origin of the tissue bounding the vascular system in the stems of many higher vascular plants dates back to the days when the concept of pericycle was being developed (Brebner, 1902; Kruch, 1889; Léger, 1897; cf. also Esau, 1943*b*, *c*, 1950), but in view of the popularity of the stelar theory the idea of the existence of a definite limiting layer of the stele seemed very attractive and was accepted even by those who recognized the inconstancy in the origin and nature of the layer called pericycle (Brebner, 1902). Now the need for a revision of the concept of pericycle is beginning to be felt (Eames and MacDaniels, 1947, p. 157; Esau, 1950; Foster, 1949, pp. 108, 155; Sterling, 1949).

Until a thorough reevaluation of the concept of pericycle is undertaken, the most practical treatment of the problem is to accept the evidence that the segregation of the different tissues in the plant body varies in distinctness; that the presence or absence of a morphologic delimitation of cortex, endodermis, pericycle, medullary rays, leaf gaps, and pith constitutes a variation in the relative distribution of the vascular and ground tissues. Thus, on the one hand, there are plant axes with an almost diagrammatic division into cortex, vascular cylinder, and pith (if present), and with a distinctly differentiated endodermis and pericycle (axes of lower vascular plants and roots of higher plants); on the other hand, there are axes having a poor delimitation between the vascular and fundamental tissues, and lacking an endodermis and pericycle (many, perhaps most, of the stems of the seed plants). In the extreme condition, the vascular system is dispersed to such an extent that no cortex or pith can be delimited (stems of many monocotyledons).

PRIMARY VASCULAR DIFFERENTIATION

As the procambium differentiates among the derivatives of the apical meristem, it eventually assumes the outlines of the future vascular system that will develop from it. Thus, one may find a solid cylinder of procambium in some plants, a hollow cylinder in certain others, and a system of procambial strands in still others. The differentiation of the primary vascular tissues from the procambium follows various developmental patterns. The maturation of the first vascular elements in the procambial strand or cylinder may occur while the procambium is still actively dividing, or it may happen after most of the divisions have been completed and the procambium clearly shows the outline and the internal pattern of the future vascular system (Wetmore, 1943). The former relation is commonly found in the aerial parts of the seed plants in which the separation between vascular and ground tissues is not precise. The relatively early delimitation of the procambial system, on the other hand, is characteristic of stems of many lower vascular plants and of most roots, that is, axes in which the different tissue systems are rather clearly delimited at maturity.

Transverse Course of Differentiation

To characterize the course of vascular differentiation as seen in transverse sections of an axis, the position of the successively appearing elements is referred to the center of the axis or, in some vascular systems, to the center of individual vascular strands. The xylem shows three fundamental patterns of differentiation. In the first, the initial mature xylem elements are located farthest from the center of the axis or bundle (see the root, chapter 17). In other words, if the differentiation is visualized in time, the progress of maturation of the xylem elements occurs in a centripetal order (fig. 17.8 and plate 74). Such xylem is called *exarch* (in Greek, beginning outside). In the second, the initial xylem elements occur nearest, and the latest occur farthest, from the center of the axis (figs. 15.8 and 15.9; plates 52 and 53, *A*, *B*); that is, the differentiation is centrifugal, and the xylem is called *endarch* (in Greek, beginning within). In the third, the differentiation progresses in two directions from the first mature xylem elements (fig. 15.11). The resulting primary xylem is called *mesarch* (in Greek, beginning in the middle). The exarch and mesarch types of primary xylem appear to be more primitive than the endarch and are commonly associated with procambial systems that are well demarcated in advance of vascular differentiation.

The phloem associated with all three types of xylem shows a centripetal direction of differentiation, unless it is located inside the xylem, as in stems with internal phloem. Such phloem differentiates centrifugally. The terms exarch and endarch are not applied to phloem, probably because they were coined with reference to the xylem before the structure and sequence in the development of the phloem were properly understood.

Chapters 11 and 12 consider the classification of primary xylem and phloem into protoxylem and metaxylem, protophloem and metaphloem, respectively. The tissues distinguished by the prefix proto are the first to differentiate and are followed by the metaxylem and the metaphloem. If the xylem is exarch, the protoxylem appears on the outer margin of the xylem system or strand, the metaxylem at or near the center (fig. 17.8). In the endarch xylem the relative positions of the two parts of the xylem are reversed (figs. 15.8 and 15.9). In the mesarch xylem the protoxylem is flanked on two sides or is surrounded by metaxylem (fig. 15.11). The protophloem usually appears farthest from the xylem, the metaphloem nearest to it (fig. 15.9). As was previously stressed (chapters 11 and 12), the proto-phloem and the protoxylem mature so early that they become more or less modified in structure before the primary body completes its development. These changes often make it difficult to recognize the position of the first vascular elements, particularly those of the proto-phloem, in the fully developed primary vascular system.

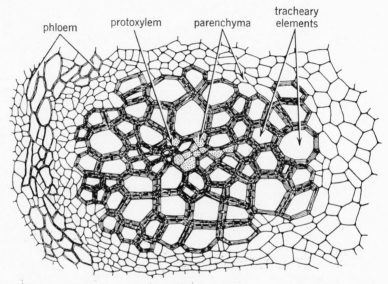

Fig. 15.11.   Transection of a vascular bundle with mesarch xylem from *Pteris* (fern) rhizome. (×160.)

The beginning of the delimitation of the procambium below the shoot apices of seed plants is recognized by the differential staining—probably mainly a result of differential vacuolation—among the deriva-tives of the apical meristem and by the distinctive patterns of growth. The ground meristem cells early show increased vacuolation, whereas the procambial cells longer remain densely cytoplasmic (plate 52, *A*). The procambial cells undergo repeated longitudinal divisions but ex-pand transversely to a limited degree (fig. 15.12). Thus, eventually the procambium becomes distinguishable by its dense narrow cells, elongated parallel with the longitudinal axis of the organ (fig. 15.13). In older parts of the axis the procambial cells become more vacuolated but retain their elongated shape and rather short transverse diameters.

The longitudinal divisions in the differentiating procambium may occur in various planes or may early become oriented in the tangential plane. Because of this difference in growth, the procambial cells may show, in transections of stems, either a random arrangement or a radial seriation resembling that in the cambial zone. The occurrence of radial alignment of cells in the procambium has led to many erro-

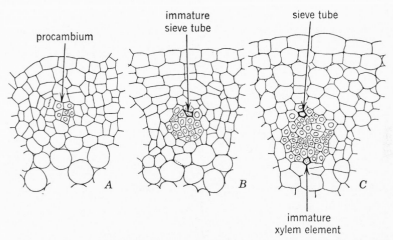

Fig. 15.12. Successive stages in the development of the procambium (cells with nuclei) in transections of a stem of *Linum perenne*. The first phloem and xylem elements begin to differentiate before the procambial strand completes its increase in diameter. This increase occurs by divisions within the strand and by addition of cells from adjacent ground meristem. (All, ×430. From Esau, 1942.)

neous assumptions concerning occurrence and time of inception of secondary growth in various groups of plants (cf. Esau, 1943c). The primary xylem differentiating from procambial cells sometimes retains the arrangement in radial files exhibited by the meristem (fig. 15.17, *A*; Esau, 1938, 1942). Sometimes subsequent divisions and changes in cell shape in the differentiating tissue obscure the initial radial seriation (plate 55, *A*; Esau, 1945). In the primary phloem, radial seriation is less commonly found than in the primary xylem.

The part of the procambium that eventually gives rise to the phloem is frequently distinct in its morphology from that forming the xylem. Often it shows denser staining and different planes of division than the xylem part. The terms *phloic procambium* and *xylary procambium* (or *xyloic procambium*; Spurr, 1950) may be used to stress the early differentiation of the meristem into the two parts. The occur-

rence of this kind of differentiation clearly indicates that the procambium is intrinsically a vascular tissue in early stages of differentiation. In this sense, it is a meristematic tissue, a provascular tissue, although in plants with secondary growth a part of it maintains meristematic characteristics and changes into the vascular cambium.

Longitudinal Course of Differentiation

Procambium. Although in a general way it is possible to picture
the procambium as forming a system similar to that later presented by
the mature primary vascular system, the developmental relation between the meristem and the final product is highly complex. The
differentiation of the vascular elements occurs simultaneously in more
than one direction, both transversely and longitudinally, and the various steps in tissue formation overlap at the same levels of the axis.
Each developmental phase—the formation of procambium, the differentiation of phloem, and the differentiation of xylem—presents special
aspects (Esau, 1943c; Philipson, 1949; Sifton, 1944; Wetmore, 1943).

The differentiation of procambium has been given most attention in
plants in which the primary vascular system can be interpreted as a
system of leaf traces. In these plants the vascularization at the shoot
apex is closely associated with the development of leaves. In fact,
initiation of leaves and initiation of the vascular tissue connected with
these leaves commonly appear as parts of the same growth process.
As was mentioned, the delimitation of the future vascular tissue becomes evident when the ground meristem cells stain lighter than the
prospective vascular region (plate 50). This differentiation in the
ground tissue, which is associated with an increasing vacuolation and
enlargement of cells, is so closely correlated in the stem and the developing leaf primordium that there is, from the beginning, a complete unity of the prospective vascular system of stem and leaf as it
is demarcated by the changes in the ground tissue (plates 50, 51).

Such initial unity has been described in shoot development in many
vascular plants of different degrees of specialization (Esau, 1942;
Helm, 1931; Kaplan, 1936, 1937; Louis, 1935; Sterling, 1949; Wardlaw, 1944a, b, 1945). However, workers disagree on the interpretation of the meristematic tissue that constitutes the precursor of the
vascular region. The first question is whether this tissue consists
wholly or in part of procambium or whether it is a precursor of the
procambium (cf. Esau, 1942, 1943c). The best-supported view is
that a part of this tissue is procambial and the rest is less determined

meristematic tissue. Some of the latter subsequently changes into additional procambium, and the remainder differentiates as parenchyma of the interfascicular areas and of the leaf gaps. In seed plants the initial procambium at a given level is that of the leaf traces of the nearest leaves above. The procambium differentiating later pertains to leaves arising at higher levels of the shoot.

The second question, and it is related to the first, is whether the less determined part of the potential vascular system is a meristematic tissue that has been delayed in its differentiation, a *residual meristem*, or whether it also is partly differentiated vascular tissue. Since the answer to this question awaits further experimental studies (Wardlaw, 1950*b*), in this book the tissue is regarded simply as less differentiated than the procambium and is called residual meristem. This term is applied also to other, nonvascular parts of the shoot that show less pronounced differentiation than the tissues associated with them (plates 50, 51). In this sense the residual meristem is not identical with the apical meristem but represents one of its derivatives.

The prospective vascular system of the shoot, as initially blocked out by the differentiation of the pith and the cortex in the stem and of the abaxial and adaxial parts of the leaf primordium (plates 50, 51), may be pictured as a cylinder of tissue with prolongations into the leaf primordia. The procambial strands constitute part of this system. The differentiation of this procambium results from the special manner of division and elongation of cells that was described in the foregoing part of this chapter. The question has been raised in the literature whether the divisions initiating the procambium progress from the leaf primordium downward toward a connection with the more mature part of the vascular system in the axis, or from the latter upward toward the leaf primordium; that is, whether the procambium differentiates basipetally (in Greek, seeking the base) or acropetally (in Greek, seeking the apex) within the youngest part of the shoot. The concept of basipetal differentiation implies an initial discontinuity of the procambium, whereas that of acropetal differentiation visualizes the procambium as extending from the existing vascular system toward the younger shoot parts.

Several investigations on vegetative shoots of dicotyledons and conifers have shown that the procambium of leaf traces differentiates continuously and acropetally from the point of connection of the trace with other vascular tissue in the stem and toward the apex, where the primordium associated with this trace is being initiated (e.g., Esau, 1942; Gunckel and Wetmore, 1946*a*; Lawalrée, 1948; Miller and Wetmore, 1946; Sterling, 1945, 1947; cf. also Esau, 1943*c*; Philipson, 1949; Sifton, 1944). The evidences of acropetal procambial de-

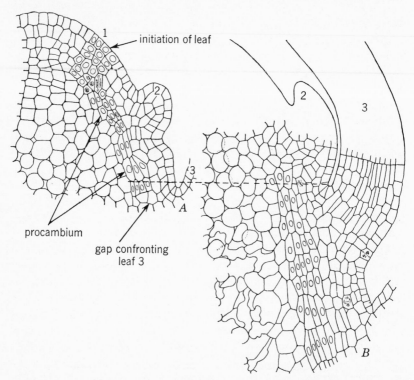

Fɪɢ. 15.13. Longitudinal sections through a shoot apex and subjacent tissues of *Linum perenne* showing an early stage in the differentiation of leaf-trace procambium pertaining to leaf primordium 1, just initiated by periclinal divisions in the second layer of tunica. Nuclei indicate cells pertaining to leaf primordium and procambium. The two drawings were made from two sections of the same shoot, 14 microns distant from each other. Leaves 2 and 3 were numbered arbitrarily, not in ontogenetic sequence. In section *A* the procambial strand deviates from the vertical path near the gap associated with leaf 3. The lower end of this strand appears in section *B*. The broken line connecting the sections *A* and *B* shows the level at which the procambial strand changed from one section to the other. The discontinuities of the procambium at the lower end in *A* and at the upper end in *B* are thus only apparent. The strand is continuous throughout and shows an intensification of the procambial characteristics in the downward direction. (Both, ×365. From Esau, 1942.)

velopment are the continuity of procambial strands associated with even the most recently formed leaf primordia and the increase in the definition of procambial characteristics in the downward direction (fig. 15.13). The acropetal differentiation of the procambium may be timed so that the divisions in the flanks of the apical meristem, which initiate a leaf primordium, are correlated with the divisions forming the procambium beneath this primordium (fig. 15.13, *A*). Thus, the leaf-trace procambium may be present before the leaf itself emerges as a visible protuberance. As the latter appears and grows into a leaf primordium, its procambium differentiates in continuity with the trace procambium below. A still more precocious differentiation of the trace procambium, before the initiation of the associated leaf primordia, has been reported in the conifers (Crafts, 1943*a*, *b*; Sterling, 1945, 1947).

It is not easy to recognize the various aspects of procambial development. The change of the derivatives of the apical meristem into procambial cells is gradual, and, therefore, investigators vary in their interpretation as to when procambium is actually present. Procambial cells are easily missed in sections where they are cut on the bias and where they deviate from the vertical path in relation to leaf gaps or other interfascicular areas. If a leaf gap occurs below a trace bundle, and if the section passes through both the trace and the gap, the trace appears as though it were interrupted at the lower end (fig. 15.13, *A*). Adjacent sections, however, may reveal its connection with older traces below (fig. 15.13, *B*). A proper study of procambial differentiation must be based on complete information on phyllotaxis, nodal anatomy, and trace connections in a given plant, and it must employ serial transverse and longitudinal sections. Furthermore, since the procambium is initiated close to the apical meristem, the activity of this meristem and the phenomena involved in leaf formation should be correlated with vascularization.

Although there is good evidence that continuous acropetal differentiation of procambium occurs in vegetative shoots, it is conceivable that the pattern of procambial development varies, depending on the manner of growth of the shoot and the type of organ, or the influence of traumatic stimuli (cf. Ball, 1948; Gifford, 1951; Wardlaw, 1950*b*).

The course of procambial initiation in the shoot apex is of considerable interest in connection with the search for causes underlying the establishment of phyllotactic patterns in plants. Many hypotheses have been formulated to explain the occurrence of phyllotaxies and the mechanics of leaf formation at the apex (cf. Gunckel and Wetmore, 1946*b*; Philipson, 1949; Snow and Snow, 1934, 1947; Wardlaw, 1948, 1950*a*). Some of these seek the causes of the specific leaf arrangements in the apex itself (see chapter 5). Others suggest that the procambium, in developing acropetally, might play a role in the organization of leaf patterns at the apex (Crafts, 1943*a*; Gunckel and Wetmore, 1946*a*, *b*; Majumdar, 1948; Sterling, 1945, 1947).

Xylem and Phloem. According to the most recent investigations on the vegetative shoot apices of seed plants, the first xylem and the first phloem differ from each other strikingly in the manner of their differentiation (fig. 15.14; Crafts, 1943*a*, *b*; Esau, 1943*a*, *c*, 1945; Gunckel and Wetmore, 1946*b*; Miller and Wetmore, 1946; Sterling, 1946, 1947). The first phloem elements (sieve tubes in the angiosperms, sieve cells or related elements in the gymnosperms) usually differentiate acropetally along the outer periphery of the procambium from their connection with the phloem of older leaf traces into the leaf primordium. This development of the phloem elements begins before there is any xylem in the trace. Therefore, if the procambium is studied in transverse sections, the first phloem elements may be found in it before the first xylem elements (fig. 15.12 and plate 52).

With some variations in details, xylem differentiation in seed plants is initiated on the inner side of the trace procambium near the base of the leaf, and from there it progresses acropetally into the leaf and basipetally into the stem. Within the stem the new xylem unites with that of the older traces. Sometimes some acropetally differentiating xylem advances toward that differentiating basipetally and the two unite within the leaf trace (De Bary, 1884, p. 392; Esau, 1943*c*; Gunckel and Wetmore, 1946*b*; Trécul, 1881). Several vertical files of tracheary elements may be initiated successively in the isolated locus before the first file becomes connected with the xylem below. In other words, isolated xylem bundles with some completely mature elements may be present near the shoot apex. In the young leaf primordium itself, a rather extensive xylem system may develop before its prolongation in the axis unites it with the system below (Esau, 1945). The physiological significance of this initial isolation of the xylem in the growing shoot still awaits a proper explanation.

This method of differentiation in the procambium concerns only the first phloem and xylem elements, the protophloem and the protoxylem. Whether all these elements and whether any of the metaphloem and metaxylem elements follow the same course has not been investigated in the seed plants. In *Equisetum*, all primary phloem and primary xylem elements in the internodal bundles differentiate basipetally from the younger nodes through the subjacent internodes until they join the vascular tissues at the next node below (Golub

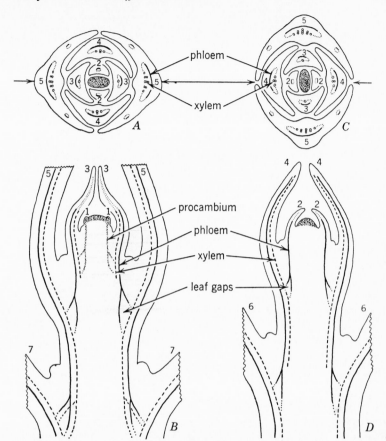

FIG. 15.14. Diagrams illustrating the initial vascular differentiation in a shoot with a decussate leaf arrangement, as seen in longitudinal (*B* and *D*) and transverse (*A* and *C*) sections. The leaves are numbered in pairs. The two longitudinal views represent the same shoot seen in two median planes oriented at right angles to each other. The planes of sectioning of *B* and *D* are indicated by means of arrows in *A* and *C*. The shoot apex and the youngest leaf primordia are densely stippled in all drawings. The sequence in the differentiation of the vascular tissues is as follows: leaf pair 1, procambium only; pair 2, some mature phloem, which is continuous with the phloem of older parts of the stem; pair 3, some phloem and xylem, the latter as isolated strands; pair 4, some phloem and xylem, the latter still isolated from the xylem of lower parts of stem; pair 5, phloem and xylem, the latter now connected with the xylem in older stem parts. (The actual connection of the young xylem and phloem with the older tissues below is not shown.) The transections show the lateral spread of vascular differentiation in the vascular bundles.

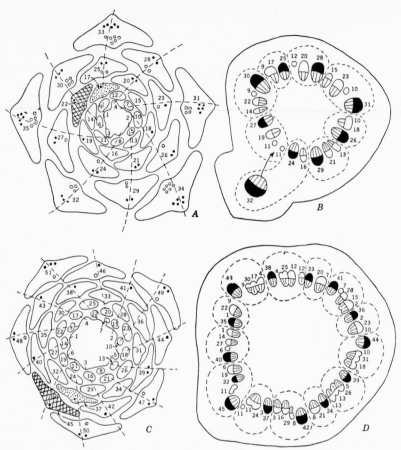

FIG. 15.15.   Relation between the vascular system of leaf and stem in *Linum perenne*. Transections through shoot apices with the uppermost leaves (*A* and *C*) and stems (*B* and *D*). The stem section in *B* was cut 5.3 mm below *A*; the one in *D*, 8.8 mm below *C*. The curved lines in *A* and *C* indicate the parastichies of leaves whose traces are most directly connected with each other. (Cf. fig. 15.3, *A*.)   The broken lines in *B* and *D* encircle parts of the vascular system. Each part is composed of traces pertaining to one of the parastichies in *A* and *C*. The numbers were assigned to the leaves and their traces following the age sequence of the leaves, beginning with the youngest. The two shoots show different leaf arrangements (see also fig. 15.2).   The shoot in *C* and *D*, as contrasted with the one in *A* and *B*, shows (1) a closer sequence of leaves, (2) a larger number of leaves without mature vascular elements (the youngest leaves with mature sieve tubes are stippled, and those with mature sieve tubes and xylem elements are crosshatched), (3) a thicker stem, and (4) a larger number of vascular bundles in transection of stem. The main trace connections in shoot *A–B* are between leaves 1 and 9, 9 and 17, 17 and 25, etc.; in shoot *C–D*, between leaves 1 and 14, 14 and 27, 27 and 40, etc. Details are: dots, sieve tubes; circles,

and Wetmore, 1948). This basipetal course of differentiation of both the xylem and the phloem is probably related to the prolonged activity of the intercalary meristems at the bases of the internodes in this plant.

Studies on initial vascularization, though still too few to permit making broad generalizations, expose the weakness of the formerly prevailing concept that leaf traces have an entirely basipetal course of differentiation within the axis. Such a course is apparently common in the initial xylem differentiation but is not necessarily followed by the procambium and the phloem. In fact, much evidence points toward the occurrence of an initial unity of the procambial system of the vegetative shoot and of a continuous acropetal phloem development. The proper interpretation of the initial vascular development in the shoots requires further extensive studies in a wide variety of vascular plants. Furthermore, such studies should include a consideration of vascularization of embryo, seedling, floral organs, and axillary buds, structures that have received some isolated attention thus far (Boke, 1949; Dauphiné and Rivière, 1946; Garrison, 1949*a*, *b*; Gifford, 1951; Lawalrée, 1948; Miller and Wetmore, 1945*a*, *b*; Nast, 1941; Reeve, 1948; Spurr, 1949, 1950; Stafford, 1948; Trécul, 1881).

Relation of Vascularization to the Growth of the Axis as a Whole

The complexities of development and of the mature structure of the primary vascular system of the shoot result, in part, from the circumstance that this system is initiated before the shoot undergoes its primary thickening and elongation. The vascular system, delimited at the apex, expands and elongates with the axis, and this growth overlaps with the differentiation and maturation of some of the vascular elements. In plants with large leaf traces (ferns and seed plants) there is the added complication that the vascular system is initiated, not uniformly within a given level of the axis, but in relation to the leaves, and therefore some parts of it develop conspicuously in advance of others.

The primary thickening of the axis occurs through cell division and cell enlargement. In dicotyledons and gymnosperms this growth

---

tracheary elements; bundles with blackened phloem, leaf traces; bundles with phloem left blank, composites of leaf traces. (*A, C, D,* ✕66; *B,* ✕79. After Esau, 1943*a*.)

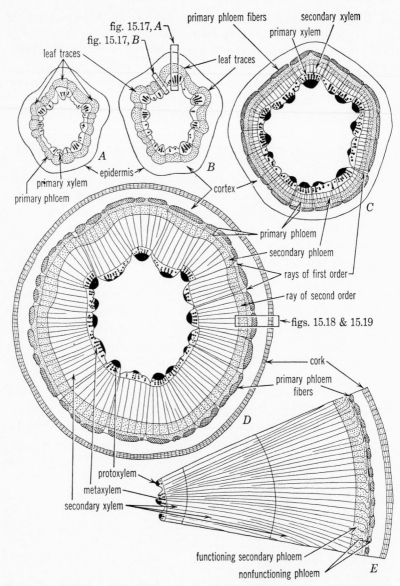

FIG. 15.16. Primary (*A* and *B*) and secondary (*C–E*) structure of the stem in a woody dicotyledon, *Prunus*, in transverse sections. *A–D*, successive developmental stages beginning with an early stage in the differentiation of primary vascular tissues and ending with the first secondary increment of xylem and phloem. *E*, segment of stem with three secondary increments. The vascular bundles in *A* and *B* vary in size. The largest are leaf traces (3 to one leaf); the others are composites of leaf traces. Narrow interfascicular areas occur between

may be rather diffuse, or more or less restricted to the pith or cortex (Troll and Rauh, 1950). In monocotyledons such thickening may be quite pronounced immediately beneath the apical meristem, and it is often localized in a peripheral mantle-like zone, the *primary thickening meristem.* This meristem somewhat resembles a cambium in that it forms cells in close radial series (fig. 15.21 and plate 54, *B*; Eckardt, 1941). The cell divisions occurring during the primary thickening of stems of seed plants are not immediately distinguishable from those that bring about the differentiation of the procambium, a circumstance that makes the recognition of the procambium in its early stages frequently quite uncertain (fig. 15.12). After the vascular system is delimited, it continues to expand, so that the first procambial bundles become farther removed from each other and new ones differentiate among them from the residual meristem (fig. 15.16, *A, B*).

The successive origin of the vascular bundles at a given level of the stem and the varied relations of the bundles to each other (some are traces, others are complexes of traces) cause the commonly observed variation in size and structure of the parts of the vascular system in a given transection of a stem of a higher vascular plant (figs. 15.15, 15.16, 15.17). Some strands are large, others small, and the composition of their vascular tissues varies conspicuously. The differences are particularly striking in the xylem where they are clearly determined by the relation between the growth of the vascular system and the elongation of the axis (Alexandrov and Alexandrova, 1929; Col, 1904; Priestley and Scott, 1936). Since the strands in a given internode are initiated at various times, some are affected more, others less, by the elongation of the internode. The early-formed bundles develop more of the kind of xylem that has extensible types of secondary walls (annular and helical) and show more destruction of xylem than those that arise later. Moreover, a single strand shows structural differences at different levels. Because of the characteris-

---

bundles (black lines). Note in *C-E* the distribution of protoxylem (solid black) and of the primary phloem fibers (crosshatched). The pith and the primary vascular system expand in width while the primary vascular tissues are differentiating and somewhat after the secondary growth is initiated (*A-C*). Rays of first order originate in the interfascicular areas; those of the second order, in the vascular bundles. The epidermis was replaced by cork in *D* and *E*. As the vascular cylinder expands the strands of primary phloem fibers become pulled apart into smaller strands with parenchyma cells filling the resulting spaces. (All, ×22.)

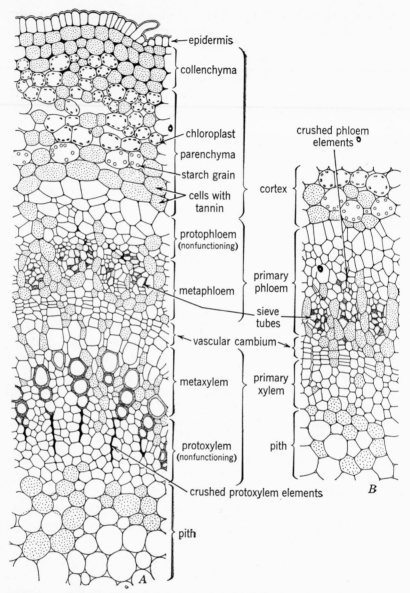

Fig. 15.17. Details of *Prunus* stem structure from fig. 15.16, *B*. The stem was sampled at the end of primary growth before the maturation of the last metaphloem and metaxylem cells but after the first cambial divisions were initiated. *A*, section through a leaf-trace region with a full complement of primary vascular tissues. *B*, sector having primary phloem (protophloem and metaphloem) and a small amount of primary xylem (metaxylem), in which the tracheary elements

tically downward differentiation of the xylem in the traces the amount of stretching and destruction of the first xylem, as well as the number of elements with extensible secondary walls, is greater at the higher levels. The phloem, too, shows more obliteration in older bundles of a given internode but is relatively uniform in structure at the different levels of the same bundle because of acropetal differentiation.

In chapters 11 and 12 the parts of the primary phloem and xylem which differentiate first and which are subjected to stretching in the elongating organs were termed protophloem and protoxylem. If this terminology is applied to the vascular system of the shoot, the protophloem and the protoxylem will be identified only in the older traces of a given internode and not in those that differentiate later. In other words, protophloem and protoxylem thus interpreted are the first vascular tissues of a system of strands and not of each individual bundle. This is a customary interpretation and was introduced by the originator of the concepts of protoxylem and protophloem (Russow, 1872; cf. also Esau, 1943c).

The distinction between bundles that differentiate early and those that differentiate late during the development of a given internode may be illustrated most conveniently by a monocotyledon having no secondary growth. In *Zea*, for example, the bundles near the center of the axis have the full complement of protoxylem and protophloem. In mature internodes the protoxylem of such bundles contains a lacuna, which is formed in connection with the destruction of the tracheary elements during the extension of the axis, and the protophloem is entirely crushed (plate 53, *B*). Bundles located closer to the stem periphery have smaller protoxylem lacunae and a smaller amount of crushed protophloem. The outermost and smallest bundles have only metaphloem and metaxylem tissues and show no evidence of destruction of vascular elements.

The relation of the structure of the vascular system to the elongation of the axis is of particular interest in plants with prolonged intercalary growth in the internodes (many monocotyledons; see chapter 4). Vascular connections are early established through the intercalary meristem, all elements of the xylem having extensible types of secondary walls. While growth occurs in this meristem,

have not yet matured. Note the tannin-containing cells (stippled) delimiting the primary phloem from the cambium and dividing it into bundles. The large cells in the outer part of the primary phloem are immature fibers (compare with fig. 15.18). (Both, $\times 350$.)

the first mature vascular elements are destroyed, but others differentiate in the meantime. The question has been raised in the literature whether the formation of new elements through the intercalary meristem keeps pace with the destruction. In some plants, intact xylem elements are constantly present—at least one file in a bundle— in the active intercalary meristem (Buchholz, 1920; Golub and Wetmore, 1948; Scott and Priestley, 1925; Stafford, 1948). In others, no intact elements appear to be present after the first ones are destroyed at the beginning of intercalary growth and until new elements differentiate at the end of this growth (Buchholz, 1920). The protoxylem lacunae are suggested as the possible conduits of water during the intercalary elongation (Buchholz, 1920). Phloem differentiation has not been investigated with special reference to the intercalary meristems.

The primary vascular system shows, at various levels of the same plant, certain structural differences which are related to the commonly observed changes in the thickness of the axis as the plant develops from a seedling into a mature plant. The primary plant axis is quite thin at first. Farther up, it increases in thickness to a certain maximum, then again becomes thinner in preparation for flowering (Troll and Rauh, 1950). The thickening of the axis is accompanied by an increase in the number of strands visible in a transection of the stem (Ball, 1949; Heimsch et al., 1950). In plants whose vascular system is essentially a system of leaf traces, such increase in the number of bundles may be brought about by an increase in the number of traces to a leaf, or an extension of the traces through a larger number of internodes, or both (Esau, 1943*a*; Mullendore, 1948). Furthermore, it may be associated with a change in leaf arrangement and a delay, as measured in plastochrons (see chapter 5), in the maturation of vascular elements (fig. 15.15; Esau, 1943*a*, 1945; Priestley and Scott, 1936).

SECONDARY GROWTH OF THE VASCULAR SYSTEM

The increase in the amount of vascular tissues by means of secondary growth from a vascular cambium is characteristic of the dicotyledons and the gymnosperms. By a special method of secondary activity some of the monocotyledons also enlarge their vascular system after the completion of primary growth. Among the lower vascular plants secondary growth appears to have been rather common in extinct forms, but it is rare in living representatives (Eames, 1936). Examples of living vascular cryptogams said to have a cambium are *Isoetes* (Lycopsida) and *Botrychium* (eusporangiate fern). It has been suggested that the occurrence of secondary growth makes it possible for plants to develop particularly large bodies (Bower, 1930). As the plant branches and produces increasing amounts of foliage, the cambium supports this growth by adding new vascular tissues, and this correlated growth can continue for a long time. Some of the monocotyledons, like the palms, attain considerable size with primary growth only, but they do not develop such elaborate and long-lived bodies as many of the dicotyledons and gymnosperms.

Origin of the Vascular Cambium

If all the procambial cells differentiate into primary vascular tissues, no cambium is formed (plates 52, 53, *A, B*). If some procambium remains in a meristematic state, after the completion of primary growth, it becomes the cambium of the secondary body (plate 55). This cambium is called *fascicular,* since it originates within the bundles or larger segments of the primary vascular system. Commonly the bands of fascicular cambium become interconnected by additional bands of meristem, the *interfascicular* cambium, which originates from the interfascicular parenchyma (plate 55, *C, D*). The completely formed cambium of the stem has the shape of a continuous cylinder extending through the nodes and internodes. If the axis is branched, the cambium of the main axis is continuous with that of the branches, and some of it may extend into the leaves.

The procambium and the cambium may be looked upon as two developmental stages of the same meristem. Such an interpretation agrees with the observation that procambium and cambium intergrade with regard to their morphologic and physiologic characteristics. The typical features of the cambium of arborescent dicotyledons and gymnosperms—the segregation of its initials into fusiform and ray initials, the occurrence of apical intrusive growth, the precise method of division in a tangential plane during the formation of xylem and phloem (see chapter 6)—are acquired gradually, and some of these characteristics appear before the primary growth is completed, that is, while the meristem is still in the stage of procambium. For instance, the procambial cells gradually become as vacuolate as the cambium, and in many plants the primary vascular tissues, or at least the xylem, are formed by repeated tangential divisions. So

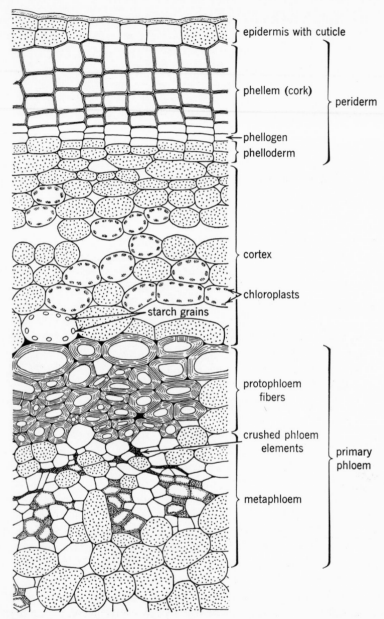

FIG. 15.18. Details of *Prunus* stem structure from the outer part of the rectangle in fig. 15.16, *D*. Note the tannin-containing cells (at bottom of figure) separating the primary from the secondary phloem (the latter is shown in fig. 15.19). (×445.)

far, the only definite character separating primary and secondary growth has been recorded in the xylem. As was discussed in chapter 11, the first secondary tracheary elements are significantly shorter than the last primary elements of the same kind (Bailey, 1944).

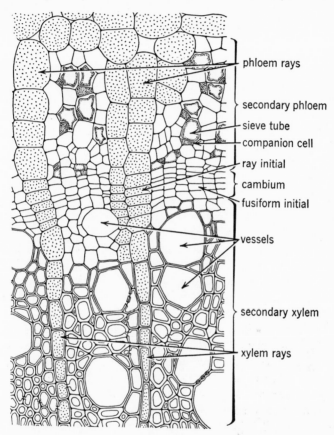

phloem rays

secondary phloem

sieve tube

companion cell

ray initial

cambium

fusiform initial

vessels

secondary xylem

xylem rays

Fig. 15.19. Details of *Prunus* stem structure from the inner part of the rectangle in fig. 15.16, *D*. Note the expansion of sieve tubes from cambium outward and increase in thickness of their walls (left white). The vessels, too, appear in different stages of differentiation, the one nearest the cambium being without secondary walls. (×445.)

The origin of the interfascicular cambium in the more or less vacuolated interfascicular parenchyma results from a resumption of meristematic activity by a potentially meristematic tissue. Usually, no cytologic changes are noticeable in connection with this return to meristematic activity (plate 55, *C*, *D*). If the interfascicular areas are relatively wide, the first divisions initiating a cambium in these areas occur next to the bundles in continuity with the fascicular cambium.

Common Form of Secondary Growth

In the ordinary types of stem of gymnosperms and dicotyledons the cambium arises in the form of a cylinder between the primary xylem and phloem and remains in the same relative position indefinitely, producing secondary xylem toward the inside of the axis, secondary phloem toward the outside (figs. 15.16–15.19; plate 42, *A*). The details of origin and activity are somewhat varied, however. The following three patterns may be encountered (cf. Esau, 1943*c*). (1) The primary vascular tissue has the form of an almost continuous vascular cylinder in the internodes (the interfascicular areas are very narrow), and the secondary vascular tissues have the form of a continuous cylinder (plate 48; *Tilia, Nicotiana, Veronica, Syringa*). (2) The primary vascular tissues form a system of strands, but the secondary vascular tissues arise as a continuous cylinder (fig. 15.16 and plate 47, *A, B*; conifers, *Sambucus, Salix, Prunus*, and many other herbaceous and woody dicotyledons). (3) The primary vascular tissues form a system of strands, the interfascicular cambium forms only ray parenchyma, and, therefore, the secondary vascular tissues also are divided into strands (plate 49, *A, B*; vine types of stems, as *Aristolochia* and *Vitis*). Further minor deviations of quantitative nature occur in relation to the phylogenetic reduction of secondary activity. In some herbaceous dicotyledons with secondary growth, the interfascicular cambium may produce only fibers or only sclerified parenchyma on the xylem side (*Medicago, Salvia*), or the secondary growth may be so small in amount that it remains limited to the vascular bundles (plate 45, *B*; *Trifolium, Cucurbita*).

Anomalous Secondary Growth

Certain dicotyledons and gymnosperms show secondary growth that deviates considerably from the form of growth just described. The deviating methods of secondary thickening are called atypical or anomalous, although the typical and atypical forms of growth are not sharply separated from one another. The developmental details of anomalous secondary growth vary considerably (De Bary, 1884, chapter 16; Eames and MacDaniels, 1947, p. 309; Pfeiffer, 1926). In some plants the cambium occurs in normal position, but the resulting tissue shows an unusual relative distribution of xylem and phloem. Some of the Bignoniaceae show an uneven growth of xylem and phloem so that the xylem becomes lobed, the lobes alternating with bands of phloem (De Bary, 1884, p. 570). In such genera as *Strychnos* (Loganiaceae), *Leptadenia* (Asclepiadaceae, fig. 15.20, *A*), and *Thunbergia* (Acanthaceae; Mullenders, 1947) strands of phloem are included in the xylem (included phloem). In other plants, part of the

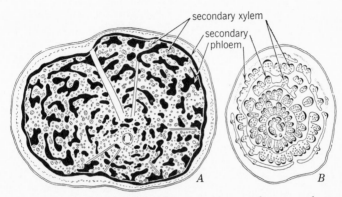

FIG. 15.20. Diagrams of transections of stems with anomalous secondary growth. *A*, *Leptadenia spartium*, Asclepiadaceae, with secondary phloem strands imbedded in the secondary xylem (included phloem). *B*, *Boerhaavia diffusa*, Nyctaginaceae, with successive increments of secondary vascular tissues, each composed of some xylem and phloem. Each of these increments arises from a separate cambial layer. The parenchyma between each two successive layers of xylem and phloem is also formed by these cambia. (Both, ×9.4.)

cambium originates in an abnormal position. For example, in the Chenopodiaceae, the Amaranthaceae, the Nyctaginaceae, the Menispermaceae, and *Gnetum* secondary growth begins from a vascular cambium in the normal position; then another vascular cambium arises in the phloem or outside it and produces xylem toward the inside and phloem toward the outside. Still another supernumerary cambium arises outside the first supernumerary layer and also forms xylem toward the inside and phloem toward the outside. In this sequence many cambia and many alternating layers of xylem and phloem may be formed (fig. 15.20, *B*). Frequently, the successive cambia are ontogenetically interrelated, in that sister cells of one cambium layer become the cambial cells of another layer. The cambia in abnormal position may be restricted in their extent and form separate units of secondary tissues (climbing Sapindaceae, De Bary, 1884, p. 581). Anomalous growth sometimes results from intensified growth of parenchyma distant from the cambium (De Bary, 1884, p. 601). In *Bauhinia* and in many Bignoniaceae, for example, the originally regularly formed continuous xylem is split into irregular units by the growth of pith and xylem parenchyma.

In view of the variability of the so-called anomalous structure, which may be primary and secondary, its precise definition is difficult and depends on how narrowly the normal type is circumscribed. Medullary bundles, for example, are often regarded as anomalous formations, although they may occur in otherwise typically formed stems. Stems of vines with discrete vascular strands in the secondary body are sometimes discussed with the ordinary dicotyledonous stem types, sometimes with the anomalous. Obviously, atypical growth represents no distinct class of phenomena. The designation anomalous serves simply to assemble growth patterns that appear to be less common, at least among plants investigated thus far.

Anomalous types of growth are widely distributed among the various taxonomic groups. Sometimes a whole family shows atypical secondary thickening; sometimes only one genus or even a smaller group. It is often associated with specific physiologic adaptations. For instance, anomalous secondary growth is often found in climbing plants and lianas, and primary and secondary anomalies occur in stems modified as storage organs in the form of rhizomes, tubers, and corms. In such storage structures there is usually a shortening of internodes and an extensive development of storage parenchyma. Anomalous growth is not restricted to stems but is equally common in roots (see chapter 17).

Secondary Growth in Monocotyledons

Although most monocotyledons lack secondary growth, by an intense and protracted primary growth they may produce such large bodies as those of the palms. As was mentioned earlier, the monocotyledons often show a rapid thickening beneath the apical meristem by means of a peripheral primary thickening meristem. The activity of this meristem resembles that concerned with secondary growth found in certain monocotyledons. Furthermore, there may be a developmental continuity between the two meristems when both are present in a given plant. It will be useful, therefore, to review briefly the primary thickening (Ball, 1941; Eckardt, 1941). The apical meristem produces directly only a small part of the

primary body. Most of the primary body is formed by the thickening meristem. This meristem is located beneath the leaf primordia and produces anticlinal rows of cells by periclinal divisions
(fig. 15.21 and plate 54, *B*). The derivatives of the meristem differ-

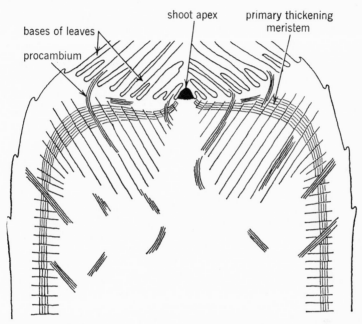

FIG. 15.21. Diagram of the upper part of shoot of a monocotyledon illustrating the
meristems concerned with its growth. The apical meristem produces derivatives
in the downward direction and forms, laterally, the leaf primordia. Beneath the
primordia the derivatives of the apical meristem divide periclinally and form
anticlinal rows (indicated by widely spaced parallel lines). These periclinal
divisions cause an increase in thickness of the axis. They may be localized in a
mantle-like tissue region, the primary thickening meristem, as shown in this
diagram. The activity of the thickening meristem may cease close to the apex
or, as shown in the diagram, thickening growth may be prolonged in the peripheral
part of the axis. After the stem ceases to elongate, the lateral meristem becomes
the cambium producing secondary tissues. The primary thickening meristem
forms ground parenchyma and procambial strands. (Based on Eckardt, 1941.)

entiate into a tissue consisting of ground parenchyma traversed by
procambial strands, which eventually mature into vascular bundles.
The internodes elongate after the axis becomes rather wide. Upon
completion of elongation, there is a further limited increase in thickness by enlargement and division of ground parenchyma cells
(Solereder and Meyer, 1928).

Secondary growth occurs in herbaceous and woody Liliflorae (*Aloe, Sansevieria, Yucca, Agave, Dracaena*) and other groups of monocotyledons (Cheadle, 1937). The meristem concerned with this growth is commonly called cambium and appears to be a direct continuation of the primary thickening meristem (Chouard, 1937; Eckardt, 1941). Unlike the latter, however, the cambium functions in the part of the axis that has completed its elongation. The cambium originates in the parenchyma outside the vascular bundles. This part of the axis is sometimes identified as cortex, sometimes as pericycle, but the difficulty of delimiting a pericycle in the stems of seed plants has been previously emphasized.

The cambial cells vary in shape. As seen in longitudinal sections, they may be fusiform or rectangular, sometimes truncated at one end, tapering at the other (Cheadle, 1937). At first, cells are produced toward the interior of the stem; later a small amount of tissue is formed also toward the periphery. The cells given off inwardly differentiate into vascular strands and parenchyma (plate 53, *C*). The outer derivatives all become parenchyma. In the development of the vascular bundles, individual derivatives of the cambium divide longitudinally; then two or three of the resulting cells form bundles by further longitudinal divisions. In a vertical direction many tiers of cells combine to make a bundle.

The mature bundles are oval in transections. In different species they are either predominantly collateral, or amphivasal. Their phloem consists of short sieve-tube members, with transverse end walls and simple sieve plates, companion cells, and phloem parenchyma. The tracheary elements are tracheids. These are very long since they undergo intensive apical intrusive growth (see chapter 4). The tracheids are associated with a small amount of xylem parenchyma which appears to be lignified. The parenchyma in which the bundles are imbedded is either thin walled or thick walled and is lignified. The small amount of parenchyma formed outwardly usually remains thin walled and contains crystals. Sometimes these parenchyma cells divide transversely and become shorter than the meristem cells.

The secondary vascular bundles and the associated parenchyma are somewhat seriated radially (plate 53, *C*). In contrast, the primary strands are arranged with no detectable order, and the ground parenchyma shows no radial seriation of cells. In general, however, the basic structure of the primary and the secondary bodies is quite similar, for both consist of a ground tissue traversed by vascular strands. The primary and the secondary bodies are also physically continuous in that the secondary bundles are connected with the peripheral prolongations of the leaf traces. With respect to this continuity the monocotyledons and the dicotyledons resemble each other (Strasburger, 1891). In both, secondary tissues differentiate higher and higher up the stem and are always in continuity with the traces of leaves appearing at successively higher levels, that is, in the new primary shoot parts. In both the dicotyledons and the monocotyledons, there is no sharp demarcation between the primary and the secondary growth.

Effect of the Activity of Vascular Cambium upon the Primary Body

In dicotyledons and gymnosperms with prolonged secondary growth the primary body is modified to various degrees. Commonly the primary xylem and the pith are simply covered by the secondary tissues without much change (fig. 15.16), except that sooner or later the protoplasts of the living cells in these tissues die. Crushing of the pith and the interfascicular areas occurs in certain vine types of stems (plate 49, *B, D*). The primary phloem is pushed toward the outside and is more or less compressed. (Loss of function by the protoxylem and the primary phloem, the frequent development of fibers in the protophloem, and the sclerification of the interfascicular parenchyma in the phloem region are phenomena that appear to be independent of cambial activity.) The effect of secondary growth upon the cortex and the epidermis varies with plant species. In some, these parts of the axis keep pace, by active growth, with the increase in circumference of the inner tissues; in others they are removed, sooner or later, by periderm formation (see chapter 14).

The features characterizing the nodal structure are not perpetuated in the secondary body. A cambium develops in the parenchyma of the leaf gap and forms vascular tissues in continuity with those bordering the gap. This phenomenon is referred to as the closing of the gap (fig. 15.22). The parenchyma cells near the margin of the gap are the first to change into cambium; those in the inner portion change later. This process occurs gradually, and the gap parenchyma is maintained as such within the secondary body until the cambium differentiates throughout the entire tangential width of the gap. Wide gaps extend farther into the secondary body than the narrow ones.

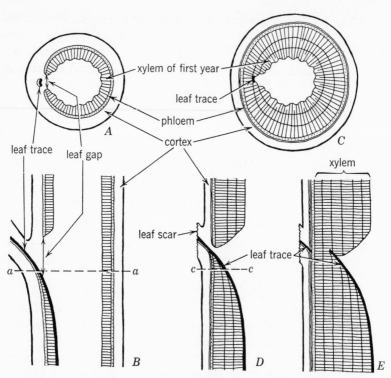

Fig. 15.22. Diagrams illustrating the closing of leaf gaps by secondary growth. *A* and *B*, transverse and longitudinal sections of stems in the first year of growth, showing the nodal region. A single leaf trace (with the xylem shown in black) confronts the single gap. In *B* the leaf trace is shown diverging into the base of the petiole. *C*, transverse and, *D* and *E*, longitudinal sections through stems several years old. In *C* secondary xylem has differentiated on the flanks and outside the xylem of the leaf trace so that, at this level, the gap is not continuous with the cortex as it is in *A*. Two stages in the closing of the gaps are shown in *D* and *E*, and rupture of leaf trace in *E*. Only one side of the stem is represented in each, *D* and *E*. In both, the leaf had abscised. The transections *A* and *C* correspond approximately with levels *aa* and *cc* in figures *B* and *D*, respectively.

In the leaf trace itself complicated changes occur during secondary growth. The lower end of the trace is affected like the other segments of the primary vascular system. The primary xylem is buried by the secondary tissues while the phloem is pushed outward. The upper part of the trace, however, diverges outwardly and crosses the plane of the cambium. The part of the cambium that differentiates above the trace, in the gap region, produces vascular tissue between the trace and the vascular cylinder. This tissue, ever increasing in amount, exerts a pressure upon the trace and eventually causes its rupture (fig. 15.22, *E*, and plate 67, *D*, *E*; Eames and Mac-Daniels, 1947, p. 184; Markfeldt, 1885). The break is filled with parenchyma which is changed into cambium and connects the cambium of the lower part of the trace with that formed in the gap. After this cambium has formed some secondary tissues, the end of the trace below the break becomes imbedded in secondary xylem (fig. 15.22, *E*). The upper severed end is carried outward, and in time it may be thrown off, together with the cortex, by the activity of the periderm. Since the cambium within the trace itself pushes the trace phloem outward, the buried part of the trace consists of xylem only. In rare instances, the trace passes through the cortex almost horizontally and is not broken. Such a trace is buried only after the secondary body extends beyond the former position of the leaf scar.

The breaking and the burial of the leaf trace occur regularly and early in deciduous species in which the trace constitutes a connection between the vascular systems of leaf and stem for one year only. In evergreen species the connection is maintained for a longer time. It has been reported that in the conifers (but not in the dicotyledonous evergreens) the leaf trace is ruptured every year and a new connection established between the xylem of the stem and the trace part above the break (Eames and MacDaniels, 1947, p. 185).

Establishment of Vascular Union in Grafting

In successful grafting, a complete union between the stock and the scion is formed. The differentiation of the connecting vascular tissues is preceded by a proliferation of parenchyma tissue—the callus—from both components of the graft. This parenchyma fills the space between the stock and the scion where their surfaces are not in complete contact with each other (plate 56, *A*). The callus may be produced by cells of the cambial zone (Küster, 1925, p. 85), and also by other living cells of the vascular region if they have no secondary walls. In certain experiments the parenchyma of the phloem rays and of the immature parts of the xylem rays was found to be particularly active in the production of callus (Juliano, 1941; Sharples and Gunnery, 1933). The contributions from the stock and the scion in a graft union may be approximately equal.

The initial phenomena involved in the formation of callus are those often considered in pathological anatomy (Küster, 1925). On the cut surfaces of the stock and the scion some of the living parenchyma cells are destroyed in cutting. The nearest intact cells enlarge until their dimensions surpass considerably those of other similar cells. Such enlargement is called *hypertrophy* (enlargement through a presumed excess of nourishment, from the Greek words meaning above and food). The increase in size may occur in several cells in depth. Subsequently, the large cells divide and produce many cells. Such multiplication of cells is called *hyperplasia* (excessive formation of tissue, from the Greek words meaning above and to shape). The calluses of the stock and the scion intermingle, and eventually vascular cambium is formed through the mixed callus in line with the cambium in the stock and the scion. The tissues resulting from the activity of this cambium are in continuity with the xylem and the phloem of both members of the graft.

The formation of vascular cambium across the callus may be studied particularly easily in connection with the process of healing of a surface exposed by removal of a strip of bark (Sharples and Gunnery, 1933). A callus develops from all the exposed surfaces and partly fills the cavity (plates 56, *B*, and 57, *A*). The cambium begins to develop in this callus—by a change of callus cells into cambial cells —wherever the intact vascular cambium impinges upon it (plate 57, *B*). Thus, the callus cambium differentiates from all margins of the wound toward the center, the process being comparable to the closing of a diaphragm. The new vascular cambium forms xylem and phloem in continuity with the same tissues in the uninjured portion of the stem (plate 57, *C*). A periderm develops in the peripheral portion of the callus in line with the original stem periderm, if the latter is present (plate 57, *B*, *C*).

The process of cambial formation is similar in grafts. The vascular meristem appears first where the cambia of the stock and the scion are in contact with the callus cells. Then divisions forming the cambium in the callus progress toward each other until they meet. Such relation between the cambia in the callus and in the components of the graft explains why a proper matching of the cambia of the stock and the scion speeds up the formation of cambial connection (Bradford and Sitton, 1929). Improper matching does not necessarily prevent union, but it usually delays it (Bradford and Sitton, 1929; Hayward and Went, 1939). A certain developmental detail of vascularization of the graft union was observed in tobacco (Crafts, 1934). A file of tracheary elements and a file of sieve-tube elements were formed through direct differentiation of callus cells into vascular elements. Then cambium differentiated between the two files of cells.

Since plant viruses appear to be rather clearly limited to the cytoplasm in the living plant body, their movement across graft unions supports the assumption of complete cytoplasmic unity between the stock and the scion (Esau, 1948*b*). A virus does not move from one member of the graft to the other until enough time elapses after grafting for the graft union to be established. Furthermore, before they can pass through a graft union, the phloem-limited viruses require a longer time than viruses readily moving through parenchyma, evidently because callus parenchyma cells unite before sieve-tube continuity is established.

TYPES OF STEMS

It is customary to distinguish woody stems from herbaceous, ordinary dicotyledonous stems from vine types, dicotyledonous from monocotyledonous, and stems with normal structure from those with anomalous structure. These groupings, however, are not necessarily based on sharp distinctions. In some instances the differences are mainly quantitative; in others stem types placed into different groups intergrade through transitional types.

Of particular interest is the separation into woody and herbaceous stem types. Evidence from many sources proves that in angiosperms the woody type of plant is more ancient than the herbaceous (Bailey, 1944; Cheadle, 1942; Sinnott and Bailey, 1914). The more primitive angiosperms are composed overwhelmingly of woody plants. In orders and families having both woody and herbaceous representatives, the primitive types are much more woody than the more recent ones. More than half the families of the dicotyledons have no herbaceous species, and the few families that are entirely herbaceous are highly specialized and are obviously of recent origins, for example, insectivorous plants, water plants, and parasites. An important anatomical evidence of the advanced state of the herbaceous plants is their possession of highly specialized xylem throughout the stems and roots. The herbaceous plants have a short life cycle and apparently have evolved as an adapatation to the change from a warm, humid climate, which prevailed in ancient geologic times, to the present colder, drier climate.

Most of the herbaceous dicotyledons arose from the woody, mainly through a decrease in the activity of the vascular cambium. In its general characteristics, therefore, the herbaceous dicotyledonous stem is much like the one-year-old stem of a related woody type. The decrease in cambial activity has often been supplemented by a widen-

ing of the interfascicular areas, a change resulting in the formation
of a many-stranded vascular system. Sometimes, instead of the individual interfascicular areas becoming high and wide, whole segments of vascular tissue became changed into fibrous or parenchymatous tissue, making the individual vascular bundles of the system
quite discrete. The distinctness of the vascular bundles is common
among certain herbaceous stems, but it does not represent a typical
state, since many herbaceous genera, and often whole families, possess
primary vascular cylinders that are conspicuously interrupted by
parenchyma only at the gaps (e.g., Caryophyllaceae, Hypericaceae,
Onagraceae, Solanaceae, Polemoniaceae, Ericaceae). Among the
monocotyledons, too, the herbaceous stem appears to have arisen
primarily through the loss of secondary thickening (Cheadle, 1942).
This evolutionary trend is one of the reasons why the monocotyledons cannot be visualized as having originated from herbaceous dicotyledons (Bailey, 1944).

In the following pages several specific examples of stems of the
higher Tracheophyta are described with the aid of illustrations.
(Further details on most of these stems may be found in Foster, 1949,
Exercise 13.)

Conifer

Pinus. The primary structure of the stem is revealed close to
the apex. Here the helically arranged foliar structures (scales) are
crowded upon the axis, whose internodes are still unextended (plate
46, *B*). The axils of the scales bear the buds of the short shoots
which later produce the needle-like leaves. Because of the crowding
of the scales on the young stem, its peripheral part (cortex and epidermis) is confluent with the bases of the scales (plate 47, *A*). The
outer boundary of the cortex becomes clearly delimited after the internodal elongation. The primary vascular system consists of collateral strands separated from one another, in transections, by interfascicular areas (plate 47, *C*). The strands are leaf traces connected
with each other in a sympodial manner (plate 46, *A*). Traces to the
buds are also present, two to each bud. The nodes are unilacunar,
with the gaps of the different nodes overlapping and with more than
one visible in each transection (*Picea*, fig. 15.5, *A*). The secondary
growth produces a continuous cylinder of xylem and phloem (plate
47, *B*). Opposite the gaps the cambium becomes continuous only
gradually so that the gap parenchyma projects into the secondary
wood (plate 47, *B, D*). After the secondary growth has been pro-

gressing for some time, the primary xylem of the original bundles may be recognized next to the pith, but the primary phloem is completely obliterated. In the secondary vascular cylinder the amount of phloem is considerably smaller than that of the xylem. The demarcation between the cortex and the vascular cylinder is obscure. There is no endodermis, no distinct starch sheath, and the primary phloem forms no peripheral fibers. During secondary growth the outer limit of the phloem may be determined by following the phloem rays to their outermost ends. Sometimes there is a concentration of tannin-containing cells outside the phloem. The cortex is typically parenchymatous, with many cells containing tannins. Early in the development of the stem, resin ducts appear in the cortex (plate 47, *A*). As the stem increases in circumference, the resin ducts become wider, especially in the tangential direction (plate 47, *B*). The initial periderm arises beneath the epidermis and is not replaced by deeper periderms for several years.

Woody Dicotyledon

Tilia. The primary vascular system consists of closely approximated segments so that in transections the vascular ring appears continuous (plate 48, *A*; Smith, 1937). The leaves are two-ranked, and the nodes are trilacunar. Beneath the epidermis is a single layer of parenchyma cells; then follows a multiseriate layer of collenchyma. The rest of the cortex is parenchymatous and contains chlorophyll. The innermost cortical layer forms a starch sheath. Fibers are formed in the protophloem, and when mature they constitute a clearly defined but discontinuous outer boundary of the vascular system. The pith is parenchymatous but early shows the development of mucilage canals. Similar canals are formed in the cortex (Strasburger, 1891).

During primary thickening the pith and the vascular cylinder increase in diameter in the presence of considerable amounts of mature xylem and phloem. (Compare young and old stems in plate 48.) The growth of the vascular cylinder probably results from a lateral expansion of the narrow interfascicular areas and the enlargement of the xylem-parenchyma cells which occur in radial rows. When the pith attains its mature size the peripheral cells have smaller lumina, thicker walls, and larger amounts of deeply colored tanniferous inclusions than the interior pith cells (plate 48, *B*). This peripheral part of the pith is the so-called medullary sheath (p. 346). Its cells remain alive and store starch while the interior cells become devoid of protoplasts relatively early. The morphologic differentiation of the peripheral pith helps to delimit the inner boundary of the xylem. Otherwise this boundary is somewhat difficult to detect because the tracheary elements of the protoxylem are destroyed during internodal elongation and the parenchyma cells long remain unlignified (Raimann, 1890). *Tilia* exemplifies a plant in which the primary xylem shows radial seriation. Its delimitation from the secondary is somewhat facilitated by the greater density of the secondary xylem as contrasted with the metaxylem (plate 48, *B*).

The secondary tissues form a continuous cylinder. The primary xylem constitutes an insignificant part of the vascular cylinder after a few years of secondary growth (plate 49, *C*). The secondary phloem has a distinctive appearance because of the alternation of fiber bands and bands containing sieve tubes and parenchyma cells and because of the lateral expansion of many of the rays (plate 49, *C*; see also chapter 12). The initial periderm arises in the layer of parenchyma located betwen the epidermis and the collenchyma and is not replaced by deeper periderms for many years (Strasburger, 1891).

Dicotyledonous Vine

In *Aristolochia* (Schellenberg, 1899; Strasburger, 1891) the primary vascular system consists of collateral strands separated from each other by wide and high interfascicular areas (plate 49, *A*). In transections of stems the strands form a discontinuous oval about a parenchymatous pith. The leaves have a two-ranked arrangement, and their bases encircle the stem halfway. The nodes are trilacunar. The median trace consists, in part of its course, of three strands (*mt* in plate 49, *A*). These three strands and the two laterals of the same set of traces are the smallest bundles in a given transection of stem (plate 49, *A*). The primary tissues outside the vascular system are the following: an epidermis; parenchyma and collenchyma of the cortex, both with chlorophyll; a cylinder of perivascular sclerenchyma (see chapter 10) composed of fibrous cells with blunt ends and concerned with starch storage; and parenchyma interpolated between the sclerenchyma and the vascular strands. A starch sheath (the innermost layer of the cortex) occurs outside the sclerenchyma. According to the stelar terminology, the sclerenchyma and the subjacent parenchyma would be called the pericycle.

During secondary growth, vascular tissues are formed only within the strands. The interfascicular part of the cambium forms parenchyma similar to that in the primary interfascicular areas, and, therefore, the strands remain discrete (plate 49, *B, D*). Growth rings are visible in the secondary xylem and also in the part of the rays associated with this xylem. In both tissues relatively small cells are formed at the end of a season's growth. The phloem contains no fibers. In the secondary phloem tangential bands of parenchyma alternate with bands containing sieve tubes and associated parenchyma cells. When the sieve tubes cease to function and are crushed, a conspicuous banding appears in the phloem, the compressed cells alternating with noncompressed parenchyma. Concomitantly with the increase in the circumference of the stem, the individual vascular strands widen out toward the periphery. From time to time new rays are interpolated in these widening vascular wedges (plate 49, *D*). The primary interfascicular areas and their secondary continuations extend mostly from node to node, whereas the rays interpolated later within the vascular strands are successively lower.

The pith and the rays which are continuous with the pith are partly crushed during secondary growth. This crushing is probably a result of the resistance offered to the expanding vascular system by the continuous perivascular sclerenchyma cylinder. Eventually this cylinder is ruptured, mostly in front of the rays, with the adjacent parenchyma invading the breaks (plate 49, *B*). In some species the first of these parenchyma cells differentiate into sclereids.

The periderm develops in the subepidermal collenchyma or somewhat deeper. The development begins in a few places, and it takes several years until the periderm spreads over the entire surface of the stem. Longitudinally the isolated periderms appear as vertical strips extending from node to node (Czaja, 1934). The cork shows layering because of an alternation of radially unextended cells with cells that are larger in radial direction (plate 49, *D*). Considerable phelloderm is formed by the phellogen.

Cucurbita (Zimmermann, 1922) has bicollateral vascular bundles appearing in two series, the outer composed of leaf traces, the inner of trace complexes (plate 45, *B*). The node is trilacunar, and three of the five bundles in the outer series belong to the leaf at the node nearest to the given transection. (See chapter 12 for further details on vascular structure.) The ground tissue system resembles that of *Aristolochia*. Beneath the uniseriate epidermis is the collenchyma, which forms wide bands and alternates with bands of chlorenchyma. The chlorenchyma bands occur beneath the parts of the epidermis bearing the stomata. The deeper lying cortical parenchyma has few chloroplasts. The innermost layer of cortex is differentiated as a starch sheath. Inside the starch sheath is a cylinder of perivascular sclerenchyma. Some parenchyma intervenes between the sclerenchyma and the vascular bundles. (This tissue region of *Cucurbita*, consisting of sclerenchyma and parenchyma, was used by Van Tieghem, 1882, when he formulated the concept of the pericycle.)

Cambial activity and associated phenomena in Cucurbitaceae are similar to those in *Aristolochia*. However, in the less woody species, secondary growth is often restricted to the vascular strands, and the sclerenchyma cylinder is not ruptured. In *Cucurbita* the pith breaks down early (plate 45, *B*).

The presence of a continuous cylinder of sclerenchyma outside the vascular system is not a constant characteristic of the vine types of stem. There may be protophloem fibers associated with the individual strands, as in *Vitis* (Esau, 1948a). The vine type of structure in this genus is expressed in the presence of relatively wide and high rays (see chapter 12). In *Vitis* the vascular strands are not displaced toward the pith during secondary growth. However, the pith breaks down early.

Herbaceous Dicotyledon

Various transitional stem structures may be found between the woody type illustrated by *Tilia* and the extreme dicotyledonous herbs with no secondary growth in the stem (plate 45, *C*). In *Pelargonium* the primary vascular system consists of closely approximated strands varying in size. During secondary growth a continuous vascular cylinder is produced (Foster, 1949, p. 167). The vascular cylinder is clearly set off from the cortex since fibers differentiate on its periphery. In the stem of *Medicago* (alfalfa) the vascular bundles, as seen in transections, are not too varied in size and are clearly separated from each other (plate 44, *B*). Some secondary growth occurs at the base of the stem, but the interfascicular cambium produces mainly sclerenchyma on the xylem side. The extremely herbaceous stem of *Ranunculus* resembles those of some monocotyledons in that it has a somewhat dispersed arrangement of the vascular bundles and lacks vascular cambium (plate 45, *C*).

The stems described above may all be considered typical of the groups of plants to which they belong. In some plants, however, parts of stems assume more or less modified aspects, often in relation to specialization as storage organs. One of the best examples of a stem that serves mainly for storage is the potato tuber (Artschwager,

1924), whose anatomy contrasts rather strikingly with that of the aerial vegetative stem (Artschwager, 1918). In the latter, normal elongation occurs during development; in the tuber, the internodes remain short, but there is lateral expansion increasing the amount of storage parenchyma. The leaf traces constitute a prominent part of the vascular system of the aerial stem. This system, therefore, shows variable structure related to the position of the leaves. In the tuber the vascular system is morphologically more homogeneous because the traces of the scale-like leaves subtending the axillary buds are very small. Both the aerial stem and the tuber have internal and external phloem, but in the tuber the internal phloem is extensively dispersed in the wide pith, so that only a narrow parenchymatous zone in the interior is free of phloem elements. The internal phloem is highly parenchymatous and appears to be the principal storage tissue of the tuber.

Herbaceous Monocotyledon

Grass Stem. Vascular systems composed of widely spaced strands and not restricted to one ring in transections are relatively uncommon in the dicotyledons (Ranunculaceae, Nymphaeaceae, Piperaceae), but in the monocotyledons similar and more complex systems are usual (Metcalfe, 1946).

In transections of the internodes of most grasses the usual three tissue systems, the epidermal, the fundamental, and the vascular, are visible. The vascular bundles are distributed according to two basic plans. Either they are in two circles, one of smaller bundles nearer the periphery, the other of larger bundles somewhat deeper within the stem (plate 45, *D*; *Triticum, Avena, Hordeum, Secale, Oryza*); or they are scattered throughout the transection (plate 54, *C*; *Zea, Saccharum, Sorghum, Bambusa*). The vascular bundles are collateral, each enclosed in a sheath of sclerenchyma (plate 53, *B*).

In grasses in which the vascular bundles are arranged in two circles there is commonly a continuous cylinder of sclerenchyma close to the epidermis, with the outer smaller bundles imbedded in it (plate 45, *D*). On the outer sides of these bundles occur fiber strands that reach to the epidermis. Bands of parenchyma with chloroplasts alternate with the fiber bands. The chlorenchyma bands extend parallel to each other through the internode and terminate at the nodes. In some places the bands coalesce. The chlorenchyma is located beneath parts of the epidermis where stomata are concentrated. Inside the ring of sclerenchyma is the fundamental parenchyma in which

the vascular bundles are imbedded. The central part of this parenchyma, which is free of vascular tissue in the internodes, may be
spoken of as pith. In many grasses the pith breaks down in the internodes, but not in the nodes (fig. 15.23 and plate 45, *D*). In others it
is retained throughout the stem (Canfield, 1934). In grasses with the
vascular bundles in a scattered arrangement, no sclerenchyma cylinder
is formed. (plate 54, *C*), but the subepidermal parenchyma may be
strongly sclerified (see also chapter 10).

The complex arrangement of the vascular bundles is related to the
variable orientations of the different traces of the same leaf. The
leaves are two-ranked, and their bases form sheaths completely around
the stem (fig. 15.3, *C*). Each leaf has numerous traces, some large,
others smaller and alternating with the larger. If the traces of a given
leaf of *Zea* are studied in successive sections downward from the node,
their course is found to be as follows (Sharman, 1942). Within the
node the large bundles bend inward, whereas the small ones remain
near the periphery (fig. 15.3, *D*). The median of the large bundles
may reach the center of the stem. The other large bundles occupy
positions intermediate between central and peripheral. With slight
alterations in their positions, the traces extend downward through one
or more internodes. Farther below, the larger traces become reoriented to a peripheral position, often appearing on the side opposite
the part of the leaf to which they are attached above (fig. 15.3, *D*).
This reorientation is accompanied by a diminution in size and fusions
with other small bundles in the peripheral portions of the stem.

In the wheat stem (Percival, 1921) the course of the vascular bundles through the internode and the leaf sheath is practically parallel
(fig. 15.23, *A*). Near the node the leaf sheath is considerably thickened, attaining its maximum thickness just above its union with the
stem (fig. 15.23, *B–D*). The stem, on the other hand, decreases in
thickness in the same direction and has the smallest diameter above
the junction with the leaf sheath. The stem is hollow in the internode,
solid at the node. The sheath is open on one side at higher levels,
closed near the node (fig. 15.23, *C*, *D*). The portion of the internode
where these strikingly different morphologic features are exhibited
constitutes the so-called joint (see chapter 4). Here the intercalary
meristematic activity continues the longest, and the tissues remain
capable of further elongation after this activity ceases. In this part
of the shoot sclerenchyma does not form, and lignification is minimum.
Massive collenchymatous bundle caps differentiate in connection with
the leaf sheath bundles (fig. 15.23, *D*).

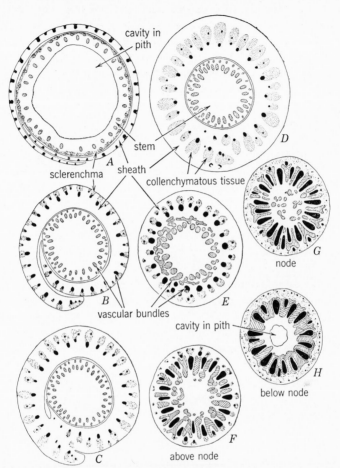

Fig. 15.23. Nodal anatomy of *Triticum* stem. Transections at various levels of stem beginning with the middle of an internode (*A*), through the lower part of the internode (*B–F*), the node (*G*), and ending just below the node (*H*). The bundles of the sheath and their prolongations as traces in the stem are shown in black; the vascular tissue of the internode and its continuation through the node is hatched. The fine stippling indicates sclerenchyma, the coarse stippling in *D*, collenchymatous tissue replacing the sclerenchyma in the joint region. Note the increase in thickness of the sheath and the decrease in thickness of the stem toward the node. Further explanations are in the text. (All, ×7.6.)

Below the junction of leaf sheath and stem the smaller of the leaf traces are prolonged in the peripheral part of the axis. The larger leaf traces become part of the inner cylinder of strands. The bundles of the internode located above the leaf insertion assume, just above the node, a horizontal and oblique course (fig. 15.23, *E, F*) and are reoriented toward a more peripheral position in the node and below it (fig. 15.23, *G, H*). In these horizontal and oblique positions the bundles variously branch and coalesce, and their total number is reduced. Through a mutual reorientation, the large leaf traces and the bundles from the internode above the insertion of the leaf together form the inner cylinder of bundles of the next lower internode (fig. 15.23, *H*). In this cylinder about half of the bundles are leaf traces from the nearest leaf above, and the other half are bundles from the internode above the insertion of this leaf. The peripheral bundles are mostly leaf traces from the nearest leaf above.

A conspicuous feature of grass stems is the presence of transverse bundles in the nodal regions (plate 54, *A*). These bundles interconnect the leaf traces of the main shoot among themselves. The transverse bundles appear somewhat late in the ontogeny of the stem, and some workers interpret them as prolongations of the small peripheral traces (Bugnon, 1920*a, c*, 1924; Sharman, 1942). The transverse bundles are sometimes associated, in the literature, with the vascular system of the axillary buds and the adventitious roots attached at the nodes. There is evidence, however, that the bud traces are prolonged vertically into the main axis, and that the roots are peripherally connected to the vascular system of the main stem (Bugnon, 1920*b*, 1924). The independence of the transverse system from the buds is indicated by its presence in nodes having no buds (Bugnon, 1924).

REFERENCES

Alexandrov, W. G., and O. G. Alexandrova. Gefässstengelbündel der Sonnenblume, als Object der Experimentalanatomie. *Bot. Arch.* 25:87–127. 1929.

Arber, A. *The natural philosophy of plant form.* Cambridge, Cambridge University Press. 1950.

Arnold, C. A. *An introduction to paleobotany.* New York, McGraw-Hill Book Company. 1947.

Artschwager, E. F. Anatomy of the potato plant, with special reference to the ontogeny of the vascular system. *Jour. Agr. Res.* 14:221–252. 1918.

Artschwager, E. F. Studies on the potato tuber. *Jour. Agr. Res.* 27:809–835. 1924.

Bailey, I. W. The development of vessels in angiosperms and its significance in morphological research. *Amer. Jour. Bot.* 31:421–428. 1944.

Bailey, I. W., and R. A. Howard. The comparative morphology of the Icacinaceae. I. Anatomy of the node and internode. *Arnold Arboretum Jour.* 22:125–132. 1941.

Bailey, I. W., and C. G. Nast. The comparative anatomy of the Winteraceae. IV. Anatomy of the node and vascularization of the leaf. *Arnold Arboretum Jour.* 25:215–221. 1944.

Bailey, I. W., and B. G. L. Swamy. The morphology and relationships of *Austrobaileya*. *Arnold Arboretum Jour.* 30:211–226. 1949.

Ball, E. The development of the shoot apex and the primary thickening meristem in *Phoenix canariensis* Chaub., with comparisons to *Washingtonia filifera* Wats. and *Trachycarpus excelsa* Wendl. *Amer. Jour. Bot.* 28:820–832. 1941.

Ball, E. Differentiation in the primary shoots of *Lupinus albus* L. and of *Tropaeolum majus* L. *Soc. Expt. Biol. Symposia.* No. 2. *Growth* 1948:246–262. 1948.

Ball, E. The shoot apex and normal plant of *Lupinus albus* L., bases for experimental morphology. *Amer. Jour. Bot.* 36:440–454. 1949.

Barthelmess, A. Über den Zusammenhang zwischen Blattstellung und Stelenbau unter besonderer Berücksichtigung der Koniferen. *Bot. Arch.* 37:207–260. 1935.

Bartoo, D. R. Origin of tissues of *Schizaea pusila*. *Bot. Gaz.* 89:137–153. 1930.

Boke, N. H. Development of the stamens and carpels in *Vinca rosea* L. *Amer. Jour. Bot.* 36:535–547. 1949.

Bond, G. The stem endodermis of the genus *Piper*. *Roy. Soc. Edinb., Trans.* 56:695–724. 1931.

Bower, F. O. *Size and form in plants.* London, Macmillan and Company. 1930.

Bower, F. O. *Primitive land plants.* London, Macmillan and Company. 1935.

Bradford, F. C., and B. G. Sitton. Defective graft unions in the apple and the pear. *Mich. Agr. Expt. Sta. Tech. Bul.* 99. 1929.

Branner, J. C. The course and growth of the fibro-vascular bundles in palms. *Amer. Phil. Soc. Proc.* 21:459–483. 1884.

Brebner, G. On the anatomy of *Danaea* and other Marattiaceae. *Ann. Bot.* 16:517–552. 1902.

Buchholz, M. Über die Wasserleitungsbahnen in den interkalaren Wachstumszonen monokotyler Sprosse. *Flora* 14:119–186. 1920.

Bugnon, P. Origin des faisceaux libéroligneux transverses formant un lacis aux noeuds des Graminées. *Acad. des Sci. Compt. Rend.* 170:671–674. 1920*a*.

Bugnon, P. Dans la tige des Graminées, certains faisceaux libéroligneux longitudinaux peuvent être des faisceaux gemmaires. *Acad. des Sci. Compt. Rend.* 170:1201–1203. 1920*b*.

Bugnon, P. Causes du parcours transversal des faisceaux libéroligneux aux noeuds des Graminées. *Acad. des Sci. Compt. Rend.* 171:673–675. 1920*c*.

Bugnon, P. Contribution à la connaissance de l'appareil conducteur chez les Graminées. *Soc. Linn. de Normandie, Mém.* 26:21–40. 1924.

Campbell, D. H. The eusporangiate ferns and the stelar theory. *Amer. Jour. Bot.* 8:303–314. 1921.

Canfield, R. H. Stem structure of grasses on the Joranda Experimental Range. *Bot. Gaz.* 95:636–648. 1934.

Caspary, R. Bemerkungen über die Schutzscheide und die Bildung des Stammes und der Wurzel. *Jahrb. f. Wiss. Bot.* **4**:101–124. 1865–66.

Cheadle, V. I. Secondary growth by means of a thickening ring in certain monocotyledons. *Bot. Gaz.* **98**:535–555. 1937.

Cheadle, V. I. The role of anatomy in the phylogenetic studies of the Monocotyledoneae. *Chron. Bot.* **7**:253–254. 1942.

Cheadle, V. I., and N. W. Uhl. Types of vascular bundles in the Monocotyledoneae and their relation to the late metaxylem conducting elements. *Amer. Jour. Bot.* **35**:486–496. 1948.

Chouard, P. La nature et le rôle des formations dites "secondaires" dans l'édification de la tige des Monocotylédones. *Soc. Bot. de France Bul.* **83**:819–836. 1937.

Church, A. H. *On the interpretation of phenomena of phyllotaxis.* London, Oxford. University Press. 1920.

Col, A. Recherches sur la disposition des faisceaux dans la tige et les feuilles de quelques Dicotylédones. *Ann. des Sci. Nat., Bot.* Ser. 8. **20**:1–288. 1904.

Crafts, A. S. Phloem anatomy in two species of *Nicotiana*, with notes on the interspecific graft union. *Bot. Gaz.* **95**:592–608. 1934.

Crafts, A. S. Vascular differentiation in the shoot apex of *Sequoia sempervirens. Amer. Jour. Bot.* **30**:110–121. 1943*a.*

Crafts, A. S. Vascular differentiation in the shoot apices of ten coniferous species. *Amer. Jour. Bot.* **30**:382–393. 1943*b.*

Czaja, A. T. Zur Entwicklungsphysiologie des Periderms und die Entstehung der Korkkrusten. *Planta* **23**:105–145. 1934.

Darwin, C. *The power of movement in plants.* New York, D. Appleton and Company. 1892.

Datta, A. Comparative study of the vegetative and flowering axes of *Leonurus sibiricus* L. *Ind. Acad. Sci. Proc.* **22**:10–17. 1945.

Dauphiné, A., and S. Rivière. Les tubes criblés de l'embryon et leur mise en évidence. *Rev. Gén. de Bot.* **53**:19–24. 1946.

De Bary, A. *Comparative anatomy of the vegetative organs of phanerogams and ferns.* Oxford, Clarendon Press. 1884.

Dormer, K. J. Observations on the vascular supply to axillary branches. *New Phytol.* **49**:36–39. 1950.

Doyle, M. H., and J. Doyle. Pith structure in conifers. I. Taxodiaceae. *Roy. Irish Acad. Proc.* Sect. B. **52**:15–39. 1948.

Eames, A. J. *Morphology of vascular plants. Lower groups.* New York, McGraw-Hill Book Company. 1936.

Eames, A. J., and L. H. MacDaniels. *An introduction to plant anatomy.* 2nd ed. New York, McGraw-Hill Book Company. 1947.

Eckardt, T. Kritische Untersuchungen über das primäre Dickenwachstum bei Monokotylen, mit Ausblick auf dessen Verhältnis zur sekundären Verdickung. *Bot. Arch.* **42**:289–334. ·1941.

Esau, K. Ontogeny and structure of the phloem of tobacco. *Hilgardia* **11**:343–424. 1938.

Esau, K. Phloem anatomy of tobacco affected with curly top and mosaic. *Hilgardia* **13**:437–490. 1941.

Esau, K. Vascular differentiation in the vegetative shoot of *Linum.* I. The procambium. *Amer. Jour. Bot.* **29**:738–747. 1942.

Esau, K. Vascular differentiation in the vegetative shoot of *Linum*. II. The first phloem and xylem. *Amer. Jour. Bot.* 30:248–255. 1943*a*.

Esau, K. Vascular differentiation in the vegetative shoot of *Linum*. III. The origin of bast fibers. *Amer. Jour. Bot.* 30:579–586. 1943*b*.

Esau, K. Origin and development of the primary vascular tissues in seed plants. *Bot. Rev.* 9: 125–206. 1943*c*.

Esau, K. Vascularization of the vegetative shoots of *Helianthus* and *Sambucus*. *Amer. Jour. Bot.* 32:18–29. 1945.

Esau, K. Phloem structure in the grapevine, and its seasonal changes. *Hilgardia* 18:217–296. 1948*a*.

Esau, K. Some anatomical aspects of plant virus disease problems. II. *Bot. Rev.* 14:413–449. 1948*b*.

Esau, K. Development and structure of the phloem tissue. II. *Bot. Rev.* 16:67–114. 1950.

Fischer, H. Der Pericykel in den freien Stengelorganen. *Jahrb. f. Wiss. Bot.* 35:1–27. 1900.

Foster, A. S. Investigations on the morphology and comparative history of development of foliar organs. IV. The prophyll of *Carya Buckleyi* var. *arkansana*. *Amer. Jour. Bot.* 19:710–728. 1932.

Foster, A. S. *Practical plant anatomy.* 2nd ed. New York, D. Van Nostrand Company. 1949.

Garrison, R. Origin and development of axillary buds: *Syringa vulgaris* L. *Amer. Jour. Bot.* 36:205–213. 1949*a*.

Garrison, R. Origin and development of axillary buds: *Betula papyrifera* Marsh. and *Euptelea polyandra* Sieb. et Zucc. *Amer. Jour. Bot.* 36:379–389. 1949*b*.

Gifford, E. M., Jr. Ontogeny of the vegetative axillary bud in *Drimys Winteri* var. *chilensis*. *Amer. Jour. Bot.* 38:234–243. 1951.

Golub, S. J., and R. H. Wetmore. Studies of development in the vegetative shoot of *Equisetum arvense* L. II. The mature shoot. *Amer. Jour. Bot.* 35:767–781. 1948.

Gris, A. Extrait d'un mémoire sur la moelle des plantes ligneuses. *Ann. des Sci. Nat., Bot.* Ser. 5. 14:34–79. 1872.

Gunckel, J. E., and R. H. Wetmore. Studies of development in long shoots and short shoots of *Ginkgo biloba* L. I. The origin and pattern of development of the cortex, pith and procambium. *Amer. Jour. Bot.* 33:285–295. 1946*a*.

Gunckel, J. E., and R. H. Wetmore. Studies of development in long shoots and short shoots of *Ginkgo biloba* L. II. Phyllotaxis and the organization of the primary vascular system; primary phloem and primary xylem. *Amer. Jour. Bot.* 33:532–543. 1946*b*.

Guttenberg, H. von. Die physiologischen Scheiden. In: K. Linsbauer. *Handbuch der Pflanzenanatomie.* Band 5. Lief. 42. 1943.

Haberlandt, G. *Physiological plant anatomy.* London, Macmillan and Company. 1914.

Hall, J. W. A morphoplastic interpretation of the amphivasal bundle in *Ranunculus*. *Lloydia* 10:235–241. 1947.

Hanstein, J. Über den Zusammenhang der Blattstellung mit dem Bau des dicotylen Holzringes. *Jahrb. f. Wiss. Bot.* 1:233–283. 1858.

Hasselberg, G. B. E. Zur Morphologie des vegetativen Sprosses der Loganiaceen. *Symb. Bot. Upsaliensis* II:3. 1937.

Hayward, H. E., and F. W. Went. Transplantation experiments with peas. II. *Bot. Gaz.* 100:788–801. 1939.

Heimsch, C., G. S. Rabideau, and W. G. Whaley. Vascular development and differentiation in two maize inbreds and their hybrid. *Amer. Jour. Bot.* 37:84–93. 1950.

Helm, J. Untersuchungen über die Differenzierung der Sprossscheitelmeristeme von Dikotylen unter besonderer Berücksichtigung des Prokambiums. *Planta* 15:105–191. 1931.

Jeffrey, E. C. The morphology of the central cylinder in the angiosperms. *Canad. Inst. Toronto, Trans.* 6:599–636. 1898–99.

Jeffrey, E. C. The structure and development of the stem in the Pteridophyta and gymnosperms. *Roy. Soc. London, Phil. Trans.* Ser. B. 195:119–146. 1903.

Jeffrey, E. C. *The anatomy of woody plants.* Chicago, University of Chicago Press. 1917.

Johnson, M. A. Origin and development of tissues in *Equisetum scirpoides. Bot. Gaz.* 94:469–494. 1933.

Juliano, J. B. Callus development in graft union. *Philippine Jour. Sci.* 75:245–251. 1941.

Kaplan, R. Die Differenzierung des Sproszscheitelmeristems bei einigen Piperaceen, kleinblättrigen Dikotylen, Monokotylen und Gymnospermen. *Planta* 25:302–306. 1936.

Kaplan, R. Über die Bildung der Stele aus dem Urmeristem von Pteridophyten und Spermatophyten. *Planta* 27:224–268. 1937.

Kruch, O. Sull' origine dei cosi detti fasci di sostegno periciclici dello stelo delle Cicoriacee. *Malpighia* 3:353–366. 1889.

Küster, E. *Pathologische Pflanzenanatomie.* 3rd ed. Jena, Gustav Fischer. 1925.

Lawalrée, A. Histogénèse florale et végétative chez quelques Composées. *Cellule* 52:215–294. 1948.

Léger, L. J. Recherches sur l'origine et les transformations des éléments libériens. *Soc. Linn. de Normandie, Mém.* 19:49–182. 1897.

Linsbauer, K. Editor. *C. K. Schneiders illustriertes Handwörterbuch der Botanik.* 2nd ed. Leipzig, Wilhelm Engelmann. 1917.

Louis, J. L'ontogénèse du système conducteur dans la pousse feuillé des Dicotylées et des Gymnospermes. *Cellule* 44:87–172. 1935.

Majumdar, G. P. Growth unit or the phyton in dictoyledons with special reference to *Heracleum. Bengal Bot. Soc. Bul.* 1947:61–66. 1947.

Majumdar, G. P. Leaf development at the growing apex and phyllotaxis in *Heracleum. Ind. Acad. Sci. Proc.* 28:83–98. 1948.

Markfeldt, O. Über das Verhalten der Blattspurstränge immergrüner Pflanzen beim Dickenwachstum des Stammes oder Zweiges. *Flora* 68:33–39, 81–90, 99–113. 1885.

Metcalfe, C. R. The systematic anatomy of the vegetative organs of the angiosperms. *Cambridge Phil. Soc. Biol. Rev.* 21:159–172. 1946.

Metcalfe, C. R., and L. Chalk. *Anatomy of the dicotyledons.* 2 vols. Oxford, Clarendon Press. 1950.

Meyer, F. J. Die Stelärtheorie und die neuere Nomenklatur zur Beschreibung der Wasserleitungsbahnen der Pflanzen. *Bot. Centbl. Beihefte* 33:129–168. 1916.

Miller, H. A., and R. H. Wetmore. Studies in the developmental anatomy of *Phlox drummondii* Hook. I. The embryo. *Amer. Jour. Bot.* 32:588–599. 1945a.

Miller, H. A., and R. H. Wetmore. Studies in the developmental anatomy of *Phlox drummondii* Hook. II. The seedling. *Amer. Jour. Bot.* 32:628–634. 1945b.

Miller, H. A., and R. H. Wetmore. Studies in the developmental anatomy of *Phlox drummondii* Hook. III. The apices of the mature plant. *Amer. Jour. Bot.* 33:1–10. 1946.

Millington, W. F., and J. E. Gunckel. Structure and development of the vegetative shoot tip of *Liriodendron tulipifera* L. *Amer. Jour. Bot.* 37:326–335. 1950.

Möbius, M. Über das Vorkommen concentrischer Gefässbündel mit centralem Phloëm und peripherischem Xylem. *Deut. Bot. Gesell. Ber.* 5:2–24. 1887.

Mullenders, W. L'origine du phloème interxylémien chez *Stylidium* et *Thunbergia*. Étude anatomique. *Cellule* 51:5–48. 1947.

Mullendore, N. Seedling anatomy of *Brachypodium distachyum*. *Bot. Gaz.* 109:341–348. 1948.

Mylius, G. Das Polyderm. Eine vergleichende Untersuchung über die physiologischen Scheiden: Polyderm, Periderm und Endodermis. *Biblioth. Bot.* 18(79):1–119. 1913

Nast, C. G. The embryogeny and seedling morphology of *Juglans regia* L. *Lilloa* 6:163–205. 1941.

Nast, C. G. The comparative morphology of the Winteraceae. VI. Vascular anatomy of the flowering shoot. *Arnold Arboretum Jour.* 25:454–466. 1944.

Ogura, Y. Anatomie der Vegetationsorgane der Pteridophyten. In: K. Linsbauer. *Handbuch der Pflanzenanatomie*. Band 7. Lief. 36. 1938.

Ozenda, P. *Recherches sur les Dicotylédones apocarpiques. Contribution a l'étude des Angiospermes dites primitives*. Thesis. Paris, École Normale Supérieure. Publ. Ser. Biol. Fasc. II. 1949.

Percival, J. *The wheat plant*. New York, E. P. Dutton and Company. 1921.

Pfeiffer, H. Das abnorme Dickenwachstum. In: K. Linsbauer. *Handbuch der Pflanzenanatomie*. Band 9. Lief. 15. 1926.

Philipson, W. R. The ontogeny of the shoot apex in dicotyledons. *Biol. Rev.* 24:21–50. 1949.

Plantefol, L. La distribution des feuilles sur les tiges. *Nature* (*Paris*) 76(3160):230–233. 1948.

Plaut, M. Untersuchungen zur Kenntnis der physiologischen Scheiden bei den Gymnospermen, Equiseten und Bryophyten. *Jahrb. f. Wiss. Bot.* 47:121–185. 1910.

Plowman, A. B. The comparative anatomy and phylogeny of the Cyperaceae. *Ann. Bot.* 20:1–33. 1906.

Posthumus, O. *On some principles of stelar morphology*. Dissertation. Amsterdam, J. H. De Bussy. 1924.

Priestley, J. H. Light and growth. II. On the anatomy of etiolated plants. *New Phytol.* 25:145–170. 1926.

Priestley, J. H., and J. Ewing. Physiological studies in plant anatomy. VI. Etiolation. *New Phytol.* 22:30–44. 1923.

Priestley, J. H., and L. I. Scott. The vascular anatomy of *Helianthus annuus* L. *Leeds Phil. Lit. Soc. Proc.* 3:159–173. 1936.

Prunet, A. Recherches sur les noeuds et les entre-noeuds de la tige de Dicotylédones. *Ann. des Sci. Nat., Bot.* Ser. 7. 13:297–373. 1891.

Raimann, R. Über unverholzte Elemente in der innersten Xylemzone der Dicotyledonen. *Akad. der Wiss. Wien, Math.-Nat. Cl. Sitzber.* Abt. 1. 98:40–75. 1890.

Reeve, R. M. Late embryogeny and histogenesis in *Pisum. Amer. Jour. Bot.* 35:591–602. 1948.

Rouffa, A. S., and J. E. Gunckel. Leaf initiation, origin, and pattern of pith development in the Rosaceae. *Amer. Jour. Bot.* 38:301–307. 1951.

Russow, E. Vergleichende Untersuchungen der Leitbündel-Kryptogamen. *Mém. Acad. Imp. Sci. St. Petérsbourg.* Ser. VII. 19:1–207. 1872.

Sachs, J. *Textbook of botany.* Oxford, Clarendon Press. 1875.

Schellenberg, H. C. Zur Entwicklungsgeschichte des Stammes von *Aristolochia sipho* L'Herit. *Botan. Untersuchungen. Festschrift für Schwendener* 1899: 301–320. Berlin, Gebrüder Borntraeger. 1899.

Schoute, J. C. *Die Stelär-Theorie.* Jena, Gustav Fischer. 1903.

Schoute, J. C. On phytonism. *Rec. des Trav. Bot. Néerland.* 28:82–96. 1931.

Schüepp, O. Über periodische Formbildung bei Pflanzen. *Biol. Rev.* 13:59–92. 1938.

Scott, L. I., and J. H. Priestley. Leaf and stem anatomy of *Tradescantia fluminensis,* Vell. *Linn. Soc. London, Jour., Bot.* 47:1–28. 1925.

Sharman, B. C. Developmental anatomy of the shoot of *Zea mays* L. *Ann. Bot.* 6:245–282. 1942.

Sharples, A., and H. Gunnery. Callus formation in *Hibiscus Rosa-sinensis* L. and *Hevea brasiliensis* Müll. Arg. *Ann. Bot.* 47:827–840. 1933.

Sifton, H. B. Developmental morphology of vascular plants. *New Phytol.* 43: 87–129. 1944.

Sinnott, E. W. Investigations on the phylogeny of the angiosperms. I. The anatomy of the node as an aid in the classification of angiosperms. *Amer. Jour. Bot.* 1:303–322. 1914.

Sinnott, E. W., and I. W. Bailey. Investigations on the phylogeny of the angiosperms, No. 4. The origin and dispersal of herbaceous angiosperms. *Ann. Bot.* 28:547–600. 1914.

Sinnott, E. W., and I. W. Bailey. Investigations on the phylogeny of the angiosperms. 5. Foliar evidence as to the ancestry and early climatic environment of the angiosperms. *Amer. Jour. Bot.* 2:1–22. 1915.

Sketch, A. F. Anatomy of the axis of banana. *Bot. Gaz.* 93:233–258. 1932.

Smith, E. P. Nodal anatomy of some common trees. *Bot. Soc. Edinb. Trans. and Proc.* 32:260–277. 1937.

Snow, M., and R. Snow. The interpretation of phyllotaxis. *Biol. Rev.* 9:132–137. 1934.

Snow, M., and R. Snow. On the determination of leaves. *New Phytol.* 46:5–19. 1947.

Solereder, H., and F. J. Meyer. *Systematische Anatomie der Monokotyledonen.* Heft III. Berlin, Gebrüder Borntraeger. 1928.

Spurr, A. R. Histogenesis and organization of the embryo in *Pinus strobus* L. *Amer. Jour. Bot.* 36:629–641. 1949.

Spurr, A. R. Organization of the procambium and development of the secretory cells in the embryo of *Pinus strobus* L. *Amer. Jour. Bot.* 37:185–197. 1950.

Stafford, H. A. Studies on the growth and xylary development of *Phleum pratense* seedlings in darkness and in light. *Amer. Jour. Bot.* 35:706–715. 1948.

Sterling, C. Growth and vascular development in the shoot apex of *Sequoia sempervirens* (Lamb.) Endl. II. Vascular development in relation to phyllotaxis. *Amer. Jour. Bot.* 32:380–386. 1945.

Sterling, C. Growth and vascular development in the shoot apex of *Sequoia sempervirens* (Lamb.) Endl. III. Cytological aspects of vascularization. *Amer. Jour. Bot.* 33:35–45. 1946.

Sterling, C. Organization of the shoot of *Pseudotsuga taxifolia* (Lamb.) Britt. II. Vascularization. *Amer. Jour. Bot.* 34:272–280. 1947.

Sterling, C. The primary body of the shoot of *Dianthera americana. Amer. Jour. Bot.* 36:184–193. 1949.

Strasburger, E. *Über den Bau und die Verrichtungen der Leitungsbahnen in den Pflanzen. Histologische Beiträge.* Band 3. Jena, Gustav Fischer. 1891.

Swamy, B. G. L., and I. W. Bailey. The morphology and relationships of *Cercidiphyllum. Arnold Arboretum Jour.* 30:187–210. 1949.

Swamy, B. G. L., and I. W. Bailey. *Sarcandra,* a vesselless genus of the Chloranthaceae. *Arnold Arboretum Jour.* 31:117–129. 1950.

Tansley, A. G. Lectures on the evolution of the filicinean vascular system. *New Phytol.* 6:25–35, 53–68, 109–120, 135–147, 148–155, 187–203, 219–238, 253–269; 7:1–16, 29–40. 1907–08.

Trécul, A. Recherches sur l'ordre d'apparition des premiers vaisseaux dans les organes aériens. *Ann. des Sci. Nat., Bot.* Ser. 6. 12:251–381. 1881.

Troll, W. *Vergleichende Morphologie der höheren Pflanzen.* Band I. *Vegetationsorgane.* Heft 1. Berlin, Gebrüder Borntraeger. 1937.

Troll, W., and W. Rauh. Das Erstarkungswachstum krautiger Dikotylen, mit besonderer Berücksichtigung der primären Verdickungsvorgänge. *Heidelberg. Akad. der Wiss., Math.-Nat. Kl. Sitzber.* 1. Abh. 1950.

Van Fleet, D. S. The development and distribution of the endodermis and an associated oxidase system in monocotyledonous plants. *Amer. Jour. Bot.* 29:1–15. 1942*a*.

Van Fleet, D. S. The significance of oxidation in the endodermis. *Amer. Jour. Bot.* 29:747–755. 1942*b*.

Van Fleet, D. S. The cell forms, and their common substance reactions, in the parenchyma-vascular boundary. *Torrey Bot. Club Bul.* 77:340–353. 1950*a*.

Van Fleet, D. S. A comparison of histochemical and anatomical characteristics of the hypodermis with the endodermis in vascular plants. *Amer. Jour. Bot.* 37:721–725. 1950*b*.

Van Tieghem, P. Sur quelques points de l'anatomie des Cucurbitacées. *Soc. Bot. de France Bul.* 29:277–283. 1882.

Van Tieghem, P., and H. Douliot. Sur la polystélie. *Ann. des Sci. Nat., Bot.* Ser. 7. 3:275–322. 1886.

Veh, R. von. Untersuchungen und Betrachtungen zum Blattstellungsproblem. *Flora* 25:83–153. 1930.

Verdoorn, F. Editor. *Manual of pteridology.* The Hague, Martinius Nijhoff. 1938.

Warden, W. M. On the structure, development and distribution of the endodermis and its associated ducts in *Senecio vulgaris. New Phytol.* 34:361–385. 1935.

Wardlaw, C. W. Experimental and analytical studies of pteridophytes. III. Stelar morphology: the initial differentiation of vascular tissue. *Ann. Bot.* 8:173–188. 1944*a*.

Wardlaw, C. W. Experimental and analytical studies of pteridophytes. IV. Stelar morphology: experimental observations on relation between leaf development and stelar morphology in species of *Dryopteris* and *Onoclea. Ann. Bot.* 8:387–399. 1944*b*.

Wardlaw, C. W. Experimental and analytical studies of pteridophytes. V. Stelar morphology: the development of the vascular system. *Ann. Bot.* 9:217–233. 1945.

Wardlaw, C. W. Experimental and analytical studies of pteridophytes. VII. Stelar morphology: the effect of defoliation on the stele of *Osmunda* and *Todea. Ann. Bot.* 9:97–107. 1946*a*.

Wardlaw, C. W. Experimental and analytical studies of pteridophytes. IX. The effect of removing leaf primordia on the development of *Angiopteris evecta* Hoffm. *Ann. Bot.* 10:223–235. 1946*b*.

Wardlaw, C. W. Experimental investigations of the shoot apex of *Dryopteris aristata* Druce. *Roy. Soc. London, Phil. Trans.* Ser. B. 232:343–384. 1947.

Wardlaw, C. W. Experimental and analytical studies of pteridophytes. XI. Preliminary observations on tensile stress as a factor in fern phyllotaxis. *Ann. Bot.* 12:97–109. 1948.

Wardlaw, C. W. Experimental and analytical studies of pteridophytes. XVI. The induction of leaves and buds in *Dryopteris aristata* Druce. *Ann. Bot.* 14:435–455. 1950*a*.

Wardlaw, C. W. The comparative investigations of apices of vascular plants by experimental methods. *Roy. Soc. London, Phil. Trans.* Ser. B. 234:583–604. 1950*b*.

Wetmore, R. H. Leaf-stem relationships in the vascular plants. *Torreya* 43:16–28. 1943.

Wetmore, R. H., and C. W. Wardlaw. Experimental morphogenesis in vascular plants. *Ann. Rev. Plant Physiol.* 2:269–292. 1951.

Wilton, O. C., and R. H. Roberts. Anatomical structure of stems in relation to the production of flowers. *Bot. Gaz.* 98:45–64. 1936.

Zimmermann, A. *Die Cucurbitaceen.* Heft 1. *Beiträge zur Anatomie und Physiologie.* Jena, Gustav Fischer. 1922.

Zimmermann, W. *Die Phylogenie der Pflanzen: ein Überblick über Tatsachen und Probleme.* Jena, Gustav Fischer. 1930.

CHAPTER

16
The Leaf

CONCEPT

The leaf is the principal appendage or lateral organ borne by the stem. As was emphasized in chapter 15, the term organ is applied to the leaf in a purely descriptive sense. The leaf and the stem are parts of one unit, the shoot. Leaves probably vary in their phylogenetic origin (Eames, 1936). In some plant groups (certain lower vascular plants) the leaf appears to have arisen as a lateral outgrowth of the stem (enation theory of leaf origin). In others (e.g., ferns and seed plants) the leaf is interpreted as a branch system, limited in growth and differing from the main branch system in form. Because of the determinate growth of such a leaf, the main branch overtops it (overtopping theory of leaf origin).

Regardless of variations in phylogenetic origin, the leaf usually contains the same tissue systems as the stem—the dermal, the vascular, and the fundamental. Also, as in the stem, the epidermis forms the outermost layer, and the vascular tissue is variously distributed in the ground tissue. Authors who emphasize the concept of the stele in the interpretation of the structure of vascular plants regard the vascular system of the leaf as a prolongation of the stelar tissue of the stem and homologize the ground tissue of the leaf with the cortex (Eames and MacDaniels, 1947, p. 317).

Although fundamentaly alike in structure, the stem and the leaf differ from each other in details of growth and in relative arrangement of tissues. The leaf shows determinate apical growth as contrasted with the continued type of growth exhibited by the stem in its apical meristem. The structural differences of the two organs appear to be related to their principal functions. In the stem the columnar shape, the vertical orientation of the vascular system, and the abundance of mechanical elements and of storage parenchyma suggest efficiency in longitudinal conduction of materials, support of the aerial body, and storage of food. In the ordinary foliage leaf the relatively large external surface, the extensive air space system, the abundance of chloroplasts in the ground tissue, and the close spatial relation between the vascular and the ground tissues suggest a specialization related to photosynthesis (Wylie, 1947). These characteristics favor exposure of the chloroplasts to the light and ready access of water and gases to the cells concerned with photosynthesis.

The structural distinction between the stem and the leaf is enhanced by certain concomitants of the specialization related to photosynthesis (Wylie, 1947). In contrast to the stem, the foliage leaf commonly lacks storage tissues, develops no periderm, and consists mainly of primary tissues. In the absence of any substantial amount of secondary growth, the leaf is restricted in its capacity to restore its tissues, which are constantly exposed to weathering and other injurious outside influences. In perennial plants new leaves are repeatedly formed and the old ones are shed. Thus, the leaves are usually limited in growth and longevity and are restricted in mass.

The concept of leaf is applied in the seed plants to many forms of lateral appendages of the axis varying in structure and function. This variation necessitates a segregation of the foliar organs into different types. A common classification distinguishes among foliage leaves, cataphylls, hypsophylls, and cotyledons. Foliage leaves are the principal photosynthetic organs. Cataphylls (from the Greek words *cata*, down, and *phyllon*, leaf, meaning leaves inserted at low levels of plant or shoot) are exemplified by scales occurring on buds and underground stems; they are concerned with protection or storage or both. Hypsophylls (from the Greek words *hypso*, high, and *phyllos*, leaf, meaning leaves inserted at high levels of the plant) are represented by the various floral bracts, possibly protective in function. The first cataphylls on a lateral branch are called *prophylls* (from the Greek *pro*, before, and *phyllon*, leaf). The monocotyledons usually have one prophyll, the dicotyledons two (see p. 353). The cotyledons are the first leaves of the plant (see chapter 1). If the flower is interpreted as a modified shoot, then the floral organs also constitute a type of foliar organ. The various kinds of leaf-like organs enumerated above may intergrade with each other by transitional forms, and each, especially the foliage leaf, varies widely in external form and anatomy.

A generalized term for the foliar members of the plant in the morphological literature is phyllome (Arber, 1950, p. 42). Phyllomes include foliage leaves (or simply leaves), scales, bracts, and floral appendages. The differences in structure and form of phyllomes result from early divergencies in method of growth, distribution of meristems, and rates of maturation (Cross, 1938; Foster, 1928, 1931, 1936; Schüepp, 1929). If phyllomes have a common origin phylogenetically, their divergences appear to have arisen as modifications of their ontogenies.

MORPHOLOGY OF THE FOLIAGE LEAF

This chapter deals almost entirely with the foliage leaf. The variations in the structure of a foliage leaf are manifold. In angiosperms the main part of the photosynthetic tissue is typically expanded into a flattened structure, the *blade*, or *limb*, or *lamina* (from the Latin, thin leaf). In sessile (from the Latin, sitting) leaves, this blade is directly attached to the stem, in others by means of a stalk, the *petiole* (meaning foot in Latin). In most monocotyledons and certain dicotyledons (for example, Polygonaceae and Umbelliferae) the base of the leaf is expanded into a *sheath* around the stem. Leaves may be simple or compound. A simple leaf has one blade. In a compound leaf two or more blades, the *leaflets*, are attached to a common axis or *rachis* (in Greek, backbone). The lamina of a leaf, or of a leaflet in the compound leaf, varies greatly in shape and size. There are lancet-shaped leaves and various broad forms. Others are cylindrical or somewhat flattened, as the needles of the conifers. In some plants the leaves are fleshy and contain relatively large amounts of nonphotosynthetic tissue; in others the foliar structures are mere scales, and the main photosynthetic activity occurs in the chlorenchyma of the stem. Sometimes the stems specialized with relation to photosynthetic activity are flattened like leaves and are then called *cladodes* (from the Greek *clados*, branch).

Leaves may have basal appendages, the *stipules* (from the Latin, stubble), or they may be exstipulate. A relationship exists between the type of nodal anatomy and the occurrence of stipules and leaf sheaths in the dicotyledons (Sinnott and Bailey, 1914). Most plants with trilacunar nodes have stipules, whereas most of those with unilacunar nodes lack these structures, and all plants with multilacunar nodes have leaves with sheathing bases.

In discussions of the form and anatomy of the leaf, it is customary to designate the leaf surface that is continuous with the surface of the part of the stem located above the leaf insertion as the upper, ventral, or adaxial side; the opposite side as the lower, dorsal, or abaxial.

HISTOLOGY OF THE MATURE LEAF

Angiosperm

Epidermis. The structure of the epidermis was considered in detail in chapter 7. The complex morphologic and physiologic organization of the leaf epidermis makes the term and the concept of epidermal tissue system highly appropriate for this part of the plant body. The principal characteristics of the leaf epidermis are reviewed below.

The epidermis of leaves is composed of the various types of cells that are encountered in the aerial parts of plants in general: epidermal cells, composing the main mass of the epidermal tissue; guard cells of the stomata, commonly accompanied by subsidiary cells; various trichomes; silica and cork cells in the Gramineae; bulliform cells in various monocotyledons (plate 59, *A*), fiber-like cells in various groups of plants (see chapter 10). Stomata are particularly characteristic of leaves and occur either on one, or the other, or both surfaces, but they are most common on the abaxial surface (fig. 16.2 and plate 60, *A*; see also chapter 7). The multiple epidermis described at some length in chapter 7 is most commonly encountered in leaves (fig. 16.2, *A*). The subsurface cells of such an epidermis often are large, thin walled, and colorless and are interpreted as water storage cells.

In the terrestrial higher vascular plants, the leaf epidermis is a living tissue and typically contains no well-differentiated chloroplasts. Certain plants, however, contain abundant chlorophyll in the epidermis, Water plants may show more abundant chloroplasts in the epidermis than in the parenchyma beneath it (Sauvageau, 1891). In many Polypodiaceae the epidermis contains chloroplasts, and in *Adiantum,* specifically, this tissue constitutes the major part of the photosynthetic tissue (Wylie, 1948, 1949*a*). Small amounts of chlorophyll are found in plastids of the leaf epidermis of angiosperms with and without relation to any special environmental conditions.

Except for the presence of intercellular spaces between the guard cells of the stomata and those associated with hydathodes (see p. 433), the epidermis of foliage leaves usually shows compact organization. The continuity of the epidermis is one of the features that contributes toward its effectiveness in protecting the leaf tissues from excessive loss of water and in offering mechanical support. The anticlinal walls of epidermal cells that are located in the interveinal areas may be undulate (plate 60, *A*).

The wall structure of the leaf epidermis varies widely, the most constant characteristics being the presence of cutin in the walls, notably the outer, and of cuticular layers on the surface. The epidermal walls may be thin in plants requiring moderately moist habitats (mesomorphic plants) and in water plants (hydromorphic plants). In xeromorphic plants, that is, plants that can subsist in dry environments, the epidermis may have thick, lignified walls. The deposition of silica in the epidermal walls is characteristic of grasses and related plants.

Mesophyll. The ground tissue of the leaf which is enclosed within the epidermis is called the mesophyll (from the Greek words *mesos*, in the middle, and *phyllon*, leaf). The mesophyll is usually specialized as a photosynthetic tissue. It is living, lacunose (that is, with many intercellular spaces) parenchyma containing chloroplasts. In many plants, particularly in dicotyledons of the mesomorphic type, the mesophyll is commonly differentiated into palisade and spongy parenchyma (figs. 16.1, 16.2 and plates 61, *A*, 63, *A*). The palisade tissue (from the Latin *palus*, stake) is so called because of the elongated shape of the cells and their arrangement like a row of stakes, as seen in transections. The spongy parenchyma appears less regular, and its name has reference to the conspicuous intercellular-space system permeating it.

The individual cells of the palisade parenchyma are commonly elongate-prismatic in shape. The ratio of length to width varies widely. It is, for example, 1:1 in the almost isodiametric cells of *Taraxacum officinale*, 6:1 in *Helianthus annuus*, and 10:1 in *Ricinus communis* (Meyer, 1923). In some plants the palisade cells are irregular in shape, having either relatively small lateral protuberances or long arm-like processes that make the whole cell appear branched ("arm-palisade cell," Haberlandt, 1914, p. 263; fig. 16.2, *B*).

Palisade cells occur beneath the epidermal surface layer (plate 61, *A*), unless there is a multiple epidermis (fig. 16.2, *A*) or a specialized hypodermis in the leaf. The palisade cells are usually oriented with their long axes at right angles to the leaf surface. There may be more than one layer of palisade cells (fig. 16.1), with a uniform or variable length of the cells in the different layers. Frequently, in such a multiseriate palisade tissue, the outermost cells are the longest, the innermost the shortest.

The palisade mesophyll commonly occurs on the adaxial side of the leaf. In certain plants it differentiates on both sides of the leaf, with a small amount of spongy parenchyma in the median part of the mesophyll (species of *Centaurea, Sarothammus, Silene, Artemisia;* Diettert, 1938; Meyer, 1923). Only rarely is the palisade limited to the abaxial side (Cupressineae; Meyer, 1923). If the palisade tissue occurs on one side of the leaf blade, and the spongy tissue on the

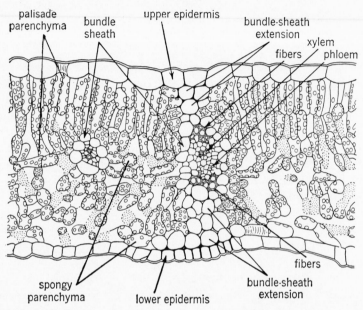

Fig. 16.1. Transverse section of pear leaf. The palisade parenchyma, above, consists of about three layers. Both vascular bundles shown are enclosed in bundle sheaths, but only the larger has bundle-sheath extensions reaching to the epidermis on both sides of the leaf. The mesophyll cells contain chloroplasts, except those having crystals. The bundle-sheath cells also have chloroplasts (not shown in the drawing), fewer than the mesophyll cells. (×247.)

other, the leaf is called *bifacial* or *dorsiventral,* that is, having distinct dorsal and ventral sides. If the palisade parenchyma is present on both sides, the leaf is *isolateral,* that is, has equal sides.

The spongy parenchyma shows many forms of cells, either nearly isodiametric, or elongated in the same direction as the palisade cells and connected with each other by lateral extensions of various lengths, or, most commonly, elongated parallel with the surface of the leaf (plate 61). The spongy mesophyll shows a wider variety in organization than does the palisade mesophyll (Wylie, 1951).

The distinction between palisade and spongy tissues varies in degree of sharpness. If the palisade mesophyll is multiseriate, there is com-

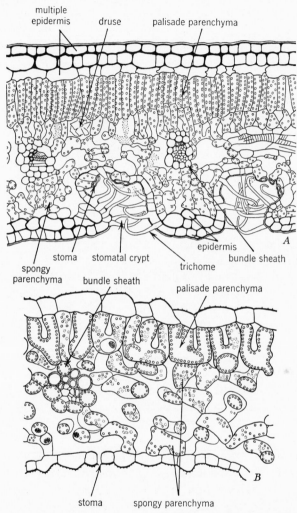

FIG. 16.2. Transections of leaves, *A*, *Nerium oleander* (dicotyledon) and, *B*, *Lilium* (monocotyledon). The oleander leaf has multiple epidermis. The stomata occur in the part of the abaxial epidermis that lines deep cavities called stomatal crypts. This epidermis also bears long slender trichomes. The distinguishing feature of the lily leaf is the presence of arm-palisade cells. (Both, ×260.)

monly a transition between the two kinds of mesophyll, the innermost layer of palisade parenchyma approaching the spongy parenchyma in shape, size, and arrangement of cells. Sometimes no distinction can be made between palisade and spongy layers, either because the mesophyll is in general little differentiated (plate 59, *B*) or
because it is composed of palisade tissue only (e.g., *Eucalyptus;* Turrell, 1936).

The degree of differentiation of the mesophyll and the proportion
of palisade and spongy parenchyma vary in relation to plant species
and habitat. Light is one of the particularly important factors influencing the final structure of the mesophyll (Paulmann, 1915; Wylie,
1949*a*, *b*, 1951). A well-known phenomenon is the stronger development of the palisade in leaves exposed to light during differentiation
(sun leaves) as contrasted with leaves differentiating in the shade
(shade leaves). Differences in mesophyll structure occur in leaves
developing at different levels of the same plant, a phenomenon ultimately related to light conditions during the growth of the various
leaves. Xeromorphic leaves have a relatively more strongly developed
palisade tissue than mesomorphic leaves (Shields, 1950).

The general organization of palisade and spongy parenchyma reveals basic contrasts that suggest different functional specialization of
the two tissues. The palisade tissue appears to be the most highly
specialized type of photosynthetic tissue (Meyer, 1923). In a leaf
with a mesophyll differentiated into palisade and spongy parenchyma,
most of the chloroplasts occur in the palisade parenchyma. This
feature is well illustrated by the comparative percentages of chloroplasts in the palisade and spongy tissues, respectively, in the following
plants: *Fragaria elatior*, 86 and 14; *Ricinus communis*, 82 and 18; *Brassica rapa*, 80 and 20; *Helianthus annuus*, 73 and 27; *Phaseolus multi-
florus*, 69 and 31 (Schürhoff, 1924). The common assumption is that,
because of the shape and arrangement of the palisade cells, the chloroplasts are brought in a most favorable position with reference to the
light. During active photosynthesis the chloroplasts line the walls,
one layer in thickness (plates 60, *B*, and 61, *A*). In the narrow cells
of the most common type of palisade tissue considerable wall surface
is present to accommodate numerous chloroplasts in a single layer.
In the wider cells arm-like protrusions or ridges increase wall surface
(fig. 16.2, *B*).

Another well-known concept is that the lacunose structure of the
mesophyll makes possible a thorough gaseous exchange between the

outside air and the photosynthetic tissue. Because of the large intercellular system in the mesophyll, an extended cell-wall surface is exposed to the intercellular air; that is, the mesophyll has a large surface.
This surface is called the internal surface of the leaf as contrasted with
the external surface of the leaf, which is the surface exposed to the
external air.

The extent of the development of the internal aerating system is
best illustrated by means of figures. The proportion of air by volume
in normal leaves varies between 77 parts per 1,000 in *Camphora officinalis* and 713 parts per 1,000 in *Pistia texensis* (Sifton, 1945). Data
comparing the internal with the external surface of leaves are also
instructive. Reference may be made here to figures obtained from a
study of the entire foliage of a 21-year-old *Catalpa* tree, in which the
internal surface of 5,100 m² was associated with 390 m² of external
surface (Turrell, 1934). The relative extent of the two surfaces varies
in different ecologic types of leaves (that is, types related to environment). In certain dicotyledon leaves the ratios of internal to external
surface were found to be relatively low in shade leaves (6.8 to 9.9),
intermediate in mesomorphic leaves (11.6 to 19.2), and high in xeromorphic sun leaves (17.2 to 31.3) (Turrell, 1936). The size of leaves
also affects this ratio. Large alfalfa leaves were found to have a larger
volume of intercellular spaces and a higher ratio of internal to external
surface than small leaves (Turrell, 1942).

As in the numbers of chloroplasts, the palisade tissue demonstrates
its extreme specialization with regard to photosynthetic activity also
in its relation to the intercellular space system. Although the spongy
parenchyma has much larger intercellular spaces than the palisade tissue (plates 60, *B*, and 61), the palisade tissue has a larger free surface.
An analysis of leaves of several species of dicotyledons showed that
per unit volume of leaf tissue the palisade tissue exposes to the intercellular air 1.6 to 3.5 times the surface exposed by the spongy parenchyma (Turrell, 1936). In view of these data the high ratio of internal to external surface in sun leaves is explained by the higher
proportion of palisade cells in such leaves (Turrell, 1936).

Certain observations suggest a correlation between the development
of an extensive intercellular system and specialization with regard to
photosynthesis. A high ratio of internal to external surface may be
accompanied by a high concentration of chlorophyll (Turrell, 1939).
Leaves with prominent intercellular spaces may produce a larger gain
in total dry matter per unit area of leaf per day than the more com-

pactly built leaves (Pickett, 1937). However, the ratio of internal to external surface is strongly and positively correlated with the rate of transpiration (Turrell, 1944) so that the structure favorable for photosynthesis induces at the same time a high loss of water. The compactly arranged, cutinized, and cuticularized epidermis and the presence of a fine film of fatty material on the walls of the mesophyll cells exposed to the intercellular spaces (see chapter 3) apparently reduce but do not completely control the high transpiration which is a concomitant of the structural specialization for photosynthesis (Wylie, 1947).

The intercellular spaces in the mesophyll are predominantly schizogenous. In some plants, however, part of the mesophyll breaks down, leaving large internal cavities. This method of space development occurs, for example, in water plants, in plants of marshy habitat (*Typha, Juncus;* Sifton, 1945), and in certain others (plate 59, *C; Musa;* Skutch, 1927). In some grasses, large cells develop in the mesophyll, and they either die and separate from each other or collapse completely during the development of the leaf (Page, 1947). The ordinary schizogenous intercellular-space system is apparently continuous throughout the leaf (Williams, 1948).

Vascular System. The arrangement of the vascular bundles, that is, the *venation*, imparts a characteristic appearance to leaves. The word venation is derived from the term *vein* (from the Latin *vena*, vein), which, in botany, is applied sometimes to a vascular bundle or a group of closely approximated bundles, sometimes to bundles together with the spatially associated nonvascular tissues. In this chapter the term vein denotes a vascular bundle or a group of closely spaced bundles.

A leaf may have a single vein or two or more. Examples of single-veined leaves are found among the conifers and in *Equisetum*, whereas multiveined leaves are common in the higher ferns and angiosperms. The two main types of venation patterns in the angiosperms are the *reticulate* (or net) and the *striate* (or parallel). In reticulate venation, which is widespread among the dicotyledons, vascular bundles of many sizes form an anastomosing network (figs. 16.4, 16.6, and plate 69, *A*), with the smaller bundles diverging from the larger. In striate veined leaves, which are so characteristic of the monocotyledons, the main bundles commonly are arranged longitudinally but converge toward each other and merge at the apex or at both ends of the blade (fig. 16.3, *A–C*). The longitudinal veins are laterally interconnected by small bundles throughout the blade. These connections are often arranged in a ladder-like manner (fig. 16.3, *B*), but they may also form various other patterns (Schuster, 1910). Some monocotyledons have a modified striate venation with the veins arranged longitudinally for a distance, then diverging laterally in a pinnate manner (fig. 16.10, *E*; Ertl, 1932; Troll, 1939, pp. 1044–1094). The longitudinally striate venation is frequently called parallel venation because in the median

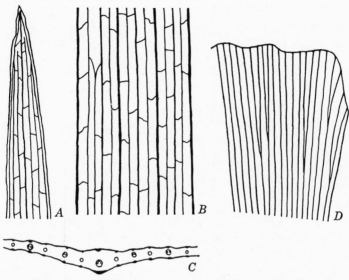

FIG. 16.3. Diagrams of leaf-venation patterns. Striate venation in a grass leaf, *Avena* (*A–C*), and open dichotomous venation in a *Ginkgo* leaf (*D*). *A* shows the convergence of longitudinal bundles at the apex of the leaf. Cross anastomoses between the longitudinal bundles appear in *A* and *B*. *C* shows the arrangement of bundles in a transection. *D* was taken from the edge of a mature leaf.

parts of long leaves the main vascular bundles approach parallelism. Striate venation is found in some dicotyledons also (e.g., *Plantago*, *Tragopogon*), and, reciprocally, some monocotyledons have netted venation (e.g., Araceae, Smilacoideae, Taccaceae, Orchidaceae; Schuster, 1910).

In the anastomosing vascular system of dicotyledonous leaves the veins are of many sizes. The largest vein often occurs in a median position and forms the midvein, and the somewhat smaller veins diverge from it laterally (fig. 16.4; pinnately veined leaf). In other leaves there may be several large veins, comparable in size, spreading out from the base of the blade toward the margins (palmately veined leaf). The large veins commonly occur in enlarged portions of the

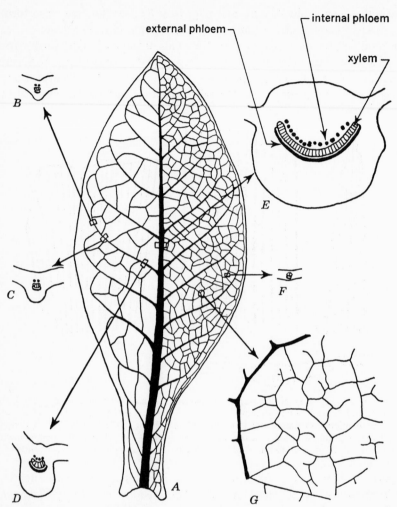

Fig. 16.4. Venation of *Nicotiana tabacum* leaf. *A*, diagram of mature leaf showing midvein, principal lateral veins, and the coarse vascular network. As indicated by the small diagrams of transections of veins of various sizes (*B–F*), xylem, external phloem, and internal phloem (the phloem is shown in solid black) occur in the midvein and the principal lateral veins. The smaller veins (*F*) lack internal phloem. *G*, small portion of blade showing smallest veins and their free endings in the mesophyll. The leaf depicted in this figure was obtained from midway on the stalk and had 543 mm of veins to a square centimeter of lamina. (*A*, ×⅓; *G*, ×20. After Avery, 1933.)

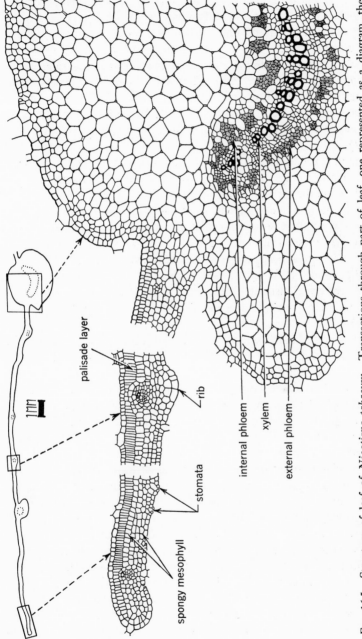

palisade layer

rib

stomata

spongy mesophyll

internal phloem

xylem

external phloem

FIG. 16.5. Structure of leaf of *Nicotiana tabacum*. Transections through part of leaf, one represented as a diagram, the others as more detailed drawings of the midvein, a smaller vein, and some mesophyll. Taken from lamina midway between the base and the tip of a leaf 135 mm long. The leaf was not fully differentiated as evidenced by the densely arranged mesophyll cells. (After Avery, 1933.)

blade which appear like ridges (ribs) on the abaxial surface of the leaf (figs. 16.4, 16.5). These ridges consist of parenchyma with a relatively small amount of chlorophyll and some supporting tissue, usually collenchyma. The vascular bundles of the large veins are imbedded in the parenchyma and are thus somewhat separated from the mesophyll proper (fig. 16.5). The small veins, in contrast, form a network among the large veins within the mesophyll. They occur in the median part of the mesophyll, usually beneath the palisade cells, that is, in the uppermost layer of the spongy parenchyma (figs. 16.1 and 16.2).

The minor venation of the dicotyledonous leaves exhibits a wide range of intergrading patterns (fig. 16.6). The branchings of these veins subdivide the mesophyll into a series of successively smaller polygons, with the ultimate branches, the bundle or vein endings, extending into the smallest subdivisions of the mesophyll and terminating there freely. In some instances the small mesophyll subdivisions lack free vein endings and appear as clearly circumscribed areas of mesophyll (fig. 16.6, A; Wylie, 1947). Plumose reticulate and arcuate venation patterns, distinct from those commonly described in dicotyledons, have been found in the Quiinaceae (plate 69, B, C; Foster, 1950a, b).

In the longitudinally striate venation of the monocotyledons the longitudinal bundles may be of almost equal thickness, or they may vary in size. If they vary, larger veins alternate with smaller. The median bundle may be larger than the others and associated with a prominent rib (fig. 16.3, C). The lateral veins may or may not form ribs. In some large grasses the median part of the blade is thickened into a midrib by the differentiation of massive colorless parenchyma on the adaxial sides of the bundles (fig. 16.10, H). Such a midrib has many vascular bundles of similar sizes and distribution as the rest of the leaf and merges imperceptibly with the green lamina halves on its sides. In many monocotyledons the smallest bundles extend from one large vein to another, but in some representatives of this plant group free vein endings occur in the mesophyll (Schuster, 1910).

The venation of the angiosperms is sometimes characterized as closed, in the sense that the veins anastomose with each other (Foster, 1950a). In many ferns and such gymnosperms as Ginkgo (fig. 16.3, D) and Stangeria the venation is classified as open type, because relatively large subdivisions of the system end freely in the interior of the leaf or at its margins. Ferns have a wide variety of venation patterns. Some are open, others are closed; some are dichotomous (re-

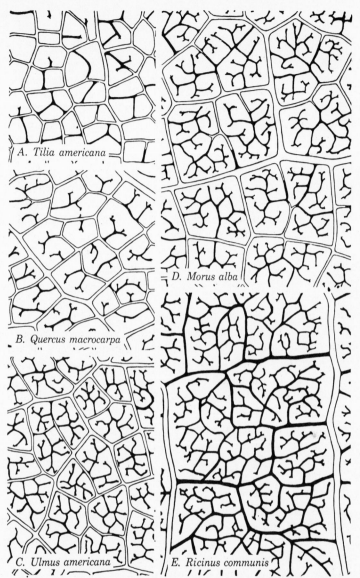

A. Tilia americana

B. Quercus macrocarpa

C. Ulmus americana

D. Morus alba

E. Ricinus communis

Fig. 16.6. Leaf venation in dicotyledons. The veins represented by double lines had bundle-sheath extensions, those in solid black had none. From A to E the proximity to each other of veins carrying bundle-sheath extensions is decreasing and the minor venation becomes more complex. There is a negative correlation between the actual smallest distance from vein to vein (vein spacing) and the spacing of sheath extensions. In the original leaves the vein spacings from A to E were in microns: 124, 103, 76, 89, and 85; the sheath-extension spacings were: 199, 225, 248, 378, 1,581. (From Wylie, 1947.)

peatedly forked, from the Greek words meaning in two and cut), others reticulate (Troll, 1939, pp. 1044–1094).

The histologic composition of the vascular bundles of various sizes shows quantitative and qualititative differences. The largest bundles contain xylem and phloem in amounts comparable to those of the bundles in the petiole (if this structure is present). The collateral bundles diverging from the stem into the leaf occupy here such a position that the xylem occurs on the adaxial, the phloem on the abaxial side (fig. 16.1). If the bundles are bicollateral, the adaxial phloem occurs also in the leaf, but only in the large veins (figs. 16.4, 16.5). The vascular tissue of the largest veins in the dicotyledonous leaves forms either one bundle or several (fig. 16.9; Plymale and Wylie, 1944). As seen in transections of veins, the vascular bundles may be arranged in a circle (fig. 16.9, *E*; *Liriodendron, Vitis*) or a semicircle (*Ambrosia*), or they may be distributed irregularly (*Silphium, Helianthus*). When the vascular bundle is single, it is crescent-shaped in some plants (fig. 16.9, *C*; *Cercis, Ulmus, Tilia, Abutilon*), circular in others (fig. 16.9, *G*; *Catalpa, Acer, Quercus*).

The larger veins in dicotyledonous leaves may have primary and secondary tissues; the smaller are entirely primary. Veins of various sizes, but not the smallest, have vessels in the xylem and sieve tubes in the phloem. In the small veins the tracheary elements are represented by tracheids. Near the ends of the ultimate vein branchings the phloem part contains only parenchyma (fig. 16.7, *G*), and the vein endings in the dicotyledons frequently contain tracheids only (fig. 16.7, *A, B, D, H*). These tracheids usually have annular and helical thickenings. At the very end of the bundle there may be a single tracheid, a pair of elements lying parallel to each other, or an irregular group of elements (Strain, 1933). Sclereids may differentiate beyond the last tracheids of the vein endings, in contact with these elements (e.g., *Hamamelis*, Melastomaceae; Foster, 1946, 1947, 1949, pp. 101–102). In some genera large ovoid or irregularly branched tracheids, frequently with pitted walls, terminate the veinlets. These cells are sometimes interpreted as water reservoirs and are called storage tracheids (Foster, 1949, p. 185; Pirwitz, 1931).

The small veinlets of monocotyledons also have few conducting elements. The transverse anastomoses in grass leaves may contain a single file of tracheary elements and a single file of sieve-tube elements (fig. 16.8, *B–E*). The notable feature of the small vascular bundles in grass leaves is that the sieve elements may occur adjacent to tracheary elements (fig. 16.8).

The principal characteristic of the vascular system of the leaf, whatever its detailed structure, is the close spatial relation between the vascular tissues and the mesophyll. Measurements performed on

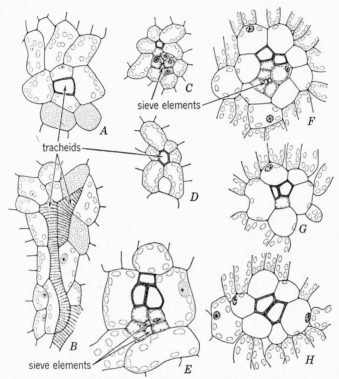

Fig. 16.7. Structure of the small leaf veins in the dicotyledons. *B* from a tangential section, all others from transverse. *A* and *B*, bundle ends consisting of tracheids enclosed by bundle-sheath cells from a *Vitis vinifera* leaf. (Stippling indicates tannins.) *C* and *D*, bundles from *Humulus* leaf, one with tracheids, sieve elements, and some parenchyma cells, the other (a bundle end) with a single tracheid. *E*, small bundle from a leaf of *Nicotiana tabacum* consisting of some tracheary elements, sieve elements, and parenchyma. *F–H*, bundles from a leaf of *Prunus* (peach). The bundle in *F* has two tracheary elements, two sieve elements, and some parenchyma; in *G*, two tracheary elements and a parenchyma cell occupying the position of the phloem; in *H*, two tracheary elements (bundle end). The bundle-sheath cells have relatively numerous chloroplasts in *A–E*, few or none in *F–H*. (*A, B*, ×470; *C–H*, ×600.)

six species of dicotyledons, herbaceous, shrubby, and arborescent, have shown that the total length of the veins averaged 102 cm per sq cm of blade (Plymale and Wylie, 1944). The thorough distribution of the vascular tissue within the mesophyll is illustrated by the

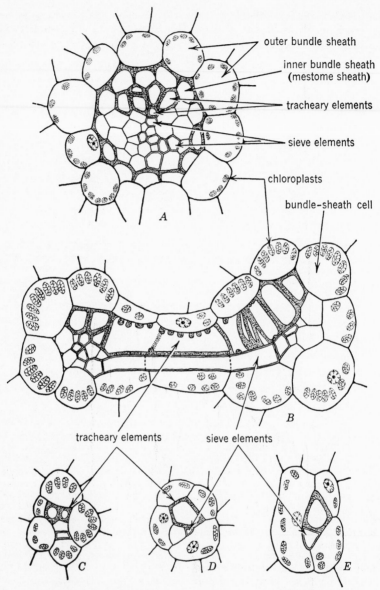

FIG. 16.8. Small vascular bundles of grass leaves. *A*, longitudinal bundle from a transection of *Triticum* leaf. *B*, two longitudinal bundles connected by a transverse bundle as seen in a transection of *Zea* leaf. *C*, one of the smallest longitudinal bundles of *Zea*. *D* and *E*, bundles constituting transverse anastomoses in *Zea* as exposed in sections cut parallel with the long axis of the leaf and perpendicular to the epidermal layers. (All, ×700.)

small size of the areas free of veins. According to some measurements, the interveinal spacings in dicotyledonous leaves average about 130 microns (Wylie, 1939, 1946).

A significant correlation has been found to exist between vein distribution and those structural features of the nonvascular tissues of the leaf that may have an influence upon conduction. Thus, the larger the volume of tissue having relatively little lateral contact among its cells (plate 60, *B*; palisade tissue)—an arrangement resulting in a comparatively low efficiency in lateral conduction—the closer together are the vascular bundles. On the contrary, the greater the amount of tissues with extensive lateral contacts among the component cells (such as the epidermis, plate 60, *A*, and the spongy parenchyma, plate 61, *B*), the larger are the interveinal distances (Wylie, 1939, 1946). In agreement with these data is the observation that sun leaves, in which the palisade tissue usually shows particularly strong development, contain a greater total length of veins than shade leaves (Schuster, 1908).

Bundle Sheaths. As has been described above, the large vascular bundles of dicotyledonous leaves are surrounded by parenchyma with small numbers of chloroplasts, whereas the small bundles occur in the mesophyll. These small bundles, however, are not in contact with intercellular spaces but are commonly enclosed within a layer of compactly arranged parenchyma, the bundle sheath (fig. 16.7). In dicotyledons the bundle-sheath parenchyma is also called border parenchyma.

The bundle sheaths of dicotyledonous leaves usually consist of cells elongated parallel with the course of the bundle and having walls as thin as those of the adjacent mesophyll. In some plants these cells have chloroplast complements similar to those of the mesophyll cells (fig. 16.7, *C–E*); in others they have few or no chloroplasts (fig. 16.7, *F–H*). Individual sheath cells may contain crystals. The bundle sheaths extend to the ends of the bundles and completely enclose the terminal tracheids (fig. 16.7, *B*).

In many dicotyledons, plates of cells similar to those in the bundle sheath extend from the bundle sheath toward one or both epidermises, some terminating in the mesophyll, others reaching the epidermis (fig. 16.1 and plate 63, *A*; Armacost, 1945; Wylie, 1943). These bundle-sheath extensions have received careful attention in the literature, and good evidence has been gathered that they are concerned with conduction in the leaves (Armacost, 1945; Wylie, 1943, 1947, 1949*b*, 1951). Originally these structures were described as *vein* *extensions* (Wylie, 1943, and following papers). In the present book they are termed *bundle-sheath extensions* or *sheath extensions* because such a designation is more precise morphologically than the one relating the extensions to the rather vague term vein.

Measurements carried out in leaves of certain dicotyledons have shown that 99 per cent of the total vein length is invested in sheath parenchyma (Armacost, 1945). In 10 species of mesomorphic species, bundle-sheath extensions were found along 58 per cent of the total vein length (Wylie, 1943). Thus, if the bundle sheaths and their extensions are concerned with conduction, their presence materially increases the contact between the mesophyll and the conducting cells (Armacost, 1945).

There is experimental evidence that the sheaths and their extensions take part in conduction. Potassium ferrocyanide solution introduced into leaves was found to move out quickly through the veins into the bundle sheaths and through the sheath extensions into the epidermis. Here the solution spread throughout. The concern of the sheath extensions with conduction is also suggested by the correlation that exists between the distribution of veins and the presence of sheath extensions. If bundle-sheath extensions are numerous and spaced close together, the vascular net is less dense and less elaborate than if sheath extensions are less numerous (fig. 16.6; Wylie, 1947). Furthermore, the ratio of sheath extension spacing to vein spacing is similar in leaves collected from shaded, intermediate, and exposed positions in a tree, although the structure and the volume of the tissues in these leaves vary greatly (Wylie, 1951). All these observations support the contention that the bundle sheaths, their extensions, and the epidermis together constitute a supplementary conducting system in mesomorphic leaves (Wylie, 1943). In this connection, the extensive lateral contact area among the epidermal cells is worthy of special mention. This contact area may be 2.5 to 6 times larger than that of all the layers of spongy mesophyll of the same leaf sample (Wylie, 1943).

The parenchymatous bundle sheaths are the most common, but in certain dicotyledons bundles of various sizes are enclosed in sclerenchyma (e.g., Winteraceae, Melastomaceae; Bailey and Nast, 1944; Foster, 1947). In some of the Winteraceae even the terminal veinlets are ensheathed by sclerenchyma.

Bundle sheaths occur in monocotyledonous leaves also. The best known are those of the Gramineae (Schwendener, 1890). Grass leaves have two kinds of sheaths: entirely parenchymatous, with chloroplasts, and relatively thick-walled sheaths, without chloroplasts. The thick-walled sheath was termed *mestom sheath* by Schwendener, because mestom was previously used to designate the conducting elements of a vascular bundle. If present, the mestom sheath occurs next to the vascular tissue, and outside it is a second thin-walled sheath with chloroplasts.

The Gramineae may be divided into two groups with reference to the occurrence of sheaths, the Panicoideae and the Pooideae. The Panicoideae, with the exception of some species of *Panicum*, have single thin-walled sheaths (fig. 16.8, *B–E*, and plate 59, *B*). (In the larger bundles the sheaths may be relatively thick walled.) The Pooideae have double sheaths, an inner thick-walled sheath and an outer thin-walled sheath (fig. 16.8, *A*, and plate 59, *A*). The inner sheath of the Pooideae consists of elongated living cells with blunt or pointed ends. The wall thickening is variable, even in different parts of the same sheath, and is often pitted. Sometimes the inner walls are thicker than the outer. In small bundles the inner sheath may be restricted to the phloem side.

In certain respects the bundle sheath of angiospermous leaves is an endodermoid layer; that is, it has features comparable to those of an endodermis (see chapters 15 and 17). Although the Casparian strip is mostly indistinguishable, the walls and the contents of the sheath cells may react to various dyes and indicators like typical endodermis cells (Guttenberg, 1943; Van Fleet, 1950). Furthermore, Casparian strips have been detected in mestom sheaths in young leaves of certain Gramineae and Cyperaceae (Van Fleet, 1950).

A bundle sheath may also exhibit characteristics of a starch sheath. In some dicotyledons and in the grasses that have single-layered bundle sheaths the parenchymatous sheath may be active in starch formation (Alexandrov, 1926; Rhoades and Carvalho, 1944). In genera like *Zea* and *Sorghum* the chloroplasts in the sheath cells are particularly large (fig. 16.8, *B–E*) and appear to be the only plastids in the leaf concerned with forming starch during active photosynthesis. In the Pooideae, having double sheaths about the bundles (fig. 16.8, *A*), the inner sheath contains no chloroplasts, and those in the outer are somewhat smaller than in the rest of the mesophyll. Starch is produced in all green cells so that the sheath is not visibly differentiated with regard to starch formation.

Developmentally, the bundle sheaths of the dicotyledons, the single parenchymatous sheaths of the Panicoideae, and the outer of the two sheaths in the Pooideae appear to be part of the ground tissue. The inner, mestom sheath of the Pooideae is probably of procambial origin.

Supporting Structures. Leaves vary considerably with regard to the development of mechanical tissues. In many leaves, supporting structures are not so prominently developed as in the stem, and much of the strength of such leaves depends on the arrangement of cells and tissues. In leaves with flat blades the soft mesophyll is partly supported by the vascular system which so completely permeates it. In dicotyledonous leaves the bundle sheaths, with their extensions reaching to the compactly arranged epidermis, probably also contribute to the support of the blade (Wylie, 1943). Typically, dicotyledonous leaves develop collenchyma beneath the epidermis of the large veins and often along the margin of the blade. Some of the bundle-sheath extensions may be collenchymatously thickened (Armacost, 1945). Many dicotyledonous leaves have sclereids within the mesophyll (Bailey and Nast, 1944; Foster, 1945, 1946, 1947; Schulze, 1902).

Monocotyledonous leaves develop relatively large amounts of sclerenchyma, in the form of fibers, in association with the vascular bundles (plate 59, *C*) or in separate strands (see chapter 10). In grasses, strands of fibers occur on one or both sides of the vascular bundles and are connected to the bundle sheaths and also to the epidermis. The epidermis frequently has fibers over the sclerenchyma strands so that all the sclerenchyma and the vascular bundles together form girder structures traversing the entire thickness of the blade.

The epidermis offers considerable support by its compact arrangement and relatively strong walls impregnated with cutin and bearing a tough cuticle on the outer surface. In some plants, notably grasses, the epidermis is lignified and silicified in varying degrees.

Secretory Structures. Leaves bear diverse organs concerned with a discharge of water from the interior, with or without appreciable amounts of dissolved materials. Among these materials are salts and complex organic substances, such as resins, mucilages, gums, oils, and nectar. The discharge may be termed secretion if the term is used in its widest sense to refer to a release of materials derived from the fluids of the plant cells. (The word secretion is derived from the Latin *secretio*, dividing, in this connection divided or separated from the fluids.) The secreted materials may issue to the outside of the cell in which they are formed, or they remain within, to be released only upon the breakdown of the cells.

Leaves have many of the secretory structures that are also found in other plant parts, such as, for example, resin ducts (Compositae, Umbelliferae) and lysigenous oil cavities (*Citrus*). Many leaves are characterized by the presence of superficial glands, hydathodes, and a variety of glandular trichomes (see chapter 7).

Glands occur on the blade margins of cataphylls, foliage leaves, and stipules, frequently on the marginal teeth or serrations. They may develop on petioles also. A gland is a complex structure consisting of proliferated parenchyma, with a vascular bundle terminating within it, and covered with glandular epidermis (Martinet, 1872; Reinke, 1876). During the development of a gland, the epidermal cells often elongate at right angles to the surface and divide both periclinally and anticlinally. A gland may be attached to the leaf by a constricted stalk-like structure (fig. 7.10, *E*).

Glands differentiate relatively early in leaf ontogeny and usually function for a short time. After the leaf matures, the glands dry up (Reinke, 1876; Sinnott and Bailey, 1914). The glands and the glandular hairs that develop on the leaves and cataphylls of buds secrete resin, mucilage, and probably other organic materials. These substances fill the spaces among the leaves in a bud and make them appear as though glued together. In *Prunus*, the leaf teeth glands secrete resins, whereas the petiolar glands produce a nectar, although both appear alike in structure (Reinke, 1876).

Hydathodes are structures that discharge water from the interior of the leaf to its surface, a process commonly called guttation (Kramer, 1945). Although the hydathodes are usually treated with the secretory structures (Haberlandt, 1914, p. 487; Sperlich, 1939), one of the common types of hydathode possesses no tissue that is exactly comparable with the glandular tissue of true secretory organs. These hydathodes eliminate water directly from the terminal tracheids of the bundle ends. In many angiosperms the terminal tracheids are in contact with a thin-walled parenchyma (the epithem), deficient in chloroplasts, and provided with intercellular spaces through which the water moves from the tracheids to the epidermis (plate 68, *A*). The epidermis has openings over the epithem, which often appear as incompletely differentiated stomata lacking the mechanism for opening and closing. Each hydathode may have one (*Primula, Aconitum, Delphinium*) or more than one pore (plate 68, *A*; Umbelliferae, Compositae). In *Equisetum* the epithem occurs along one side of the vascular bundle, rather than at the end, and the number of pores for each hydathode varies from three to fifty (Johnson, 1937). The epithem may be enclosed by suberized cells or by cells having Casparian strips (Johnson, 1937; Sperlich, 1939). In some plants the hydathodes are without epithem, and the water moves toward the

pore through ordinary mesophyll (Haberlandt, 1914, p. 495). In
others the hydathodes are rather complex and appear to be associated
with secretory tissue (Sperlich, 1939). Such hydathodes may be
interpreted as structures intergrading between nectaries and typical
hydathodes (Agthe, 1951; see also chapter 18). Hydathodes may be
also differentiated as secretory trichomes (Haberlandt, 1914, p. 491).

Guttation is a widespread phenomenon among plants, but it is
observed only when there is a combination of proper conditions,
namely, active growth in plants, closed stomata, high humidity, and
a soil temperature above that of the air (Frey-Wyssling, 1941).
Guttation has been recorded in more than 340 genera in 115 families
(Frey-Wyssling, 1941). Whether all these plants possess specialized
hydathodes or whether they discharge water through ordinary stomata
has apparently not been investigated. Hydathodes are, however,
widely distributed among vascular plants, except the gymnosperms
(Sperlich, 1939; Ziegenspeck, 1949).

The guttated water contains dissolved salts, which may occur in
such large amounts that upon evaporation of the water they cover
the surface of the leaf with a crust-like deposit (Curtis, 1943; Haberlandt, 1914, p. 499). The presence of salts in the guttated water is
suspected to be the possible cause of the physiological disease, tip
burn, characterized by necrosis of leaf apices in certain economic
plants (Curtis, 1943). It is also thought to be associated with the
various behavior of insecticides and pesticides applied to foliage
(Curtis, 1944).

Petiole. The tissues of the petiole are comparable to primary tissues
of the stem. There is a close similarity between petiole and stem with
regard to the structure of epidermis. The ground parenchyma of
the petiole is like the stem cortex in arrangement of cells and in
number of chloroplasts, which are fewer in these plant parts than
in the mesophyll of the leaf blade. The supporting tissue of the
petiole is collenchyma or sclerenchyma. These may have both disposition and structure similar to those in the stem. Sometimes, however, the petiole has one or the other kind of supporting tissue that
may be absent in the stem. In relation to the arrangement of the
vascular tissues in the stem, the vascular bundles of the petiole may
be collateral (*Syringa*), bicollateral (*Cucurbitaceae, Solanaceae*), or
concentric (many dicotyledons and some ferns). Primary phloem
fibers may differentiate in both the stem and the petiole, or the corresponding phloem cells may develop only thickened primary walls
in the petiole (see chapter 10).

The petioles of different plants show considerable variation in the distribution of the vascular tissues within the body of the petiole (figs. 16.9 and 16.10; Bouygues, 1902; Petit, 1887). As seen in transections, the vascular tissues frequently form a continuous or a multi-stranded arc open toward the adaxial side of the petiole (fig. 16.9, *B, D, L; Adiantum, Olea, Euonymus, Stellaria, Nicotiana*). The

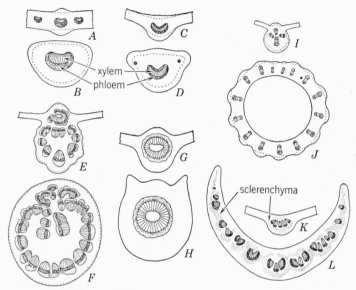

FIG. 16.9. Arrangement of vascular tissues in transections of midribs and petioles of dicotyledonous leaves. *A, B, Euonymus; C, D, Nerium; E, F, Platanus; G, H, Citrus; I, J, Cucurbita; K, L, Mahonia*. In each pair of drawings the midrib appears above the petiole, and both are oriented with the adaxial side upward. (*A, B,* ×9; *C, D,* ×4.7; *E, F, K, L,* ×8; *G, H,* ×6; *I, J,* ×3.)

bundles may form a circle (*Ricinus, Paeonia, Aquilegia, Hedera, Geranium, Smilax*), sometimes with additional bundles within the circle and outside it (fig. 16.9, *F; Tilia; Robinia, Juglans, Wistaria, Rhododendron*). The bundles may be numerous and arranged in several superposed arcs (fig. 16.10, *G; Canna, Eryngium, Petasites*), or they may be scattered (fig. 16.10, *D;* many monocotyledons, *Rumex*). The petiolar bundles are variously interconnected among themselves, so that their numbers and the patterns of their arrangement may vary from level to level (Gerresheim, 1913; Rippel, 1913).

If the petiole has only one collateral bundle, the phloem is on the abaxial side, the xylem on the adaxial (fig. 16.9, *B*). In bicollateral

bundles the phloem occurs on both sides of the xylem (fig. 16.9, *D*).
If the vascular tissues occur in arcs or circles, as seen in transections,
the phloem is usually oriented toward the periphery of the petiole
(fig. 16.9, *B*, *H*). Other arrangements are found in petioles with

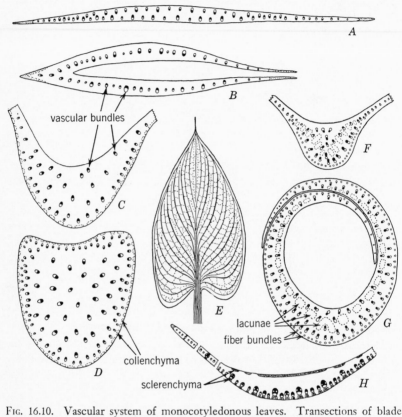

Fig. 16.10. Vascular system of monocotyledonous leaves. Transections of blade
(*A*) and sheath (*B*) of *Iris* leaf. Transections of midrib (*C*) and petiole (*D*)
of *Zantedeschia*. *E*, surface view of *Zantedeschia* leaf showing venation. Transections of midrib (*F*) and sheath (*G*) of *Canna*. *H*, transection of midrib and
parts of blade of *Zea*. In the vascular bundles the xylem is shown in black and
the phloem is white. (*A–D, F, G*, ×4; *H*, ×6; *E*, approx. ½ size.)

numerous vascular strands (fig. 16.9, *F*, *L*). If endodermoid layers are
present in the petiole, these may encircle individual bundles or an
entire complex of bundles.

The rachis and the pedicels of leaflets in compound leaves are
comparable in structure to the petioles of simple leaves, but the
amounts of tissues in the pedicels are relatively small.

Gymnosperm: Conifer Leaf

The histology of the conifer leaf is described here mainly with reference to the needle of *Pinus* because the leaf of this genus has been investigated in most detail (e.g., Abagon, 1938; Huber, 1947; Strasburger, 1891; Sutherland, 1933). However, considerable work has also been done on leaves of other gymnosperms, some of comparative and systematic nature (e.g., Feustel, 1921; Florin, 1931; Fulling, 1934), some more limited in scope.

The needle-like leaves of conifers illustrate many of the characteristics of xeromorphic leaves (Shields, 1950), including the most obvious one, the low ratio of surface to volume expressed in the absence of an expanded flattened blade. The pine needle, as seen in transection, is semicircular (plate 64, *A*), or triangular, or, rarely, terete in shape. The center of the needle is traversed by one or two vascular bundles surrounded by a peculiar vascular tissue, called *transfusion tissue*, and a thick-walled layer, commonly designated as endodermis. Outside the endodermis is the mesophyll. The peripheral layers are the epidermis and the morphologically differentiated hypodermis.

As in other conifers the leaf epidermis in the pine is heavily cuticularized and has such thick walls that the cell lumina are almost obliterated (figs. 7.4, *D*, and plate 65). The fiber-like cells of the hypodermis also have thick walls and form a compact layer interrupted only beneath the stomata (plate 65). The occurrence and the arrangement of the hypodermal sclerenchyma vary in different conifers, and some lack this tissue entirely (Fulling, 1934; Mahlert, 1885). The epidermis bears numerous stomata on one or all sides in the different conifers. In many genera, including *Pinus*, the stomata occur in longitudinal rows parallel with the vascular bundles. The front cavity of the stoma is typically filled with a whitish or dark, granular or alveolate occluding material (see chapter 7). Since this material is porous and the pores are filled with air, the stomata appear white superficially, a circumstance that facilitates their recognition from the surface. The guard cells are sunken and are overtopped by the subsidiary cells (fig. 7.4 and plate 65, *A*).

The mesophyll cells have internal ridges on the walls projecting into the cell lumina (plate 65, *B*; see also chapter 8). In the pine and some other conifers the mesophyll is not differentiated into palisade and spongy parenchyma (plate 64, *A*). Certain conifers and other gymnosperms, however, show such differentiation, with the elongated cells on the adaxial side of the leaves distinguishable as palisade from the short-celled spongy mesophyll on the abaxial side (e.g., *Abies, Araucaria, Ginkgo, Sequoia, Cunninghamia,* and various Cycadaceae; Cross, 1942; Fulling, 1934; Lamb, 1923; Mahlert, 1885). The mesophyll cells of *Pinus* and other conifers are arranged in horizontal layers separated from one another by intercellular spaces (plate 63, *C*). The horizontal strata are not completely detached from each other. There are interconnecting files of cells, making the whole tissue appear like an anastomosing system with a prevailingly horizontal orientation of the spaces (Cross, 1940).

Gymnosperm leaves have resin ducts in the mesophyll. Their number varies even in individual genera, although there appears to be a constant minimum. In *Pinus* two lateral ducts occur almost invariably (plate 64, *A*). The resin ducts of *Pinus* are lined with thin-walled secretory epithelial cells. Outside these cells is a sheath of fibers with thickened lignified walls (plate 65, *B*). This sclerenchyma is in contact with the hypodermis. The resin ducts of conifer leaves vary in length. Some are continuous from the leaf into the cortex of the stem (*Cryptomeria, Cunninghamia;* Cross, 1941, 1942); others are restricted to the leaf, sometimes in the form of elongated cysts or sacs (e.g., *Picea;* Marco, 1939).

In transverse sections of pine needles the vascular bundles are oriented somewhat obliquely, with the xylem pointing toward the adaxial side, the phloem toward the abaxial side (plate 64, *A*). The xylem is endarch. The protoxylem is partly crushed in mature needles. Outwardly from the crushed elements are some helically thickened tracheids—probably also part of the protoxylem—then some metaxylem tracheids with bordered pits. The primary xylem elements are in radial rows, and the rows of tracheary elements are interspersed with rows of parenchyma cells oriented like the rays in a secondary tissue. The individual parenchyma cells are vertically elongated and have transverse end walls. The sieve cells are also in radial rows alternating with rows of parenchyma cells. The parenchyma of the phloem is more abundant than that of the xylem. In the xylem the parenchyma forms starch. In the phloem some parenchyma cells form starch, whereas others appear to be albuminous cells (see chapter 12) which lack starch but have dense cytoplasm. The difference between starch-containing and starch-free cells is most conspicuous in the fall when starch is most abundant. Some parenchyma cells have crystals. As a rule pine needles are shed in the third year, sometimes in the fourth. The vascular bundles increase somewhat in thickness after the first year through the activity of a vascular cambium (Strasburger, 1891).

The transfusion tissue surrounding the vascular bundles in a pine needle consists mainly of two kinds of cells, living parenchyma cells with nonlignified walls, and thin-walled but lignified tracheids with bordered pits. The parenchyma cells contain deeply staining tanniferous and resinous substances, and also starch during part of the year. Next to the xylem, the transfusion tracheids are somewhat elongated; farther away from the bundles they are shorter and more like the parenchyma cells in shape. The tracheids appear to be nonliving cells. Their thin walls seem unable to offer sufficient resistance to the turgid living cells adjacent to them, and their lumina are somewhat compressed (plate 64, *B*; Huber, 1947). Next to the phloem the transfusion tissue contains cells similar to the albuminous cells in having dense cytoplasm and prominent nuclei (plate 64, *B*).

The transfusion tracheids and the transfusion parenchyma cells form continuous systems, and the two systems interpenetrate each other (Huber, 1947). Parenchyma cells are more abundant near the endodermis; tracheids are abundant closer to the vascular bundles. The vascular bundles appear to be separated from the transfusion cells by sclerenchyma except on their flanks where the transfusion tracheids and the marginal albuminous cells are concentrated (Strasburger, 1891).

The transfusion tissue is of universal occurrence in gymnosperms, but it shows various spatial relations with respect to the vascular bundles (Van Abbema, 1934; Wordsell, 1897). Regarding the phylogenetic origin of this tissue, some investigators consider it to be derived from the so-called centripetal xylem (Bernard, 1904; Wordsell, 1897). Others interpret it simply as transformed parenchyma outside the vascular tissue (Takeda, 1913; Van Abbema, 1934). The function of the transfusion tissue is also a matter of disagreement. The most common concept is that it represents an auxiliary conducting system serving to bring the vascular tissue closer to the mesophyll (Van Abbema, 1934; Worsdell, 1897). Some workers, however, regard it as a water storage tissue (Takeda, 1913).

The endodermis surrounding the transfusion tissue in the pine needle consists of relatively thick-walled cells, sometimes containing starch. This cell layer is clearly differentiated in the pine and in certain other conifers, but it is ill defined in others. In the Abietineae it is reported as having no Casparian strips but as being provided with a suberin lamella on the inside of the lignified radial and transverse walls (Soar, 1922). The tangential walls may be lignified. Some of the walls are pitted. The endodermal cells are tangentially and vertically somewhat elongated and are flattened radially. Intercellular spaces are lacking between the endodermal cells and throughout most of the vascular region (Strasburger, 1891).

DEVELOPMENT OF THE LEAF

Origin from the Apical Meristem

The morphologic and cytohistologic aspects of leaf initiation at the shoot apex were considered in chapter 5. A brief summary of the events will suffice here. Divisions in the flank of the apical meristem initiate a lateral protrusion, the leaf buttress, upon which the erect portion of the leaf later develops. In many plants, the leaf primordium arises so close to the shoot apex that the latter changes its shape and size periodically in relation to the lateral extension of the buttress. In some others, the primordium is initiated relatively low on the apical cone, which remains unaffected in its appearance in the part above the leaf primordium. In still other plants, the leaves, besides being inserted low on the apical cone, are also so small that they form no protrusion meriting the name of a leaf buttress (e.g., *Hippuris, Elodea*).

The initial lateral protrusion of the axis formed during the growth of a leaf primordium commonly results from periclinal divisions in the flank of the apical meristem. In a wide variety of angiosperm these divisions occur in one or more of the layers near the surface, but not in the surface layer itself. The surface layer grows by anti-clinal divisions as the subsurface divisions produce a bulge. In some angiosperms (e.g., certain grasses), however, the surface layer is directly concerned with the initiation of the first protrusion by dividing periclinally (see below). In such instances the outer covering is formed by the anticlinally dividing outer derivatives of the superficial layer.

The two growth zones of angiospermous shoot apices, the tunica and the corpus, variously participate in the formation of the leaf primordium (Foster, 1936). The degree of their participation is determined by the quantitative relationship between the tunica and the corpus and by the depth at which the periclinal divisions initiat-ing the leaf are located. In *Scrophularia nodosa*, for example, the apical meristem has a single tunica layer, and the first divisions to form a leaf occur in the corpus. In *Vinca minor*, with a three-layered tunica, the leaf is initiated in the innermost layer of the tunica (Schmidt, 1924). The *Acacia* phyllodes (that is, leaf-like structures homologous with the petiole rachis of the pinnate foliage leaf) involve both the

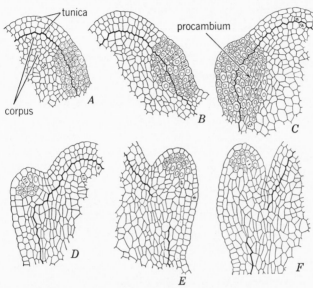

Fig. 16.11. Origin and development of the foliar organ (phyllode) in *Acacia* as seen in longitudinal sections through shoot apices. The heavy lines serves to indicate the delimitation of the tunica and its derivatives from the corpus and its derivatives. The nuclei have been drawn in those cells which were most directly concerned with the growth of the primordium. *A*, periclinal divisions have occurred in the outer layer of the corpus and the third layer of the tunica. *B*, periclinal divisions are spreading into the second layer of the tunica. *C*, leaf buttress is well developed and beneath it, in the stem, the procambium of the leaf trace is recognizable. *D*, concentration of meristematic activity in one part of the buttress initiates the upward growth of the primordium. *E* and *F*, continuation of the upward growth of the primordium through periclinal and other divisions in subapical initials of the primordium and the concomitant growth in surface of the protoderm. (All, ×175. After Boke, 1940.)

tunica and the corpus in their initiation, although the tunica is three-layered (fig. 16.11 and plate 66; Boke, 1940). In the Gramineae, some of which have one layer of tunica, others two, the leaf primordia arise through periclinal divisions in the first two layers of the apex, regardless of the number of tunica layers (figs. 16.17 and 16.18; Hsü, 1944; Sharman, 1942, 1945; Thielke, 1951). The gymnosperms, with a less precise apical zonation than that expressed in the tunica-corpus complex, appear to show variations in the initiation of the leaf primordia similar to those in the angiosperms. In *Taxodium distichum*, for example, leaf growth starts with periclinal divisions in the subsurface layer, accompanied by anticlinal divisions in the surface layer (Cross, 1940), whereas in many other conifers (Korody, 1937) and in *Zamia* (Johnson, 1943) periclinal divisions occur in the surface and the subsurface layers.

Whereas the location and the orientation of the divisions initiating leaf primordia may be readily observed in sections, the degree of participation of the various layers of the shoot apex in the final constitution of a leaf is difficult to judge (figs. 16.17 and 16.18). Periclinal cytochimeras have been successfully employed for the determination of the numbers of initial layers in the shoot apices of certain dicotyledons (see chapter 5) and are proving equally useful for the analysis of the composition of leaves in relation to the initial layers of the shoot apex (Dermen, 1947; Satina and Blakeslee, 1941). Such analysis of the cranberry leaf may be cited as an example (Dermen, 1947). Three layers of the apical meristem take part in the formation of this leaf, the two layers of the biseriate tunica and the outermost layer of the corpus. The leaf epidermis is derived from the outer layer of the tunica entirely by anticlinal divisions. The derivatives of the second layer of the tunica and those of the corpus together contribute toward the formation of the mesophyll and the vascular tissues. The derivatives of the tunica are represented at the leaf tip and the margins, those of the corpus in its central part.

Early Growth and Histogenesis

After the leaf is initiated at the apex of the shoot, its further growth in herbaceous and in some woody plants is an uninterrupted process of cell division, cell enlargement, and maturation, until the full size is attained. In many trees, however, such as *Aesculus*, *Fagus*, and *Platanus*, the leaves arise during one season, interrupt their growth during the winter, and resume growth the following spring. The winter buds contain the full complement of foliar structures to be borne by the mature shoot, and these structures are considerably advanced in their development as regards the delimitation of the various meristems. The following spring the leaves unfold by cell division and particularly cell expansion. In some woody species some of the leaves borne by a new shoot are present in the bud; the others are initiated during the same season that they reach maturity (*Syringa vulgaris, Ligustrum vulgare, Tilia vulgaris, Ulmus campestris, Ulmus montana*).

Dicotyledonous Foliage Leaf. The direction and the amount of growth in a leaf, following its initiation by the apical meristem, vary in relation to the eventual form assumed and the size attained at maturity. In dicotyledons with ordinary leaves having an expanded

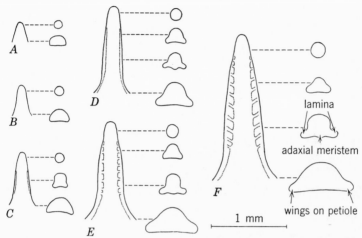

Fig. 16.12. Growth of leaf of *Nicotiana tabacum*. Diagrams of longitudinal and transverse sections of primordia in successive stages of development. In the transverse sections the adaxial sides of the primordia are turned downward. The figure illustrates in particular the growth of primordium in height and its change from the state when it is only an axis without a blade (*A* and *B*) to one when the marginal-meristem activity on two flanks begins to form the blade (*C–F*). Marginal activity of limited duration occurs in the petiole, forming wings. The dotted lines indicate the external boundaries of the midvein and the lateral veins. (After Avery, 1933.)

blade and a relatively narrow base, with or without a petiole, the development of the leaf may be divided into the following stages: (1) formation of the foliar buttress (fig. 16.11, *A–C*), (2) formation of the leaf axis (fig. 16.11, *D–F*), and (3) formation of the lamina (figs. 16.12 and 16.13). This division is somewhat artificial because the successive stages overlap.

The initiation and development of the foliar buttress was outlined in the preceding part of this chapter. Commonly a primordium at the leaf-buttress stage is associated with a procambial strand (the leaf-trace procambium) within the part of the axis bearing the buttress (fig. 16.11, *C*).

Through a change in the direction of growth an erect peg-like protuberance (fig. 16.11, *D–F*), often somewhat flattened on the adaxial side (fig. 16.12, *A*), arises upon the buttress. This protuberance is the axis of the young leaf. It may be regarded as consisting of the midrib-petiole part of the primordium (only midrib part in

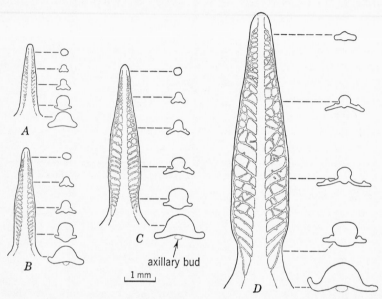

FIG. 16.13. Growth of leaf of *Nicotiana tabacum*. Diagrams of longitudinal and transverse sections of primordia in several developmental stages succeeding those illustrated in fig. 16.12. The dotted lines indicate the external boundaries of the veins. The figure illustrates in particular: continued increase in the height of primordium; further growth of the lamina and the appearance on it of ridges associated with some of the veins; increase in thickness of the parenchyma associated with the midvein, both on abaxial and on adaxial sides; lack of adaxial thickening in the petiole region; and development of the network of veins in basipetal direction. (After Avery, 1933.)

sessile leaves) bearing the meristematic initials of the future lamina. In other words, it is a complete leaf which has not yet attained its differentiation into petiole, midrib, and lamina. The growth of the leaf axis is at first most active at the apex (fig. 16.11, *D–F*). Later it occurs throughout; that is, apical growth is followed by intercalary growth. Apical growth is generally of short duration, and the distinctness of the cells concerned with this growth varies in different plants (Avery, 1933; Boke, 1940; Cross, 1937*b*). In some leaves, apical growth results from the activity of a *subapical initial* which gives rise to the internal tissue of the leaf axis, while the protoderm divides anticlinally concomitantly with the increase in length of the primordium (e.g., *Nicotiana, Viburnum;* fig. 16.14, *D*). Others may have a group of subapical initials (e.g., *Acacia;* fig. 16.11, *F*).

As the leaf axis is elevated above the buttress, a procambium is differentiated in its median part in continuity with the procambium in the buttress (plate 66, *C*, *D*). The axis also increases in thickness, often through the activity of a strip of cells beneath the adaxial protoderm, the *adaxial meristem* (plates 66, *D*, and 68, *C*; Cross, 1938; Foster, 1936; Troll, 1939, pp. 1005–1009). The divisions in this meristem may be so orderly that the resulting derivatives appear like a cambial tissue.

The lamina is initiated in the early stages of elongation of the leaf axis from two strips of meristematic cells located along two margins of the leaf axis (figs. 16.12, 16.13, and plate 68, *C*). These bands of cells are called the *marginal meristems* (Foster, 1936). Since the sides bearing the marginal meristems are turned toward the shoot axis, they are sometimes referred to as the adaxial margins (Foster, 1949, p. 187). The leaf primordia attain somewhat variable heights before the activity of the marginal meristems begins, but in general they are still quite small at this time—less than 1 mm in length—and may not have completed their apical growth (Avery, 1933; Cross, 1937*b*, 1938; Fitzpatrick, 1934; Foster, 1936; MacDaniels and Cowart, 1944).

The marginal meristem often is composed of a file of superficial initials, the *marginal initials,* which extend the protoderm of the lamina by anticlinal divisions, and a file of subsurface initials, the *submarginal initials,* located beneath the marginal initials and forming the interior tissue of the lamina (Foster, 1936). In dicotyledonous leaves the marginal initials usually divide only in the anticlinal plane (Foster, 1949, p. 188). Exceptions have been found in variegated plants in which periclinal divisions in the protoderm may produce white margins on green leaves (Renner and Voss, 1942). The submarginal initials show various combinations of periclinal, anticlinal, and oblique divisions (cf. Foster, 1936; Troll, 1939, pp. 998–1005; fig. 16.14, *A–C*). Like the apical growth of the leaf axis, the marginal growth of the lamina varies in duration and in distinctness of the initials. During marginal growth and after its cessation the lamina expands also by intercalary growth throughout its extent.

Through divisions of the marginal and submarginal initials and of their immediate derivatives a certain number of layers is established in the young lamina (fig. 16.14, *C*). This number remains constant in the further intercalary expansion of the lamina, except in the regions of procambial differentiation where additional divisions occur in various planes (Avery, 1933; Cross, 1937*b*, 1938; Foster, 1936; Gifford, 1951; Smith, 1934). The relative constancy in the number of

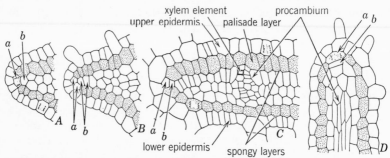

Fig. 16.14. Leaf development in *Nicotiana tabacum*. *A–C*, transections through the edges of young laminae in three successive stages of development illustrating the activity of the marginal meristem. The submarginal initial may divide periclinally, producing two sister cells, one inner and one outer (*a* and *b* in *A* and *C*). The outer is now the initial and may divide next by an anticlinal wall (between cells *a* in *B*). The anticlinal derivatives of this initial form, by subsequent anticlinal divisions, the adaxial and abaxial layers of the mesophyll (stippled cells). The periclinal derivatives usually divide first periclinally (compare *b* in *A* and *B*). Farther away from the margin various divisions occur and give rise to the middle mesophyll layers (unstippled cells enclosed by the stippled cells in *A–C*). The vascular bundles arise in this part of the mesophyll (*C*). The protoderm increases in surface by anticlinal divisions and remains uniseriate, except where trichomes arise (*C*). *C* shows, to the right, plate meristem structure. (Cf. plate 62.) *D*, median longitudinal section of primordium illustrating the meristematic activity at its apex during the initial growth in length. The subapical initial (*a*) gives rise to all the interior tissue of the primordium by alternating periclinal (wall between *a* and *b*) and anticlinal (division figure in *a*) divisions. The anticlinal derivatives are further multiplied by anticlinal divisions (stippled cell layer). The periclinal derivatives form the inner mass of the primordium by various divisions. The procambium differentiates among these derivatives. (Adapted from Avery, 1933.)

layers in the growing primordial lamina and its consequent stratified appearance result from the manner of division of cells. In each layer, the cells divide by walls oriented at right angles to the surface of the leaf (anticlinal divisions), so that each layer increases in surface but not in thickness. As was mentioned in chapter 4, a meristematic tissue composed of parallel cell layers growing in one plane is termed plate meristem. The establishment of the characteristic number of layers of mesophyll occurs more or less close to the submarginal initials, depending on the sequence of divisions of these initials and their derivatives (fig. 16.15). This sequence may vary markedly in different genera (Foster, 1936; Gifford, 1951).

The cell layers established by the activity of the marginal meristems may be said to comprise a protoderm on the surface and a ground meristem in the interior. Close to the marginal meristem localized divisions in the ground meristem result in the formation of the procambium. In conformity with the final position of the procambium in the middle of the mesophyll, it arises in a median layer of the ground meristem, which may be formed directly by the submarginal initials or by periclinal divisions of derivatives of the submarginal initials.

The above description considers the early developmental phenomena only in a simple dicotyledonous leaf. A compound leaf also is initiated as a leaf axis upon a buttress. Such a leaf axis is a primordium of the petiole-rachis part of the leaf bearing the meristematic initials of the leaflets. These arise at the margins of the leaf axis as hemispherical protuberances. If the leaf has a terminal leaflet, the leaflet is formed at the apex of the axis. Each leaflet resembles a simple leaf in its development and histogenesis. It appears first as a leaflet axis, which shows apical and later intercalary growth, and eventually develops a lamina from two bands of marginal meristem (Foster, 1935a). The direction of appearance of the leaflet primordia on the leaf axis may be basipetal, acropetal, or divergent (starting in the middle and progressing in two directions; Foster, 1936; Troll, 1939, pp. 1426–1676).

The formation of a compound leaf by the development of independent units, the leaflets, along a continuous axis must be distinguished from the compounding of a leaf that occurs by splitting of an initially single lamina more or less late in the life of the leaf. Such splitting occurs in a still meristematic state in palm leaves (Deinega, 1898) and after expansion of the blade in the banana leaf (Skutch, 1927).

Dicotyledonous Cataphyll. As was mentioned at the beginning of this chapter, the cataphylls show early growth peculiarities that determine their development as cataphylls rather than as foliage leaves (Cross, 1936, 1937a, b; Foster, 1931, 1935a, b). When compared with foliage leaves, the cataphylls may exhibit the following deviating anatomic characteristics (Foster, 1928, 1949, p. 194): poorly differentiated mesophyll, usually without palisade; inextensive vascular system, often of an open dichotomous type, as though vascular anastomoses were arrested in their development; stomata few or absent.

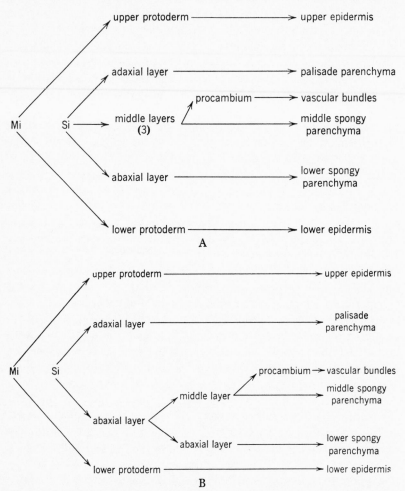

Fig. 16.15. Diagrams depicting histogenesis of leaf lamina in *Nicotiana tabacum* (*A*) and *Carya Buckleyi* (*B*). In both leaves the protoderm is increased in surface by anticlinal divisions. The origin of the mesophyll differs in the two leaves. In tobacco the submarginal initials divide both periclinally and anticlinally, and the inner mesophyll is derived from the periclinal derivatives. In hickory the submarginal initials divide only anticlinally and the inner mesophyll is formed from periclinal derivatives of the lowermost layer of mesophyll. In both leaves the veins originate in the spongy mesophyll layers beneath the palisade. Mi, marginal initials; Si, submarginal initials. (Adapted from Foster, 1936.)

In some cataphylls sclerenchyma is small in amount or absent, in others there may be fibers or sclereids (e.g., *Camellia, Fagus, Quercus, Populus*). The outer bud scales may produce a periderm beneath the abaxial epidermis (e.g., *Aesculus*).

Like the foliage leaf, the cataphyll originates by periclinal and anticlinal divisions in the flank of the apical meristem and forms a leaf axis as the first structure distinct from the stem. Sooner or later, the development of this primordium begins to deviate from that of the foliage leaf of the same plant. The following are some of the common developmental differences between the scales and the leaves. Whereas the axis of a foliage leaf increases in thickness by the activity of the adaxial meristem, a cataphyll shows little or no adaxial growth. The marginal activity, however, is accelerated in the scale and is also directed more definitely laterally, rather than adaxially as in the foliage leaf. The rapid marginal growth, combined with the lack of thickening of the midrib, gives the scale its characteristic vaginant (sheathing) form. In the bud scales of *Rhododendron* the marginal initials divide periclinally and contribute cells to the ground meristem (Foster, 1937). The cataphyll tissues mature rapidly, usually without such a high degree of differentiation as the foliage leaf tissues.

Monocotyledonous Leaf. The development of the leaf in this group of plants is here illustrated by the use of a grass leaf (Abbe et al., 1941; Bugnon, 1921; Sharman, 1942, 1945). The grass leaf has a narrow blade and a base sheathing the stem (figs. 15.3, *C*, and 16.16, *C*). The leaf sheath is open on one side. The sheathing nature of the grass leaf results from a characteristic manner of development of the leaf primordium. The periclinal divisions initiating the leaf appear at one side of the apical cone and are then propagated to both sides of this initiation center until they encircle the stem (figs. 16.16, *A*, *B*, and 16.18, *B–E*). The center of initiation of divisions occurs above and opposite the median part of the next lower leaf in conformity with the two-ranked arrangement of grass leaves (fig. 16.18, *A*). The lateral spread of divisions results in the formation of a crescentic protrusion and then, with further growth, a collar-like structure encircling the stem (fig. 16.16, *B*, and plate 81, *A*). When the edges of this protrusion meet, at the side of the stem opposite the point of initiation of the divisions, one of the edges is prolonged above the other and they overlap without growing together (fig. 16.16, *C*).

If the concept of the leaf buttress is to be applied to the grass shoot, this structure must be identified as the protrusion encircling the stem (figs. 16.17, *B–F*, and 16.18, *B–E*). The upward growth of the grass leaf from its buttress differs from similar growth of a dicotyledon leaf having a narrow insertion on the stem. The elevation of the grass leaf begins at the point where the initial divisions occur (fig. 16.17, G). This growth, which may be termed apical growth, starts before the encirclement of the axis is completed, and throughout its development the leaf remains highest at the point of its origin and slopes down along the margins (fig. 16.16, B). The upward growth of the margins

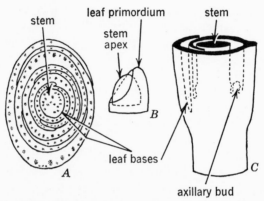

Fig. 16.16. The development of a grass leaf, *Zea mays.* *A*, transection of a young shoot, showing the stem surrounded by the successively older leaf primordia in two-ranked arrangement. Stippling indicates the vascular bundles. *B*, diagram of the shoot apex partly enclosed by the youngest leaf primordium. *C*, diagram of part of the shoot, including a node bearing the base of the leaf ensheathing the stem. To the left the margins of the leaf overlap each other. Compare with leaf 9 in fig. 16.18, *A*. (*B*, *C*, after Sharman, 1942.)

constitutes the marginal growth. Thus the apical and marginal growth processes in a grass leaf are not as distinctly separated from one another as in a dicotyledonous leaf with a narrow base, and the grass leaf does not pass through the two stages, namely, the formation of the midrib-petiole leaf axis, and the development of the blade. The combined apical and marginal growth of the grass leaf lasts a short time, but intercalary growth at the base of the primordium continues the process of elongation.

In the early stages of development of a grass leaf no boundary is evident between the leaf blade and the leaf sheath. Some workers consider that the initial part of the primordium represents only the leaf blade and that the leaf sheath is initiated somewhat later by intercalary growth near the foliar buttress (Bugnon, 1921; Sharman, 1942). The blade itself owes the major part of its growth to the activity of the intercalary meristem at its base. The intercalary activity forming the sheath occurs below that responsible for the growth of the blade. Since it originates relatively late, the sheath lags behind the blade in

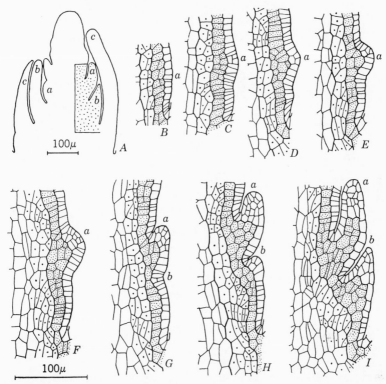

Fig. 16.17. Origin and development of a grass leaf, *Agropyron repens*. *A–I*, median longitudinal sections in the plane of leaves. The stippling in *A* delimits the area represented in detail in *I*. *B–I* illustrate the origin and early development of the median part of a leaf primordium (*a*) and of the base of the older primordium located one node lower (*b*). (Compare with fig. 16.18.) *B–F*, stages in the emergence of a leaf buttress through periclinal divisions in the two outer cell layers. *G–I*, initial stages in the upward growth of the primordium. The derivatives of the second tunica layer have been stippled and those of the outermost part of the corpus indicated by single dots. (Adapted from Sharman, 1945.)

development. Before the blade attains much length, a ligule (a thin projection from the top of the leaf sheath) develops from the adaxial protoderm and demarcates the sheath from the blade (Thielke, 1951).

In the marginal growth of monocotyledonous leaves marginal and submarginal initials may be distinguishable. The derivatives of these

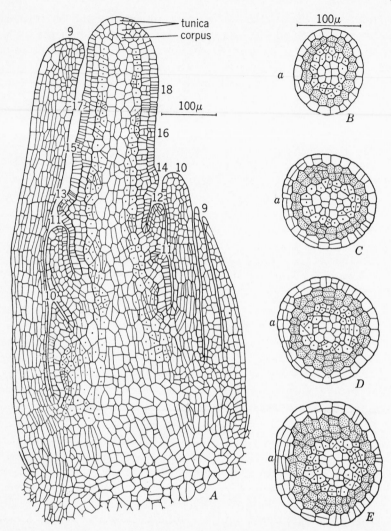

Fɪɢ. 16.18. Origin and development of leaves in a grass, *Agropyron repens.* *A,* median longitudinal section in the plane of the leaves through the shoot apex and leaf primordia 9–18. Primordia 12–18 had not completed the encircling growth around the stem so that only their median parts are indicated by the numbers. Primordia 9–11 had completed the encirclement, and therefore parts of them appear on both sides of the stem. In leaf 9 the overlapping edges appear as a double structure to the right in the figure. The shoot apex has three sets of initials, two pertaining to the biseriate tunica, one to the corpus. The outer corpus derivatives are indicated by single dots as far down as they can be identified as such. *B–E,* transections of shoot at level of origin of a leaf primordium

initials become oriented in parallel layers and divide anticlinally (plate meristem) during the increase in the surface of the leaf (Mericle, 1950). The procambial strands originate in a middle layer through divisions in various planes and thus disturb the original parallel stratification. During the apical and marginal growth, periclinal divisions often occur in the protoderm in the monocotyledonous leaf so that part of the inner tissue is of protodermal origin. In the sheath of many grasses two-layered margins develop from the protoderm and sharply distinguish this part of the leaf from the blade (Thielke, 1951).

The development of the leaves in representative members of the Monocotyledoneae varies in complexity. In the Gramineae, the Amaryllidaceae, the Liliaceae, and certain other families, the leaf primordium is clearly bifacial (that is, it has distinct abaxial and adaxial surfaces), and its initial development, as outlined above, results from the activity of one continuous meristematic layer extending from the apex down along the entire free margin (Roth, 1949). In certain other monocotyledons, however, the initial apical activity is interrupted and another growth center is established abaxially from the initial apex (fig. 16.19). The structure developing from the new apex is unifacial, in the sense that it consists of the abaxial side of the leaf only (Knoll, 1948; Roth, 1949; Thielke, 1948). The unifacial leaf part may be short (Araceae) or long (*Allium, Iris*); it may be tubular in shape (*Allium cepa; Juncus glaucus*) or flattened, either along the median plane of the leaf (*Iris*, fig. 16.10, *A, B*) or at right angles to this plane (*Allium lineare*). In view of the complexity of structure and development of monocotyledonous leaves, it is difficult to draw a parallel between the parts of these leaves and those of dicotyledonous leaves. Some workers suggest that the monocotyledonous leaf has no counterpart of the lamina of the dicotyledonous leaves, that it is a phyllome lacking a lamina (Arber, 1950, p. 108).

As in the dicotyledons, the cataphyll and the foliage leaf in the monocotyledon diverge from one another at an early stage of development (Chang and Sun, 1948; Sun, 1948).

Conifer Leaf. Among gymnosperms the development of the leaf was investigated in modern times in three genera of the Taxodiaceae (Cross, 1940, 1941, 1942) and in *Zamia* (Johnson, 1943). All these genera show fundamental similarity with the angiosperms regarding

---

showing the initiation of periclinal divisions (at *a* in *B*) and their spread around the circumference of the shoot during formation of the sheathing base of the leaf. Letter *a* indicates location of the apex of the primordium. The stipples and dots are used as in fig. 16.17. (Adapted from Sharman, 1945.)

leaf development. In the conifers (Taxodiaceae) periclinal divisions
near the surface in the flank of the apical meristem give rise to a buttress. Apical growth of short duration and a longer-lasting intercalary

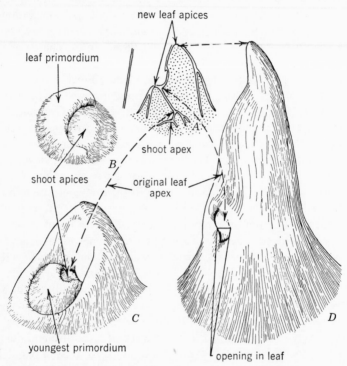

new leaf apices

leaf primordium

shoot apex

A

B

shoot apices

original leaf
apex

youngest primordium

C

D

opening in leaf

Fig. 16.19. Origin and early development of leaf in *Allium cepa*. *A*, diagram
of a median section through a shoot apex with the associated primordia. *B–D*,
three-dimensional aspects of the shoot apex with primordia in three stages of
development. The leaf primordium of onion arises on one side of the shoot apex
(*B*) and encircles it completely (*C*). The sheath of the onion leaf is completely
closed (*C* and *D*). The original leaf apex early ceases growth and is supplanted
by another apex located somewhat abaxially (new leaf apices in *A*, *C*, and *D*).
This apex forms a tubular blade. Since this blade results from meristematic
activity on the abaxial side of the original primordium, it consists of only the
abaxial part of the leaf and is spoken of as being unifacial. (*B–D* drawn by Alva
D. H. Grant.)

growth form the leaf axis. Marginal activity of short duration initiates the leaf blade. The intercalary growth concerned with the formation of the blade is also small in amount and does not assume the
form of plate meristem activity (as is common in dicotyledons) but
that of a rib meristem (plate 63, *B*). This kind of growth, combined

with the short duration of marginal growth, results in the development of a long, relatively narrow organ.

Regulation of Shape

The factors determining the final shape of the leaf may be classified as follows: (1) shape of the leaf primordium; (2) number, distribution, and orientation of cell divisions; (3) amount and distribution of cell enlargement (Ashby, 1948*a*). A comparison between the prevailing type of monocotyledonous leaf with its stem-ensheathing base and a dicotyledonous leaf having a narrow base illustrates the influence of the shape of primordium upon the final leaf form. In contrast, a comparison of such leaves as those of *Taxodium* with leaves of a *Nicotiana* or a *Syringa* shows that similar peg-like primordia may develop into leaves unlike in shape.

The development of the leaf, as determined by cell division and cell enlargement, follows various patterns (Bower, 1884; Foster, 1936; Papen, 1935). Fern leaves, for example, characteristically show a prolonged apical activity and an acropetal progression of intercalary growth and maturation of the tissues. In contrast, the leaves of seed plants show an early cessation of apical growth and a prolonged intercalary growth. In some leaves cessation of the intercalary activity and the following maturation of tissues occur in a more or less strict basipetal direction. This method of differentiation is particularly well expressed in monocotyledonous leaves, but it is also found in conifers and in dicotyledons with narrow leaves (*Tragopogon, Thesium, Linum, Plantago;* Ziegenspeck, 1944). In other leaves with a restricted apical activity a distinct leaf axis is formed first; then an intense meristematic activity occurs on the flanks of the axis (marginal meristems), extending the lamina laterally. The marginal activity may be followed by a rather uniform extension of the leaf or by a growth and maturation directed basipetally. This complex growth pattern is common among the dicotyledons (Avery, 1933; Fitzpatrick, 1934). As was mentioned in chapter 7, the pattern of leaf development may be well judged by following the differentiation of the stomata (Ziegenspeck, 1944). In leaves maturing strictly basipetally, the stomata differentiate in the same direction. In leaves combining basipetal maturation and a lateral growth the different developmental stages of the stomata are mixed in a mosaic fashion.

Measurements carried out on the growth of different parts of the same leaf of tobacco (fig. 16.20; Avery, 1933) suggest that the final form of a leaf is determined by the differential distribution of growth in different leaf areas (localized growth) and by the greater growth in one dimension than in another (polarized growth). The growth of such a leaf may be characterized as being anisotropic (Ashby, 1948*a*). The anisotropy of leaf growth is expressed in both differen-

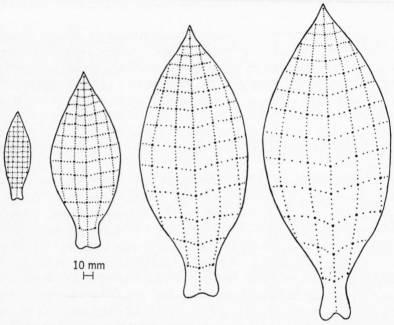

10 mm

FIG. 16.20. Development of the leaf of *Nicotiana tabacum*. Diagrams of a leaf depicting four stages of development as seen in surface view. When the leaf was ¼ final size (left), its entire surface was marked into 5-mm squares. Their unequal change in shape and size shows that the expansion is variable in the different parts of the leaf. (After Avery, 1933.)

tial cell division and differential cell enlargement. These two phenomena are genetically controlled (Delisle, 1938; Hammond, 1941; Stephens, 1944; Whaley and Whaley, 1942), perhaps, in part, through the activity of growth substances (Avery, 1935; Delisle, 1938).

The growth characteristics, although basically determined by heredity, are also influenced by environmental conditions, external and internal. Among the external factors may be named the supply of water and mineral nutrients, light, and length of day (Ashby, 1948*b*; Morton and Watson, 1948). Internal factors appear to be involved in establishing differences between leaves at different levels of the same plant (Ashby, 1948*b*).

Differentiation of the Mesophyll

The origin of the mesophyll from the marginal meristem has been considered in the preceding parts of this chapter, and some variations are illustrated in the diagrams in fig. 16.15. The establishment of the characteristic differences between the palisade and the spongy parenchyma results from an unequal growth in the various layers of the leaf. This inequality is expressed in the different durations of cell division and cell enlargement in the epidermis and in the various layers of the mesophyll. Several observations indicate that, in bifacial dicotyledonous leaves, cell division ceases first in the upper epidermis and continues longest in the future palisade tissue (Avery, 1933; Fitzpatrick, 1934; MacDaniels and Cowart, 1944; Mounts, 1932; Tetley, 1932, 1936). The areas where the procambial strands occur must be excluded from consideration in this connection, since new procambium may be initiated by cell division after the meristematic activity has ceased elsewhere in the mesophyll (Avery, 1933). On the other hand, in areas where vascular bundles have been formed, the associated mesophyll may cease dividing early (MacDaniels and Cowart, 1944).

The early cessation of cell division and commencement of cell enlargement in the upper epidermis and the protracted division in the palisade parenchyma are clearly illustrated by the numerical relationships between cells of the two tissues in young and old apple leaves (MacDaniels and Cowart, 1944). The ratios between the numbers and diameters of the epidermal and the palisade cells were 1:1 in a young leaf. In the mature leaf the diameters of the epidermal cells were 3 to 4 times larger than those of the palisade cells, and there were 8 to 10 palisade cells to one epidermal cell. While the division and enlargement of the palisade cells keeps pace with the enlargement of the epidermal cells, the palisade cells remain closely packed (plate 62, *A*, *B*). When the palisade cells cease dividing and enlarging—and apparently they cease enlarging before the epidermal cells—the further adjustment of the palisade to the continued increase in surface of the epidermis involves the development of intercellular spaces (plates 62, *C*, and 61, *A*). The palisade cells divide mainly at right angles to the surface. They also elongate in the same direction, and during the formation of intercellular spaces they separate from each other along the anticlinal walls. All these phenomena are responsible for the characteristic appearance of the palisade, that is, of a tissue composed of orderly rows of elongated cells largely separated from each other along their anticlinal walls.

The developmental relation between the lower epidermis and the spongy mesophyll in bifacial leaves appears to be somewhat variable. This epidermis may cease cell division before the spongy mesophyll but continue longer with cell enlargement (Avery, 1933; Fitzpatrick, 1934), or it may show cell division after this activity has stopped in the spongy tissue (MacDaniels and Cowart, 1944). In both situations the epidermis shows active growth in surface without formation of intercellular spaces, while the spongy parenchyma grows in a tangential plane by some enlargement of cells and by a loosening of contacts (plates 61, 62).

Among the various tissue elements of the leaf, the epidermal hairs, the stomata, and the large veins complete their differentiation before the mesophyll (Fitzpatrick, 1934; MacDaniels and Cowart, 1944). The stomata develop concomitantly with the development of the intercellular spaces in the mesophyll (Tetley, 1932; see also chapter 7).

Vascularization

The development of the vascular system of foliage leaves is a relatively little-explored subject, particularly with reference to the procambium and the phloem. The most complete studies on the differentiation of the procambial system were carried out in leaves of *Nicotiana tabacum* (Avery, 1933) and *Zea mays* (Sharman, 1942). In the tobacco leaf the procambium of the midvein is differentiated in the leaf axis before the development of the lamina. As the lamina is formed, procambium differentiates in its middle layers, giving rise first to the largest lateral veins, then to the successively smaller veins of various orders, until a reticulate venation is formed (figs. 16.12, 16.13). The development of this network does not occur uniformly throughout the blade but progresses basipetally (fig. 16.13). In the leaf of *Zea* the median and the main lateral procambial strands differentiate in the developing leaf in an acropetal direction. The small lateral strands alternating with the larger differentiate from the tip of the leaf downwardly after some protophloem appears in the larger strands. The transverse anastomoses are the last strands to appear and they, too, follow a basipetal course. Thus, in both kinds of leaves there is first an acropetal sequence initiating the procambial system in the form of the largest strands, then a basipetal sequence completing the procambial differentiation with the smaller veins. In both kinds of leaves the apices are the first to have a complete procambial system.

As in the stem, the vascular elements mature in the leaf before its procambial system is completely differentiated. The course of vascular differentiation has been investigated in *Zea* in some detail (Sharman, 1942). The protophloem differentiates acropetally, first in the median vein, then in the large lateral veins before the basipetally differentiating procambium is initiated. The protoxylem follows the protophloem and differentiates in the same direction. The differentiation of the protophloem and the protoxylem coincides with the period of elongation of the leaf. After this extension is completed, metaphloem and metaxylem differentiate basipetally in the larger strands, which first developed protophloem and protoxylem, and in the smaller basipetally differentiating strands, which have no protophloem and no protoxylem. This course of development of the metaphloem and the metaxylem is associated with the basipetal maturation of the leaf as a whole and with the prolonged intercalary growth at the base of the leaf.

The initial differentiation of xylem of leaves has been studied in many other plants (Esau, 1943; Pellisier, 1939; Scott and Priestley, 1925; Trécul, 1881). These studies indicate that the double wave of differentiation of the xylem, first in acropetal and then in basipetal direction, is common in monocotyledonous leaves. In dicotyledons the initial differentiation of xylem is also characteristically acropetal, but the subsequent development of this tissue follows a less orderly sequence than in the monocotyledons, probably in conformity with the less strictly basipetal course of differentiation of dicotyledonous leaves. (For data on establishment of vascular connection between leaf and stem, cf. chapter 15.)

ABSCISSION OF LEAVES

The periodic defoliation of perennial plants is a complex phenomenon involving the development of features bringing about the separation of the leaf from the stem, without injury to the living tissues in the stem, and giving protection to the newly exposed surface from desiccation and invasion by microorganisms. This development occurs in a region commonly called the *abscission region* or *zone* (from the Latin *abscissus*, cut off; Eames and MacDaniels, 1947, p. 267). Within this zone it is commonly possible to distinguish between the *separation layer* through which the actual break occurs, and the *protective layer* (plate 67, *A–C*). The separating leaf may be said to abscise.

The characteristics of the abscission region vary widely in different plants, as may be learned from the voluminous literature on the subject (see Pfeiffer, 1928). Efforts have been made to classify the methods of abscission with reference to the nature of the abscission zone and the timing in the development of its special features (Lee, 1911; Mühldorf, 1925; Pfeiffer, 1928; Tison, 1900). Most studies on leaf abscission pertain to dicotyledons, but monocotyledons, conifers, and ferns also have received attention (Pfeiffer, 1928).

In simple dicotyledonous leaves the abscission zone occurs within the petiole or at its base. In compound leaves abscission zones develop in the petiole of the leaf as a whole and also at the base of the individual leaflets. The various abscission zones of such leaves are similar in structure although those associated with the leaflet separation may be somewhat simpler.

The features facilitating the separation are of two kinds: (1) peculiarities of histologic structure of the part of the petiole where the abscission zone is located and (2) the presence of a separation layer directly concerned with the severing of the connection between the leaf and the stem. The abscission zone differs from the adjacent parts of the petiole in having a minimum of strengthening tissues. Except in the vascular tissues, the cells are mainly parenchymatous; in the vascular tissues the lignified cells may be represented by tracheary elements only. Moreover, these elements may be exceptionally short (Scott et al., 1948). Thus, the abscission region is structurally weak. It is sometimes visible externally by being somewhat constricted, although such constrictions do not always coincide with abscission zones.

A common characteristic of the separation layer is that its cell walls are chemically changed during leaf abscission in such a way that the cells separate from each other or are easily broken. The cell walls increase in volume, swell, and assume a gelatinous appearance. Sometimes the gelatinization is observed only in the intercellular layer, sometimes also in the primary wall (Facey, 1950; Hewitt, 1938; Hodgson, 1918; Lee, 1911). Microchemically the change in the wall has been described as involving conversions of calcium pectate into pectic acid and of the latter into water-soluble pectin, with the cellulose remaining as such but assuming a gelatinous consistency (Facey, 1950).

The cells may separate from each other without breakage, along the middle lamellae, or the walls themselves may break (Facey, 1950).

The separation layer consists of at least two superposed rows of cells in which chemical changes in the cell walls take place. The morphologic distinctness of these cell layers varies. Sometimes they are hardly differentiated from the ground parenchyma of the abscission zone (*Aristolochia sipho, Aesculus hippocastanum*); sometimes they are relatively small and either many sided (*Picea, Abies, Populus, Sambucus, Salix*) or tabular in shape (*Pseudotsuga, Gleditschia, Robinia*). In many woody plants the separation layer is prepared by divisions in the ground tissue, which range in number from one or two to several in each cell (plate 67, *C*; Pfeiffer, 1928). The separation of leaves withering on the plant apparently occurs by mechanical breakage without the development of a definite separation layer (Addicott, 1945; Hoshaw and Guard, 1949).

The process of separation commonly starts from the periphery of the petiole and progresses toward the interior (plate 67, *B*). In the vascular bundles the separation layer is continued through the living cells, but the sieve elements and the tracheary and other nonliving cells that may be present are broken mechanically. The tracheary cells may be occluded by tyloses before the leaf abscises, and then the living tylose cells complement the separation layer.

The protection of the surface exposed after leaf fall occurs in several ways. Two main phenomena may be distinguished: (1) the formation of a scar, or cicatrice, and (2) the development of periderm beneath the scar. The basic feature of cicatrization is the deposition of substances that are usually said to protect the new surface from outside injuries and loss of water. These substances are localized beneath the separation layer in a region several cell layers in depth. Together these layers constitute the protective layer of the abscission zone. Sometimes modifications similar to those of the protective layer occur above the separation layer on the leaf side (Pfeiffer, 1928). The materials deposited in the protective layer are commonly referred to as suberin and lignin. Suberin gives the usual reactions of fatty substances and is laid down, as in cork cells, in the form of a lamella on the inside of the cellulose wall. The presence of lignin is inferred from the positive staining reaction with phloroglucinol and hydrochloric acid. There is some evidence, however, that the substance identified as lignin might be wound gum, which shows many of the same microchemical reactions as lignin but is not identical with it

(Hewitt, 1938). This wound gum appears in the walls, the intercellular spaces, and frequently also in the tracheary elements. The cicatrization may affect ground tissue cells without any previous changes in the tissue. In other instances, divisions occur in preparation for the development of the protective layer. The periderm which develops beneath the protective layer is continuous with the periderm of the stem. In some plants periderm develops immediately as part of the abscission phenomenon (*Salix, Aesculus*). The timing of the various changes connected with leaf fall varies widely. The separation layer may be prepared early, during leaf differentiation, or it may become discernible only shortly before abscission. Similarly, cicatrization may occur in advance of leaf fall (*Morus nigra, Magnolia acuminata, Juglans nigra*; Tison, 1900), or after leaf fall (*Mespilus germanica, Ficus carica, Olea europea*; Hewitt, 1938; Tison, 1900). The development of the cicatrice is affected by environmental conditions.

The internal factors determining the characteristics and the timing of development of the abscission zone in plants—those concerned with leaf fall and also with the abscission of other organs—are not known, but work with growth substances suggests that these are in some way connected with the phenomenon; at least the application of these substances has been found to retard abscission (Gardner and Cooper, 1943; Gawadi and Avery, 1950; Myers, 1940).

REFERENCES

Abagon, M. A. A comparative anatomical study of the needles of *Pinus insularis* Endlicher and *Pinus merkusii* Junghun and de Vriese. *Philippine Univ. Nat. and Appl. Sci.* 6:29–58. 1938.

Abbe, E. C., L. F. Randolph, and J. Einset. The developmental relationship between shoot apex and growth pattern of leaf blade in diploid maize. *Amer. Jour. Bot.* 28:778–784. 1941.

Addicott, F. T. The anatomy of leaf abscission and experimental defoliation in guayule. *Amer. Jour. Bot.* 32:250–256. 1945.

Agthe, C. Über die physiologische Herkunft des Pflanzennektars. Thesis. Zürich, Eidgenössische Technische Hochschule. 1951.

Alexandrov, W. G. Über tägliche Veränderungen des Stärkegehalts in Blättern. *Deut. Bot. Gesell. Ber.* 44:217–226. 1926.

Arber, A. The natural philosophy of plant form. Cambridge, Cambridge University Press. 1950.

Armacost, R. R. The structure and function of the border parenchyma and vein-ribs of certain dicotyledon leaves. *Iowa Acad. Sci. Proc.* 51:157–169. 1945.

Ashby, E. Studies in the morphogenesis of leaves. I. An essay on leaf shape. *New Phytol.* 47:153–176. 1948a.

Ashby, E. Studies in the morphogenesis of leaves. II. The area, cell size and cell number of leaves of *Ipomoea* in relation to their position on the shoot. *New Phytol.* 47:177–195. 1948*b*.

Avery, G. S., Jr. Structure and development of the tobacco leaf. *Amer. Jour. Bot.* 20:565–592. 1933.

Avery, G. S., Jr. Differential distribution of a phytohormone in the developing leaf of *Nicotiana*, and its relation to polarized growth. *Torrey Bot. Club Bul.* 62:313–330. 1935.

Bailey, I. W., and C. G. Nast. The comparative morphology of the Winteraceae. V. Foliar epidermis and sclerenchyma. *Arnold Arboretum Jour.* 25:342–348. 1944.

Bernard, C. Le bois centripète dans les feuilles des Conifères. *Bot. Centbl. Beihefte* 17:241–310. 1904.

Boke, N. H. Histogenesis and morphology of the phyllode in certain species of *Acacia*. *Amer. Jour. Bot.* 27:73–90. 1940.

Bouygues, H. Structure, origine et développement de certaines formes vasculaires anormales du pétiole des Dicotylédones. *Soc. Linn. de Bordeaux, Actes* 57:41–176. 1902.

Bower, F. O. On the comparative morphology of the leaf in the vascular cryptogams and gymnosperms. *Roy. Soc. London, Phil. Trans.* Ser. B. 175:565–615. 1884.

Bugnon, P. La feuille chez les Graminées. *Soc. Linn. de Normandie, Mém.* 21:1–108. 1921.

Chang, C. Y., and C.-N. Sun. Morphology and development of the vegetative shoot of *Arisaema consanguineum* Schott with special reference to the development of the cataphyll and the foliage leaf. *Natl. Peking Univ. Seme-Cent. Papers, Coll. Sci.* 1948:169–182. 1948.

Cross, G. L. The structure of the growing point and the development of the bud scales of *Morus alba*. *Torrey Bot. Club Bul.* 63:451–465. 1936.

Cross, G. L. The origin and development of the foliage leaves and stipules of *Morus alba*. *Torrey Bot. Club Bul.* 64:145–163. 1937*a*.

Cross, G. L. The morphology of the bud and the development of the leaves of *Viburnum rufidulum*. *Amer. Jour. Bot.* 24:266–276. 1937*b*.

Cross, G. L. A comparative histogenetic study of the bud scales and foliage leaves of *Viburnum opulus*. *Amer. Jour. Bot.* 25:246–258. 1938.

Cross, G. L. Development of the foliage leaves of *Taxodium distichum*. *Amer. Jour. Bot.* 27:471–482. 1940.

Cross, G. L. Some histogenetic features of the shoot of *Cryptomeria japonica*. *Amer. Jour. Bot.* 28:573–582. 1941.

Cross, G. L. Structure of the apical meristem and development of the foliage leaves of *Cunninghamia lanceolata*. *Amer. Jour. Bot.* 29:288–301. 1942.

Curtis, L. C. Deleterious effects of guttated fluids on foliage. *Amer. Jour. Bot.* 30:778–781. 1943.

Curtis, L. C. The influence of guttation fluid on pesticides. *Phytopathology* 34:196–205. 1944.

Deinega, V. Beiträge zur Kenntnis der Entwickelungsgeschichte des Blattes und der Anlage der Gefässbündel. *Flora* 85:439–498. 1898.

Delisle, A. L. Morphogenetical studies in the development of successive leaves in *Aster*, with respect to relative growth, cellular differentiation, and auxin relationships. *Amer. Jour. Bot.* 25:420–430. 1938.

Dermen, H. Periclinal cytochimeras and histogenesis in cranberry. *Amer. Jour. Bot.* 34:32–43. 1947.

Diettert, R. A. The morphology of *Artemisia tridentata* Nutt. *Lloydia* 1:3–74. 1938.

Eames, A. J. *Morphology of vascular plants. Lower groups.* New York, McGraw-Hill Book Company. 1936.

Eames, A. J., and L. H. MacDaniels. *Introduction to plant anatomy.* 2nd ed. New York, McGraw-Hill Book Company. 1947.

Ertl, O. Vergleichende Untersuchungen über die Entwicklung der Blattnerven der Araceen. *Flora* 26:115–248. 1932.

Esau, K. Origin and development of primary vascular tissues in seed plants. *Bot. Rev.* 9:125–206. 1943.

Facey, V. Abscission of leaves in *Fraxinus americana* L. *New Phytol.* 49:103–116. 1950.

Feustel, H. Anatomie und Biologie der Gymnospermenblätter. *Bot. Centbl. Beihefte* 38:177–257. 1921.

Fitzpatrick, R. E. The ontogeny of the peach leaf. *Roy. Canad. Inst. Trans.* 20:73–76. 1934.

Florin, R. Untersuchungen zur Stammesgeschichte der Coniferales und Cordaitales. *Svenska Vetensk. Akad. Handl.* Ser. 3. 10:1–588. 1931.

Foster, A. S. Salient features of the problem of bud-scale morphology. *Biol. Rev.* 3:123–164. 1928.

Foster, A. S. Phylogenetic and ontogenetic interpretations of the cataphyll. *Amer. Jour. Bot.* 18:243–249. 1931.

Foster, A. S. A histogenetic study of foliar determination in *Carya buckleyi* var. *arkansana. Amer. Jour. Bot.* 22:88–147. 1935*a.*

Foster, A. S. Comparative histogenesis of foliar transition forms in *Carya. Calif. Univ., Pubs., Bot.* 19:159–186. 1935*b.*

Foster, A. S. Leaf differentiation in angiosperms. *Bot. Rev.* 2:349–372. 1936.

Foster, A. S. Structure and behavior of the marginal meristem in the bud scales of *Rhododendron.* Amer. Jour. Bot. 24:304–316. 1937.

Foster, A. S. The foliar sclereids of *Trochodendron aralioides* Sieb. & Zucc. *Arnold Arboretum Jour.* 26:155–162. 1945.

Foster, A. S. Comparative morphology of the foliar sclereids in the genus *Mouriria* Aubl. *Arnold Arboretum Jour.* 27:253–271. 1946.

Foster, A. S. Structure and ontogeny of the terminal sclereids in the leaf of *Mouriria Huberi* Cogn. *Amer. Jour. Bot.* 34:501–514. 1947.

Foster, A. S. *Practical plant anatomy.* 2nd ed. New York, D. Van Nostrand Company. 1949.

Foster, A. S. Morphology and venation of the leaf in *Quiina acutangula* Ducke. *Amer. Jour. Bot.* 37:159–171. 1950*a.*

Foster, A. S. Venation and histology of the leaflets in *Touroulia guianensis* Aubl. and *Froesia tricarpa* Pires. *Amer. Jour. Bot.* 37:848–862. 1950*b.*

Frey-Wyssling, A. Die Guttation als allgemaine Erscheinung. *Schweiz. Bot. Gesell. Ber.* 51:321–325. 1941.

Fulling, E. H. Identification, by leaf structure, of the species of *Abies* cultivated in the United States. *Torrey Bot. Club Bul.* 61:497–524. 1934.

Gardner, F. E., and W. C. Cooper. Effectiveness of growth substances in delaying abscission of *Coleus* petioles. *Bot. Gaz.* 105:80–89. 1943.

Gawadi, A. G., and G. S. Avery, Jr. Leaf abscission and the so-called "abscission layer." *Amer. Jour. Bot.* 37:172–179. 1950.

Gerresheim, E. Über den anatomischen Bau und die damit zusammenhängende Wirkungsweise der Wasserbahnen in Fiederblättern der Dicotyledonen. *Biblioth. Bot.* 19(81):1–67. 1913.

Gifford, E. M., Jr. Early ontogeny of the foliage leaf in *Drimys Winteri* var. *chilensis*. *Amer. Jour. Bot.* 38:93–105. 1951.

Guttenberg, H. von. Die physiologischen Scheiden. In: K. Linsbauer. *Handbuch der Pflanzenanatomie*. Band 5. Lief. 42. 1943.

Haberlandt, G. *Physiological plant anatomy*. London, Macmillan and Company. 1914.

Hammond, D. The expression of genes for leaf shape in *Gossypium hirsutum* L. and *Gossypium arboreum* L. *Amer. Jour. Bot.* 28:124–150. 1941.

Hewitt, W. B. Leaf-scar infection in relation to the olive knot disease. *Hilgardia* 12:41–71. 1938.

Hodgson, R. W. An account of the mode of foliar abscission in *Citrus*. *Calif. Univ., Pubs., Bot.* 6:417–428. 1918.

Hoshaw, R. W., and A. T. Guard. Abscission of marcescent leaves of *Quercus palustris* and *Q. coccinea*. *Bot. Gaz.* 110:587–593. 1949.

Hsü, J. Structure and growth of the shoot apex of *Sinocalamus Beecheyana* McClure. *Amer. Jour. Bot.* 31:404–411. 1944.

Huber, B. Zur Mikrotopographie der Saftströme im Transfusionsgewebe der Koniferennadel. *Planta* 35:331–351. 1947.

Johnson, M. A. Hydathodes in the genus *Equisetum*. *Bot. Gaz.* 98:598–608. 1937.

Johnson, M. A. Foliar development in *Zamia*. *Amer. Jour. Bot.* 30:366–378. 1943.

Knoll, F. Bau, Entwicklung und morphologische Bedeutung unifazialer Vorläuferspitzen an Monokotylenblättern. *Österr. Bot. Ztschr.* 95:163–193. 1948.

Korody, E. Studien am Spross-Vegetationspunkt von *Abies concolor*, *Picea excelsa* und *Pinus montana*. *Beitr. z. Biol. der Pflanz.* 25:23–59. 1937.

Kramer, P. J. Absorption of water by plants. *Bot. Rev.* 11:310–355. 1945.

Lamb, Sister M. A. Leaflets of Cycadaceae. *Bot. Gaz.* 76:185–202. 1923.

Lee, E. The morphology of leaf-fall. *Ann. Bot.* 25:51–106. 1911.

MacDaniels, L. H., and F. F. Cowart. The development and structure of the apple leaf. *N. Y. (Cornell) Agr. Exp. Sta. Mem.* 258. 1944.

Mahlert, A. Beiträge zur Kenntnis der Anatomie der Laubblätter der Coniferen mit besonderer Berücksichtigung des Spaltöffnungs-Apparates. *Bot. Centbl.* 24: 54–59, 85–88, 118–122, 149–153, 180–185, 214–218, 243–249, 278–282, 310–312. 1885.

Marco, H. F. The anatomy of spruce needles. *Jour. Agr. Res.* 58:357–368. 1939.

Martinet, J. Organes de sécrétion des végétaux. *Ann. des Sci. Nat., Bot. Ser. 5.* 14:91–232. 1872.

Mericle, L. W. The developmental genetics of the Rg mutant in maize. *Amer. Jour. Bot.* 37:100–116. 1950.

Meyer, F. J. Das trophische Parenchym. A. Assimilationsgewebe. In: K. Linsbauer. *Handbuch der Pflanzenanatomie.* Band 4. Lief. 9. 1923.

Morton, A. G., and D. J. Watson. A physiological study of leaf growth. *Ann. Bot.* 12:281–310. 1948.

Mounts, B. T. The development of foliage leaves. *Iowa Univ. Studies in Nat. Hist.* 14(5):1–19. 1932.

Mühldorf, A. Über den Ablösungsmodus der Gallen von ihren Wirtspflanzen nebst einer kritischen Übersicht über die Trennungserscheinungen im Pflanzenreiche. *Bot. Centbl. Beihefte* 42:1–110. 1925.

Myers, R. M. Effect of growth substances on the absciss layer in leaves of *Coleus.* *Bot. Gaz.* 102:323–338. 1940.

Page, V. M. Leaf anatomy of *Streptochaeta* and the relation of this genus to the bamboos. *Torrey Bot. Club Bul.* 74:232–239. 1947.

Papen, R. von. Beiträge zur Kenntnis des Wachstums der Blattspreite. *Bot. Arch.* 37:159–206. 1935.

Paulmann, R. Über die Anatomie des Laubblattes. *Flora* 7:227–258. 1915.

Pellisier, F. Sur la différenciation vasculaire dans les feuilles de *Cucurbita pepo.* *Soc. Bot. de France Bul.* 86:187–190. 1939.

Petit, L. Le pétiole des Dicotylédones au point de vue de l'anatomie comparée et de la taxinomie. *Soc. des Sci. Phys. et Nat. Bordeaux, Mém.* Ser. 3. 3:217–404. 1887.

Pfeiffer, H. Die pflanzlichen Trennungsgewebe. In: K. Linsbauer. *Handbuch der Pflanzenanatomie.* Band 5. Lief. 22. 1928.

Pickett, W. F. The relationship between the internal structure and photosynthetic behavior of apple leaves. *Kans. Agr. Expt. Sta. Tech. Bul.* 42. 1937.

Pirwitz, K. Physiologische und anatomische Untersuchungen an Speichertracheiden und Velamina. *Planta* 14:19–76. 1931.

Plymale, E. L., and R. B. Wylie. The major veins of mesomorphic leaves. *Amer. Jour. Bot.* 31:99–106. 1944.

Reinke, J. Beiträge zur Anatomie der an Laubblättern, besonders an den Zähnen derselben vorkommenden Secretionsorgane. *Jahrb. f. Wiss. Bot.* 10:117–178. 1876.

Renner, O., and M. Voss. Zur Entwicklungsgeschichte randpanaschierter Formen von *Prunus, Pelargonium, Veronica, Dracaena. Flora* 35:356–376. 1942.

Rhoades, M. M., and A. Carvalho. The function and structure of the parenchyma sheath plastids of the maize leaf. *Torrey Bot. Club Bul.* 71:335–346. 1944.

Rippel, A. Anatomische und physiologische Untersuchungen über die Wasserbahnen der Dicotylen-Laubblätter mit besonderer Berücksichtigung der handnervigen Blätter. *Biblioth. Bot.* 19(82):1–74. 1913.

Roth, I. Zur Entwicklungsgeschichte des Blattes, mit besonderer Berücksichtigung von Stipular- und Ligularbildungen. *Planta* 37:299–336. 1949.

Satina, S., and A. F. Blakeslee. Periclinal chimeras in *Datura stramonium* in relation to development of leaf and flower. *Amer. Jour. Bot.* 28:862–871. 1941.

Sauvageau, C. Sur les feuilles de quelques Monocotylédones aquatiques. *Ann. des Sci. Nat., Bot.* Ser. 7. 13:103–296. 1891.

Schmidt, A. Histologische Studien an phanerogamen Vegetationspunkten. *Bot. Arch.* 8:345–404. 1924.

Schüepp, O. Untersuchungen zur beschreibenden und experimentellen Entwicklungsgeschichte von *Acer Pseudoplatanus* L. *Jahrb. f. Wiss. Bot.* 70:743–804. 1929.

Schulze, H. Beiträge zur Blattanatomie der Rutaceen. *Bot. Centbl. Beihefte* 12: 55–98. 1902.

Schürhoff, P. N. Die Plastiden. In: K. Linsbauer. *Handbuch der Pflanzenanatomie.* Band 1. Lief. 10. 1924.

Schuster, W. Die Blattaderung des Dicotylenblattes und ihre Abhängigkeit von äusseren Einflüssen. *Deut. Bot. Gesell. Ber.* 26:194–237. 1908.

Schuster, W. Zur Kenntnis der Aderung des Monocotylenblattes. *Deut. Bot. Gesell. Ber.* 28:268–278. 1910.

Schwendener, S. Die Mestomscheiden der Gramineenblätter. *Preuss. Akad. der Wiss., Phys.-Math. Kl., Sitzber.* 22:405–426. 1890.

Scott, L. I., and J. H. Priestley. Leaf and stem anatomy of *Tradescantia fluminensis,* Vell. *Linn. Soc. London, Jour., Bot.* 47:1–28. 1925.

Scott, F. M., M. R. Schroeder, and F. M. Turrell. Development, cell shape, suberization of internal surface, and abscission in the leaf of the Valencia orange, *Citrus sinensis. Bot. Gaz.* 109:381–411. 1948.

Sharman, B. C. Developmental anatomy of the shoot of *Zea mays* L. *Ann. Bot.* 6:245–282. 1942.

Sharman, B. C. Leaf and bud initiation in the Gramineae. *Bot. Gaz.* 106:269–289. 1945.

Shields, L. M. Leaf xeromorphy as related to physiological and structural influences. *Bot. Rev.* 16:399–447. 1950.

Sifton, H. B. Air-space tissue in plants. *Bot. Rev.* 11:108–143. 1945.

Sinnott, E. W., and I. W. Bailey. Investigations on the phylogeny of the angiosperms. 3. Nodal anatomy and the morphology of stipules. *Amer. Jour. Bot.* 1:441–453. 1914

Skutch, A. F. Anatomy of leaf of banana, *Musa sapientum* L. var. Hort. Gros Michel. *Bot. Gaz.* 84:337–391. 1927.

Smith, G. H. Anatomy of the embryonic leaf. *Amer. Jour. Bot.* 21:194–209. 1934.

Soar, I. The structure and function of the endodermis in the leaves of Abietineae. *New Phytol.* 21:269–292. 1922.

Sperlich, A. Das trophische Parenchym. B. Exkretionsgewebe. In: K. Linsbauer. *Handbuch der Pflanzenanatomie.* Band 4. Lief. 38. 1939.

Stephens, S. G. The genetic organization of leaf-shape development in the genus *Gossypium. Jour. Genet.* 46:28–51. 1944.

Strain, R. W. A study of vein endings in leaves. *Amer. Midland Nat.* 14:367–375. 1933.

Strasburger, E. *Über den Bau und die Verrichtungen der Leitungsbahnen in den Pflanzen. Histologische Beiträge.* Band 3. Jena, Gustav Fischer. 1891.

Sun, C.-N. Morphology and development of the vegetative shoot of *Amorphophallus rivieri* Dur. with special reference to the ontogeny of the cataphyll and the foliage-leaf. *Natl. Peking Univ. Seme-Cent. Papers, Coll. Sci.* 1948:183–193. 1948.

Sutherland, M. A microscopical study of the structure of leaves of the genus *Pinus. New Zeal. Inst. Trans. and Proc.* 63:517–568. 1933.

Takeda, H. A theory of "transfusion-tissue." *Ann. Bot.* 27:359–363. 1913.

Tetley, U. The development and cytology of the leaves of healthy and 'silvered' Victoria plum trees. *Ann. Bot.* 46:633–652. 1932.

Tetley, U. Tissue differentiation in some foliage leaves. *Ann. Bot.* 50:523–557. 1936.

Thielke, C. Beiträge zur Entwicklungsgeschichte unifazialer Blätter. *Planta* 36: 154–177. 1948.

Thielke, C. Über die Möglichkeiten der Periklinalchimärenbildung bei Gräsern. *Planta* 39:402–430. 1951.

Tison, A. Recherches sur la chute des feuilles chez les Dicotylédones. *Soc. Linn. de Normandie, Mém.* 20:121–327. 1900.

Trécul, A. Recherches sur l'ordre d'apparition des premiers vaisseaux dans les organes aériens. *Ann. des Sci. Nat., Bot.* Ser. 6. 12:251–381. 1881.

Troll, W. *Vergleichende Morphologie der höheren Pflanzen.* Band 1. *Vegetationsorgane.* Heft 2. Berlin, Gebrüder Borntraeger. 1939.

Turrell, F. M. Leaf surface of a twenty-one-year-old catalpa tree. *Iowa Acad. Sci. Proc.* 41:79–84. 1934.

Turrell, F. M. The area of the internal exposed surface of dicotyledon leaves. *Amer. Jour. Bot.* 23:255–264. 1936.

Turrell, F. M. The relation between chlorophyll concentration and the internal surface of mesomorphic and xeromorphic leaves grown under artificial light. *Iowa Acad. Sci. Proc.* 46:107–117. 1939.

Turrell, F. M. A quantitative morphological analysis of large and small leaves of alfalfa with special reference to internal surface. *Amer. Jour. Bot.* 29:400–415. 1942.

Turrell, F. M. Correlation between internal surface and transpiration rate in mesomorphic and xeromorphic leaves grown under artificial light. *Bot. Gaz.* 105:413–425. 1944.

Van Abbema, T. Das Transfusionsgewebe in den Blättern der Cycadinae, Ginkgoinae und Coniferae. *Rec. des Trav. Bot. Néerland.* 31:309–390. 1934.

Van Fleet, D. S. The cell forms, and their common substance reactions, in the parenchyma-vascular boundary. *Torrey Bot. Club Bul.* 77:340–353. 1950.

Whaley, W. G., and C. Y. Whaley. A developmental analysis of inherited leaf patterns in *Tropaeolum. Amer. Jour. Bot.* 29:195–200. 1942.

Williams, W. T. The continuity of intercellular spaces in the leaf of *Pelargonium zonale,* and its bearing on recent stomatal investigations. *Ann. Bot.* 12:411–420. 1948.

Worsdell, W. C. On "transfusion-tissue": its origin and function in the leaves of gymnospermous plants. *Linn. Soc. London, Trans., Bot.* Ser. 2. 5:301–319. 1897.

Wylie, R. B. Relations between tissue organization and vein distribution in dicotyledon leaves. *Amer. Jour. Bot.* 26:219–225. 1939.

Wylie, R. B. The role of the epidermis in foliar organization and its relations to the minor venation. *Amer. Jour. Bot.* 30:273–280. 1943.

Wylie, R. B. Relations between tissue organization and vascularization in leaves of certain tropical and subtropical dicotyledons. *Amer. Jour. Bot.* 33:721–726. 1946.

Wylie, R. B. Conduction in dicotyledon leaves. *Iowa Acad. Sci. Proc.* 53:195–202. 1947.

Wylie, R. B. The dominant role of the epidermis in leaves of *Adiantum*. *Amer. Jour. Bot.* 35:465–473. 1948.

Wylie, R. B. Variations in leaf structure among *Adiantum pedatum* plants growing in a rock cavern. *Amer. Jour. Bot.* 36:282–287. 1949a.

Wylie, R. B. Differences in foliar organization among leaves from four locations in the crown of an isolated tree (*Acer platanoides*). *Iowa Acad. Sci. Proc.* 56:189–198. 1949b.

Wylie, R. B. Principles of foliar organization shown by sun-shade leaves from ten species of deciduous dicotyledonous trees. *Amer. Jour. Bot.* 38:355–361. 1951.

Ziegenspeck, H. Vergleichende Untersuchungen der Entwicklung der Spaltöffnungen von Monokotyledonen und Dikotyledonen im Lichte der Polariskopie und Dichroskopie. *Protoplasma* 38:197–224. 1944.

Ziegenspeck, H. Zur Phylogenie der Hydathoden. *Phyton* 1:302–318. 1949.

CHAPTER

17

The Root

CONCEPT

The root constitutes the underground part of the plant axis, specialized as an absorbing and anchoring organ. It occurs in the sporophytes of the vascular plants (Troll, 1949). As a group among the vascular plants, only the Psilotales lack such an organ. The sporophytes of these most primitive tracheophytes are attached to the ground by means of rhizomes bearing hair-like absorbing structures, the rhizoids (Eames, 1936).

The morphologic relation between the root and the stem is variously interpreted. Since the two organs have many similarities in structure and show physical continuity, they are commonly treated as two parts of the same unit axis, and similar terms are applied to their tissue systems. In such treatment the designation of the stem and the root as organs serves to bring out their morphological and physiological specialization. Certain concepts deny the existence of complete homology between the two organs. According to one view, only part of the shoot, namely its inner region, is represented in the root (Arber, 1950). Another entirely opposite suggestion is that the vascular cylinder of the root, the stele, may be homologous with the entire shoot axis, the peripheral root tissues having no counterparts in the shoot (Allen, 1947).

It is particularly common to question the morphologic equivalence of the epidermis in the two organs because of the developmental and structural differences of this tissue system in the stem and in the root (see chapter 7). There is also some difficulty in correlating the morphology of the primary vascular cylinder in root and stem. The old view that the entire primary vascular cylinder (or central cylinder) of the root is a single bundle was superseded by the interpretation of this cylinder as a system of bundles corresponding to the system of bundles in the shoot (Kattein, 1897; Russow, 1875); and when the concept of stele was introduced, the vascular cylinder of the root was interpreted as the stele of this organ (Guttenberg, 1940). The concept of the composite nature of the primary vascular cylinder of the root is now prevalent, but reference to this cylinder as a vascular bundle has not been completely abandoned (e.g., Guttenberg, 1940; Haberlandt, 1914; Meyer, 1925).

No complete agreement exists regarding the interpretation of the parenchymatous region that occurs in the center of the vascular cylinder of many roots, particularly in the monocotyledons. Commonly this region is referred to as pith or pith-like, but there is some question whether it should not rather be regarded as potential vascular tissue that fails to differentiate as such (Russow, 1875). The introduction of the stelar concept did not resolve the problem because of the different views on the phylogenetic origin of the pith in the stele (Bower, 1911). According to one interpretation, the pith is stelar in origin (Schoute, 1903). According to another, the pith was derived from the cortex and appeared in the evolution of the siphonostele with the development of leaves and leaf gaps (Jeffrey, 1898–99). Such pith would not be present in roots because they lack leaves.

In view of the uncertain state of the interpretation of homologies between the root and the stem, in this book a simple topographic-morphologic definition of the tissue systems of the root is adopted, conforming with that used in the treatment of the stem. The superficial layer of the root in the primary state of growth is the epidermis. Beneath this layer is the fundamental tissue system in the form of a cortex, which surrounds the vascular system. If a clearly defined parenchymatous core appears in the center of the root, it is considered a part of the fundamental tissue system and is called pith.

ORIGIN OF THE ROOT

As was mentioned in chapter 1, the root and the stem appear to be closely related phylogenetically. The primitive axis-like plant body is considered to have differentiated into a shoot and a root with reference to different habitats and functions of the aerial and underground parts. The greater uniformity of the underground habitat, as contrasted with the aerial, is thought to be one of the factors causally connected with the relative simplicity of the root and its retention of some of the primitive structural features which eventually disappeared in the stem.

Ontogenetically the root origin is somewhat variable (Troll, 1949). The seed plants possess a radicle or simply a root meristem at the root end (root pole) of the embryo from which the first root of the plant develops upon germination. In gymnosperms and dicotyledons this root (the taproot) commonly produces, by elongation and branching, the root system of the plant. In monocotyledons the first root, derived from the root meristem of the embryo, usually dies early in the growth of the plant, and the root system of the mature plant develops as a composite structure from numerous roots borne on the stem above the place of origin of the first root. Some of these stem-borne roots may be initiated in the embryo; others arise later. In the vascular cryptogams, also, the main root system consists of roots that arise on the stem (Troll, 1949).

The first apical meristem of the root of seed plants arises not superficially like that of the epicotyl, but more or less deeply in the tissue of the root end of the embryo (Allen, 1947; see also chapter 20). The deep-seated origin of the lateral roots (plate 15, *B*) and of those occurring adventitiously on the stem is even more clearly expressed. Thus, roots typically originate endogenously, whereas shoots arise exogenously. (Troll, 1949, however, regards the embryo root as exogenous.)

The roots originating at the root pole of the embryo and all their branches formed in normal sequence are usually distinguished from roots originating in various other manners by the designation of the latter as *adventitious roots*. This broad usage of the term is employed in the present book. It refers to roots that arise on aerial plant parts, on underground stems, and on relatively old roots (Eames and Mac-Daniels, 1947, p. 289; Guttenberg, 1940). Some workers prefer to restrict the appellation adventitious to roots arising from mature tissues or from parts of the plant where roots would not arise under ordinary conditions of growth. In this strict usage the stem-borne roots of some dicotyledons, the monocotyledons, and the lower vascular plants would not be called adventitious (*cladogenous roots*, according to Troll, 1949).

MORPHOLOGY OF THE ROOT

Roots vary widely in their morphology (Weaver, 1926; Weaver and Voigt, 1950) and exhibit structural and developmental differences correlated with more or less pronounced physiological specializations (Guttenberg, 1940). Most dicotyledons and gymnosperms possess a

root system based on the taproot and its branches. The taproot produces the lateral or branch roots in an acropetal sequence, that is,
with the youngest laterals located nearest the apical meristem, the oldest nearest the base (end of taproot merging with the hypocotyl).
The taproot is often called the primary root; branches of the first
order, the secondary roots; and branches of the secondary roots, the
tertiary roots. Some plants may have root branches of fourth and
even fifth orders (Dittmer, 1948). In perennial species the taproots
and the older laterals undergo secondary growth. At this stage of
development they serve as conductors of food and water, and as storage and anchorage organs. Absorption, on the other hand, is carried
on mainly by the ultimate branchings which are in primary state of
growth. The fine absorptive branches—the feeder roots—remain short
and are often fragile and short-lived (Guttenberg, 1940; Jones, 1943;
Preston, 1943). Adventitious roots also may constitute normal complements of the root system in these groups of plants. Many gymnosperms develop such roots from the hypocotyl (Guttenberg, 1941).
Some dicotyledons, usually rhizome-bearing plants, resemble the
monocotyledons in having mainly adventitious roots.

The root systems of the monocotyledons are commonly composed
of stem-borne adventitious roots. As in the dicotyledons, there may
be several orders of branches in the individual roots, or branching
may be lacking. The roots are devoid of secondary growth and vary
less in size from one another than the various parts of a similar root
system in a perennial dicotyledon or gymnosperm. Familiar examples
of the monocotyledonous, so-called fibrous root systems are found in
the grasses and on bulbs and rhizomes of such families as Liliaceae,
Iridaceae, and others (Guttenberg, 1940). In the grasses some of the
adventitious roots may start developing in the embryo so that the
embryo possesses two or more root primordia in the hypocotyl, in
addition to the terminal radicle. All these primordia together are
commonly spoken of as seminal roots. Some or all of these die after
other adventitious roots develop. The formation of numerous adventitious roots in the Gramineae is associated with the important
phenomenon of tillering characteristic of many representatives of this
family. It consists in the production of numerous shoots with un-
elongated internodes from axillary buds and the development of
adventitious roots in connection with these shoots (Jackson, 1922).

The above description characterizes the most common and widespread types of root systems, concerned with absorption, conduction,
storage, and anchorage of the plant in the soil. Some roots are more

definitely specialized with reference to one particular function and correspondingly show morphologic peculiarities (Guttenberg, 1940). Many roots develop as fleshy storage organs, with or without anomalous secondary growth. Others serve mainly as supporting organs, such as the prop roots in the mangrove plants and, on a smaller scale, in the grasses and sedges. Roots may be specialized as aerating organs or modified into thorns. Certain vines (e.g., *Ficus pumila*) and epiphytes develop aerial roots that attach the shoots to the surface upon which the plant may be growing.

Reference to morphologic forms of roots is incomplete without mention of mycorrhizae and root nodules. Mycorrhizae are associations of roots and fungi, usually interpreted as symbiotic. They occur widely among woody and herbaceous angiosperms and in the gymnosperms (Dittmer, 1949; Guttenberg, 1940, 1941; Kelley, 1950; McDougall, 1914). The mycorrhizal roots are often short, and their internal structure deviates somewhat from that of noninvaded roots (Clowes, 1951). The development of root nodules is caused by bacteria's entering through the root hairs and stimulating a proliferation of cortical cells. Root nodules are particularly characteristic of the Leguminosae (Bond, 1948; Bottum, 1941; Guttenberg, 1940) but are found also in some other families (Podocarpaceae; Guttenberg, 1941).

THE PRIMARY STRUCTURE OF THE ROOT

Epidermis

The histologic and developmental details of the epidermis of various plant parts appear in chapter 7. In brief, the root epidermis consists of closely packed elongated cells with thin walls that usually lack a cuticle. An eventual cutinization of the epidermal walls, sometimes only of the outer ones, is not uncommon, however, and appears to be associated with the longevity of the epidermis (Guttenberg, 1940; Kroemer, 1903). Thickened outer walls occur in root parts growing in air and also in roots that retain their epidermis for a long time (many monocotyledons and some dicotyledons). The walls of a long-persisting epidermis may also show lignification or may be impregnated with dark-colored substances of uncertain identity (Guttenberg, 1940).

The root epidermis is typically uniseriate. A well-known example of a multiseriate epidermis is the velamen (see p. 162) of air roots of tropical Orchidaceae and epiphytic Araceae (Guttenberg, 1940, pp.

81–84; Haberlandt, 1914, pp. 231–235). The velamen is a parchment-like sheath consisting of compactly arranged nonliving cells with thickened walls. During dry weather the cells are filled with air. When it rains, however, the velamen cells become filled with water. Because of this behavior the velamen is commonly interpreted as absorptive tissue.

An outstanding characteristic of the root epidermis is the development of root hairs. Ordinarily, the root hairs are confined to a region between one and several centimeters in length near the tip (Farr, 1928). They are absent in the nearest proximity of the apical meristem, and they die off in the older root parts. Exceptional longevity and persistence of the root hairs—probably with a loss of the function of absorption—has been observed in a number of plants (see chapter 7). Root hairs vary in width and length (Dittmer, 1949). In some plants all epidermal cells are capable of initiating root hairs; in others, only certain ones. Furthermore, the actual development of root hairs is much affected by the environment (Cormack, 1949). The formation of root hairs from a subepidermal layer has been recorded in *Citrus* (Hayward and Long, 1942).

Rootcap

The rootcap (plate 15, *A*) is commonly regarded as a structure that protects the root meristem and assists the root in the penetration of the soil during its growth (Guttenberg, 1940). The latter function is suggested by the mucilaginous consistency of the walls of the outermost rootcap cells, a characteristic that presumably reduces the friction between the growing root tip and the soil. In some plants the rootcap cells are mechanically strong and possibly could serve to force soil particles apart (Guttenberg, 1940).

The cells of the rootcap are living parenchyma cells, often containing starch. The starch is rather persistent, in the sense that it is not readily utilized, except under conditions of extreme starvation (Netolitzky, 1935). The mucilaginous alteration of the rootcap-cell walls is probably comparable to that commonly found in the epidermis of young roots (see chapter 7). Mucilaginous walls occur between the rootcap and the protoderm (plate 72, *B*) and also in the peripheral cells of the cap. The mucilaginous condition of the walls is assumed to facilitate the separation of the rootcap from the flanks of the growing root and the sloughing of the cells on the outer surface of the rootcap. During the sloughing process the separating cells show turgid protoplasts surrounded by a continuous wall layer, even after they are obviously disconnected from the rootcap (Guttenberg, 1940). Environmental conditions affect the structure of the rootcap. For example, rootcaps of roots ordinarily growing in the soil undergo a reduction in size and a structural loosening when the plants are transferred to a water culture. In true water plants, however, rootcaps are usually prominently developed, a phenomenon suggesting that this part of the root may have other functions besides those mentioned above.

Cortex

The root cortex may be homogeneous and simple in structure, or it may contain a variety of cell types. The degree of differentiation is apparently related to the longevity of this part of the root. In the roots of gymnosperms and dicotyledons, which possess secondary growth and shed their cortex early, the cortex consists mainly of parenchyma. In roots retaining their cortex, as in many of the monocotyledons, abundant sclerenchyma may develop in addition to parenchyma. The innermost cortical layer of roots of seed plants growing in soil differentiates as an *endodermis* (fig. 17.2, *A*, and plate 70, *A*). Some roots also develop a specialized layer—the *exodermis*—beneath the epidermis (plate 70, *A*).

As seen in transverse sections, the cortical cells may be arranged in orderly radial rows (plate 76, *A*, *B*), or they may alternate with one another in the successive concentric layers (plate 70, *A*; Cormack, 1947; Guttenberg, 1940). Sometimes the radial alignment is combined with a pronounced concentric layering, a pattern especially common in water plants and often associated with the presence of large intercellular spaces. In many roots a radially seriated inner cortex is combined with a less orderly appearing outer cortex. The presence of schizogenous intercellular spaces is typical of the root cortex. These spaces arise in the early ontogeny of the root, usually before the divisions forming the cortex are completed and before any vascular elements mature in the vascular cylinder (plate 76, *B*). In addition to the schizogenous spaces, some plants (e.g., Gramineae, Cyperaceae) develop lysigenous lacunae by the breakdown of cells (Freidenfelt, 1904; Guttenberg, 1940). Some experiments suggest that the development of such lacunae may be causally related to scarcity of oxygen (Bryant, 1934a; McPherson, 1939). Large lacunae may develop also by schizogeny, division and separation of cells combining in the process (Boeke, 1940; Guttenberg, 1940). In contrast to the lysigenous lacunae, the schizogenous ones have smooth walls and are sometimes symmetrically arranged.

The orderly arrangement of cortical cells frequently observed in roots results from the method of cell division during the origin of this tissue region. As was shown in chapter 5, the root cortex often develops from one or two layers of cells derived from the apical initials (plate 72, *B*). Repeated periclinal divisions augment the number of layers in radial extent, while anticlinal divisions increase the circumference and length of the cortex. In most roots, the sequence of periclinal divisions is centripetal; that is, of the two cells formed by a given periclinal division only the inner cell repeats the periclinal division. Thus, a series of cells is cut off toward the periphery of the root, and, developmentally, the outer cortex is older than the inner (Guttenberg, 1940, 1943; Kroemer, 1903; Williams, 1947). After the periclinal divisions are completed, the innermost layer differentiates into an endodermis.

The centripetal sequence of divisions in the root cortex is common in the dicotyledons but it also occurs in many monocotyledons (e.g., Typhaceae, Pontederiaceae, Alismaceae, Cannaceae). In some dicotyledons (Ranunculaceae) and in many monocotyledons (Gramineae, Cyperaceae, Juncaceae, Commelinaceae, Aroideae) the internal part of the cortex shows centripetal growth; the external, centrifugal or irregular growth (Flahault, 1878; Janczewski, 1874*a*). Apparently in the lower vascular plants also part or all of the root cortex grows by centripetal divisions (Janczewski, 1874*a*; Williams, 1947).

The cortical parenchyma of roots is usually devoid of chlorophyll. Exceptions are roots of some water plants (Cormack, 1937) and aerial roots of many epiphytes. Starch is frequently present. Various idioblasts and secretory structures may occur in the root cortex. If sclerenchyma is present, it usually assumes a cylindrical arrangement, several cell layers in depth, either beneath the epidermis directly, or beneath an exodermis, or next to the endodermis. The sclerenchyma cells may be elongated like fibers, or they may be short. Sclerification is often found in the monocotyledons, but it is rare in dicotyledons (Guttenberg, 1940). The cortical cells in roots of many gymnosperms have band-like or reticulate thickenings which may be lignified (Guttenberg, 1941, pp. 29–31; Van Fleet, 1948). Some dicotyledons (Cruciferae, Pomoideae, Prunoideae, Spiraeoideae, Caprifoliaceae) also develop prominent reticulate or band-like thickenings in cortical cells outside the endodermis (fig. 17.10; Guttenberg, 1940, pp. 121–122). The cortex of lower vascular plants shows thin-walled parenchymatous and variously sclerified cell complexes (Ogura, 1938). Sometimes collenchymatous differentiation occurs in roots (Freidenfelt, 1904; Guttenberg, 1940, p. 112; Van Fleet, 1950).

Endodermis. An endodermis characterized by Casparian strips on its anticlinal walls (figs. 17.1 and 17.2) is almost universally present in roots. The strip is formed during the early ontogeny of the cell and is a part of the primary wall. It apparently results from a localized

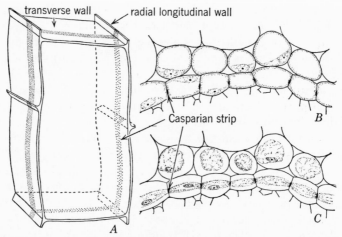

transverse wall   radial longitudinal wall

Casparian strip   *B*

A   *C*

Fig. 17.1. Details of endodermal structure. *A*, diagram of a cell showing location of Casparian strip. *B* and *C*, illustration of the effect of treatment with alcohol upon cells of endodermis and of ordinary parenchyma. *B* shows the cells before treatment, *C* after. Casparian strip is seen only in sectional views in drawings *B* and *C*.

impregnation of the primary wall with certain substances. The intercellular substance also is modified in the strip region and becomes less soluble than elsewhere (Guttenberg, 1943). In fact, according to one study (Van Fleet, 1942*a*), the Casparian strip originates as an intercellular deposit. The strip varies in width and is often much narrower than the wall in which it occurs. It is typically located close to the inner tangential wall.

Despite the numerous and careful studies carried out on the Casparian strip, its chemistry is a matter of controversy (Guttenberg, 1943). Many workers agree that the strip shows some of the reactions of lignin. Certain workers find also suberin or related fatty substances in it (e.g., Van Fleet, 1942*a*; Van Wisselingh, 1924), although others deny the presence of such substances (e.g., Elisei, 1941).

The evidence for the presence of suberin-like materials is more generally accepted than the opposite view (Guttenberg, 1943).

One of the most remarkable features of an endodermal cell is that its cytoplasm is relatively firmly attached to the Casparian strip, so

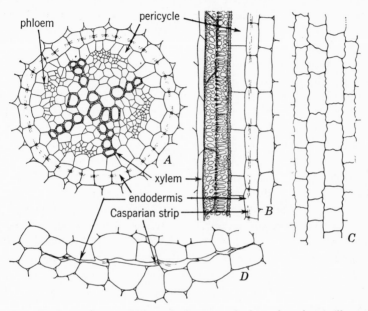

Fɪɢ. 17.2. Sections of root of *Convolvulus arvensis* (morning-glory) illustrating the endodermis in relation to other tissues. *A*, transection of vascular cylinder and part of cortex. Note the following details: tetrarch xylem, uniseriate pericycle, uniseriate endodermis with Casparian strips, presence of intercellular spaces outside the endodermis and their absence in the vascular cylinder. *B*, radial longitudinal section through the xylem, the pericycle, and the endodermis. *C*, tangential longitudinal section through the endodermis, showing the characteristic waviness of the walls. This appearance is sometimes explained as resulting from differential shrinkage of wall parts with and without the Casparian strip. *D*, transection from an older root showing crushing of the endodermis in connection with the expansion of the vascular cylinder during secondary growth. (*A–C*, ×225; *D*, ×135. After Kennedy and Crafts, 1931.)

that it does not readily separate from it when the tissue is subjected to the effects of plasmolytic or other agents normally causing a contraction of protoplasts (fig. 17.1, *B, C*; Behrisch, 1926; Bryant, 1934*b*; Guttenberg, 1943; Schnee, 1936). Some ascribe this adherence of the cytoplasm to a particularly strong penetration of the band by the cytoplasm (Schnee, 1936); others to a high degree of viscosity of endodermal cytoplasm (Behrisch, 1926). Whatever may be its cause, the phenomenon is considered highly important by the physiologists in the interpretation of the function of the endodermis (see p. 506).

The Casparian strips differentiate after the centripetal growth of the cortex is completed. At this level of the root, primary xylem development in the vascular cylinder may be more or less advanced. In gymnosperms and dicotyledons having secondary growth, the roots commonly develop no other kind of endodermis than that with Casparian strips. In many of these plants the endodermis is discarded, together with the cortex, when the periderm develops in the pericycle. If the periderm is superficial and the cortex is retained, either the endodermis is stretched and crushed (fig. 17.2, *D*), or it keeps pace with the expansion of the vascular cylinder by radial anticlinal divisions, the new walls developing Casparian strips in continuity with the old ones (Bond, 1931; Guttenberg, 1943; Warden, 1935).

Without secondary growth (most monocotyledons and a few dicotyledons) the endodermis commonly undergoes certain wall modifications. Workers distinguish two developmental states, sometimes very distinct, in addition to the primary state when only the Casparian strip is present. In the secondary state a suberin lamella covers the entire wall on the inside of the cell, so that the Casparian strip is separated from the cytoplasm and the peculiar relation between the two ceases to be evident. In the tertiary state a thick cellulose layer is deposited over the suberin lamella, sometimes mainly on the inner tangential wall (figs. 17.3, 17.4; Guttenberg, 1943). The thick wall, as well as the original wall in which the Casparian strip is located, may become lignified. The Casparian strip may or may not be identifiable after the thickening of the endodermal wall. The thick endodermal wall, which probably could be classified as secondary, may have pits. The successive development of endodermal walls is clearly expressed in the monocotyledons. In the dicotyledons the distinction between the secondary and tertiary states of endodermis may not be sharp (Guttenberg, 1943), and in the lower vascular plants the differentiation is terminated with the secondary state (Ogura, 1938).

The development of the wall structures distinguishing the different states of endodermal differentiation does not occur simultaneously throughout the entire endodermis at a given level. There are, therefore, more or less extended parts of the root where the endodermis is partly in one state, partly in another, and often cells in all three states of development are found at the same level. The change from one state to another usually follows a pattern suggesting a relation of this change to the proximity of the phloem. The Casparian strips and the subsequent wall modifications appear first on the face of the phloem strands and then spread toward the parts of the endodermis opposite the xylem (Clowes, 1951; Guttenberg, 1943; Kroemer, 1903; Van Fleet, 1942*a*, *b*). Such unequal development of the endodermis opposite the xylem and the phloem often results in the occurrence of

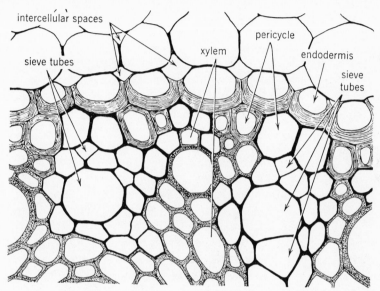

Fig. 17.3. Transection from part of *Zea* root illustrating endodermis in tertiary state of development characterized by the presence of thick walls. The wall thickening is confined to the radial and inner tangential walls. The pericycle consists in part of sclerenchyma. Part of a xylem strand and two phloem strands flanking the xylem are shown. In the phloem, one narrow sieve tube, located next to the pericycle, is flanked by two parenchyma cells. Inward from these are one or more wide sieve tubes. Parenchyma occurs between the phloem strands and the xylem. The parenchyma associated with the xylem is sclerenchymatous. (Compare with plate 73, *B*.) ($\times$690.)

a thick-walled endodermis facing the phloem and cells with only Casparian strips facing the xylem. These cells are called passage cells because they are assumed to be the passageways for a limited transfer of material between the cortex and the vascular cylinder (Guttenberg, 1940, 1943; Kroemer, 1903). The passage cells either remain unmodified as long as the root lives or develop thick walls like the rest of the endodermis.

Exodermis. The subepidermal cortical layers of the root are often differentiated as a protective tissue containing suberin in its walls. Some workers apply the general term of hypodermis to the morphologically specialized subepidermal layers in both root and shoot (Eames and MacDaniels, 1947, pp. 163, 281); others distinguish the root hypodermis under a special designation of exodermis because of its distinctive histologic characteristics (Foster, 1949; Guttenberg, 1943).

endodermis   pericycle

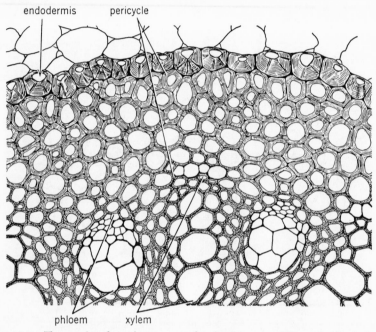

phloem   xylem

FIG. 17.4. Transection from inner part of a *Smilax* root. The endodermis is in tertiary state of development characterized by thick walls. The thickening is most pronounced in the radial and the inner tangential walls. (Compare with fig. 17.3.) The pericycle is many-layered and sclerenchymatous. Part of a xylem strand is flanked by two phloem strands, each with many sieve tubes. The parenchyma between the xylem and the phloem is sclerenchymatous. (×257.)

The exodermis resembles the endodermis histochemically and structurally (Van Fleet, 1950). Also, the causal factors of development of these tissues appear to be similar, since both show suberization of cell walls in roots and underground stems but not in aerial stems (Van Fleet, 1950). The most commonly reported characteristic of the exodermis is the presence of a suberin lamella on the inside of the primary wall (Guttenberg, 1940, 1941; Kroemer, 1903). Usually the suberin lamella is covered by centripetally developing cellulose layers. Thus, the exodermal cells resemble cork cells derived from phellogen, except that in contrast to the cork cells they retain their protoplasts and may have much thicker walls (fig. 17.5). The exodermal cells are often lignified. In some species Casparian strips were observed in the exodermis (Van Fleet, 1950).

Exodermis is common in roots of gymnosperms and angiosperms but is mostly lacking in vascular cryptogams (Guttenberg, 1943, p. 5). It is rarely absent in roots of monocotyledons. Sometimes the subepidermal layers reveal an impregnation of cell walls with substances showing certain reactions of fatty materials and of lignin,

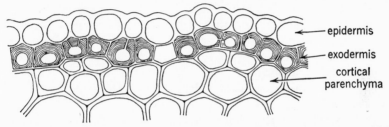

epidermis

exodermis

cortical
parenchyma

Fɪɢ. 17.5. Transection from the outer part of a *Smilax* root illustrating a thick-walled exodermis beneath the epidermis. One exodermal cell is not thickened. (×400.)

but develop no suberin lamella. Finally, in some roots no histologic specialization of these layers has been demonstrated (Guttenberg, 1943, p. 4).

The exodermis varies in thickness from one to several layers and is sometimes accompanied by sclerenchyma in the subjacent parts of the cortex (e.g., pineapple root; Krauss, 1949). The exodermis contains either one kind of cells, all elongated and suberized (some Gramineae, *Linum usitatissimum, Lactuca sativa*), or some of the cells are short and unsuberized (*Allium cepa; Asparagus officinalis;* Guttenberg, 1943).

Vascular Cylinder

The central part of the root is occupied by the vascular cylinder composed of the vascular system and the associated parenchyma. The vascular system of the root is more clearly delimited from the cortex than that of the shoot because of several distinctive anatomic features of the root. First, the vascular tissue is compactly arranged and is not interrupted by leaf gaps; second, this tissue is surrounded by a commonly distinct uniseriate or multiseriate tissue zone, the pericycle (pericambium of some authors, Guttenberg, 1940, 1943); and third, a specialized endodermis (the innermost layer of the cortex in the seed plants) typically surrounds the pericycle (fig. 17.2 and plate 70, *A*).

Pericycle. The pericycle of relatively young roots consists of thin-walled parenchyma (fig. 17.2). In the angiosperms and gymnosperms it is concerned with meristematic activities. The lateral roots in these groups of plants arise in this tissue; the phellogen originates here in most roots having secondary growth; and part of the vascular cambium is formed from pericyclic cells. (These activities, however, are not characteristic of the root pericycle of the non-seed-bearing plants; Guttenberg, 1943; Ogura, 1938.) In the monocotyledons, which usually lack secondary growth, the pericycle often undergoes sclerification in older roots, partly (fig. 17.3) or entirely (fig. 17.4).

In the angiosperms the pericycle is commonly uniseriate, but in many monocotyledons (e.g., some Gramineae, *Smilax, Agave, Dracaena,* palms) and a few dicotyledons (*Celtis, Morus, Salix, Castanea, Calycanthus*) it consists of several layers (fig. 17.4). The gymnosperms characteristically show a multiseriate pericycle (Guttenberg, 1941, 1943). Sometimes the pericycle is uniseriate opposite the phloem and wider opposite the xylem. Roots without pericycle are rare but may be found among water plants and parasites. The pericycle may be interrupted by the differentiation of xylem (many Gramineae and Cyperaceae) or phloem elements (Potamogetonaceae) next to the endodermis (Guttenberg, 1943). The pericycle may contain laticifers and secretory ducts.

Vascular System. The phloem of the root occurs in the form of strands distributed near the periphery of the vascular cylinder, beneath the pericycle (figs. 17.2–17.4). The xylem either forms discrete strands, alternating with the phloem strands (fig. 17.4 and plate 70, *A*) or occupies the center as well, with the strand-like parts projecting from the central core like ridges (figs. 17.2 and 17.8). If no xylem differentiates in the center, the center is occupied by a pith (plate 70, *A*). Plants with internal phloem may have such phloem in the root as well as in the stem (Russow, 1875; Van Tieghem, 1891*b*).

The arrangement of the vascular tissues and its variations in the root are best understood if the tissues are considered from the developmental standpoint. The classification of the patterns of xylem differentiation, based on the relative position of the successively maturing elements, has been discussed in chapter 15. The root typically shows an exarch xylem; that is, its elements mature in the centripetal direction (fig. 17.8). Since the earliest xylem in a given plant organ is commonly called protoxylem, the root may be said to have the protoxylem located near the periphery of the vascular cylinder, the metaxylem farther inward (fig. 17.8). In the phloem, too, differentiation is centripetal, the protophloem occurring closer to the periphery than the metaphloem. Since the protophloem and the protoxylem mark, by their appearance, the beginning of vascular differentiation and thus may be used later as points of reference for the determination of the direction of vascular differentiation in the transverse plane, the location of these first vascular cells may be referred to as poles, *protophloem* and *protoxylem poles*, or simply phloem and xylem poles. The number of such poles in different roots varies, but commonly there are as many protophloem as protoxylem poles.

Depending on the number of protoxylem poles, one, two, three, or more, the roots are called monarch, diarch, triarch, and so on (fig. 17.6). The term polyarch may be used when the number is high. In these designations the last part of the word, arch, stems from the Greek word meaning beginning. Monarch, diarch, and the other words thus indicate the number of loci where xylary differentiation begins, whereas exarch signifies that this beginning is peripheral with reference to the later xylem.

The number of protoxylem poles is in general characteristic in the different large groups of plants, but it is not stable. Like the presence or absence of pith, it is related to the diameter of the vascular cylinder. If the diameter is long, the number of poles is larger, and pith is more likely to be present than in roots with narrow vascular cores. Such variations may occur in the same plant (cf. Cheadle, 1944; Guttenberg, 1940; Preston, 1943). Frequently the number of xylem strands is higher in the proximal (basal) end of a given root than in its distal (apical) end, but the change may occur in the opposite direction as well.

Most dicotyledons have few xylem strands. The taproot is frequently di-, tri-, or tetrarch, but it may have five to eight and even more poles (e.g., many Amentiferae, *Castanea*). Only one xylem strand occurs in the slender root of the hydrophyte *Trapa natans*. The seedling taproots of monocotyledons show numbers of protoxylem strands similar to those of dicotyledons, but the adventitious roots often have considerably higher numbers, as many as 100 and more in the Palmae and the Pandanaceae. High numbers of xylem strands in adventitious roots are associated with large transverse di-

ameters and presence of pith. The roots of many gymnosperms are
diarch. Polyarch roots with the number of strands reaching seven
have been recorded in the genus *Pinus*. A monarch condition has
been observed in the smallest roots of the Araucariaceae (Guttenberg,
1941). The roots of the non-seed-bearing vascular plants have one to
many protoxylem and protoploem strands (Ogura, 1938).

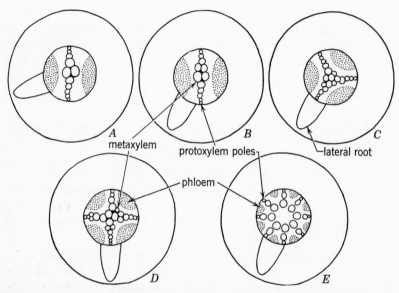

Fɪɢ. 17.6. Diagrams illustrating arrangement of primary vascular tissues and the
orientation of the lateral root with reference to the vascular tissues of the main
root. In relation to the number of radially arranged ridges in the xylem system,
the roots are diarch (*A* and *B*), triarch (*C*), tetrarch (*D*), and polyarch (*E*).
A–D illustrate common patterns in dicotyledonous roots, *E* in a monocotyledonous root. The lateral roots are shown as having originated opposite a protoxylem
pole (*C*, *D*), between the xylem and phloem poles (*B*), and opposite the phloem
(*A*, *E*).

In the monocotyledons the arrangement of the primary xylem of
roots is more varied than in the dicotyledons. In the latter the principal
differences result from the presence or absence of pith and internal
phloem, but in the monocotyledons there is, in addition, a varied
spatial relation between the peripheral xylem strands (usually composed partly of protoxylem, partly of metaxylem) and the more
interior wide metaxylem vessels (Cheadle, 1944; Guttenberg, 1940).
In some roots a single vessel occupies the center and is separated by
nontracheary elements from the peripheral strands (plate 71, *A*). In

others variable numbers of large metaxylem vessels are arranged in a circle around the pith (plate 73). The number of these large vessels is not necessarily correlated with that of the peripheral strands. In some roots each strand terminates toward the center with a large vessel; in others two strands converge toward one large vessel. In the woody monocotyledons the inner metaxylem elements may form two to three circles (*Latania*), or they may be rather widely separated from each other (*Phoenix dactylifera*), or even scattered throughout the center (*Raphia Hookeri*). In some monocotyledons (e.g., *Cordyline, Musa*, Pandanaceae) phloem strands are scattered among the tracheary elements in the center of the root.

Although in transections the different strands and individual vessels might seem isolated from one another, they are commonly interconnected by lateral anastomoses (Guttenberg, 1940; Meyer, 1925). Where the xylem has the form of a star or of a diarch plate in transections, the tracheary elements are thoroughly interconnected. If there are peripheral radiating strands terminating at the central pith, the xylem and phloem strands have here and there lateral connections with strands of their own kind. In some roots, however, the strands are apparently isolated from one another and, in some monocotyledons, also from the large central metaxylem vessel.

As seen in transections, the xylem elements at the poles are smaller in diameter than the more central ones (fig. 17.8). The transition between narrow and wide elements is usually gradual, and therefore it is difficult to draw a line of demarcation between the protoxylem and metaxylem elements on the basis of size differences. The sculpture of the secondary walls may be of little assistance too. The elongation of the axial part subjacent to apical meristem is much more limited in the root than in the shoot, and therefore the extensible types of primary xylem elements are few or absent in roots. If the two criteria, maturation of elements before completion of growth in length by the organ and the presence of more or less extensible secondary walls, are applied for the delimitation of the protoxylem (see chapters 11 and 15) in the root, the number of elements of such xylem at each pole may be quite small, sometimes limited to one. The exact morphology of the tracheary elements of the protoxylem —whether they are tracheids or vessel members—has not been definitely established. The metaxylem contains tracheids and vessel members in the angiosperms.

The structure of the primary phloem of roots is less well known than that of the xylem, and the first sieve elements of this tissue are often mistaken for secretory structures. In angiosperm roots the first mature sieve elements are easily recognized, because in contrast to the surrounding, still meristematic cells they contain only small amounts of stainable material in their lumina (plates 73, *A*, and 76, *A*, *C*). These sieve tubes differentiate on the outer periphery of the phloem strands and may not be associated with any companion cells. Their number in each strand is somewhat variable. In the more mature portions of the root other sievè tubes appear centripetally from the first (fig. 17.8). Some or all of these later sieve tubes are part of the metaphloem. They are commonly associated with companion cells. In very small roots the metaphloem may be absent. Fibers occur in the primary phloem of some plants (e.g., Papilionaceae, Annonaceae, Malvaceae; Guttenberg, 1943). The structure of the first phloem elements of gymnosperm roots is not well understood. They appear to be transitional between sieve cells and parenchyma cells (see chapter 12). The subsequently formed phloem contains elements with the usual characteristics of the primary sieve cells of gymnosperms.

The cells separating the tracheary elements from each other and from the phloem strands are apparently comparable to the vascular parenchyma occurring in the primary vascular region of the shoot. In older roots of species having no secondary growth this parenchyma often becomes sclerified (fig. 17.4 and plate 70, *A*). The pith of roots consists of parenchyma essentially similar to that located among the vascular elements, but sometimes having thinner walls (plates 70, *A*, and 73, *B*).

Certain Coniferae show a characteristic distribution of resin ducts in the primary vascular region of the seedling taproot (Guttenberg, 1943; Thomson and Sifton, 1925). The Araucariaceae have resin ducts in the primary phloem, four to five in each phloem strand in the larger roots, fewer in the smaller. In the Pinaceae there is either a single central resin duct (e.g., *Abies, Cedrus, Tsuga*) or one duct at each protoxylem pole (e.g., *Picea, Larix, Pseudotsuga*). The Taxaceae, the Taxodiaceae, and the Cupressaceae lack resin ducts in the primary vascular cylinder.

ROOT DEVELOPMENT

Histogenesis and Initial Vascularization

The apical meristem of the root and the developmental relation between it and the primary tissue systems of this organ have been dealt with in chapter 5. At somewhat variable distances from the apical initials the meristems of the epidermis, the cortex, and the vascular cylinder become delimited from each other (plate 72, *B*). In the root this delimitation is usually more precise and occurs closer to the apical initials than in the shoot. In angiosperms the boundary between the primordial cortex and the future vascular region is particularly definite because the innermost layer of the cortex repeatedly divides by periclinal walls and contributes cells toward the outside (plate 76, *A, B*), while independent cell divisions in the central part of the root are forming the vascular cylinder. The pericycle becomes distinct from the central part of the vascular cylinder usually quite close to the apical meristem (fig. 17.7).

The histogenetic terminology regarding the vascular cylinder in the roots is in an unsettled state. According to some authors, the histogenesis of this region involves a differentiation of procambial strands in a meristematic core (the plerome, see chapter 5), some forming phloem, others xylem (Guttenberg, 1943). The part not occupied by procambium is ground meristem. The pericycle, the pith (if present), and any nonvascular cells between the xylem and the phloem are derived from this ground meristem. Such interpretation seems to stress the concept that the vascular tissues of the root form, not a single bundle, but a system of strands. However, the phloem and the xylem of the root are spatially so closely associated that it is also common to treat the potential vascular region as one procambial unit (cf. Esau, 1943*a*). If such treatment is adopted, the presence of the pith in some roots could be interpreted as a differentiation of a potentially vascular meristem into ground tissue or as evidence that the procambium of such roots has the shape of a hollow cylinder enclosing some ground meristem. The position of the pericycle in the histogenetic pattern of the root is also problematical. In view of the present uncertain state of the interpretation of homologies beween the stem and the root and of the treatment of the stelar concept, it is not obvious whether the precursor of the pericycle in roots should be regarded as procambium or as ground tissue. All these terminological difficulties are clearly traceable to the circumstance that the vascular and nonvasculár tissues are not definitely separated from each other in their origin and ontogeny.

Although it may be difficult to delimit the phloic and xylary parts of the procambium of the root as separate strands, these parts show a morphologic differentiation close to the apical meristem. The prospective xylem may be early distinguished from the prospective phloem by the increasing size and vacuolation of cells (plate 76, *A*, *B*). The phloic procambium shows not merely a delay in the enlargement of cells but also a decrease in the size of cells because of repeated divisions not followed by a conspicuous cell enlargement. The vacuolation, the concomitant reduction in stainability, and the enlargement of cells in the xylary procambium usually occur in a reverse order from that followed by the maturation of the xylem cells. That is, the future metaxylem cells enlarge and vacuolate before the protoxylem cells (plate 73, *A*), although the latter are eventually the first to develop secondary walls. Because of this developmental pattern the metaxylem cells attain a larger ultimate size than the protoxylem cells. This size contrast is particularly conspicuous in the monocotyledons and in those dicotyledons whose roots lack secondary growth. In such plants the primordia of the largest metaxylem elements may be recognized among the most recent derivatives of the apical initials (plate 72; Heimsch, 1951; Young, 1933). Once these primordia are individualized, they cease dividing longitudinally and, after having undergone some transverse divisions, begin to increase in width and length, while the surrounding cells are still dividing (plate 72, *A*; Young, 1933).

The early delimitation of the phloic and xylary parts of the procambium makes vascular differentiation in the root appear simpler than in the shoot in which, at a given level, the maturation of elements overlaps with active procambial divisions that enlarge the earlier procambial strands and add new ones. As was stressed in chapter 15, the vascular ontogeny of the shoot is complex because the vascular system of this organ differentiates largely or entirely in relation to leaf primordia. In contrast, the vascular system of the root differentiates as an axial structure independent of lateral organs. Concomitantly, the recognition of the direction of differentiation of the primary vascular meristem in the root constitutes no problem. As the apical meristem adds new cells to the root, the delimitation of the procambial tissue follows into the new portions of the root. In other words, the procambium differentiates acropetally.

Judging by the available studies on root vascularization, the differentiation and maturation of the xylem and the phloem follow the procambium in its acropetal course (fig. 17.7; Esau, 1940, 1941; Heimsch, 1951). The first phloem elements are typically in advance of the first xylem elements; that is, they mature closer to the apex (cf. Esau, 1943*a*). Thus, the maturation of the first vascular elements also follows a relatively simple pattern in the root as contrasted with this phenomenon in the shoot, in which the xylem has a discontinuous initiation and a subsequent bidirectional sequence of development in relation to the leaf primordia (see chapter 15).

The timing of the maturation of the first vascular elements is related to the growth of the root as a whole (fig. 17.7). Periclinal divisions in cortex cease near the level where the sieve tubes mature. Beyond this region the root elongates rapidly (Goodwin and Stepka, 1945). The protoxylem of the root typically matures after most of the elongation is completed. At the same level or slightly farther from the apex, Casparian strips develop in the endodermis, and the epidermis forms root hairs.

There seems to be a causal relation between the rate of growth of the root and the proximity of mature elements to the apical meristem, and both are affected by environmental conditions, by the type of root, and by the developmental stage of the root. A detailed study of barley roots (Heimsch, 1951), for example, has shown that the main roots of the adventitious system which were rapidly elongating had mature tracheary elements farther from the apices than the following two kinds of roots: (1) main roots which were approaching their maximum length and (2) small lateral roots. Considering all these roots, the various vascular elements have been found maturing the following distances from the apical meristem: sieve tubes, 250 to 750 microns; protoxylem elements, 400 to 8,500 or more microns; the early metaxylem, 550 microns to 1.5 or more cm; and the large central metaxylem vessels at still greater distances.

Primary and Secondary Growth

Like stems, roots show a wide variation in the amount and characteristics of secondary growth. Some herbaceous dicotyledons lack secondary growth, others have mere vestiges of such growth, and still others produce considerable amounts of secondary tissue (plate 70, *B*). The taproot and the main branch roots of gymnosperms and arborescent dicotyledons typically have secondary growth (plate

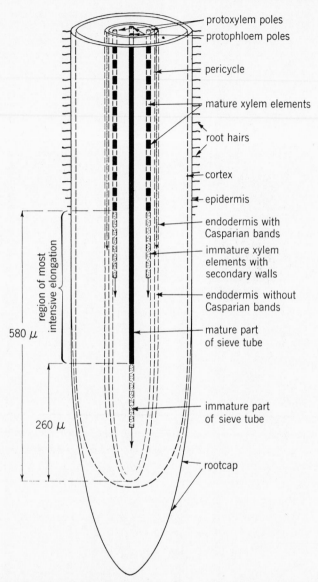

protoxylem poles

protophloem poles

pericycle

mature xylem elements

root hairs

cortex

epidermis

endodermis with
Casparian bands

immature xylem
elements with
secondary walls

endodermis without
Casparian bands

mature part
of sieve tube

immature part
of sieve tube

rootcap

region of most
intensive elongation

580 μ

260 μ

Fɪɢ. 17.7. Diagram of longitudinal section of a root tip of tobacco illustrating certain features of differentiation. The rootcap and the epidermis have common origin. The cortex and the vascular cylinder have separate initials in the apical meristem. The pericycle is delimited close to the apical meristem. Within the vascular cylinder the sieve tubes mature first. The region of most intensive elongation occurs between the levels of first mature sieve tube and first mature xylem elements. The root hairs develop beyond this region. The endodermis

70, *C, D*), but the small branch roots are devoid of it. The roots, as well as the stems, of most monocotyledons are entirely primary (plate 70, *A*). Among the monocotyledons showing secondary growth in stems, *Dracaena* has been mentioned most often as having secondary tissues in roots also (Cheadle, 1937; De Silva, 1936). The secondary tissues in roots of dicotyledons and gymnosperms are basically similar to those in the stems of the same plants, but the initiation of cambial activity has its distinctive features in the two organs in relation to the differences in the arrangement of the primary vascular tissues. The details of development of secondary tissues in roots, like that of the primary, varies in relation to type of root and environmental conditions (Nightingale, 1935).

Roots without Secondary Growth. Absence of secondary growth is characteristic of monocotyledonous roots. Several figures illustrate various stages of development of monocotyledonous roots: the delimitation of the tissue regions subjacent to the apical meristem (plate 72, *B*); the maturation of the first sieve tubes, one at each phloem pole, and the enlargement of the metaxylem elements (plate 73, *A*; compare with plate 72, *A*); the maturation of the protoxylem and the development of an endodermis with Casparian strips (plate 71). The completion of primary growth is attained with the maturation of all metaxylem and metaphloem and the sclerification of parenchyma cells associated with the vascular elements (plates 70, *A*, and 73, *B*), the development of thick secondary walls in the endodermis (figs. 17.3 and 17.4), and the differentiation of an exodermis (fig. 17.5 and plate 70, *A*). Since no secondary growth occurs, the cortex is retained and no periderm develops. The peripheral protective tissues are the epidermis and the exodermis.

A dicotyledonous root with small amount of secondary growth may be illustrated by the tetrarch root of *Ranunculus*. Figure 17.8, *B*, shows the central part of such a root at the level where the first sieve tubes and xylem elements are mature. The outermost sieve tube at each phloem pole is the protophloem sieve tube; the others are part of the metaphloem. In the xylem region the smallest outermost elements constitute the protoxylem. A uniseriate pericycle appears outside the vascular elements and is surrounded by the similarly uniseriate endodermis with Casparian strips. The central metaxylem

develops Casparian strips close to the position of the first mature xylem elements, although it is delimited before the sieve tubes mature. (Compare with plate 76, *A* and *B*.) (After Esau, 1941.)

elements have no secondary walls but are conspicuously enlarged. In figure 17.8, *C*, all the primary phloem is present. This phloem is

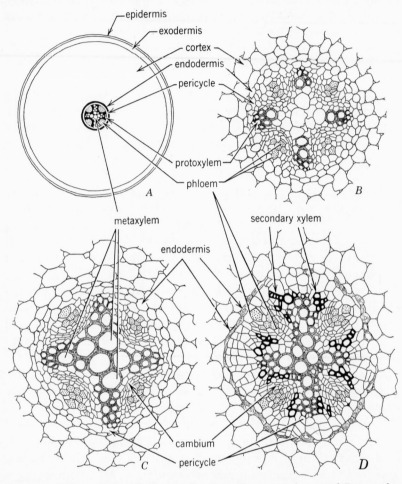

FIG. 17.8. Differentiation of the vascular tissues in a tetrarch root of *Ranunculus*. *A*, diagram of entire root in mature state. *B–D*, detailed drawings of the vascular cylinder and adjacent cortical layers in three stages of development. Further details are in the text. (*A*, ×27; *B–D*, ×150.)

composed of sieve tubes and companion cells (the sieve tubes are stippled). Some cambial divisions initiating secondary growth have occurred on the inner edges of the phloem strands. The metaxylem elements have thickened their walls. Figure 17.8, *D*, depicts the central part of the root with the primary vascular cells all mature. The cambium has produced a few cells between the phloem and the xylem. Some of these cells have differentiated into secondary tracheary elements (with walls shown in solid black); the others have remained parenchymatous. Pericyclic cells outside the xylem poles have divided. The endodermis has developed secondary walls, mainly opposite the phloem; elsewhere it has been crushed. In some *Ranunculus* roots all endodermal cells develop secondary walls. Because the secondary growth is so small in amount, the cortex is retained in the mature state (fig. 17.8, *A*). A multiseriate, relatively thin-walled exodermis differentiates in the cortex.

Roots with Secondary Growth. Secondary growth of a woody dicotyledon root is exemplified by the root of *Pyrus*, pear (Esau, 1943*b*). Figure 17.9 illustrates the growth of this root diagrammatically, and plates 74 and 75 *A, B*, give some of the histologic details. The xylary procambium becomes delimited from the phloic procambium by a decrease in density of staining (plate 74, *A*). Sieve tubes differentiate at each phloem pole (plate 74, *B*), followed by the protoxylem elements at the xylem poles (fig. 17.10 and plate 74, *C*). Centripetal differentiation of further xylem and phloem cells in successively older root parts completes the primary differentiation of the vascular tissues (plate 74, *D–F*). The late metaxylem elements enlarge relatively little and mature when the secondary growth is initiated (plate 74, *F*). The pericycle is uniseriate at first (plate 74, *B*). The endodermis, in addition to developing faintly defined Casparian strips (fig. 17.10), also accumulates considerable amounts of tanniferous compounds (plate 74, *D–F*). Tannin deposition is frequently first restricted to cells facing the phloem (plate 74, *C*). Later it spreads to all endodermal cells and also to some cortical cells farther out and to pericyclic cells (plate 74, *D–F*). The cortical cells outside the endodermis develop thickenings resembling those of a collenchyma (fig. 17.10).

The vascular cambium appears first on the inner edges of the phloem strands (fig. 17.9, *C*, and plate 74, *E*). While these cambial cells form some secondary elements, the pericyclic cells outside the protoxylem poles divide (plate 74, *F*) in a manner similar to that previously shown in the root of *Ranunculus* (fig. 17.8, *D*). The inner derivatives of these divisions complete the cylinder of cambium by joining the strips located on the inner faces of the phloem strands. The vascular cambium assumes a circular outline in transections because on the inner boundary of the phloem the secondary xylem

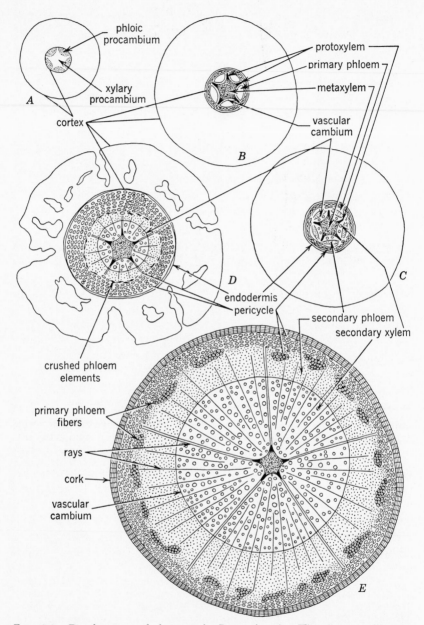

Fig. 17.9. Development of the root in *Pyrus* (pear). The diagrams illustrate five stages of development as follows: *A*, vascular cylinder in procambial state. *B*, primary growth completed. *C*, strips of vascular cambium between the phloem and the xylem have produced some secondary vascular tissues. *D*, the vascular

is deposited earlier than outside the protoxylem (fig. 17.9, *C*, *D*, and plate 74, *F*). The secondary vascular tissues assume the form of a

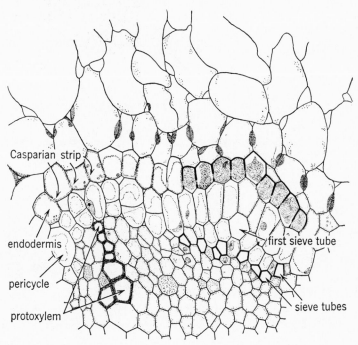

Fig. 17.10. Transection through part of pear root illustrating one phloem and one xylem pole and adjacent tissues. The drawing was made from the same section as plate 74, *C* (area in rectangle). The pericyclic cells in front of the protoxylem pole have divided tangentially. The faint areas in the radial walls of the endodermis are the sectional views of the Casparian strips. The endodermis outside the phloem has accumulated tannins. The cortical cells outside the endodermis have collenchymatous wall thickenings. ($\times$540. From Esau, 1943.)

continuous cylinder and completely imbed the primary xylem (fig. 17.9, *E*, and plate 75, *B*). The sieve elements of the primary phloem are crushed, and some of the remaining cells differentiate into fibers

cambium has assumed the shape of a cylinder and has produced secondary tissues around the entire circumference of the root; the pericycle has increased in width by periclinal divisions; the endodermis is partly crushed and the cortex is breaking down. *E*, secondary growth has progressed considerably, a periderm has been formed, and the cortex has been shed. The cambium formed in the pericycle opposite the protoxylem poles has formed wide rays (*D*, *E*). Further details are in the text and in plates 74 and 75, *A*, *B*. (All, $\times$36.)

(plate 75, *B*). The cambium which arises in the pericycle outside the xylem poles forms wide vascular rays (fig. 17.9, *E*, and plate 75, *B*).

The periclinal divisions in the pericycle which are not involved in the formation of the vascular cambium occur not only outside the xylem poles but spread around the circumference of the root (plate 75, *A*). These are divisions preparatory for the formation of the periderm. Their number varies with growth conditions (Mylius, 1913). A phellogen arises among the outer cells of the proliferated pericycle. Outwardly this phellogen forms cork tissue (fig. 17.9, *E*); inwardly it may produce phelloderm. It is difficult to distinguish between the phelloderm and the parenchyma derived from the growth of the pericycle preceding the initiation of phellogen activity. The expansion of the vascular cylinder by secondary growth causes the rupture and sloughing of the cortex together with the endodermis (fig. 17.9, *D*; compare with plate 75, *C*, *D*).

Dicotyledonous roots with a limited amount of secondary growth may retain their cortex (*Actaea, Convolvulus arvensis;* Kennedy and Crafts, 1931). Such roots may develop an exodermis or a superficial periderm (*Convolvulus arvensis*). In *Citrus sinensis* there first appears a periderm of subepidermal origin; later a deeper periderm arises in the pericycle (Hayward and Long, 1942). A tissue related to periderm and designated as polyderm has been described in certain Rosaceae, Myrtaceae, Onagraceae, and Hypericaceae (Guttenberg, 1943; Mylius, 1913). This tissue consists of rows of parenchyma interspersed with single rows of cells having Casparian strips and other wall modifications characteristic of endodermal cells. The tissue arises in the pericycle by tangential divisions and may consist of many layers, parenchyma cells alternating with endodermoid cells. With the death of the cortex, the polyderm becomes exposed to the surface.

Development of Lateral Roots

In contrast to the lateral organs of the shoot, lateral roots arise at some distance from the apical meristem and in a deep tissue region (endogenous). In both the gymnosperms and the angiosperms the branch roots commonly are initiated in the pericycle of the parent root and subsequently grow through the cortex of the latter (plate 15, *B*; Guttenberg, 1940, 1941). In the lower vascular plants the branch roots originate, as a rule, in the endodermis, although exceptions may occur (Ogura, 1938).

During the initiation of a lateral root in ,an angiosperm, a group of pericycle cells undergoes periclinal and anticlinal divisions (fig. 17.11, *A*, *B*), which eventually result in the formation of a protrusion, the lateral root primordium (fig. 17.11, *C*). By continued growth, the lateral root primordium gradually penetrates the cortex (fig. 17.6). Before the primordium emerges on the surface of the parent root, the apical meristem, the primary tissue regions of the young root axis, and the rootcap become delimited by oriented cell divisions (fig. 17.12, *A*). The apical meristem has not necessarily the same architecture as that of the parent root, but it may develop such with further growth. Regarding the mechanism of growth of the lateral root through the cortex of the parent root, some workers assume that the lateral root partly digests the cortical tissue as it advances, whereas others consider that the penetration is entirely mechanical (Guttenberg, 1940). There is common agreement, however, that the advancing lateral root forms no connection with the tissues it penetrates.

In many plants the endodermis of the parent root takes part in the initial growth of the branch root. Sometimes it undergoes only anticlinal divisions and forms a single layer on the surface of the primordium (figs. 17.11 and 17.12); sometimes it divides periclinally also and forms more than one layer. Before or soon after the lateral root emerges on the surface, the tissue derived from the endodermis dies and eventually is shed. In certain angiosperms (e.g., Cucurbitaceae, Papilionaceae, certain water plants) the innermost cortical layers, one or more, are involved in the formation of the lateral root by contributing part of the cells that become incorporated into the lateral primordium (cf. Berthon, 1943; Janczewski, 1874*b*). In such instances, the innermost layer of the cortex of the parent root is an immature endodermis. Whether or not the endodermis takes part in the formation of the lateral primordium apparently depends on the proximity of the lateral root origin to the apical meristem. If the lateral roots arise rather far from the apical meristem, at the level where some xylem is mature and the endodermis has Casparian strips (most common timing of lateral root initiation), the endodermis is little or not at all concerned with the phenomenon. If the new primordium is initiated while the endodermis is still essentially meristematic, the endodermis may be as active as the pericycle in forming the lateral organ (Berthon, 1943).

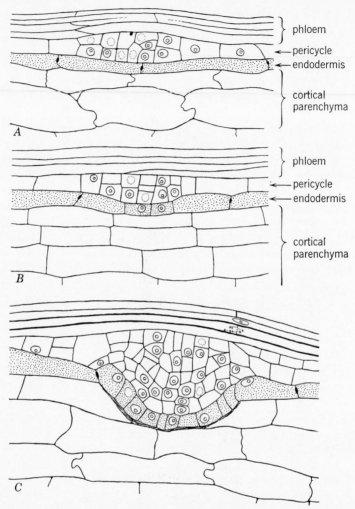

phloem
pericycle
endodermis

cortical
parenchyma

A

phloem
pericycle
endodermis

cortical
parenchyma

B

C

FIG. 17.11. Lateral root development. Longitudinal sections through young tap-roots of carrot, showing three stages in the development of a branch root. Divisions in the pericycle initiate the root primordium (*A*). The endodermis divides anticlinally and keeps pace with the growth of the primordium (*B, C*). Note the compression of cortical parenchyma cells in front of the primordium in *C*. (All, ×400. From Esau, 1940.)

There is certain regularity in the spacing of lateral roots with reference to the xylem and phloem poles of the parent root (fig. 17.6; Guttenberg, 1940). If the parent root has more than two xylem

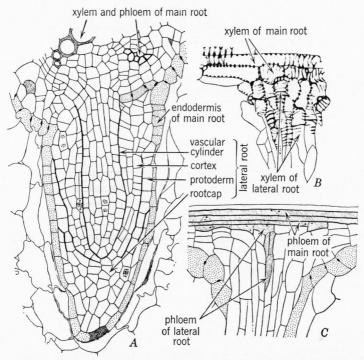

Fig. 17.12. Lateral root development. Longitudinal sections through lateral roots of carrot. *A*, entire section of a root that had not yet completely traversed the cortex of the main root. It shows organization into primary meristematic regions. The layer of endodermis enclosing the root primordium is beginning to break down. At the base of the lateral root some cells have developed Casparian strips. These cells constitute a connection between the endodermis of the main root and the prospective endodermis of the lateral root. *B* and *C*, sections through bases of lateral roots, illustrating the elements connecting the vascular tissues of the main and lateral roots. The xylem and phloem elements at the base of the lateral root are derived from pericyclic cells. (All, ×196. From Esau, 1940.)

poles, the branch roots arise either opposite these poles (most common pattern), or opposite the phloem poles (e.g., Gramineae, Cyperaceae, Juncaceae). In diarch roots the lateral primordia are formed close to the phloem poles or somewhat to the sides of the xylem poles. In roots of this kind, there may be a row of primordia on both sides of each xylem pole. Thus the number of rows of branch roots may equal the number of xylem poles or may be double that number. In the fleshy root of the carrot, additional branch roots arise at the bases of the earlier ones as the earlier ones die. They are formed in cushions of tissue of pericyclic origin (Esau, 1940; Thibault, 1946).

The vascular systems of the main and the lateral roots are delimited independently of each other, and the connection between the two is established through the intervening cells. Since the lateral root arises partly or entirely in the pericycle, the distance between its vascular region and that of the parent root is small. The intervening cells are derivatives of the pericycle. They differentiate into tracheary and sieve elements in continuity with similar elements in the main and the lateral roots (fig. 17.12, B, C). The timing of this differentiation, that is, whether vascular elements mature first nearest the vascular tissues of the main root and then successively farther into the lateral root (Rywosch, 1909), or whether some elements mature in the lateral root before the connection with the main root is established (Thibault, 1946) has not been adequately investigated.

The connection between lateral and parent roots varies in degree of complexity. In the seed plants, when the lateral root is diarch, the longer transverse diameter of its xylem plate (the diameter connecting the two xylem poles) is oriented parallel with the long axis of the parent root, and when, at the same time, the lateral root faces a protoxylem pole of the main root, there is a most direct connection between the xylem systems of the two roots. The two phloem strands of such a branch root are united with two phloem poles of the parent root. If the lateral root is formed between a xylem and a phloem pole of the main root, it is connected to these two poles. In the monocotyledons the xylem of the lateral root is often joined to two or more xylem strands of the main root (e.g., Monstera; Guttenberg, 1940; Rywosch, 1909). Moreover, the connection may occur not only with the peripheral xylem strands but also with the innermost large metaxylem vessels through the modification into tracheary elements of the vascular parenchyma cells intervening between the peripheral strands and the late metaxylem vessels (Rywosch, 1909). Such differentiation may extend considerably to the sides of the actual insertion of the lateral root. Thus, sometimes the insertion of a lateral root has a marked although localized influence upon the structure of the vascular cylinder of the parent root (Fourcroy, 1942). In plants with secondary growth, the secondary tissues of the main and the lateral roots differentiate in continuity with each other, and the xylem of the bases of the lateral roots is imbedded in the xylem of the main root.

Development of Adventitious Roots

Adventitious roots, in the wide sense of the term as adopted on p. 472, may occur on the hypocotyl of a seedling, at nodes and internodes of stems, and in roots. They may arise in connection with buds or independently (Bannan, 1942; Carlson, 1938; Guttenberg, 1940; Van der Lek, 1924). They may be formed in young organs (e.g., embryos and intercalary meristems in Gramineae) or in older tissues that have not lost their meristematic potentialities. Most adventitious roots arise endogenously, although examples of exogenous origin are known also (Guttenberg, 1940; Hayward, 1938, p. 54; McVeigh, 1938). Adventitious roots may arise from primordia laid down previously and remaining dormant until stimulated to growth, or they may be new formations (Carlson, 1938, 1950; Siegler and Bowman, 1939; Van der Lek, 1924).

Stem-borne adventitious roots constitute the main vascular system in lower vascular plants, in most monocotyledons, in dicotyledons propagating by means of rhizomes or runners, in water plants, in saprophytes, and in parasites. Roots that form on cuttings, directly from the stem or from the callus tissue, are also adventitious. The subject of adventitious roots in cuttings has been considerably explored, particularly in connection with the research on growth-promoting substances (Carlson, 1950; Swingle, 1940; Van der Lek, 1924).

The principal histologic aspects of the origin of adventitious roots may be summed up in a statement that such roots usually are initiated in the vicinity of differentiating vascular tissues of the organ which gives rise to them (Datta and Majumdar, 1943; Priestley and Swingle, 1929; Siegler and Bowman, 1939; Smith, 1942; Swingle, 1940). If the organ is young, the adventitious primordium is initiated by a group of cells near the periphery of the vascular system. If it is older, the seat of this origin is located deeper, near the vascular cambium. In young stems, the cells forming the root primordium are commonly derived from the interfascicular parenchyma; in older stems, from a vascular ray. Sometimes the adventitious roots appear to be initiated by divisions in the cambial zone (Smith, 1936). Often the seat of the first divisions forming a root primordium in stems is identified in the literature as pericycle. As has been discussed in chapter 15, in many stems the region formerly defined as pericycle is, by origin, part of the primary phloem or the interfascicular parenchyma between two parts of the primary phloem. The origin of the adventitious roots in the interfascicular region, in the vascular ray, or in the cambium places the young root close to both the xylem and the phloem of the parent axis and facilitates the establishment of vascular connection between the two organs.

The organization of the apical meristem of the adventitious root, of its rootcap, and of the vascular connection with the main axis parallels similar phenomena associated with the origin of a lateral root. There is also the same problem of mechanics of emergence of the adventitious root to the surface through the peripheral tissues of the parent axis; this problem still awaits solution.

STRUCTURE OF THE ROOT IN RELATION TO FUNCTION

The Root as an Absorbing Organ

Many studies have been carried out to determine the part of the root concerned with the intake of water and salts (Kramer, 1945, 1949), but only a few have attempted, at the same time, to consider accurately the structure of the absorbing zone. Workers agree that absorption of water and salts occurs mainly in the young part of the root that has not passed beyond the development of the primary state. This primary development involves various phenomena of growth and differentiation, changing from level to level between the apical meristem and the mature primary structure. Therefore, the zone engaged in absorption is structurally heterogeneous, and, since it is also growing, it is constantly changing in its structural and physiologic characteristics. The assumptions are justified, and are supported by experimental evidence, that at least certain phenomena of absorption are dependent on metabolic activity associated with growth and that the factors determining salt intake are not necessarily the same as those responsible for the entry of water (Hoagland, 1937).

The common opinion is that little water enters through the rootcap and the apical meristem (Kramer, 1945). In plants grown in culture solutions the maximum rates of absorption of water are usually observed several centimeters from the apical meristem (Hayward et al., 1942; Hayward and Spurr, 1943; Kramer, 1945; Rosene,

1937, 1941). At this level, *Zea* roots were found to have mature or almost mature primary xylem (Hayward and Spurr, 1943).

The distribution of the rates of water absorption along the root is known to vary in relation to the length of the root, its age, and other internal conditions (Kramer, 1945). Some of these variations are probably associated with structural differences. Thus, when growth slows down at the approach of winter, the absorbing zone may be eliminated completely by the formation of various impermeable layers. A suberized exodermis and an endodermis develop to within a short distance of the apical meristem, and fatty substances appear in the superficial rootcap cells and in the epidermal cells intervening between the suberized exodermis and the rootcap (Guttenberg, 1943; Hayward and Long, 1942; Müller, 1906; Scott and Priestley, 1928). The difference between slowly and rapidly growing roots with regard to proximity of mature xylem to the apical meristem (see p. 491) might also be related to variable rates of absorption. The intake of soil solution is a particularly outstanding function of young roots. Some experimental evidence, however, suggests that to a limited extent this activity may occur also in older root parts where secondary vascular tissues are present and the surface is covered by periderm (Kramer, 1949).

The most intensive accumulation of salts appears to take place close to the apical meristem where cells may be expected to be concerned mainly with division and enlargement (Jacobson and Overstreet, 1947; Overstreet and Jacobson, 1946; Prevot and Steward, 1936; Steward et al., 1942). The experiments supporting this conclusion do not prove, however, that the most active absorption occurs necessarily at the same level as the most intense accumulation.

The root hairs are usually interpreted as structures substantially increasing the absorbing surface of the roots (Farr, 1928; Kramer, 1945; see also chapter 7). In agreement with this concept, the root hairs come to their full development in the root zone where the most active absorption of water takes place. The ability of these structures to absorb water has been demonstrated experimentally, but hairless epidermal cells are also capable of absorbing water (Rosene, 1943).

The structure of the root is of particular interest with regard to the movement of water and salts from the absorbing cells to the conducting tissues, and their release from the living cells of the vascular cylinder into the nonliving tracheary elements. Figure 17.13 illustrates the pathway of the soil solution in the root by means of a drawing of a part of a wheat root in transection. The arrows indicate the direction of movement in certain selected cells. Among these the living cells are stippled. The most notable features of this pathway are: (1) the presence of abundant intercellular spaces in the cortex, (2) the lack of such spaces in the vascular cylinder, and (3) the presence of a specialized endodermis between the two systems.

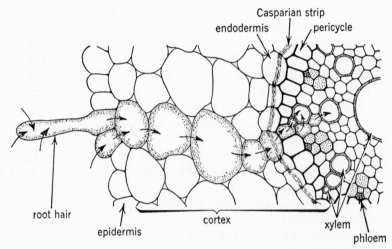

FIG. 17.13. Part of transection of wheat root, illustrating the kinds of cell that may be traversed by water and salts absorbed from the soil before they reach the tracheary elements of the xylem. The arrows indicate the direction of the movement through a selected series of cells. Among these, the living cells are partly stippled. The Casparian strip in the endodermis is shown as though exposed in surface views of the end walls. (×330.)

Some investigators stress the contrasting environments of the cortex and of the vascular cylinder. The well-aerated cortex is high in metabolic activity and capable of accumulating salts; the poorly aerated vascular cylinder is low in activity and unable to hold salts (Crafts and Broyer, 1938). The endodermis located between the two distinct systems acts as a barrier that facilitates the development of hydrostatic pressure in the vascular cylinder by preventing a leakage of solutes from the vascular cylinder into the cortex and thereby also having to do with the entry of the solutes into the nonliving tracheary cells. The fatty materials of the Casparian strip are supposed to hinder the movement of substances through the walls, whereas the connection of the cytoplasm to the strip prevents the passage between the protoplast and the wall. Hence, all materials crossing the endodermis would be forced to pass the living protoplasm and be subjected to its regulatory activity. (See also Strugger, 1939–46.)

Many primary features of the root seem to be associated with absorption. Numerous investigations show that, during the period of active absorption by the plant, new primary root areas bearing functional root hairs are constantly added by growth (Kramer, 1945). Furthermore, the extensive branching characteristic of most roots is responsible for the presence of numerous apical meristems that produce new primary root tissues and extend the existing ones. Quite commonly, plants with well-developed root systems produce special absorbing roots that are periodically renewed. All these developmental features are important not only because they create new absorbing surfaces but also because they bring these surfaces into contact with new areas of soil (Farr, 1928; Kramer, 1945).

The Root as a Storage Organ

Roots of ordinary structure are important storage organs of the plant; in addition, roots may become specifically adapted for this function by distinct developmental peculiarities. Primary roots store food, notably starch, in the cortex, which is often wide. In roots having a limited amount of secondary growth, the cortex may remain as a storage tissue (e.g., morning glory, Kennedy and Crafts, 1931). The secondary tissues of the root accumulate starch in the same kind of cells as those of the stem, that is, in various parenchymatous and some sclerenchymatous cells of the xylem and the phloem. In general, roots possess a higher proportion of parenchyma cells than do stems.

The special adaptations for storage are commonly expressed in the development of fleshy bodies in parts of the root system. Frequently, the hypocotyl and the base of the taproot form jointly one fleshy structure (e.g., *Daucus*, *Pastinaca*, *Beta*). Some fleshy organs have large amounts of storage parenchyma associated with an otherwise ordinary arrangement of tissues. This type of development is exemplified by the carrot, in which the hypocotyl and the upper part of the taproot, after sloughing off the cortex in a normal manner, become fleshy through a massive development of parenchyma in the phloem and the xylem (Esau, 1940).

In contrast to the carrot, the sugar beet forms its fleshy hypocoytl-root organ by anomalous growth (Artschwager, 1926; Seeliger, 1919;

see also chapter 15). Both the table beet and the sugar beet show a usual type of primary and early secondary development. Later, however, a series of supernumerary cambia arise outside the normal vascular core and produce several increments of vascular tissue, each consisting of a layer of parenchyma, parenchymatous xylem and parenchymatous phloem (plate 77). Sugar occurs as a storage product in parenchyma cells, particularly those closely associated with the vascular elements.

Anomalous growth of a different kind is found in the sweet potato, *Ipomoea batatas* (Hayward, 1938). In the normally developed but highly parenchymatous primary and secondary xylem, anomalous cambia arise around individual vessels or vessel groups and produce phloem rich in parenchyma and with some laticifers away from the vessels, and tracheary elements toward them. The fleshy roots, the rhizomes, and the stems of many Cruciferae (turnip, radish, kohlrabi, rutabaga, and others) show a proliferation of parenchyma in the pith (if pith is present) and in the secondary xylem, and a differentiation of concentric vascular bundles within this parenchyma (Hayward, 1938; Lund and Kiaerskou, 1885; Soeding, 1924; Weiss, 1880).

Despite their variations in structure, the storage organs all have in common an abundance of parenchyma and a thorough permeation of this parenchyma with vascular elements. The close association between the two kinds of tissues may be brought about by (1) a proliferation of the parenchyma among the normally located vascular elements, (2) a massive development of parenchyma followed by a differentiation of additional vascular elements in this parenchyma, or (3) a development of whole new systems of parenchyma-vascular tissues outside the normally placed system of the same kind.

The Root as an Anchorage Organ

The well-known function of the root as an organ fastening the plant to the soil need not be emphasized here. The development of sclerenchyma in the old root leads to the formation of a strong rigid anchorage organ, but the firm attachment to the soil is also dependent upon the development of the many branches in the branched type of a root system and of the many adventitious roots in the fibrous type. Of the two types of systems the fibrous generally penetrates the soil less deeply but binds the surface soil more tightly than the branched type (Dittmer, 1940). The root hairs, too, play a part in binding the soil (Dittmer, 1948). They are particularly efficient in anchoring young plants and preventing their being pushed upward by the growth of the root apex (Farr, 1928). One aspect of the anchorage of the plant to the soil deserving the anatomist's attention is the contraction of roots that during a certain stage of development of the plant draws the shoot apex near or below the ground level and places it in an optimal environment for growth and for development of adventitious roots. Root contraction is a common phenomenon and is widely distributed among herbaceous perennial dicotyledons and monocotyledons (Arber, 1925; Gravis, 1926; Rimbach, 1929). In one study, the contraction of roots was recorded, by actual testing, in 450 species of 315 genera in 82 families (1 gymnosperm family, 15 monocotyledonous, 66 dicotyledonous; Rimbach, 1929). The Gramineae appear to lack contractile roots (Arber, 1934). Examples of well-known economic plants showing root contraction are alfalfa (Jones, 1928), sugar beet, carrot, and sweet clover (Bottum, 1941). Contraction of roots is also observed in the bulbous monocotyledons which draw the bulbs to considerable depths into the soil. In *Rubus* the terminal bud may become rooted when it is brought into contact with the soil and is subsequently pulled into the ground by a shortening of the roots (Rimbach, 1898).

The contraction occurs in taproots, in lateral roots, and in adventitious roots. In root parts showing maximum contraction, 10 to 70 per cent shortening has been reported (Rimbach, 1898). The contraction begins soon after the elongation of the root is completed and continues for variable lengths of time. In some plants it continues from 1 to 5 months, and in *Taraxacum* it is said to occur for years in the same root (Rimbach, 1898). In some plants only certain of the roots undergo contraction, and these are rather specialized morphologically; in others, no morphologic differentiation of contractile roots occurs. The highly specialized contractile roots, or contractile root parts, exhibit histologic peculiarities. They show relatively little lignification, have a high proportion of parenchyma, and, in general, appear little differentiated. Noncontractile roots undergo most of their primary thickening during elongation. Contractile roots thicken during the contraction, that is, after the elongation is completed, and may become twice as thick as they were before contraction (Rimbach, 1932). In some species this thickening is associated with the development of the root as a storage organ (fig. 17.14, *A, B; Melilotus, Asparagus officinalis;* Bottum, 1941; Rimbach, 1899); in others the parenchyma collapses with age and the root appears wrinkled.

Apparently the histologic details of root contraction vary considerably in different plants. In some (e.g., *Medicago, Melilotus,* sugar beet) a radial extension of parenchyma cells and an assumption of a sinuous course by the lignified tissues (particularly of the central xylem core; fig. 17.14, *C*) have been observed in connection

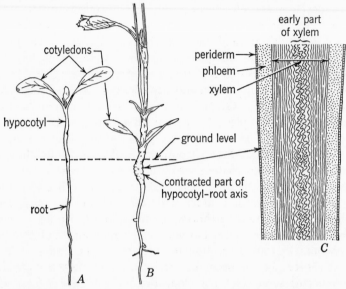

Fig. 17.14. Illustration of root contraction. *A* and *B*, habit sketches of alfalfa (*Medicago sativa*) seedlings. The younger seedling in *A* bears its cotyledons high above the ground level; the older seedling in *B* has pulled the cotyledons close to the ground by contracting the hypocotyl and the upper part of the root. The contracted part is considerably thickened. *C*, drawing of a cleared longitudinal section of an alfalfa root. The central xylem system (consisting of primary and some secondary xylem) became undulate after the contraction of the root. (*A, B*, drawn by R. H. Miller.)

with root shortening (Bottum, 1941; Jones, 1928; Rimbach, 1929). One must postulate that in these plants the radial extension of the parenchyma cells is combined with their vertical contraction. In some monocotyledons the contraction has been found restricted to the inner cortex, the outer cortex dying and becoming wrinkled (Rimbach, 1929). In the Umbelliferae certain cell groups, located among those that are expanding radially, die and collapse. This change in the volume of the tissue apparently permits the mutual adjustment between the expanding cells and those elements that are oriented longitudinally and are undergoing a bending (Berckemeyer,

1929). In certain species of *Oxalis* the collapsing cells occur in transverse zones, and the reduction in length of the root is thought to result from a reduction in volume rather than from growth phenomena (Davey, 1946; Thoday and Davey, 1932).

COMPARATIVE STRUCTURE OF SHOOT AND ROOT

Primary Body

The preceding pages of this chapter give ample evidence that the root has many distinctive characteristics differentiating it from the shoot, particularly in the seed plants. It will be useful to assemble the data comparing the two organs. The dissimilarities between the root and the shoot are evident in their earliest stages of development. The apical meristem of the shoot is truly apical, for it occupies a superficial position; that of the root is subterminal, for it is covered by the rootcap. The architecture of the two meristems differs also in that the relation between the regions of the primary body and the apical initials is often more precise in the root than in the shoot. It is not uncommon, for example, that in the root the vascular cylinder and the cortex have separate initials, whereas in the stem these two tissue regions are closely related in their early ontogeny. The leaf primordia arise directly from the apical meristem of the shoot, and the branches more or less directly; and both are exogenous. The lateral roots arise independently of the apical meristem and are endogenous.

In the higher vascular plants the vascular system of the shoot differentiates largely or entirely in relation to the leaves. The root develops its vascular system as an axial structure independent of the lateral organs. The lack of influence of the lateral organs upon the organization of the root is also reflected in the absence of a segmentation into nodes and internodes in the root. Leaf gaps and pith are characteristic of the vascular cylinder in the stems, except in certain lower vascular plants. There are no gaps in the root and frequently no pith.

The primary vascular tissues of the shoot are commonly arranged in the form of more or less discrete bundles, each containing both xylem and phloem, in collateral or in bicollateral combinations. The root lacks vascular bundles, in the sense of units combining xylem and phloem, but develops radially alternate phloem and xylem strands, the latter being discrete or united in the center into one continuous body. In the seed plants the root and the stem contrast strikingly with regard to the direction of differentiation of primary xylem in the horizontal plane. This direction is centrifugal in the shoot (endarch xylem) and centripetal in the root (exarch xylem). In lower vascular plants (i.e., Psilopsida and Lycopsida) the primary xylem is exarch in both root and stem (cf. Foster, 1949, p. 204), in ferns, commonly mesarch in the stem.

The boundaries between the tissue systems are quite precise in the root. The vascular cylinder forms a compact core delimited from the cortex by an endodermis and surrounded by a distinct nonvascular tissue region, the pericycle. In the stem of the higher vascular plants, the vascular tissues are not compactly arranged, a specialized endodermis is rare, and commonly no distinct region meriting the special name of pericycle occurs between the cortex and the vascular tissues. The difference in the precision of tissue delimitation is evident in the two organs of the same plant, and, therefore, if the tissue regions are followed upward from the root, their limits will appear more diffuse as the level of the shoot is approached.

The root and the stem show some differences in the manner of primary growth. The root has a shorter elongation region than the shoot, and a sharper transition between the region of small, actively dividing cells and that composed of large, expanding cells (Sinnott and Bloch, 1941). Concomitantly with the small amount of elongation, the root frequently develops no extensible types of protoxylem elements (with annular and helical secondary walls), whereas in the shoot such elements are common.

Secondary Body

Whereas the primary bodies of the shoot and the root show fundamental differences, which can be traced directly into the meristems, the secondary bodies of the two organs are much alike in both origin and structure, and the existing differences are of a quantitative rather than a qualitative kind. The secondary vascular tissues of the root commonly have a greater proportion of living to nonliving cells than similar tissues in the stem (Beakbane, 1941; Liese, 1924; Riedl, 1937). This difference appears to be related to the different environments under which the root and the stem develop, for the underground stems (rhizomes) have more similarities with roots than with stems in the structure of their secondary tissues. Furthermore, root and stem can be made to produce tissues resembling those of the opposite organ by reversing their environmental conditions, that is, by exposing the root to an aerial environment and, contrarily, burying the stems in the soil (Bannan, 1934; Beakbane, 1941). The quantitative nature of the difference is also suggested by its variability in the roots of the same plants. In conifer roots, for example, the secondary xylem may differ more and less from that in the stem, depending on the part of the root system in which it occurs (Bannan, 1941).

In detail, the differences between the structure of secondary vascular tissues of stem and root may be enumerated as follows. Compared with the stem, the root may have: a higher bark-to-wood ratio (assuming that the bark includes all extracambial tissues; see chapter 14); a lower percentage of area of bark occupied by fibers; a smaller number of fibers in the xylem; larger vessels of more uniform size, although sometimes fewer in numbers; a poor differentiation of growth increments; in the gymnosperms, wider and longer tracheids with multiseriate arrangement of pits and frequent occurrence of pits on tangenital walls; larger ratio of area of living cells to area of nonliving cells in both the phloem and the xylem; more starch; and less tanniferous substances. The rays of the secondary body are also distinct in stems and roots (Barghoorn, 1940a, b; Riedl, 1937). The loss of ray initials is less pronounced in roots than in stems. This difference results in the establishment of a larger volume of ray tissue in the root, expressed in a larger number and larger size of rays. Disregarding some exceptions, the first periderm of the roots arises in the pericycle, that of the stem in the peripheral layers of the axis.

VASCULAR CONNECTION BETWEEN THE SHOOT AND THE ROOT

Concept of the Transition Region

The connection between the morphologically distinct primary vascular systems of the shoot and the root in the seed plants is of interest from the developmental as well as from the phylogenetic viewpoint and is, therefore, extensively treated in the botanical literature. Since this connection involves spatial adjustments between systems with differently oriented parts and with different directions of differentiation in the horizontal plane, it shows some features that are intermediate or transitional between those of the shoot and the root. The change from one type of structure to the other, as viewed in successive levels of the root-shoot connection, is commonly called vascular transition, and the region of the plant axis where it occurs is called the transition region.

As was shown in chapters 1 and 15, the shoot of a higher vascular plant arises at one end of the embryo axis (the hypocotyl), the root at the other. Accordingly, the connection between the two is established through the hypocotyl. The basic features of this connection are delimited in the form of a procambial system during the development of the embryo (Miller and Wetmore, 1945; Spurr, 1950). The differentiation of the vascular elements from the procambial cells follows the delimitation of the procambium (it may begin during the development of the embryo or after germination). Its sequence and direction are determined not only by the form of the initial procambial pattern but also by the distribution of growth in the different parts of the seedling. Therefore, a proper understanding of the transition region may be gained only if this plant part is studied throughout its development. Most of the literature on vascular transition deals with partly differentiated seedlings, so that despite its volume it gives only a partial picture of the phenomenon.

Although the structure of the transition region is variable in the different groups of plants and is generally complex, an understanding of this structure has been unnecessarily obscured by the interpretation that there is a transition between the root and the stem (Eames and MacDaniels, 1947), rather than between the root on the one hand, and the cotyledons and the epicotylary shoot on the other. The transition region represents a connection, not between two axial organs with somewhat different arrangements of tissues, but between an organ with an axial vascular system and one whose vascular system develops in relation to leaves. A study of the transition region must, therefore, explain the relation between the vascular system of the root and the traces of the first foliar organs of the plant.

Structure of the Transition Region

In most dicotyledons and gymnosperms, the characteristics intermediate between those of the vascular systems of root and shoot are present within the system connecting the root and the cotyledons (Chauveaud, 1911; Guttenberg, 1941; Hill and de Fraine, 1908–10; Thomas, 1914). In other words, the transition in these plants occurs between the root and the cotyledons. Whereas the root has a more or less compact core of vascular tissue, the levels intermediate between the root and the cotyledonary node show strands diverging above into the cotyledons. Using the concept of leaf traces, one can say that in the transition region the cotyledonary traces diverge from the vascular system of the root. This divergence differs from that of the leaf traces in the shoot in that the cotyledonary traces are connected with a system with exarch xylem and an alternate arrangement of xylem and phloem. The cotyledonary traces are more or less affected in their structure by this association. The matter may be explained best by a simple example.

The seedling in fig. 17.15 has two cotyledons, a small epicotylary shoot between the cotyledons, a hypocotyl, and a root with a diarch xylem plate flanked on both sides by phloem strands. Each cotyledon has, in median position, a double vascular bundle composed of two partially merged strands. Such structure of the median cotyledonary strands is common in various groups of plants (Hill and de Fraine, 1913; Thomas, 1907, 1914). In some seedlings the double nature of the median strand may be less pronounced than in fig. 17.15, in others more pronounced, and in still others there may be two separate strands in median position. The double nature of the median cotyledonary strands is considered to have phylogenetic significance.

The median parts of the cotyledons are located in direct line above the protoxylem poles. In the root the xylem is strictly centripetal in its differentiation, the metaxylem occupying the center. In the lower parts of the hypocotyl the protoxylem maintains its peripheral position, but the metaxylem, instead of differentiating toward the center, diverges laterally from the protoxylem. Such order of differentiation leaves the center of the axis unoccupied by vascular elements. In other words, a pith differentiates in this part of the seedling. At successively higher levels the distance between the protoxylem poles increases, for the hypocotyl axis widens toward the cotyledonary node. Concomitantly, the plates of metaxylem associated with each protoxylem pole do not join in the intercotyledonary plane. Thus, instead of one xylem plate as in the root, there are, higher up, two distinct xylem complexes, each pertaining to one double cotyledonary trace. In the upper hypocotyl and in the bases of the cotyledons the direction of xylem differentiation is such that in each cotyledonary trace the protoxylem pole occupies a deeper position in the axis than the metaxylem. This orientation signifies that the xylem approaches the endarch condition. It is entirely endarch still higher in each cotyledon, where the metaxylem differentiates, not in the form of two diverging plates, but as one double plate directed outwardly from the protoxylem pole. Thus fig. 17.15 illustrates the transition from exarch to endarch xylem.

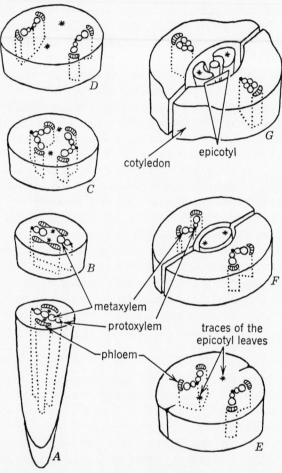

Fig. 17.15. Diagrams illustrating the connection between the root and the cotyledons (the transition region) in a dicotyledonous seedling (*Beta vulgaris*). The root is diarch (*A*). The primary vascular system of the root diverges, above, into the two cotyledons. Further explanations are in the text.

The differences in the orientation of the phloem at various levels of the seedling are less pronounced than those of the xylem. Instead of the two phloem strands appearing in the root, there are four in the hypocotyl. Considering the structure from the base upward, one could say that the phloem branches, each phloem strand of the root giving two branches in the hypocotyl. Each of the four hypocotylary phloem strands is associated with one metaxylem plate (fig. 17.15, C). In the part of each cotyledon where the xylem is endarch, the phloem differentiates as one mass on the abaxial side of the double cotyledonary bundle. This bundle is, therefore, collateral. Thus fig. 17.15 shows the transition from the radially alternate arrangement in the root to the collateral in the cotyledons.

The epicotylary shoot of seedlings having such a transition region as that depicted in fig. 17.15 develops after the primary vascular system of the root-hypocotyl-cotyledon unit is delimited and partly differentiated. The traces of the first two leaf primordia of the epicotyl (these usually appear almost at the same time, opposite each other and alternating with the cotyledons) alternate with the cotyledonary traces in the hypocotyl, and all these traces together encircle a central pith. In the root, where the xylem of the cotyledonary traces is merged with the diarch primary xylem plate, the vascular tissues of the epicotylary traces are prolonged directly without change in orientation along the flanks of the diarch plate and along the inner margins of the primary phloem strands. In other words, the epicotylary traces are connected with the part of the xylem that occurs on the flanks of the diarch plate and with the part of the phloem developing centripetally from the initial phloem. These tissues may be entirely secondary or partly secondary and partly primary. The traces of the first leaves on the epicotyl are collateral and have endarch xylem. Since they are connected in the root with similarly oriented tissues, there is no transition between the root and the epicotyl in the type of seedling depicted in fig. 17.15, but rather a simple direct connection between similarly oriented tissues. The epicotyl seems to be superimposed over the initially complete root-hypocotyl-cotyledon unit.

The type of transition region just described is common among the dicotyledons. However, there are many deviations from this type. Seedlings may have several traces to each cotyledon, one double median and two or more lateral. Frequently, the lateral traces are relatively small and are connected with the root in a manner described for the epicotylary traces in the preceding paragraphs, that is, without any change in the orientation of tissues. The cotyledon-root connection varies also in relation to the structure of the vascular system of the root. If, for example, this vascular system has tetrarch xylem, two of the xylem poles may be continuous with two median cotyledonary traces, the other two with the two pairs of the lateral cotyledonary traces. In some plants, like the Cucurbitaceae, each cotyledon has many vascular bundles and a highly complex vascular system in the transition region (Hayward, 1938).

The epicotyl-root relation also varies in the dicotyledons, and apparently the closeness of connection between the two parts depends on the timing in the development of the epicotyl. If it initiates leaf primordia relatively early, the first traces may be connected with the primary tissues of the root; if the foliar organs appear later, the connection is formed with the secondary tissues (Compton, 1912*a*; see also fig. 17.15). In some plants the epicotyl is connected with the root apparently only indirectly through the cotyledonary traces (certain Cucurbitaceae, Hufford, 1938; Whiting, 1938; *Cynara*, Phillips, 1937). A notable deviation in the vascular transition is found in the dicotyledons with hypogeous cotyledons, that is, cotyledons remaining below the surface of the ground after germination. Such method of germination is well exemplified by certain Leguminosae (*Pisum sativum, Vicia sativa, Vicia faba, Lens esculenta, Cicer arietinum*). In the representatives of this group of Leguminosae the traces of the first foliage leaves may be connected with the primary vascular tissues of the root. Depending on the closeness of connection between the root and the epicotyl, the transitional characteristics of the vascular system are extended more or less far into the epicotylary shoot, sometimes through more than one internode (Compton, 1912*a*; Muller, 1937).

Evidently the extent of the dicotyledonous seedling axis which shows the features of transition is variable. The transition region, in other words, may be short or long; or, with reference to the position of the root, it may be high or low. In some plants transitional characteristics are evident throughout the hypocotyl; in others they are restricted to the upper hypocotyl and part of the cotyledons. In the latter types of seedlings the hypocotyl is said to have root structure. In the seedlings with hypogeous cotyledons the transition region is particularly long, for it extends into one or more of the internodes above the cotyledons.

The specific characteristics of the vascular transition in the monocotyledons are related to the presence of a single cotyledon and the shortness of the lower internodes. The latter feature is probably the main cause of the frequently close connection between the epicotyl and the root in this group of plants (Arber, 1925). In many monocotyledons one part of the root system is connected with the cotyledon, the other with the first leaf of the epicotyl, and both connections exhibit transitional features (e.g., *Allium cepa*, Hayward, 1938; *Asparagus officinalis*, Mullendore, 1935; palms, Drabble, 1906). However, in some of the monocotyledons the transition occurs, like in so many dicotyledons, only between the root and the cotyledon, with the whole primary vascular system of the root prolonged into the single cotyledon (*Anemarrhena*, Arber, 1925).

The transition region of the Gramineae is particularly complex (Avery, 1930; Boyd and Avery, 1936; McCall, 1934), because the vascular system of the root is connected with more than one leaf above the scutellum, which many workers consider to be the single cotyledon in this group of plants. The vascular transition of *Triticum* may be used as an example (fig. 17.16; Boyd and Avery, 1936). The polyarch vascular cylinder of the root is connected with the vascular system of the foliar organs through the plate-like vascular system located below the insertion of the scutellum (nodal plate of the scutellum according to some authors). The vascular tissue prolonged upward from the nodal plate is separated into strands which, at lower levels, show irregular arrangement and transitional features and, at higher levels, form a hollow cylinder, all parts of which have endarch xylem and collateral arrangement of xylem and phloem. This system consists of traces and trace complexes of the scutellum, the coleoptile, and the first and second foliage leaves. Thus, there is a relatively abrupt transition from the vascular cylinder of the root with exarch xylem and alternate arrangement of xylem and phloem, and a system of leaf traces with endarch xylem and collateral arrangement of xylem and phloem.

The transition region of the gymnosperms resembles that of many dicotyledons in that it represents primarily a connection between the root and the cotyledons (Guttenberg, 1941; Hill and de Fraine, 1908–10). The variations in the structure of the transition region in these plants result, in part, from the variable numbers of cotyledons and of traces to each cotyledon. A similar direct continuity between the vascular tissue of the root and that of the first leaves exists also in the sporelings of the lower vascular plants (Campbell, 1921; Hill and de Fraine, 1913).

The vascular system showing transitional characteristics is entirely primary. When cambial activity occurs in plants having secondary growth, the secondary tissues are formed in complete continuity between the stem and the root (fig. 1.2). The vascular cambium arises in the same position, between the metaxylem and metaphloem, in the root, the hypocotyl, and the epicotyl and produces derivatives

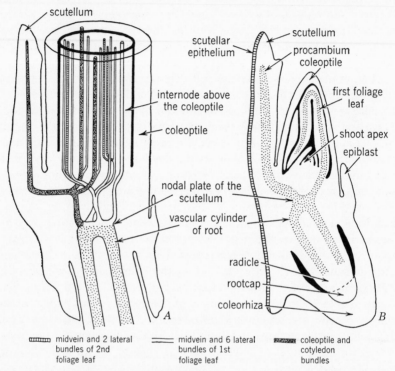

| ▭ midvein and 2 lateral bundles of 2nd foliage leaf | ▭ midvein and 6 lateral bundles of 1st foliage leaf | ▭ coleoptile and cotyledon bundles |

Fig. 17.16. Diagrams of longitudinal sections of the transition region of wheat seedling (*A*) and of an entire wheat embryo (*B*). The scutellum of the embryo is the cotyledon. Its epithelial surface is appressed to the endosperm in the seed. (Cf. fig. 19.2.) The epicotylary shoot is enclosed by the coleoptile, the radicle by the coleorhiza. (*B*, ×35. *A*, after Boyd and Avery, 1936; *B*, adapted from McCall, 1934.)

in the same direction, phloem toward the outside, xylem toward the inside, in all three parts of the plant. Thus, the secondary growth obscures the initial differences in the structure of root, hypocotyl, and epicotyl. Moreover, it separates the primary phloem from the primary xylem by carrying the primary phloem outward and leaves only the xylem pattern of the transition region buried in the center of the axis.

Morphologic Significance of the Transition Region

The peculiar structure of the transition region makes it difficult to classify this part in relation to the other organs of the plant. As a result, more than one theory has been formulated with reference to the structural and evolutionary significance of this region of the plant (cf. Compton, 1912*b*; Duchaigne, 1950). One common concept is that the seedling plant has a unit vascular system, morphologically equivalent in all its parts, and that the difference in orientation of its parts at the various levels may be described, figuratively, as branching, twisting, rotation, and inversion (e.g., Eames and Mac-Daniels, 1947; Lenoir, 1920; Van Tieghem, 1891*a*). The proponents of this concept recognize that the elements differentiate in the same positions where they occur in the mature state and use the expressions implying motion of parts merely to emphasize the unity of the system. The opposite view is that the seedling system is initially discontinuous, consisting of a radicular hypocotylary part on the one hand, and a cotyledonary part on the other, and that the two are joined in the upper hypocotyl (Dangeard, 1889, 1913).

A double origin of the vascular system of the seedling is also postulated in a physiologic interpretation of the transition region (Thoday, 1939). The seedling is pictured as having a unique structure in that it consists of a short axis bearing at opposite ends, but at close proximity to each other, two self-determining centers of different kind. Each of these two opposite poles, the shoot pole and the root pole, is capable of impressing its own inherent pattern on the meristematic tissues to which it gives rise. The cotyledons, and, if the epicotyl is precocious, the first foliar primordia also, influence the structure of the upper part of the seedling axis, and the root leaves its impression at the base of it. In the intervening region the two patterns are mutually accommodated.

One of the most elaborately developed theories postulates that, from the evolutionary standpoint, the different arrangements of the vascular system in the different plant parts are not equivalent, but that the alternate arrangement in the root is primitive, the collateral or superposed arrangement in the shoot, advanced. The different structures at the successive levels of the transition region result from an acropetal acceleration in the development of the different evolutionary types in the transition region; that is, at higher levels the more advanced evolutionary stages appear earlier than at the lower levels, and at the highest position the primitive stage is completely omitted (Bouvrain, 1941; Chauveaud, 1911).

The understanding of the structure and the evolution of the transition region would seem to be of much importance for the interpretation of homologies between the root and the shoot. Although the vascular system of the root and the cotyledons is a unit from the early stages of embryogeny, the epicotyl often appears to be a separate structure attached to the root-hypocotyl-cotyledon unit. The study of the relation between the various tissue systems of the epicotyl and the axis below it might prove highly significant in the interpretation of such matters as the comparative nature of the epidermis and the cortex of root and shoot, the morphologic value of the region called pericycle, the meaning of protoxylem and metaxylem, protophloem and metaphloem, and the developmental relation between the primary and secondary tissues.

REFERENCES

Allen, G. S. Embryogeny and the development of the apical meristems of *Pseudotsuga*. III. Development of the apical meristems. *Amer. Jour. Bot.* 34: 204–211. 1947.

Arber, A. *Monocotyledons. A morphological study*. Cambridge, Cambridge University Press. 1925.

Arber, A. *The Gramineae*. Cambridge, Cambridge University Press. 1934.

Arber, A. *The natural philosophy of plant form*. Cambridge, Cambridge University Press. 1950.

Artschwager, E. Anatomy of the vegetative organs of the sugar beet. *Jour. Agr. Res.* 33:143–176. 1926.

Avery, G. S., Jr. Comparative anatomy and morphology of embryos and seedlings of maize, oats, and wheat. *Bot. Gaz.* 89:1–39. 1930.

Bannan, M. W. Origin and cellular character of xylem rays in gymnosperms. *Bot. Gaz.* 96:260–281. 1934.

Bannan, M. W. Variability in wood structure in roots of native Ontario conifers. *Torrey Bot. Club Bul.* 68:173–194. 1941.

Bannan, M. W. Notes on the origin of adventitious roots in the native Ontario conifers. *Amer. Jour. Bot.* 29:593–598. 1942.

Barghoorn, E. S., Jr. Origin and development of the uniseriate ray in the Coniferae. *Torrey Bot. Club Bul.* 67:303–328. 1940a.

Barghoorn, E. S., Jr. The ontogenetic development and phylogenetic specialization of rays in the xylem of dicotyledons. I. The primitive ray structure. *Amer. Jour. Bot.* 27:918–928. 1940b.

Beakbane, A. B. Anatomical studies of stems and roots of hardy fruit trees. III. The anatomical structure of some clonal and seedling apple rootstocks stem- and root-grafted with a scion variety. *Jour. Pomol. and Hort. Sci.* 18: 344–367. 1941.

Behrisch, P. Zur Kenntnis der Endodermiszelle. *Deut. Bot. Gesell. Ber.* 44:162–164. 1926.

Berckemeyer, W. Über kontraktile Umbelliferenwurzeln. *Bot. Arch.* 24:273–318. 1929.

Berthon, R. Sur l'origine des radicelles chez les Angiospermes. *Acad. des Sci. Compt. Rend.* 216:308–309. 1943.

Boeke, J. E. On the origin of the intercellular channels and cavities in the rice root. *Buitenzorg Jard. Bot. Ann.* 50:199–208. 1940.

Bond, G. The stem endodermis of the genus *Piper. Roy. Soc. Edinb., Trans.* 56:695–724. 1931.

Bond, L. Origin and developmental morphology of root nodules of *Pisum sativum. Bot. Gaz.* 109:411–434. 1948.

Bottum, F. R. Histological studies on the root of *Melilotus alba. Bot. Gaz.* 103:132–145. 1941.

Bouvrain, G. *Recherches ontogéniques sur les Angiospermes Dicotylédones.* Dissertation. Paris, R. Foulon. 1941.

Bower, F. O. Medullation in Pteridophyta. *Ann. Bot.* 25:555–574. 1911.

Boyd, L., and G. S. Avery, Jr. Grass seedling anatomy: the first internode of *Avena* and *Triticum. Bot. Gaz.* 97:765–779. 1936.

Bryant, A. E. Comparison of anatomical and histological differences between roots of barley grown in aerated and non-aerated culture solutions. *Plant Physiol.* 9:389–391. 1934*a*.

Bryant, A. E. A demonstration of the connection of protoplasts of the endodermal cells with the Casparian strips in the roots of barley. *New Phytol.* 33:231. 1934*b*.

Campbell, D. H. The eusporangiate ferns and the stelar theory. *Amer. Jour. Bot.* 8:303–314. 1921.

Carlson, M. C. The formation of nodal adventitious roots in *Salix cordata. Amer. Jour. Bot.* 25:721–725. 1938.

Carlson, M. C. Nodal adventitious roots in willow stems of different ages. *Amer. Jour. Bot.* 37:555–561. 1950.

Chauveaud, G. L'appareil conducteur des plantes vasculaires et les phases principales de son évolution. *Ann. des Sci. Nat., Bot.* Ser. 9. 13:113–438. 1911.

Cheadle, V. I. Secondary growth by means of a thickening ring in certain monocotyledons. *Bot. Gaz.* 98:535–555. 1937.

Cheadle, V. I. Specialization of vessels within the xylem of each organ in the Monocotyledoneae. *Amer. Jour. Bot.* 31:81–92. 1944.

Clowes, F. A. L. The structure of mycorrhizal roots of *Fagus sylvatica. New Phytol.* 50:1–16. 1951.

Compton, R. H. An investigation of the seedling structure in the Leguminosae. *Linn. Soc. London, Jour., Bot.* 41:1–122. 1912*a*.

Compton, R. H. Theories of the anatomical transition from root to stem. *New Phytol.* 11:13–25. 1912*b*.

Cormack, R. G. H. The development of root hairs by *Elodea canadensis. New Phytol.* 36:19–25. 1937.

Cormack, R. G. H. A comparative study of developing epidermal cells in white mustard and tomato roots. *Amer. Jour. Bot.* 34:310–314. 1947.

Cormack, R. G. H. The development of the root hairs in angiosperms. *Bot. Rev.* 15:583–612. 1949.

Crafts, A. S., and T. C. Broyer. Migration of salts and water into the xylem of the roots of higher plants. *Amer. Jour. Bot.* 25:529–535. 1938.

Dangeard, P. A. Recherches sur le mode d'union de la tige et de la racine chez les Dicotylédones. *Botaniste* Ser. 1. 1:75–125. 1889.

Dangeard, P. A. Observations sur la structure des plantules chez les Phanérogames dans ses rapports avec l'évolution vasculaire. *Soc. Bot. de France Bul.* 60:73–80, 113–120. 1913.

Datta, A., and G. P. Majumdar. Root initiation in the adult axes of a few dicotyledonous species. *Indian Acad. Sci. Proc.* 18:109–118. 1943.

Davey, A. J. On the seedling of *Oxalis hirta* L. *Ann. Bot.* 10:237–256. 1946.

De Silva, B. L. T. Secondary thickening in the roots of *Dracaena*. *Ceylon Jour. Sci. Sec. A, Bot.* 12:127–135. 1936.

Dittmer, H. J. A quantitative study of the subterranean members of soybean. *Soil Conservation* 6:33–34. 1940.

Dittmer, H. J. A comparative study of the number and length of roots produced in nineteen angiosperm species. *Bot. Gaz.* 109:354–358. 1948.

Dittmer, H. J. Root hair variations in plant species. *Amer. Jour. Bot.* 36:152–155. 1949.

Drabble, E. The transition from stem to root in some palm seedlings. *New Phytol.* 5:56–66. 1905.

Duchaigne, A. Une nouvelle étude ontogénique de l'appareil conducteur des Dicotylédones. *Rev. Gén. de Bot.* 57:129–156. 1950.

Eames, A. J. *Morphology of vascular plants. Lower groups.* New York, McGraw-Hill Book Company. 1936.

Eames, A. J., and L. H. MacDaniels. *An introduction to plant anatomy.* 2nd ed. New York, McGraw-Hill Book Company. 1947.

Elisei, F. G. Ricerche microfluoriscopiche sui punti di Caspary. *Ist. Bot. della R. Univ. Pavia Atti* 13:3–66. 1941.

Esau, K. Developmental anatomy of the fleshy storage organ of *Daucus carota*. *Hilgardia* 13:175–226. 1940.

Esau, K. Phloem anatomy of tobacco affected with curly top and mosaic. *Hilgardia* 13:437–490. 1941.

Esau, K. Origin and development of primary vascular tissues in seed plants. *Bot. Rev.* 9:125–206. 1943*a*.

Esau, K. Vascular differentiation in the pear root. *Hilgardia* 15:299–324. 1943*b*.

Farr, C. H. Root hairs and growth. *Quart. Rev. Biol.* 3:343–376. 1928.

Flahault, C. Recherches sur l'accroissement terminal de la racine chez les Phanérogames. *Ann. des Sci. Nat., Bot.* Ser. 6. 6:1–168. 1878.

Foster, A. S. *Practical plant anatomy.* 2nd ed. New York, D. Van Nostrand Company. 1949.

Fourcroy, M. Perturbations anatomiques interessant le faisceau vasculaire de la racine au voisinage des radicelles. *Ann. des Sci. Nat., Bot.* Ser. 11. 3:177–198. 1942.

Freidenfelt, T. Der anatomische Bau der Wurzel in seinem Zusammenhange mit dem Wassergehalt des Bodens. *Biblioth. Bot.* 12(61):1–118. 1904.

Goodwin, R. H., and W. Stepka. Growth and differentiation in the root tip of *Phleum pratense*. *Amer. Jour. Bot.* 32:36–46. 1945.

Gravis, A. Contribution à l'étude anatomique du raccourcissement des racines. *Acad. Roy. de Belg., Bul. de Cl. des Sci.* Ser. 5. 12:48–69. 1926.

Guttenberg, H. von. Der primäre Bau der Angiospermenwurzel. In: K. Lins-bauer. *Handbuch der Pflanzenanatomie*. Band 8. Lief. 39. 1940.

Guttenberg, H. von. Der primäre Bau der Gymnospermenwurzel. In: K. Lins-bauer. *Handbuch der Pflanzenanatomie*. Band 8. Lief. 41. 1941.

Guttenberg, H. von. Die physiologischen Scheiden. In: K. Linsbauer. *Handbuch der Pflanzenanatomie*. Band 5. Lief. 42. 1943.

Haberlandt, G. *Physiological plant anatomy*. London, Macmillan and Company. 1914.

Hayward, H. E. *The structure of economic plants*. New York, The Macmillan Company. 1938.

Hayward, H. E., W. M. Blair, and P. E. Skaling. Device for measuring entry of water into roots. *Bot. Gaz.* 104:152–160. 1942.

Hayward, H. E., and E. M. Long. The anatomy of the seedling and roots of the Valencia orange. *U. S. Dept. Agr. Tech. Bul.* 786. 1942.

Hayward, H. E., and W. B. Spurr. Effects of osmotic concentration of substrate on the entry of water into corn roots. *Bot. Gaz.* 105:152–164. 1943.

Heimsch, C. Development of vascular tissues in barley roots. *Amer. Jour. Bot.* 38:523–537. 1951.

Hill, T. G., and E. de Fraine. On the seedling structure of gymnosperms. Part I. Taxaceae, Podocarpaceae, Cupressaceae, Abietineae. *Ann. Bot.* 22:689–712. 1908. Part II. Abietineae and Araucarieae. *Ann. Bot.* 23:189–227. 1909*a*. Part III. Ginkgoaceae and Cycadaceae. *Ann. Bot.* 23:433–458. 1909*b*. Part IV. Gnetales. *Ann. Bot.* 24:319–353. 1910.

Hill, T. G., and E. de Fraine. A consideration of facts relating to structure of seedlings. *Ann. Bot.* 27:257–272. 1913.

Hoagland, D. R. Some aspects of the salt nutrition of higher plants. *Bot. Rev.* 3:307–334. 1937.

Hufford, G. N. Development and structure of the watermelon seedling. *Bot. Gaz.* 100:100–122. 1938.

Jackson, V. G. Anatomical structure of the roots of barley. *Ann. Bot.* 36:21–39. 1922.

Jacobson, L., and R. Overstreet. A study of the mechanism of ion absorption by plant roots using radioactive elements. *Amer. Jour. Bot.* 34:415–420. 1947.

Janczewski, E. de. Recherches sur l'accroissement terminal des racines dans les Panérogames. *Ann. des Sci. Nat., Bot.* Ser. 5. 20:162–201. 1874*a*.

Janczewski, E. de. Recherches sur le développement des radicelles dans les Phanérogames. *Ann. des Sci. Nat., Bot.* Ser. 5. 20:208–233. 1874*b*.

Jeffrey, E. C. The morphology of the central cylinder in the angiosperms. *Canad. Inst. Toronto, Trans.* 6:599–636. 1898–99.

Jones, F. R. Winter injury to alfalfa. *Jour. Agr. Res.* 37:189–211. 1928.

Jones, F. R. Growth and decay of the transient (noncambial) roots of alfalfa. *Amer. Soc. Agron. Jour.* 35:625–634. 1943.

Kattein, A. Der morphologische Werth des Centralcylinders der Wurzel. *Bot. Centbl.* 72:55–61, 91–97, 129–139. 1897.

Kelley, A. P. *Mycotrophy in plants*. Waltham, Mass., Chronica Botanica Company. 1950.

Kennedy, P. B., and A. S. Crafts. The anatomy of *Convolvulus arvensis*, wild morning-glory or field bindweed. *Hilgardia* 5:591–622. 1931.

Kramer, P. J. Absorption of water by plants. *Bot. Rev.* 11:310–355. 1945.

Kramer, P. J. *Plant and soil water relationships.* New York, McGraw-Hill Book Company. 1949.

Krauss, B. H. Anatomy of the vegetative organs of the pineapple *Ananas comosus* (L.) Merr. III. The root and the cork. *Bot. Gaz.* 110:550–587. 1949.

Kroemer, K. Wurzelhaut, Hypodermis und Endodermis der Angiospermenwurzel. *Biblioth. Bot.* 12(59):1–159. 1903.

Lenoir, M. Évolution du tissu vasculaire chez quelques plantules des Dicotylédones. *Ann. des Sci. Nat., Bot.* Ser. 10. 2:1–123. 1920.

Liese, J. Beiträge zur Anatomie und Physiologie des Wurzelholzes. *Deut. Bot. Gesell. Ber.* 42:(91)–(97). 1924.

Lund, S., and H. Kiaerskou. Morphologisk-anatomisk Beskrivelse af *Brassica oleracea* L., *B. campestris* (L.) og *B. Napus* (L.) (Havekaal, Rybs og Raps), samt Redegjörelse for Bestövnings-og Dyrkningsforsög med disse Arter. *Bot. Tidsskr.* 15 (1–3):1–150. 1885. (Review in *Bot. Centbl.* 27:326–331. 1886.)

McCall, M. A. Developmental anatomy and homologies in wheat. *Jour. Agr. Res.* 48:283–321. 1934.

McDougall, W. B. On the mycorhizas of forest trees. *Amer. Jour. Bot.* 1:51–74. 1914.

McPherson, D. C. Cortical air spaces in the root of *Zea mays* L. *New Phytol.* 38:190–202. 1939.

McVeigh, I. Regeneration in *Crassula multicava. Amer. Jour. Bot.* 25:7–11. 1938.

Meyer, F. J. Untersuchungen über den Strangverlauf in den radialen Leitbündeln der Wurzeln. *Jahrb. f. Wiss. Bot.* 65:88–97. 1925.

Miller, H. A., and R. H. Wetmore. Studies in the developmental anatomy of *Phlox drummondii* Hook. II. The seedling. *Amer. Jour. Bot.* 32:628–634. 1945.

Müller, H. Über die Metakutisierung der Wurzelspitze und über die verkorkten Scheiden in den Achsen der Monokotyledonen. *Bot. Ztg.* 64:53–84. 1906.

Mullendore, N. Anatomy of the seedling of *Asparagus officinalis. Bot. Gaz.* 97:356–375. 1935.

Muller, C. La tige feuillée et les cotylédons des Viciées a germination hypogée. *Cellule* 46:195–354. 1937.

Mylius, G. Das Polyderm. Eine vergleichende Untersuchung über die physiologische Scheiden: Polyderm, Periderm und Endodermis. *Biblioth. Bot.* 18(79):1–119. 1913.

Netolitzky, F. Das trophische Parenchym. C. Speichergewebe. In: K. Linsbauer. *Handbuch der Pflanzenanatomie.* Band 4. Lief. 31. 1935.

Nightingale, G. T. Effects of temperature on growth, anatomy, and metabolism of apple and peach roots. *Bot. Gaz.* 96:581–639. 1935.

Ogura, Y. Anatomie der Vegetationsorgane der Pteridophyten. In: K. Linsbauer. *Handbuch der Pflanzenanatomie.* Band 7. Lief. 36. 1938.

Overstreet, R., and L. Jacobson. The absorption by roots of rubidium and phosphate ions at extremely small concentrations as revealed by experiments with Rb[86] and P[32] prepared without inert carrier. *Amer. Jour. Bot.* 33:107–112. 1946.

Phillips, W. S. Seedling anatomy of *Cynara scolymus. Bot. Gaz.* 98:711–724. 1937.

Preston, R. J., Jr. Anatomical studies of the roots of juvenile lodgepole pine. *Bot. Gaz.* 104:443–448. 1943.

Prevot, P., and F. C. Steward. Salient features of the root system relative to the problem of salt absorption. *Plant Physiol.* 11:509–534. 1936.

Priestley, J. H., and C. F. Swingle. Vegetative propagation from the standpoint of plant anatomy. *U. S. Dept. Agr. Tech. Bul.* 151. 1929.

Riedl, H. Bau und Leistungen des Wurzelholzes. *Jahrb. f. Wiss. Bot.* 85:1–75. 1937.

Rimbach, A. Die kontraktilen Wurzeln und ihre Thätigkeit. *Beitr. z. Wiss. Bot.* 2:1–28. 1898.

Rimbach, A. Beiträge zur Physiologie der Wurzeln. *Deut. Bot. Gesell. Ber.* 17:18–35. 1899.

Rimbach, A. Die Verbreitung der Wurzelverkürzung im Pflanzenreich. *Deut. Bot. Gesell. Ber.* 47:22–31. 1929.

Rimbach, A. Nachträgliche Dickenzunahme kontraktiler Monokotylen-Wurzeln. *Deut. Bot. Gesell. Ber.* 50:215–219. 1932.

Rosene, H. F. Distribution of the velocities of absorption of water in the onion root. *Plant Physiol.* 12:1–19. 1937.

Rosene, H. F. Comparison of rates of water intake in contiguous regions of intact and isolated roots. *Plant Physiol.* 16:19–38. 1941.

Rosene, H. F. Quantitative measurement of the velocity of water absorption in individual root hairs by a microtechnique. *Plant Physiol.* 18:588–607. 1943.

Russow, E. *Betrachtungen über das Leitbündel- und Grundgewebe aus vergleichend morphologischem und phylogenetischem Gesichtspunkt.* Dorpat, Schnackenburg. 1875.

Rywosch, S. Untersuchungen über die Entwicklungsgeschichte der Seitenwurzeln der Monokotylen. *Ztschr. f. Bot.* 1:253–283. 1909.

Schnee, L. Bandplasmolyse der Endodermiszellen von *Cobaea scandens. Protoplasma* 26:97–99. 1936.

Schoute, J. C. *Die Stelär-Theorie.* Jena, Gustav Fischer. 1903.

Scott, L. I., and J. H. Priestley. The root as an absorbing organ. II. The delimitation of the absorbing zone. *New Phytol.* 27:141–174. 1928.

Seeliger, R. Untersuchungen über das Dickenwachstum der Zuckerrübe (*Beta vulgaris* L. var. *rapa* Dum.). *Biol. Reichsanst. f. Land u. Forstw. Arb.* 10:149–194. 1919.

Siegler, E. A., and J. J. Bowman. Anatomical studies of root and shoot primordia in 1-year apple roots. *Jour. Agr. Res.* 58:795–803. 1939.

Sinnott, E. W., and R. Bloch. Division in vacuolate plant cells. *Amer. Jour. Bot.* 28:225–232. 1941.

Smith, A. I. Adventitious roots in stem cuttings of *Begonia maculata* and *B. semperflorens. Amer. Jour. Bot.* 23:511–515. 1936.

Smith, A. I. Adventitious roots in stem cuttings of *Tropaeolum majus* L. *Amer. Jour. Bot.* 29:192–194. 1942.

Soeding, H. Anatomie der Wurzel-, Stengel- und Rübenbildung von Oelraps und Steckrübe (*Brassica Napus* L. var. *oleifera* und var. *napobrassica*). *Bot. Arch.* 7:41–69. 1924.

Spurr, A. R. Organization of the procambium and development of the secretory cells in the embryo of *Pinus strobus* L. *Amer. Jour. Bot.* 37:185–197. 1950.

Steward, F. C., P. Prevot, and J. A. Harrison. Absorption and accumulation of rubidium bromide by barley roots. Localization in the root of cation accumulation and of transfer to the shoot. *Plant Physiol.* 17:411-421. 1942.

Strugger, S. I. Zellphysiologie und Protoplasmatik (Pflanzenzellen). *Naturforsch. und Med. in Deutschl.* Vol 52. *Biologie.* Part 1. 1939-46.

Swingle, C. F. Regeneration and vegetative propagation. *Bot. Rev.* 6:301-355. 1940.

Thibault, M. Contribution à l'étude des radicelles de carotte. *Rev. Gén. de Bot.* 53:434-460. 1946.

Thoday, D. The interpretation of plant structure. *Nature* 144:571-575. 1939.

Thoday, D., and A. J. Davey. Contractile roots. II. On the mechanism of root-contraction in *Oxalis incarnata. Ann. Bot.* 46:993-1005. 1932.

Thomas, E. N. A theory of the double leaf-trace founded on seedling structure. *New Phytol.* 6:77-91. 1907.

Thomas, E. N. Seedling anatomy of Ranales, Rhoedales, and Rosales. *Ann. Bot.* 28:695-733. 1914.

Thomson, R. B., and H. B. Sifton. Resin canals in the Canadian spruce (*Picea canadensis* (Mill.) B. S. P.)—an anatomical study, especially in relation to traumatic effects and their bearing on phylogeny. *Roy. Soc. London, Phil. Trans.* Ser. B. 214:63-111. 1925.

Troll, W. Über die Grundbegriffe der Wurzelmorphologie. *Österr. Bot. Ztschr.* 96:444-452. 1949.

Van der Lek, H. A. A. Over de wortelvorming van houtige stekken. *Landbouwhoogesch. te Wageningen Lab. v. Tuinbouwplantentielt. Meded.* 28:1-230. 1924.

Van Fleet, D. S. The development and distribution of the endodermis and an associated oxidase system in monocotyledonous plants. *Amer. Jour. Bot.* 29: 1-15. 1942a.

Van Fleet, D. S. The significance of oxidation in the endodermis. *Amer. Jour. Bot.* 29:747-755. 1942b.

Van Fleet, D. S. Cortical patterns and gradients in vascular plants. *Amer. Jour. Bot.* 35:219-227. 1948.

Van Fleet, D. S. A comparison of histochemical and anatomical characteristics of the hypodermis with the endodermis in vascular plants. *Amer. Jour. Bot.* 37:721-725. 1950.

Van Tieghem, P. *Traité de Botanique.* 2nd ed. Paris, Librairie F. Savy. 1891a.

Van Tieghem, P. Sur les tubes criblés extralibériens et les vaisseaux extraligneux. *Jour. de Bot.* 5:117-128. 1891b.

Van Wisselingh, C. Die Zellmembran. In: K. Linsbauer. *Handbuch der Pflanzenanatomie.* Band 3. Lief. 11. 1924.

Warden, W. M. On the structure and distribution of the endodermis and its associated ducts in *Senecio vulgaris. New Phytol.* 34:361-385. 1935.

Weaver, J. E. *Root development of field crops.* New York, McGraw-Hill Book Company. 1926.

Weaver, J. E., and J. W. Voigt. Monolith method of root-sampling in studies on succession and degeneration. *Bot. Gaz.* 111:286-299. 1950.

Weiss, J. E. Anatomie und Physiologie fleischig verdickter Wurzeln. *Flora* 38: 81-89, 97-112, 113-123. 1880.

Whiting, A. G. Development and anatomy of primary structures in the seedling of *Cucurbita maxima. Bot. Gaz.* 99:497-528. 1938.

Williams, B. C. The structure of the meristematic root tip and origin of primary tissues in the roots of vascular plants. *Amer. Jour. Bot.* 34:455–462. 1947.

Young, P. T. Histogenesis and morphogenesis in the primary root of *Zea Mays*. Thesis. New York, Columbia University. 1933.

CHAPTER

18

The Flower

CONCEPT

The present and the following two chapters deal with the angiospermous flower and the structures derived from it, the fruit and the seed. The flower consists of an axis bearing appendages, the floral parts or floral organs (fig. 18.1). Some of the floral parts form reproductive structures; others are sterile appendages.

The floral organs concerned with megasporogenesis constitute, collectively, the *gynoecium* (from the Greek words meaning woman and house). The basic unit of the gynoecium is the *carpel* (from the Greek word for fruit), which is commonly regarded as a megasporophyll. One or more carpels may enter into the composition of a gynoecium. The carpels form *ovules* (from the Greek word for egg). The *nucellus*, which is the central part of the ovule, is usually interpreted as the megasporangium. The functioning megaspore germinates within the megasporangium and gives rise to the female gametophyte, the *embryo sac*.

The floral parts forming the microspores are called, collectively, the *androecium* (from the Greek words meaning man and house). The individual units of the androecium are the *stamens* (in Latin, a filament). A stamen is usually interpreted as a microsporophyll, and the part of the stamen called *pollen sac*, as the microsporangium. A microspore develops into the male gametophyte, the *pollen grain*.

The sterile parts of the flower are the *petals* (in Greek, flower leaves), collectively called the *corolla* (in Latin, small crown), and the *sepals* (from the Greek, a covering) composing the *calyx* (in Greek, a cup). The calyx and the corolla constitute the *perianth* (from Greek words meaning about and flower). If the perianth is not differentiated into sepals and petals (fig. 18.11, *A*), the individual members of the perianth are called *tepals* (from the Latin *tepalum*, which is an anagram of *petalum*).

Much of the research on floral anatomy is conducted with reference to the fundamental morphologic nature of the flower and its parts. The literature dealing with the interpretation of floral morphology is voluminous, but it has been extensively reviewed in many articles (e.g., Arber, 1937, 1950; Bancroft, 1935; Chadefaud, 1946; Douglas, 1944; Eames, 1929, 1931; Ozenda, 1949; Plantefol, 1948; Schaffner, 1937; Wilson and Just, 1939). The oldest and most popular concept is that the flower consists of an abbreviated axis of determinate growth that bears floral parts which are members of the same category as the leaves. In other words, the flower is regarded as a short shoot bearing modified leaves. The modern proponents of this concept usually assume that the floral organs are appendicular structures in the same sense as leaves, both kinds of appendages possibly having undergone parallel evolutionary development (Arber, 1937, 1950; Bancroft, 1935; Wilson and Just, 1939). Emphasis is thus placed upon unity of types of structures; that is, foliage leaves and floral organs are both regarded as leaf-like appendages or phyllomes (Arber, 1937, 1950).

The degree of resemblance to foliage leaves varies in different floral organs. Sepals and petals are basically leaf-like in external form. They may intergrade with one another and with the small bracts (bracteoles) subtending the flower. The flowers of certain of the Ranales clearly reveal stages in specialization of sterile appendages to form typical bracteoles, sepals, and petals (I. W. Bailey, personal communication). Some workers, however, consider that petals evolved through sterilization of stamens (e.g., Baum, 1950a; Ozenda, 1949).

The specialized types of stamens, characterized by a distinct differentiation into a filament, an anther, and a connective, appear rather unlike the leaves, but in many Ranales the stamens are wide leaf-like structures with no differentiation of a filament (Bailey and Nast, 1943a; Bailey and Smith, 1942; Bailey et al., 1943; Wilson, 1942). The nature of the carpel has been the subject of more debate than that of any other floral organ (cf. Arber, 1937; Bancroft, 1935; Douglas, 1944; Eames, 1931; Ozenda, 1946; Swamy, 1945; Unruh, 1939; Wilson and Just, 1939). Some interpret the carpel as a leaf-like appendage (e.g., Arber, 1937; Bailey and Swamy, 1951; Boke, 1949; Joshi, 1947; Troll, 1939); others consider that its ontogeny makes it quite distinct from the leaves (e.g., Brooks, 1940; Grégoire, 1938; Plantefol, 1948). Some workers distinguish between two types of carpels, the solid fertile and the valve-like sterile ones (Saunders,

1937); others recognize only one, the fertile type (Bonner, 1947–48; Puri, 1950; Swamy, 1945). The literature deals extensively with the question regarding the type of a leaf to which the carpel may be compared. The concept has been advanced that many carpels have the same growth form as a peltate leaf, that is, a leaf in which a stalk is attached to the lower surface of the blade. The degree of peltation is considered to be variable and absent in some forms (Juhnke and Winkler, 1938; Leinfellner, 1950; Wilson and Just, 1939). Peltation is recognized in stamens and perianth parts as well (e.g., Baum, 1949c, 1950a).

Certain efforts to reveal the evolution of the floral parts have culminated in the concept that the stamens and the carpels are derived from branch systems (telome systems) rather than from foliar structures (Hunt, 1937; Wilson, 1942, 1950; cf. also Bancroft, 1935, and Wilson and Just, 1939). This view is being criticized on the basis that in ontogeny the stamens and the carpels arise as units which give no evidence that they might have originated from branch systems (Baum, 1950c).

Although not all the features of the flower can be explained on the basis of homology between the flower and the shoot, the concept of the shoot-like nature of the flower and the leaf-like nature of the flower parts make possible a coherent and consistent treatment of floral structures and their variations. These concepts are, therefore, more generally used than the opposing ones and are also adopted in this book.

STRUCTURE

The Flower Parts and Their Arrangement

Before considering the anatomy of the flower it will be useful to review its morphology. The flower does not show the open, indeterminate type of growth characteristic of the vegetative shoot (see chapter 5); instead, its apical meristem usually ceases its activity after the reproductive structures have been initiated. In certain groups of angiosperms considered to be primitive this determinate growth of the flower is less pronounced than in the more advanced families. In the primitive groups, the activity of the apical meristem is prolonged and therefore the number of floral parts is large and indefinite. Moreover, these parts occur on a rather elongated axis, with sepals, petals, stamens, and carpels succeeding each other acropetally in the order named. The similarity between such a flower and a vegetative shoot is not difficult to visualize, especially if the flower parts are arranged helically.

In the more highly specialized flower types the growth period is shorter and the number of floral parts is smaller and more definite. Moreover, the shortening of the period of activity of the apical meristem is associated with development of distinguishing characteristics that obscure or even efface the evidences of similarity between a flower and a vegetative shoot. Such characteristics are: whorled (or cyclic) instead of helical arrangement of parts; cohesion of parts within one whorl; adnation of parts of two or more different whorls; loss of parts; zygomorphy (bilateral symmetry) instead of actinomorphy (radial symmetry); and epigyny (inferior ovary) instead of hypogyny (superior ovary). The words synsepalous, sympetalous, and syncarpous are used to characterize flowers with united sepals, petals, and carpels, respectively. If the gynoecium occupies a position similar to that in an epigynous flower but is not adnate to the noncarpellary tissue, the flower is called perigynous and the ovary superior (fig. 18.10, *J*). Epigynous flowers (those with inferior ovaries) are especially difficult to interpret morphologically because the gynoecium is imbedded in noncarpellary tissue and appears to be inserted below the other floral parts (fig. 18.10, *H*).

The flowers of different degrees of specialization form an intergrading series of morphologic types. The degree of fusion of sepals, petals, stamens, and carpels varies widely, and the union is not necessarily equally pronounced in the different whorls of the same flower. The perianth may not be differentiated into calyx and corolla, or the sepals and petals may intergrade with each other. Transitional forms may also occur between the petals and the stamens.

The Vascular System

Investigations on the vascular system of the flower occupy a prominent place in the literature on the anatomy of the flower. Interest in vascularization of the flower has resulted from the common acceptance of the postulate that the vascular system is conservative and, therefore, might be expected to reveal at least some of the evolutionary changes that have been obliterated in the external form (cf. Puri, 1951). Thus, the vascular anatomy of the flower has been studied mainly to find an explanation of some of the perplexing structural details of flowers (e.g., Bonne, 1928; Douglas, 1944; Jackson, 1934; MacDaniels, 1940; Smith and Smith, 1942a; Wilkinson, 1948;

Wilson and Just, 1939) and to obtain additional data for the classification of angiosperms (e.g., Baehni and Bonner, 1947–48; Bonner, 1947–48; Eames, 1929; Nast, 1944; Wilkinson, 1948, 1949).

The vascular system of relatively unspecialized flowers with superior ovaries is comparable to that of a vegetative shoot in which strands diverge into the lateral organs from an axial system of bundles. Commonly, a complete parallel is drawn between the patterns of vascularization in the shoot and the flower, and the concepts of stele, traces, and gaps are applied with reference to both structures (Eames, 1931; Eames and MacDaniels, 1947). The shortness of internodes, and still more the union of parts and the epigyny, make the floral vascular pattern less regular than that of a shoot (Nast, 1944) and considerably obscure, in the flower, the relation between the vascular systems of the appendages and that of the axis.

In a hypogynous flower, with relatively little fusion of parts, the vascular system may be easily depicted in terms of traces to the various floral appendages (fig. 18.1, *A*). The pedicel shows a cylindrical vascular region enclosing a pith and delimited on the outside by the cortex (fig. 18.1, *B*). In the receptacle or torus (the part of the axis bearing the floral parts), at the level of attachment of sepals, traces diverge into these appendages (fig. 18.1, *C, D*). Each sepal usually has as many traces as a foliage leaf of the same plant. Above this level, traces diverge into the corolla, one to each petal in most dicotyledonous flowers (fig. 18.1, *D, E*), one to many to each tepal in the monocotyledonous flowers (Kausmann, 1941). Still higher, the traces to the stamens become discernible, typically one to each stamen (fig. 18.1, *E–G*), and finally the carpellary supply of one, three, five, or more traces to each carpel (fig. 18.1, *E–G*). The common number is three traces to each carpel, one median and two lateral (fig. 18.7). Small branches of carpellary vascular bundles, usually derived from the laterals, connect the carpellary system with the ovules (fig. 18.1, *A, F, G*). There is also a prolongation of the vascular system into the style (fig. 18.1, *A, H*).

Some of the common deviations in the arrangement of the vascular system are associated with the fusion of floral parts. In many flowers the lateral bundles of the adjacent carpels are fused with each other. Similar fusions occur in other floral organs. The reduction in the numbers of traces and bundles may also occur through nondevelopment of some of them.

The vascular system of epigynous flowers shows additional complications related to the apparently basal position of the gynoecium.

The vascularization of such flowers has been frequently studied (Douglas, 1944; Smith and Smith, 1942*b*) with the result that rather definite ideas have been developed on the nature of the noncarpellary

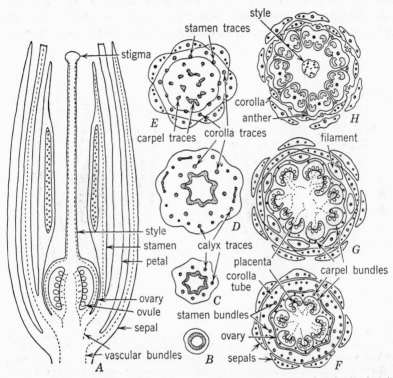

FIG. 18.1. Diagrams of a cultivated tomato flower shown in a longitudinal (*A*) and transverse (*B–H*) sections. The broken lines in *A* represent the vascular tissue. At the right, vascular bundles are shown diverging from the floral axis into the sepal and the stamen, to the left into the petal. Vascular bundles also diverge into the ovary wall and into the central part of the ovary and the ovules. The bundles traversing the ovary wall are continuous throughout the style. The transections were taken, *B–H*, at successively higher levels. *B* was taken through the pedicel. The vascular tissue is indicated by stippling and broken lines. The stamen bases are adnate to the corolla tube. The blackened areas in the style in *H* represent stigmatoid tissue; the circles near periphery, vascular bundles. Further details are in the text. (×8.)

tissue enclosing the gynoecium. In most epigynous flowers this tissue is interpreted as appendicular in origin, composed of the bases of sepals, petals, and stamens that underwent a concrescence during the evolution of the flower. The vascular system is thought to reflect this structure in that the bundles pertaining to members of different whorls are variously fused but all show the usual orientation of xylem and phloem (fig. 18.2, *A*). Some few epigynous flowers (Calycanthaceae, Santalaceae, and probably Juglandaceae) show evidence that the ovary is partially enclosed in receptacular tissue. The vascular bundles are prolonged from the axis to the level below the insertion of floral parts, other than the carpels, where traces to these

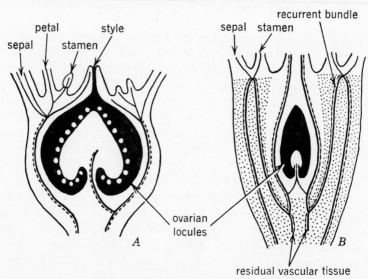

FIG. 18.2. Diagrams illustrating the vascular system in longitudinal sections of flowers with inferior ovaries. The xylem is shown by solid lines; the phloem by broken lines. *A*, *Samolus floribundus*, with the ovary imbedded in the floral tube. *B*, *Darbya*, with the ovary imbedded in the invaginated receptacle (stippled part). The receptacular nature of the outer tissue in *B* is indicated by the presence of recurrent bundles with inverted orientation of xylem and phloem, and of the residual vascular tissue at the base of the ovary. (Adapted from Douglas, 1944.)

parts diverge. The main bundles, instead of ending here, continue farther from the periphery in a downward direction—with a corresponding inverse position of the xylem and the phloem—and at lower levels give branches to the carpels (fig. 18.2, *B*). This orientation of the vascular system is interpreted as a result of the invagination of the axis.

In general, the vascular elements in the bundles of the flower are comparable to those in foliage leaves. The tissues are mostly primary, although some secondary growth may occur later, during fruit development, particularly in the pedicel. The vascular system of the sepals, the petals, and the carpels is more or less elaborately ramified

(Sprotte, 1940; Unruh, 1941). Stamens rarely show a branched vascular system (cf. Puri, 1951). In general character the venation of the perianth parts of the monocotyledons and the dicotyledons shows distinctive characteristics similar to those in the foliage leaves of these two groups of plants (Kausmann, 1941).

The Sepal and the Petal

The sepal and the petal are essentially leaf-like in form and anatomy but generally simpler in detailed structure than a foliage leaf. They consist of ground parenchyma, often called mesophyll, a vascular system permeating the ground tissue, and epidermal layers on the abaxial and adaxial sides (plate 79, *D*, *E*). Crystal-containing cells, idioblasts, and laticifers may occur in the ground tissue or in association with the vascular elements. The sepals are commonly green. The chloroplast distribution in the sepals depends on their position. If the sepals are upright and are closely applied to the petals, most chloroplasts are on the abaxial side; if the sepals are recurved, the chloroplasts are most abundant on the adaxial side. The mesophyll is rarely differentiated into palisade and spongy parenchyma. Commonly it is simple in structure and consists of approximately isodiametric cells loosely arranged into a lacunose tissue. The epidermis of the sepals shows a deposition of cutin and a development of stomata and trichomes similar to those in the foliage leaves. The vascular system resembles that in the leaves but is less elaborate.

Petals show a wider variety of shapes than the sepals and are usually distinguished from the sepals by their color. The vascular system may consist of one or several large veins and a system of small veinlets. The patterns formed by these veinlets vary greatly (Glück, 1919; Gumppenberg, 1924). Commonly the veinlets are dichotomously branched. The mesophyll is few cells in thickness, except in flowers with fleshy corollas. The tissue is parenchymatous, with the cells either closely packed or loosely arranged.

The epidermis of petals shows certain peculiarities in the shape of cells (Hiller, 1884) and in the structure of cuticle (Martens, 1934). The anticlinal cell walls may be straight or wavy or may bear internal ridges. The undulation and ridging vary widely in degree of expression in different plants. In some, the anticlinal walls are only slightly wavy; in others the undulations are so deep that the cells are star-like in shape as seen from the surface. The ridges, which arise through a localized centripetal growth of cell walls (see chapter 8), may appear as small buttons in sectional views, or as long bars, straight or bent, solid or hollow. The degree of waviness or ridging may vary in the same petal. For instance, the anticlinal walls are usually straight at the base of the petal and along the veins, even if they are wavy elsewhere. Frequently, the undulate walls are restricted or are more pronounced on the lower side as contrasted with the upper.

Intercellular spaces may develop in the epidermis in connection with the differentiation of ridges. In some species the two wall layers composing a ridge split apart and the space between the two layers becomes filled with air. These spaces are open toward the interior of the petal but appear to be closed with a cuticle on the exterior (Hiller, 1884). Ridged walls occur mainly in the dicotyledons, although they have been found in some members of the Liliaceae also.

The tangential walls of the epidermis may be horizontal or convex to various degrees. The inner tangential wall is commonly slightly convex over the entire extent. The outer wall, on the contrary, is often strongly convex, or it may bear one or more capitate or cone-shaped papillae (*Viola, Nasturtium*). The papillose structure is more common in the adaxial epidermis than in the abaxial and does not develop at the base of the petals. Various trichomes may occur on the petals, usually similar to those found on the leaves of the same plants. The stomata which occur on the petals either resemble those on the foliage leaves or are incompletely differentiated.

The cuticle of the corolla is rarely smooth. Commonly it is striated, and the lines form various patterns in different plants (plate 21, *A*). The development of these patterns has been suggested as resulting from two phenomena: first, a temporarily excessive production of cutin and the consequent increase in surface and folding of the cuticle; second, a stretching of the cuticle and a reorientation of the initial folds by cell extension (Martens, 1934).

The color of petals is caused by the presence of chromoplasts or pigments in the cell sap (see chapter 2). Starch is often formed in young petals. Volatile oils imparting the characteristic fragrance to the flowers commonly occur in the epidermal cells of the petals.

The Stamen

The well-known type of stamen, with a single-veined filament bearing at the upper end a two-lobed, four-loculed anther, is phylogenetically an advanced structure (figs. 18.3, *A*, and 18.14, *A*). Among the Ranales there are stamens that are leaf-like in shape and, in the least modified form, have three veins and bear the microsporangia on the abaxial surface between the midvein and the lateral veins (Bailey and Nast, 1943*a*; Bailey and Smith, 1942; Bailey and Swamy, 1949; Bailey et al., 1943). The reduction of the three veins to one is apparently a concomitant of the reduction in width of the sporophyll, and particularly of the modification of the base of the sporophyll into a filament. The presence of a single vascular bundle is the prevailing condition in the existing angiosperms. An extensive survey (Wilson, 1942) has shown that 95 per cent of angiosperms have a single vascular bundle in the stamen. This strand traverses the filament and may end at the base of the anther or may be prolonged into the tissue between the anther lobes, the so-called connective, terminating blindly near the apex. The vascular bundle is not connected by any vascular elements with the sporogenous tissue, but if the ground parenchyma of the anther develops secondary thickenings the cells in the vicinity of the sporogenous tissue remain thin walled and there are also vertical bands of similar thin-walled cells interpolated between the vascular strand and the anther lobes. The vascular bundle of the anther may be amphicribral.

The ground tissue of the filament is vacuolated parenchyma without a prominent intercellular-space system. It often contains pigments in the vacuoles. The epidermis is cutinized and bears trichomes in some species. The ground tissue of the anther and the connective is also parenchymatous but is highly specialized in the vicinity of the sporogenous cells (plate 79, *B–E*). This specialized tissue forms the wall layers or the parietal layers of the microsporangia (anther locules or pollen sacs). The wall layers vary in number and are established through a series of divisions parallel to the periphery of the anther locule (fig. 18.4, *A*; plate 79, *B, C*). The parietal layers facing the epidermis are ontogenetically related to the sporogenous tissue. Both the parietal cells and the pollen mother cells arise from the same initial cells, the archesporial cells. The wall layers occurring internally to the pollen sacs, however, arise from the ground tissue in contact with the archesporial cells (plate 79, *B*).

The outermost wall layer, the *endothecium* (from the Greek words for inner and case), is located beneath the epidermis. In anthers that open at maturity by longitudinal slits, the endothecium develops secondary thickenings as the stamen approaches maturity (fig. 18.3, *C*). These thickenings are restricted to the cell walls that are not in

contact with the epidermis. In the radial and transverse cell walls
that interconnect the endothecial cells the secondary thickenings have

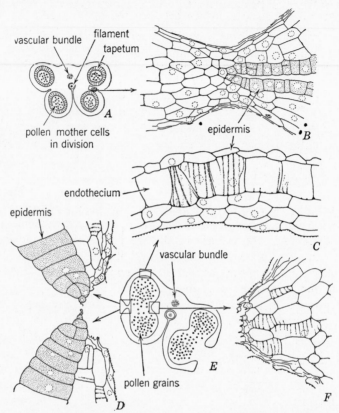

FIG. 18.3. Structure of the anther in *Lilium*. *A*, diagrammatic drawing of transection of a stamen taken during the division of pollen mother cells into tetrads.
The wall part between the members of a pair of locules of one anther lobe is
shown in detail in *B*. *E*, diagrammatic drawing of a dehisced anther containing
mature pollen grains. Rectangles in *E* mark the areas from which *C*, *D*, and *F*
were drawn. During dehiscence a break occurred between the epidermis (stippled in *D*) and the subjacent cells (partly collapsed in *F*). A break also occurred
between certain epidermal cells (the small epidermal cells in *D*) and caused the
opening of the anther locules. *C* shows details of wall structure somewhat removed from the dehiscence region. An endothecium with secondary wall thickenings is present here. Similar thickenings occur elsewhere in the parenchyma
of the anther (*F*). (*A, E,* ×9; *B–D, F,* ×120.)

the form of strips or ridges that are oriented perpendicularly to the
epidermal layer. The cell walls facing the sporogenous tissue may
have uniform or irregular thickenings. The protoplasts either dis-

appear from the endothecium as it completes its development, or they remain alive until the pollen is shed. Wall thickenings similar to those in the endothecium may develop rather generally throughout the ground parenchyma of the anther.

The innermost of the parietal layers is the *tapetum* (from the Greek, carpet), which is apparently concerned with the nutrition of the developing pollen mother cells (fig. 18.4, *B*; plate 79, *E*). The tapetal cells are characterized by densely staining protoplasts and prominent nuclei. The nuclei show various behavior in different plants (Cooper, 1933). In some, they do not divide after all the tapetal cells have been formed; in others, one or more nuclear divisions occur without being followed by cytokineses so that the cells become bi- or multinucleate (fig. 18.4, *B*; *Lactuca, Taraxacum*). Sometimes the nuclear divisions are not carried to completion: the chromosomes divide but do not form separate nuclei. Such behavior results in the polyploidy of the tapetal nuclei (Cooper, 1933; Witkus, 1945). The tapetal layer attains its maximal development at the tetrad stage in the microspore formation. In some angiosperms the tapetum remains as a discrete layer—apparently functioning as a secretory tissue—until the pollen is mature. In many others, however, the cell walls disintegrate and the cells assume the appearance of plasmodial masses. The latter gradually disintegrate as the pollen develops (Schnarf, 1927).

The parietal layers intervening between the endothecium and the tapetum frequently are crushed and destroyed so that, after the maturation of the pollen and the disintegration of the tapetum, the anther locule is bordered on the outside only by the epidermis and the endothecium.

In many plants the release of the pollen occurs through dehiscence (from the Greek, to yawn), that is, spontaneous opening of the anther. The opening, or *stomium*, may be a longitudinal slit located between the two pollen locules of each half of the anther. Before the dehiscence the partition between the two locules of the same anther lobe may break down (fig. 18.3, *D–F*). After such disintegration, only one cell layer, the epidermis, separates the locule from the outside in the region of dehiscence. This part of the epidermis consists of particularly small cells and is easily broken when the pollen is mature (fig. 18.3, *D*). Another common type of stomium is oriented transversely near the apex of the anther lobe. When such a stomium is formed, the apex of each anther lobe separates like a cap and leaves a pore (e.g., many Ericaceae, *Solanum*). Pores may be formed laterally also. In anthers possessing secondary wall thickenings in the endothecium, dehiscence is commonly ascribed to the differential shrinkage of the various walls of this layer. The unthickened outer wall apparently shrinks more rapidly than the secondarily thickened walls. Thus, a transverse pull is created which ruptures the delicate tissue in the region of the stomium. In some plants,

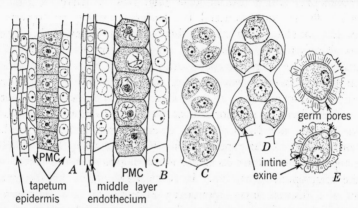

FIG. 18.4. Pollen differentiation in *Cichorium endivia* (endive) as seen in longitudinal sections of anthers. *A*, pollen mother cells (PMC) compactly arranged, tapetum present, the wall layer between the tapetum and epidermis in division. *B*, pollen mother cells rounding off, all wall layers present, the tapetum multinucleate. *C*, the protoplasts of the tetrads of microspores are imbedded within the pollen mother cell wall (left blank in the drawings). Some of the microspores are still connected with one another by cytoplasmic bridges. *D*, the microspores show the beginning of development of the exine. *E*, pollen grains with exine and intine wall layers. (×470.)

anthers do not dehisce but open by an irregular breaking and exfoliating of tissue fragments (Coulter and Chamberlain, 1912).

The development of the sporogenous tissue in the anther involves certain characteristic phenomena of wall formation. The cells that eventually undergo meiosis, the pollen mother cells, are closely packed in their early stages of development (fig. 18.4, *A*). During meiosis these cells usually separate from one another, and the protoplasts round off and become enclosed in a thick gelatinous wall giving the staining reaction of callose. This wall is designated as the pollen mother cell wall or special wall. As is well known, normal meiosis results in the formation of four nuclei, the microspore nuclei (fig. 18.4, *C*). Each nuclear division may be followed immediately by cytokinesis (successive formation of walls), or the four protoplasts may be walled off simultaneously at the end of meiosis (simultaneous formation of walls; Maheshwari, 1950; Schnarf, 1927). The first type of division is particularly common in the monocotyledons, the second in the dicotyledons. The simultaneous wall formation may occur by development of cell plates or by furrowing (Sharp, 1934; see also chapter 3). The first wall delimiting the microspore protoplasts from each other is of the same material, callose, as the special wall around the entire tetrad of microspores (fig. 18.4, C; Reeves, 1928; Sharp, 1934). Later, each microspore forms its own wall which commonly consists of two layers (fig. 18.4, E), the *exine* (outer wall) and the *intine* (inner wall).

Usually the exine is formed first, against the inner surface of the callose wall (fig. 18.4, D). In pollen grains having germ pores or germinal furrows the exine is laid down as a partially interrupted layer. The pores and furrows are the openings in the exine (fig. 18.4, E) through which the pollen tube may emerge upon germination of the pollen grain. The exine frequently has spines, depressions, areolations (divisions into distinct spaces), and other types of ornamentations. These external markings of the exine and the shape of the pollen grains give the grains their characteristic appearance that may be utilized in the classification of plant groups (Wodehouse, 1935, 1936). The exine consists of cellulose and pectic substances and is strongly cutinized.

If an exine is present, the intine is deposited on the inside of the exine. The intine varies in thickness, consists of cellulose and pectic substances, and is not cutinized. It is a continuous wall layer, without ornamentations (fig. 18.4, E). It is sometimes thickened in the regions of the germ pores, but elsewhere it is usually uniform in thickness (fig. 18.4, E). The development of the pollen tube results from localized extension growth of the intine. The pollen tube emerges through a germ pore and grows by addition of wall material at its apex (Schoch-Bodmer, 1945). The cytoplasm accumulates here and may completely disappear from the basal part of the tube. In such instances, the older parts of the elongating pollen tube are successively sealed off by plugs of wall material giving the staining reactions of callose (fig. 18.8, H; Brink, 1924; Schoch-Bodmer, 1945). In plants forming no plugs of callose (*Fagopyrum esculentum*) the whole tube probably has a thin layer of cytoplasm in addition to the accumulation at the apex (Schoch-Bodmer, 1945).

The Carpel

The Carpel in Relation to the Gynoecium. The gynoecium may consist of free carpels (apocarpous gynoecium, fig. 19.1, *A, C*) or of united carpels (syncarpous gynoecium, fig. 19.1, *B*). An apocarpous gynoecium may have a single carpel (e.g., *Prunus* and Leguminosae). A carpel not united with others is commonly referred to as *simple pistil* (from the Latin, pestle). If two or more carpels are united into one structure, this structure constitutes a *compound pistil.*

The carpel of an apocarpous gynoecium is a leaf-like folded structure, differentiated, in the specialized condition, into a basal fertile part, the *ovary*, and an upper sterile part, the *style* (figs. 18.10, *J*, and 19.1, *A, C*). The folded carpel is commonly described as having infolded or involuted margins, that is, margins turned toward the interior of the folded carpel. Furthermore, these margins are pictured as bearing the placentae that give rise to the ovules. The carpel of woody Ranales shows, however, that in the primitive form the carpel is a conduplicately (from the Latin, doubling) folded structure, that is, a structure folded lengthwise without involution of margins (fig. 18.6, *D*). Such a carpel shows laminar placentation; the ovules are borne not on the margins but on the inner (ventral) surface, more or less distant from the margins (fig. 18.5, *B*; Bailey and Swamy, 1951). The superficial appearance of involution and marginal placentation (fig. 18.5, *D*, and plate 79, *A*) resulted from phylogenetic change in the ontogeny of the carpel. This change was a decrease in the extension of the folded ventral part of the carpel (the unstippled areas in fig. 18.5, *C, D*).

The differentiation of the dicotyledonous carpel into ovary, style, and stigma is also a result of phylogenetic modification of a primitively leaf-like conduplicate carpel as is found in the woody Ranales (fig. 18.6, *D*; Bailey and Nast, 1943*b*; Bailey and Smith, 1942; Bailey and Swamy, 1949, 1951; Swamy, 1949). Such an unspecialized carpel is a styleless, unsealed, conduplicate leaf-like structure with laminar placentation. It has three veins, one dorsal or midvein and two lateral or ventral veins. The stigmatic tissue occurs on the free margins of the carpel (fig. 18.6, *D, E*), on its inner surface, and at times also on the outer surface. Successive phylogenetic stages involve closure of the carpel, reduction in the number of ovules and their restriction to the lower part of the carpel (the ovary), and differentiation of the upper part into the style with a stigma localized on its

ovules

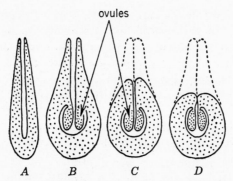

A   B   C   D

FIG. 18.5. Diagrams of transections of carpels of the Ranales. *A*, open folded sterile carpel. *B*, open folded fertile carpel with a locule, toward the dorsal side of the carpel, enclosing ovules. *C* and *D* illustrate stages in phylogenetic closure of folded carpels. The folded ventral part of the carpels (delimited by broken lines) is retracted phylogenetically; that is, it becomes less and less extended during ontogeny. (After Bailey and Swamy, 1951.)

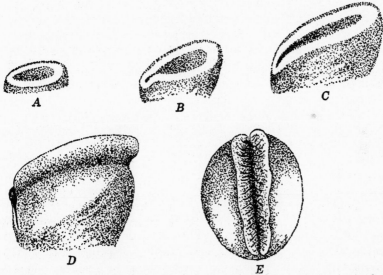

FIG. 18.6. Carpel of *Degeneria vitiensis*—an example of a primitive carpel—in several stages of development. *A*, carpel primordium in the form of a shallow cup. The cessation of divisions on the ventral side results in the formation of a notch (*B*). Uneven growth of the rim transforms the carpel into a conduplicate structure (*C*). The free edges grow out into flanges with flaring margins (*D*, side view, and, *E*, surface view). The internal surfaces of the flanges become stigmatic in the mature carpel. (After Swamy, 1949.)

apex. The closure of the carpel occurs through a growing together (concrescence) of the ventral surfaces along the margins that are in contact with each other. The concrescence occurs during the ontogeny and may leave a conspicuous suture; or the union may be so complete that the evidence of a suture is partly or entirely obliterated (Bailey and Swamy, 1949; Baum, 1949*a*, 1950*b*; Leinfellner, 1950).

The evolutionary changes in the structure of the gynoecium of the angiospermous flower also involve various manners of union of

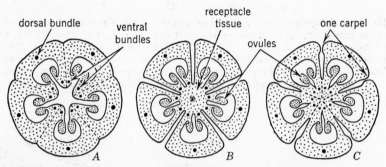

FIG. 18.7. Diagrams of transections of gynoecia of Ranales illustrating syncarpous tendencies. *A*, a whorl of five open folded carpels laterally concrescent. *B*, a whorl of folded carpels adnate to the receptacle with their free margins. *C*, a whorl of folded carpels concrescent in their ventral parts. (After Bailey and Swamy, 1951.)

carpels of the same flower (Bailey and Swamy, 1951; Baum, 1948*c*, 1949*b*; Leinfellner, 1950). The carpels may become joined by their margins to the receptacle (fig. 18.7, *B*), or they may grow together laterally in a closed folded condition (fig. 18.7, *C*), or they may become laterally united in an open folded condition (fig. 18.7, *A*). The union of carpels may occur during their ontogeny (figs. 18.11, *F*, *G*, and 18.12) or they may be fused from their inception and grow as a unit structure (plate 83; Baum, 1949*a*). In relation to the differences in the manner of concrescence, the ovaries show different internal structure. The junction of carpels in an open condition may result in a unilocular ovary (parietal placentation, fig. 18.7, *A*). Folding combined with union of carpels with each other or with receptacular tissue may form an ovary with as many locules as there are carpels. In such ovaries the ovules are borne mostly on the central column of tissue where the carpels come together (axile placentation, fig. 18.7, *B*, *C*).

Various deviations from the basic structures of the ovary just described are encountered in different angiosperms. Division of the ovary into compartments may occur in other ways than by the folding of carpels. The placentae may be borne upon a central column of tissue not connected by partitions with the ovary wall (free central placentation), or at the very base of a unilocular ovary (basal placentation, plate 80, *A*, *B*).

The morphologic nature of the various parts of syncarpous gynoecia is in many instances an unsettled matter. In some hypogynous flowers with axile and free central placentations the column of tissue bearing the ovules apparently may be derived from the receptacle (fig. 18.7, *B*; Bailey and Swamy, 1951; Murray, 1945). In the epigynous flowers there are the problems of determination of the morphology of the noncarpellary tissue (whether it is appendicular or receptacular) in which the ovary is imbedded and of the relative amounts of carpellary and noncarpellary tissues (fig. 18.2; Douglas, 1944).

The ovary wall is not highly differentiated before and during anthesis (time when fertilization takes place in the flower). It consists largely of parenchyma and vascular tissue and bears a cuticularized epidermis on the outer surface. However, the ovary wall undergoes more or less profound changes during the development of the fruit and then may show varied and striking specializations (see chapter 19).

The Style. As was mentioned in the outline of the evolution of the gynoecium, the development of the style (from the Greek, column) occurred as a concomitant of the sterlization of the apical part of the carpel (Bailey and Swamy, 1951). In an apocarpous gynoecium each carpel usually has one simple style. In syncarpous gynoecia the styles of the component carpels may be variously united with each other (Baum, 1948*d*). The carpels may be united only at their bases, leaving the styles free, or partly so (fig. 18.8; Theaceae, Hypericaceae). In highly modified flowers the carpels are united from base to apex and form a gynoecium with a single ovary, style, and stigma (fig. 18.1; Solanaceae, Oleaceae). If the styles are free, the stylar portions derived from the individual carpels are often called style branches. This term, however, gives an erroneous concept of the structure of the compound style, for these branches are morphologically entire styles (Baum, 1948*d*).

The style and the stigma have structural and physiological peculiarities that make possible the germination of the pollen and the growth of the pollen tube from the stigma to the ovules. Upon the stigma the protoderm differentiates into a glandular epidermis with cells rich in cytoplasm, often papillate in shape, and covered with a cuticle (Schnarf, 1928). This epidermis excretes a sugary liquid. Thus, the stigma resembles a nectary in structure and function. (In *Koelreuteria* the stigmatic secretion appears to be resinous, Baum, 1950*d*.) The cells beneath the epidermis may be as rich in cytoplasm as the epidermis, and then they constitute a part of the glandular tissue. In many plants, the stigmatic epidermal cells develop into short, densely crowded hairs (cherry, bean) or into long, branched hairs (grasses and other wind-pollinated plants; plate 83, *F*).

An outstanding feature of the organization of the carpel is that the stigma is connected with the interior of the ovary by a tissue cytologically similar to glandular stigmatic tissue (Coulter and Chamberlain, 1912; Schnarf, 1928). This tissue is interpreted as a medium facilitating the progress of the pollen tube through the style and supplying the developing pollen tube with food. It is commonly called conducting tissue, a term easily confused with that referring to the vascular tissue. The terms transmitting tissue and pollen-transmitting tracts have been proposed as substitutes (Arber, 1937). In the following discussion this tissue is referred to as *stigmatoid tissue* on the basis of its apparent cytologic and physiologic similarity to the tissue of the stigma.

The most primitive carpels of the dicotyledons (e.g., fig. 18.6) do not show a differentiation into stigmatic and stigmatoid tissues, for, as was stated previously, the surfaces of the flaring margins and the inner surface of the open carpel are lined with stigmatic glandular hairs. With the increase in specialization of the carpels, characterized by their gradual closure and the development of the style, the stigma proper became restricted to a part of the style, but the continuity of the stigmatic tissue with the placentae was maintained. The internal glandular surfaces became modified into pollen-transmitting (Bailey and Swamy, 1951) or stigmatoid tissue.

In relation to the variation in degree of concrescence of carpels and in methods of growth of the styles, the styles may be open or solid in both the apocarpous and the syncarpous gynoecia. The open styles are described as having a canal. In a syncarpous gynoecium the compound style may have one common canal (*Viola, Erythronium*), or each component style may have its own canal (*Lilium, Citrus*). The stigmatoid tissue lining the stylar canal resembles the glandular tissue of the stigma and may be papillose. In some plants

starch has been observed in this tissue, and a cuticle has been identified on the surface exposed to the canal. The stigmatoid tissue may
line the entire canal, or it may be restricted to localized parts in the
form of one or more longitudinal bands. In many plants the stigmatoid tissue is several cells in thickness and if, at the same time, it
is distributed in longitudinal bands, one can speak of strands of stigmatoid tissue. Stigmatoid tissue occurs on the placenta within the
ovary and in some species on the funiculus of the ovule as well. In
certain plants the stigmatoid tissue is brought close to the micropyle
by a placental proliferation in the form of a small protuberance, the
obturator (Schnarf, 1928). Developmental studies on the styles of
Datura and *Cucurbita* have shown that the multilayered stigmatoid
tissue lining the stylar canals and placentae in these plants originates
from the epidermis by periclinal divisions (Kirkwood, 1906; Satina,
1944).

In most angiosperms the styles are solid; that is, they have no canals
(fig. 18.1). The stigmatoid tissue is present, nevertheless, usually
in the form of strands of considerably elongated cells staining deeply
with cytoplasmic stains. If the gynoecium with a single solid style
is syncarpous, the stigmatoid tissue of the style forms several strands,
each leading to a different placenta. Commonly the stigmatoid tissue
has a course independent from that of the vascular bundles, but it
may be associated with the bundles (e.g., *Zea*, Kiesselbach, 1949).

The possible factors that might direct the growth of pollen toward
the ovule have been discussed in the literature. Some workers
stress the evidence that there is a chemotactic attraction between the
pollen tube and the tissues of the stigma and of the ovule; others consider that the structure of the stigmatoid tissue and its distribution in
the pistil are sufficient to account for the direction of growth of the
pollen tube (Brink, 1924; Renner and Preuss-Herzog, 1943; Schnarf,
1928). The presence of pollen tubes within the stigmatoid tissue has
been repeatedly ascertained in various plants (fig. 18.8; Borthwick,
1931; Doak, 1937; Maheshwari, 1950; Pope, 1946; Schnarf, 1928;
Schoch-Bodmer and Huber, 1947).

The relation of the pollen tube to the stigmatoid tissue is somewhat
different in styles with and without open canals. In the former, the
pollen tubes may have an entirely superficial course. After the
germination of the pollen grain on the stigma the pollen tube grows
among the papillae or hairs or on the surface of the nonpapillate cells.
The course in the stylar canal is essentially the same as on the stigma.
Frequently the cuticle disappears in the stylar canal before pollina-

tion, and the walls of the glandular tissue become swollen and soft (Schnarf, 1928). The pollen tube may also penetrate the lining of

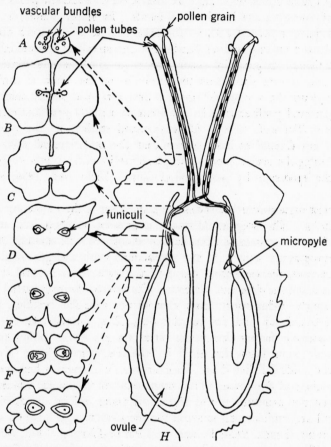

Fig. 18.8. Path of pollen tubes within a flower. Transverse *(A–G)* and longitudinal *(H)* sections of *Daucus carota* (carrot) flowers showing the course of pollen tubes diagrammatically. The blackened parts of the pollen tubes represent plugs of callose. The pollen tube passes through the tissue of the style *(A, B)*, then emerges into the stylar canal *(C)*. Farther down it follows the funiculus *(D, E)* and finally enters the micropyle *(F, G)*. At the level where the stylar canals are interconnected, the pollen tubes may cross over from one carpel to the other *(C, H)*. *(A–G,* ×13; *H,* ×24. After Borthwick, 1931.)

the stylar canal to somewhat deeper layers and proceed there by growing between cells.

If the style is solid, the pollen tube usually passes through the stigmatoid tissue by intercellular growth. Reports that pollen tubes penetrate the cells themselves are not well substantiated (Schnarf, 1928). In grasses, the pollen tube may take an intercellular course on the stigma itself. As was mentioned previously, the grass stigma commonly bears long hairs. These may be multicellular columns, both vertically and horizontally (e.g., *Zea, Hordeum;* Kiesselbach, 1949; Pope, 1946). The pollen tube penetrates into the interior of the column of cells and proceeds from there into the stigmatoid tissue of the style. After the pollen tube reaches the ovarian cavity, it

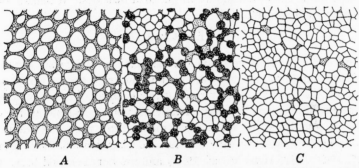

A   *B*   *C*

Fig. 18.9. Relation between the pollen tube and the stigmatoid tissue. Transections of stigmatoid tissue of *Lythrum salicaria* without pollen tubes (*A*), with young, densely cytoplasmic pollen tubes (*B*), and with old pollen tubes having scanty cytoplasm (*C*). The undisturbed mature stigmatoid tissue has thick collenchymatous walls (*A*). The pollen tubes remove these wall thickenings (*B*). The cell lumina of the stigmatoid tissue also shrink. In the exhausted stigmatoid tissue the old pollen tubes are almost indistinguishable (*C*). (All, ×400. After Schoch-Bodmer and Huber, *Naturf. Gesell, Zürich, Vrtljschr.* 92, 1947.)

follows the stigmatoid tissue lining the ovary wall and the placenta and eventually comes in contact with the ovule.

The intercellular growth of the pollen tube appears to involve a digestion of the intercellular substance (Schoch-Bodmer and Huber, 1947). This assumption is supported by the report that pollen tubes give a positive reaction for an enzyme capable of digesting pectic substances (Paton, 1921). However, the stigmatoid tissue appears to undergo a partial weakening in its structure before the pollen tube passes through it. Its walls assume a swollen aspect (the tissue resembles collenchyma in this state, fig. 18.9, *A*), and the connection between cells is loosened, as demonstrated by the ease with which the tissue may be macerated. In fact, the walls appear as though they have been converted into a mucilage (Schnarf, 1928). When the pollen tube passes through the stigmatoid tissue, it occupies the space formerly filled with cell wall material (fig. 18.9, *B*). The protoplasts of the stigmatoid tissue may also become exhausted and sometimes even shrivel and die. Because of these relationships the entry of pollen tubes, even if these are very numerous, does not cause the expansion of the stigmatoid tissue (Schoch-Bodmer and Huber, 1947). The pollen tubes may be said to replace some of the stigmatoid tissue (fig. 18.9, *C*).

The stigmatoid tissue and the vascular bundles constitute the most specialized parts of the style. The ground tissue is parenchymatous, and the outer epidermis shows no peculiar features. It bears a cuticle and may have stomata.

The Ovule

The ovule developing from the placenta of the ovary is the seat of formation of the megaspores (or macrospores) and of the development of the embryo sac (female gametophyte) from a megaspore. Sporogenesis, the development of the embryo sac, and the many variations in the details of these phenomena, have been the subject of numerous investigations (cf. Coulter and Chamberlain, 1912; Schnarf, 1927, 1928, 1931; Maheshwari, 1950) and are not reviewed here. Concomitant with the development of the embryo from the fertilized egg, and of the endosperm from the product of the triple fusion (two polar nuclei and one sperm nucleus), the ovule develops into a seed. Histologically, the ovule is rather simple as compared with the resulting seed.

Commonly the ovule is differentiated into the following morphologic parts (plate 80, *C*): the *nucellus* (from the Latin, small kernel), a central body of tissue containing some vegetative and some sporogenous cells; one or two *integuments* (from the Latin, covering) enclosing the nucellus; the *funiculus* (from the Latin, rope), the stalk by means of which the ovule is attached to the placenta. The size of the nucellus, the number of integuments, and the shape of the ovule are important distinguishing characteristics of ovules in different groups of angiosperms. If the nucellar apex points away from the funiculus, the ovule is termed *atropous* (synonym of *orthotropous; a*, not; *tropos*, turned, in Greek), that is, not turned. If the ovule is completely inverted so that the nucellar apex is turned toward the funiculus, it is called *anatropous* (*ana*, up, in Greek; plate 80, *C*). Between these two extreme forms of ovules, there are several variously named intermediate ones with various degrees of curvature (Maheshwari, 1950; Schnarf, 1927).

The ovule primordium arises from the placenta as a conical protuberance with a rounded apex. The first sporogeneous cell (archesporial cell) becomes evident, in the still undifferentiated protuberance, by its size and often also by a certain density of cytoplasm. This cell appears beneath the protoderm at the apex of the primordium. Slightly below the apex the inner integument (or the integument, if only one is formed) is initiated by periclinal divisions in the protoderm. It arises as a ring-like welt and grows upward (fig. 18.12, *B*). With the appearance of the integument, the nucellus of the primordium becomes delimited as the part enveloped by the integument (plate 80, *A*). The latter grows faster than the nucellus and encloses it partially or completely. Usually a narrow, canal-like opening remains at the top of the integument. This is the *micropyle* (fig. 18.12, *C*, and plate 80, *C*; from the Greek, *micros*, small, and *pyle*, gate-like). The outer integument, if such develops at all, arises in the protoderm slightly below the inner integument and develops in a manner similar to that of the inner (fig. 18.12, *C*, and plate 80, *B*). It frequently does not reach the apex of the ovule in its upward growth. In the anatropous and other curved ovules the growth of the integuments is asymmetrical, being more pronounced on the side of the ovule which eventually becomes convex (plate 80).

There is no complete agreement on the morphologic nature of the ovule and its parts. Some workers consider the ovule a foliar structure, others an axial (Coulter and Chamberlain, 1912). The nucellus is commonly regarded as the megasporangium, but the interpretation of the homology of the integuments constitutes a major morphologic problem (Chadefaud, 1946).

The nucellus, the integuments, and the funiculus cannot be sharply delimited from one another either morphologically or cytologically (e.g., Satina, 1945). The nucellus is usually clearly outlined above the level where the integuments originate (plate 80). From this level upward the nucellus and the integument (or integuments) have each their distinct epidermal layers (plate 80, *B*). Below this level, that is, at the base of the nucellus, the nucellus and the integuments are confluent with the funiculus. The region of the ovule where all its parts merge with one another is called the *chalaza* (plate 80, *C*; from the Greek, small tubercle).

The ovules of certain plants show considerable deviations from·the structure just outlined (Maheshwari, 1950; Schnarf, 1927). Some have no integuments, and others have more than two. The nucellus may be entirely confluent with the integuments, a condition supposedly different from that interpreted as absence of integument. Ovules may have other outgrowths than the integuments, such as the aril (*Euonymus europaeus*) derived from the funiculus, and the caruncle (*Ricinus*), an integumentary protuberance near the micropyle. In some plants the integument so completely overgrows the nucellus that no micropyle remains; in others, on the contrary, the integuments never reach the apex of the nucellus.

The nucellus varies in size in different groups of plants. It may be so small that it comprises little more than an epidermis and the sporogenous tissue enclosed by it (plate 80, *A, C*). In other plants a more or less massive vegetative tissue envelops the sporogenous tissue (plate 80, *B*). The integuments also show variations in thickness. The thinnest integument is two cells thick; that is, it consists only of the two epidermal layers (plate 80, *B*). Sometimes the micropylar end is somewhat thicker in the two-layered integuments. Most angiosperms have two-layered integuments, although some dicotyledonous families have integuments of three and more layers (Netolitzky, 1926). Ovules with large nucelli and two integuments are considered to be more primitive than those with small nucelli and a single integument.

The ovules have a vascular system connected with that of the placenta. The presence of integumentary bundles is sometimes considered a primitive characteristic, but such bundles occur in the more specialized as well as in the less specialized angiosperms, and therefore their phylogenetic significance is uncertain (Kühn, 1928). Most commonly there is a single strand ending in the chalaza with no prolongations into the integuments (Kühn, 1928). In some species the bundle extends beyond the chalaza as a single strand or is variously branched. Such an intraovular system occurs in the integument. If two integuments are present, vascular tissue may be found in both integuments or only in the outer. Rarely does vascular tissue occur in the nucellus (Kühn, 1928; Maheshwari, 1950; Schnarf, 1931). The vascular bundles, though collateral in the funiculus, are usually amphicribral higher in the ovule. The vascular tissue is primary and appears to be in a functioning state during the maturation of the seed.

The distribution of cuticles in the ovules deserves special mention because of their prominence and physiologic importance in the seed that develops from the ovule. The cuticles of the ovules and seeds are called by various names: cuticles, suberized membranes, semipermeable membranes, and fatty membranes. They are here referred to as cuticles in keeping with the most prevalent designation (Schnarf, 1927). Cuticles are reported to be present in ovules in relatively early stages of development (Schnarf, 1927). The entire surface of the ovule primordium bears a cuticle. After the development of the integuments three cuticular layers may be distinguished: the outer, on the outside of the outer integument and the funiculus; the median, double in nature, between the two integuments; the inner, also double in nature, between the inner integument and the nucellus. In ovules with a single integument the median cuticle is absent. If the nucellus is small and its vegetative tissue is disorganized during the development of the embryo sac, the cuticle of the micropylar part of the nucellus may be dissolved also (e.g., Scrophulariaceae, Labiatae, Campanulaceae).

Parts of the ovule are disorganized during the development of the embryo sac, and the resulting materials are presumably utilized by the growing female gametophyte. The vegetative tissue of the nucellus is partly or entirely resorbed. In the latter instance the embryo sac comes in contact with the inner epidermis of the integument. Large nucelli may be partially retained, and in some plant groups they form a storage tissue (*perisperm*) in the seed (e.g., Centrospermae; fig. 20.4, *A*). The nucellar epidermis is sometimes highly resistant and may proliferate into a nucellar cap with relatively thick walls (*Allium*).

The integuments undergo certain histologic changes or are disorganized to varying degrees. Particularly common is the differentiation of the inner epidermis of the integument into the so-called nutritive jacket or *integumentary tapetum* consisting of deeply staining cells elongated perpendicularly with reference to the surface of the embryo sac (plate 80, *C*). Such differentiation is characteristic of families in which the nucellus is early disorganized and the integument comes in contact with the embryo sac (Sympetalae). The physiologic significance of the integumentary tapetum is not agreed upon, and it might be variable (Schnarf, 1927). Some connection with the nutrition of the embryo is suggested by the disintegration of the ovule tissue located next to the tapetum (fig. 19.4) and the persistence of the tapetum until the contents of the embryo sac complete their development (fig. 19.5).

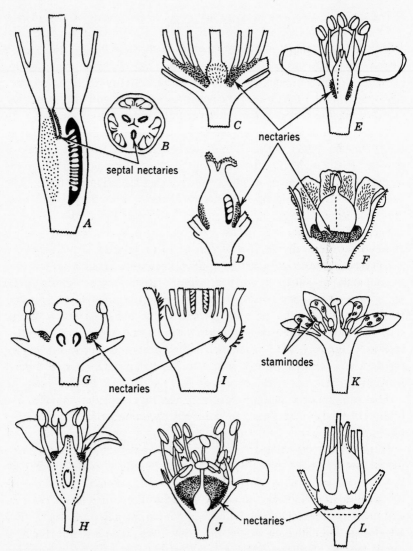

Fɪɢ. 18.10. Diagrams illustrating location of nectaries (densely stippled) as seen in longitudinal (*A*, *C–L*) and transverse (*B*) sections of flowers. Septal nectaries in Liliales, *Narcissus* (*A*) and *Gladiolus* (*B*). *C*, external nectaries in basal parts of stamens (*Thea*, Theales). *D*, ring in base of ovary (*Euyra*, Theales). *E*, ring below stamens (*Coccoloba*, Polygonales). *F*, disc below ovary (*Jatropha*, Euphorbiales). *G*, disc between ovary and stamens (*Perrottetia*, Celastrales). *H*, disc above the inferior ovary (*Mastixia*, Umbellales). *I*, cushion of hairs at base of sepal (*Corchorus*, Tiliales). *J*, secretory tissue lining the perigynous floral cup (*Prunus*, Rosales). *K*, nectaries as modified stamens, the staminodes (*Cin-*

The Nectary

The sugar-containing nectar of insect-pollinated flowers is secreted either by special structures borne directly on the receptacle or by glandular surfaces on various floral parts (Martinet, 1872; Porsch, 1913; Sperlich, 1939). Both the differentiated structures and the glandular surfaces are called nectaries or glands.

Many types of nectaries are recognized in the dicotyledons (Brown, 1938; Porsch, 1913). Nectar may be secreted by the basal parts of stamens (fig. 18.10, *C*) or by a ring-like nectary below the stamens (fig. 18.10, *E*; Caryophyllales, Polygonales, Chenopodiales). The nectary may be a ring or a disc at the base of the ovary (fig. 18.10, *D*, *F*; Theales, Ericales, Polemoniales, Solanales, Lamiales) or a disc between the stamens and the ovary (fig. 18.10, *G*). Several discrete glands may occur at the base of the stamens (fig. 18.10, *L*). In the Tiliales the nectaries consist of multicellular glandular hairs, usually packed close together to form a cushion-like growth (fig. 18.10, *I*). Such nectaries occur on various floral parts, frequently on sepals. In the perigynous Rosaceae the nectary is located between the ovary and the stamens, lining the interior of the floral cup (fig. 18.10, *J*). In the epigynous flower of the Umbellales the nectary occurs on the top of the ovary (fig. 18.10, *H*). In the Compositae it is a tubular structure at the top of the ovary, encircling the base of the style. In most of the insect-pollinated genera of the Lamiales, Berberidales, and Ranunculales the nectaries are modified stamens, or staminodes (fig. 18.10, *K*).

In the monocotyledons the nectaries frequently occur in the partitions or septae of the ovaries (fig. 18.10, *A*, *B*; septal nectaries; Brown, 1938; Okimoto, 1948; Sperlich, 1939). These nectaries have the structure of pockets with a glandular lining and arise in parts of the ovary where the carpel walls are incompletely fused. If they are deeply imbedded in the ovary, they have outlets in the form of canal§ leading to the surface of the ovary.

The secretory tissue of the nectary may be restricted to the epidermal layer. Usually the secretory epidermal cells have dense cytoplasm and may be papillate or elongated like palisade cells (Agthe, 1951). In some plants, however, the secretory epidermis shows no

namomum, Laurales). *L*, small glands at bases of stamens (*Linum*, Geraniales). (Adapted from Brown, *Amer. Phil. Soc. Proc.* 79, No. 4, 1938.)

distinguishing cytological characteristics. In many nectaries the cells beneath the epidermis also are rich in cytoplasm, are closely packed, and have thin walls. These cells, together with the epidermis, constitute the secretory tissue. Laticifers may be present in the nectary.

The nectaries that are differentiated as organized structures are associated with vascular tissues. These approach the secretory tissue and may branch below it, but they do not occur among the secretory cells. There is good evidence (Agthe, 1951) that the vascularization of nectaries varies and that these variations are related to the type of nectar secreted. In nectaries secreting a highly concentrated sugar solution, the ultimate branches of the vascular system terminating below the secretory tissue consist of phloem elements only (*Euphorbia pulcherrima, Abutilon striatum*). Such nectaries contrast strikingly with hydathodes (see chapter 16) in which the ultimate branchings of the vascular system contain only tracheary elements. Nectaries and hydathodes also differ in cell arrangement. In the nectary the parenchyma cells are closely packed, whereas in the hydathodes the tissue is permeated with intercellular spaces (plate 68, *A*). Certain nectaries (e.g., *Ranunculus, Fritillaria*) occupy an intermediate position between the most highly specialized nectaries and the hydathodes. In such nectaries the ground tissue is moderately compact, xylem and phloem occur in the final branchings of the vascular system, and the nectar shows moderate concentration of sugar.

A cuticle is present on the nectaries. Studies on *Hevea* nectaries indicate that the nectary cuticle may have a different composition from the ordinary cuticle; at least in this plant it has been found to be isotropic, whereas usually the cuticle shows some double refraction attributed to the presence of wax (Sperlich, 1939; see also chapter 3).

ORIGIN AND DEVELOPMENT OF THE FLOWER

The change from vegetative to reproductive activity in the apical meristem follows a sequence that is determined by the nature of the plant (Grainger, 1939). Herbaceous annuals pass, during one season, through an uninterrupted sequence of vegetative growth, floral initiation, and floral development. Woody species, at least in the North Temperate zone, commonly initiate the flowers in one season and complete their development during the next. The degree of differentiation that the flowers attain before the end of the first season is highly variable (Roberts, 1937). Floral initiation is affected by external factors, but only within the limits of reactivity of the plant to a given environment. Plants show, for example, characteristic responses to length of day and to temperature and produce flowers under specific combinations of these two factors (Verdoorn, 1948).

The Floral Meristem

Flowers arise at the apex of the main shoot, or on lateral branches, or on both. The lateral branches may form further branches of various orders before producing flowers. In different angiosperms the groupings of the flowers, called inflorescences, are highly variable and bear special names (Rickett, 1944). The formation of all types of inflorescences involves, in the activity of a given apical meristem, a cessation of the vegetative phase and the initiation of the reproductive phase.

Questions pertaining to the developmental relation between the apical meristems in the vegetative and reproductive states and to the significance of the structural differences of the meristem in the two states have been considered in chapter 5. To recapitulate briefly, some workers consider that the floral apex belongs to a different morphological category from the vegetative (e.g., Grégoire, 1938); others regard the floral apex as a developmental continuation of the vegetative apex and fundamentally similar to it (e.g., Boke, 1947; Eames and MacDaniels, 1947, p. 74; Lawalrée, 1948; Philipson, 1949; Sass, 1944; Satina and Blakeslee, 1941). The two most commonly cited differences between the two kinds of apices pertain to their shape and to the cytohistological details. The floral apex, often broad and flat, bears a relatively thin covering of eumeristem (p. 82) and beneath it a vacuolated core. This cytohistologic pattern is related to the mode of growth of the reproductive apex. The emphasis in this growth is not upon increase in length and maintenance of the apical meristem but upon a uniform expansion and the production of a limited number of appendages.

Organogenesis

Much can be learned about floral development by comparing flowers in different stages of development in material dissected under magnifications of moderate degrees. Payer (1857) employed this method in his classic comparative study of organ development in flowers, and in modern times it has been applied with particular success to investigations of floral differentiation in the Gramineae (Bonnett, 1935, 1936, 1937, 1940, 1948; Evans and Grower, 1940; Sharman, 1947). A correlation of the observations on dissected material with those on flowers sectioned with a microtome gives a rather comprehensive picture of the main phenomena in the development of the specific form of flowers and their parts.

Depending on the structure of the flower, the parts may appear in acropetal order at successively higher levels like the leaves on a vegetative shoot (e.g., *Ranunculus*), or the parts of a given kind may arise at the same level or nearly so (e.g., *Capsella*). In the former instance the floral parts are arranged helically; in the latter they are in whorls (cycles). If the parts arise in a helical sequence, the helices of the various parts are usually not continuous with one another. The calyx members, however, may appear along helices that are continuations of those of the foliage leaves (Plantefol, 1948). The flower parts either arise in a continuous acropetal sequence of sepals, petals, stamens, and carpels, or else this sequence is more or less modified. In *Capsella*, for example, the stamen and carpel primordia appear before those of the petals.

As was mentioned previously, the floral parts may remain discrete at maturity, or they may become variously united within the whorls and between whorls. Three developmental patterns may bring about the union of parts: (1) the whorl arises as a unit structure; that is, the parts of the whorl show congenital unity (congenital, from the Latin, born together); (2) the parts of a whorl or of adjacent whorls become joined during ontogeny; (3) the union of parts results from a combination of the two phenomena, the ontogenetic and congenital unions. The calyx and corolla tubes in *Datura*, for example, arise by ontogenetic fusion (Satina, 1944). Those of *Frasera* are congenitally united, for they are formed by intercalary growth of a ring of tissue at the base of the primordia of calyx and corolla (McCoy, 1940). In *Vinca*, however, the corolla tube consists of two parts, one formed by intercalary growth of receptacular tissue at the base of the petals, the other resulting from the union of the bases of the initially free petals (Boke, 1948).

The development of an initially open carpel into a closed structure involves a clearly expressed ontogenetic union of carpel margins (Baum, 1948*a*, *b*, *d*). The lower part of the carpel, however, may have a sac-like seamless form from the inception of the primordium (fig. 18.6). Many workers interpret this developmental feature as a result of the peltation mentioned on p. 532 (Baum, 1949a; Juhnke and Winkler, 1938; Sprotte, 1940; Troll, 1939). The formation of syncarpous gynoecia is associated with congenital and ontogenetic union in varying proportions (Baum, 1948a, b, 1949b, d; Boke, 1949; Leinfellner, 1950). There may be also an ontogenetic union between the carpels and the stamens (Baum, 1948c). On the other hand, the perianth parts and the stamens may originate together from unit primordia and become distinct during later growth (Ehrenberg, 1945; Jones and Emsweller, 1936).

The features discussed above may be elucidated by means of specific examples of floral development. The flower of *Allium cepa* (onion) is relatively unspecialized in having an undifferentiated perianth of free parts and a superior ovary (fig. 18.11, *A*). Its carpels are united, however. The six-parted perianth consists of two whorls of tepals, an outer and an inner. The six stamens occur in the axils of the six perianth members. The three carpels are united into a gynoecium with a three-loculed ovary and an axile placentation. The style is thin and has a slightly three-lobed stigma. An individual flower is a globose protuberance before the flower parts appear. The outer three tepals arise first. The stamens in the axils of these tepals arise simultaneously with the tepals and from the same primordia (fig. 18.11, *B*). The outer tepals and the associated stamens arise in a clockwise direction. The inner tepals and the stamens subtended by them also arise together, but in a counterclockwise direction (fig. 18.11, *B*, *C*). With further growth, the tepals overarch the stamens (fig. 18.11, *D*, *E*). When this stage is reached, the carpels are initiated. They occur within the inner staminal whorl in alternation with its members. At first they project over the surface of the receptacle in the form of three horseshoe-shaped welts of meristematic tissue (fig. 18.11, *F*). Then they grow upward and toward the center where their margins meet and fuse (fig. 18.11, *G*). The compound style is formed by apical growth of the three carpels, the three parts uniting completely (fig. 18.12, *A–D*). The base of the style eventually appears deeply imbedded in the center of the ovary because the carpels bulge upward during the differentiation of the ovules (fig. 18.12, *D*). The ovules are initiated before the carpel margins fuse. They are anatropous and have two integuments (fig. 18.12).

The flower of *Lactuca sativa* (lettuce) may be used to illustrate the growth of a highly specialized flower, one with an inferior ovary (epigynous flower) and a zygomorphic sympetalous corolla (Jones,

1927). Lettuce belongs to the Compositae in which the flowers occur in capitate (head-like) inflorescences. The individual flowers arise acropetally on the flattened receptacle, so that the outermost

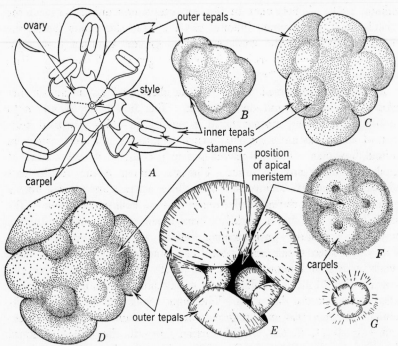

FIG. 18.11. Development of the flower of *Allium cepa* (onion). *A*, diagrammatic drawing of an opened flower seen from above. Three outer tepals and three inner tepals constitute the perianth. Each tepal subtends a stamen. Those in the axils of the inner tepals have widened bases. The gynoecium consists of three fused carpels (syncarpous gynoecium). The solid lines divide the ovary into the three component carpels. The lines of dehiscence (broken lines) alternate with the lines of union (loculicidal dehiscence). *B–E*, four stages in the development of tepals and stamens as seen from above. *F* and *G*, two stages in the development of carpels as seen from above. Further details are in the text. (*A*, ✕9; *B–F*, ✕70; *G*, ✕28. *B–G*, after Jones and Emsweller, 1936.)

flowers of a head are the oldest, the innermost the youngest (fig. 18.13, *A–C*). In an individual flower, the petal lobes appear first, as five protuberances on the margin of the floral primordium. However, immediately upon their appearance they are thrust upward by intercalary growth of a ring of tissue upon which the corolla is inserted. As a result of this growth the central part of the flower primordium becomes cup-shaped (fig. 18.13, *C*, primordium in center). The stamens, which are initiated after the corolla, seem to be inserted below the corolla, but actually they occur closer to the center or apex of the flower than the other floral parts (fig. 18.13, D). The pappus, which is interpreted sometimes as a set of epidermal trichomes (Puri, 1951), sometimes as the calyx, appears al-

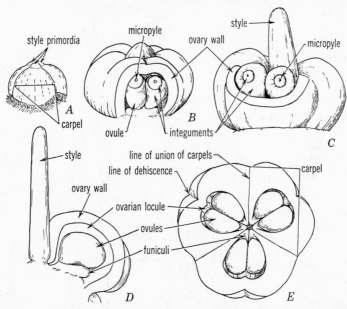

Fɪɢ. 18.12. Development of the gynoecium of *Allium cepa* (onion). *A*, young gynoecium in side view. The apices of the three carpels have begun to extend, forming jointly a compound style. *B–D*, side views of gynoecia in three developmental stages, partly cut open to expose the ovules. *E*, ovary opened by a transverse cut and seen from above. Further details are in the text. (All, ×28. After Jones and Emsweller, 1936.)

most at the same time as the stamens. It arises below and opposite the stamens on the outer surface of the rim of the cup-like primordium which higher up bears the corolla and the stamens (fig. 18.13, *D*, *E*).

In its further growth the corolla develops as a tubular structure with a unilateral strap-shaped prolongation (zygomorphic ligulate corolla). Two phases may be distinguished in the growth of the corolla tube. First, intercalary growth above the insertion of the stamens forms the upper part of the corolla tube (fig. 18.13, *G*). Second, intercalary growth below the insertion of the stamens forms the lower part of the tube (fig. 18.13, *H*) in which the bases of the

corolla and of the stamens are congenitally fused (epipetalous stamens). The second phase occurs comparatively late in the development of the flower. In the Compositae with actinomorphic tubular

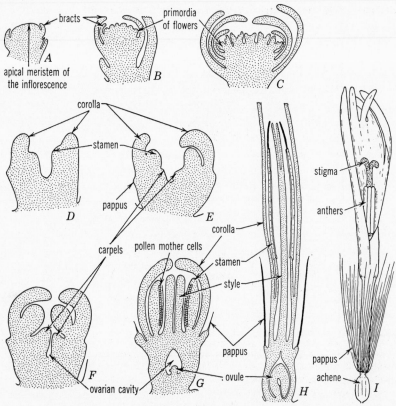

Fig. 18.13. Development of the flower of *Lactuca sativa* (lettuce). *A–H*, outline
drawings of longitudinal sections of young inflorescences (*A–C*) and flowers
(*D–H*). *I*, sketch of entire flower. *Lactuca* flower has an inferior ovary and
a sympetalous zygomorphic corolla. The stamens are adnate to the corolla
(epipetalous), and their anthers are joined into a column. The style is compound (composed of two styles, one from each of the two carpels). The two
strap-shaped ends of the style bear stigmatic hairs. Further details are in the text.
(*A–C*, ×29; *D–F*, ×153; *G, H*, ×27; *I*, ×7. After Jones, 1927.)

corollas the growth of the upper part of the corolla is uniform
throughout. In zygomorphic corollas, as in lettuce, the upper part
grows asymmetrically (fig. 18.13, *I*). The free parts of the stamens
elongate also, and each becomes differentiated into a filament and
an anther (fig. 18.13, *H*).

The carpels develop at the morphologically highest position of the flower, that is, within the cavity of the cup-like primordium. The two carpels become visible as two protuberances located seemingly below the stamens (fig. 18.13, *E, F*). These two carpel units over-arch the ovarian cavity (fig. 18.13, *F*) and become prolonged above into a solid compound style with a two-part stigma (fig. 18.13, *G, H*). As was pointed out previously, the identification of the part of the epigynous flower investing the ovary (that is, the cup bearing the calyx, the corolla, and the stamens), constitutes one of the major problems of floral morphology (Douglas, 1944). The view most widely accepted at present with regard to the Compositae is that this cup consists of adnate bases of the floral whorls joined to the carpel bases; that, in other words, the ovary is enclosed by the floral tube, or the tube is lined internally by carpellary tissue.

The development of an inflorescence and flower of a representative of the Gramineae may be illustrated by reference to the study on *Triticum* and *Avena* (Bonnett, 1936, 1937). The wheat inflorescence is a spike and consists of several groups of flowers, each referred to as a spikelet. In *Triticum*, the spikelets are attached directly to the main axis, the rachis (plate 82, *A*). A spikelet of a grass (fig. 18.14, *D*, and plate 82, *D*) consists of a short axis, the rachilla, bearing several chaff-like, two-ranked (distichous), overlapping bracts (commonly called glumes). The two lowermost bracts bear no flowers in their axils and are called empty glumes. Above the empty glumes are others that subtend flowers, usually referred to as florets (fig. 18.14, *A–C*). The wheat spikelet has four to six florets, each subtended by two bracts: the lower or abaxial, called the lemma, and the upper or adaxial, called the palea. The reproductive parts of a grass floret consist of three stamens with thread-like filaments and rather large anthers, and a single, three-carpellate unilocular pistil with a short style and two feathery stigmas (fig. 18.14, *A*, and plate 83, *F*). At the base of the ovary and opposite the palea are two lodicules (fig. 18.14, *A*, and plate 83, *E*), small scales involved in the opening of the bracts during anthesis.

The reproductive phase of a wheat plant begins while the plant is still in the rosette stage. The initiation of reproductive phase is quickly followed by a sudden and vigorous elongation of the shoot, the subsequent culm. The addition of leaf primordia ceases, and even the further development of the existing leaf buttresses is stopped. Some of the younger buttresses may be obliterated as the apex expands in length and width. Whereas the foliage leaf primordia

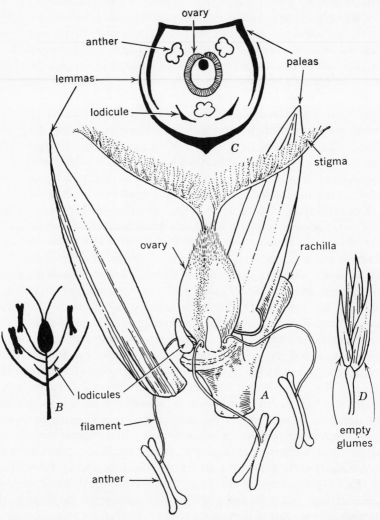

Fig. 18.14. The grass flower. *A*, partly dissected grass flower at anthesis. *B*, longitudinal and, *C*, transverse diagrams of the flower. *D*, spikelet. The lodicules are small scales outside the stamens. (From A. M. Johnson, *Taxonomy of the Flowering Plants*, Appleton-Century-Crofts, Inc., 1931.)

arise as single ridges gradually encircling the shoot axis (plate 81, *A–D*; see also chapter 16), the spikelet development is initiated by the appearance of double ridges (plate 81, *E–H*). The spikelet proper differentiates from the upper of the paired ridges (plates 81, *F–H*, and 82, *B*). A spikelet is interpreted as an axillary bud, and the lower ridge as the subtending leaf. The first spikelets differentiate in the middle of the spike (plate 81, *F–H*), and differentiation then progresses acropetally and basipetally (plate 82, *B*, *C*). Within the individual spikelet differentiation is acropetal, the parts appear in the sequence of: empty glumes, first flower, second flower, and so forth (plate 82, *B–D*). Within an individual floret the parts arise in the following sequence: lemma, anthers, palea, and gynoecium.

The development of the gynoecium is here discussed mainly with reference to the flower of *Avena* (oat), since it has been studied in detail in this plant rather than in wheat (Bonnett, 1937). The gynoecium originates as a crescent-shaped ridge which is highest on the side toward the lemma (plate 83, *A*). The ovule primordium appears at the same time in the opening between the margins of the crescent (plate 83, *A*). The ridge extends entirely around the ovule primordium (plate 83, *B*). On two sides the margins of the primordium of the gynoecium extend into two styles (plate 83, *C*, *D*). The continued upward growth of the margins below the styles brings about the closure of the ovarian cavity. The stigmatic hairs are the last parts of the gynoecium to develop (plate 83, *E*, *F*). Thus, the grass gynoecium arises as a unit and does not reveal, ontogenetically, the three-carpellate structure ascribed to the flowers of the Gramineae.

The rhythm of the development of a flower as a whole has certain distinguishing characteristics that are closely correlated with the important phenomena of mitosis and meiosis occurring during the formation of spores and gametes (Erickson, 1948). Morphologic observations and studies on comparative weights of developing flowers and their parts show that these parts may have divergent rates of growth after they are initiated (Sosa-Bourdouil, 1945). The petals, for example, may appear before the stamens but may develop more slowly. Sometimes the principal period of growth of the petals occurs only after the stamens cease to grow entirely. Both the petals and the stamens may accelerate their growth rate shortly before anthesis (Pearson, 1933). The remarkable speed with which the stamens may attain their final length is well illustrated by the rate of elongation of 2.5 mm per minute observed in the growing anther filaments of rye (Schoch-Bodmer, 1939). The stamens may lag behind the gynoecium in development at first, then rapidly attain the final length which brings the anther into a most favorable position for release of pollen (fig. 18.14, *A*). The ovary usually enlarges uniformly like a vegetative organ. Sometimes, however, the enlargement of the ovary slows down before fertilization, and if fertilization fails to take place the gynoecium dies. Comparative studies on floral parts show that the reproductive parts constitute a relatively large mass of the flower as a whole (Sosa-Bourdouil, 1945).

Histogenesis

Studies relating the histogenesis of floral parts to the present concept of the structure and activity of the apical meristem are comparatively few (Boke, 1947, 1948, 1949; Brooks, 1940; Engard, 1944; Kausmann, 1941; Lawalrée, 1948; Satina, 1944; Satina and Blakeslee, 1943). The sepals and petals originate, like the foliage leaves, from periclinal divisions in one or more subsurface layers of the apical meristem. Such origin of the perianth parts is apparently common in both the dicotyledons and the monocotyledons (Kausmann, 1941). In their upward growth (plate 78, *B–D*), the perianth parts show apical activity of short duration followed by some intercalary growth. Marginal activity followed by intercalary growth is responsible for the increase in width of the perianth primordia. In *Vinca* the marginal meristem of the petals is more active than that of the sepals and is involved in the formation of the upper part of the floral tube which arises through the ontogenetic fusion of the corolla lobes (Boke, 1948).

Most workers agree that the stamens and the carpels are initiated just like the members of the perianth (Boke, 1948, 1949; Kausmann, 1941; Lawalrée, 1948; Wilson and Just, 1939). In *Datura*, however, the foliage leaves and the perianth parts have a somewhat more superficial origin than the stamens and the carpels (Satina, 1944; Satina and Blakeslee, 1941, 1943).

After their initiation the stamens (plate 78, *D*) show apical growth of short duration, followed by intercalary growth. In *Vinca*, apical and subapical initials have been recognized during apical growth (Boke, 1949). If the stamen filament is flattened, it shows marginal growth; otherwise such growth is suppressed (Kausmann, 1941). The anthers show a special form of marginal activity which produces the characteristic two-lobed, four-loculed structure, rather than a flat blade (plate 79, *D*; Boke, 1949). The carpels (plates 78, *E*, *F*, and 79,

A) also undergo apical and marginal growth after they are initiated (Boke, 1949; Sprotte, 1940).

Histologic studies have revealed the manner of ontogenetic union of flower parts. As was mentioned previously, the union of perianth parts or of the carpels may be congenital, or it may occur, partly or entirely, during ontogeny. The ontogenetic union is brought about by fusion of the margins of parts that come in contact with each other during growth. In the petals of *Vinca* such union occurs through apposition of two epidermal layers, with the line of union eventually becoming obscured (plate 79, *D, E*; Boke, 1948). Evidence of the fusion of perianth parts is thoroughly obliterated if divisions, periclinal and others, occur in the apposed epidermal layers (e.g., *Datura*; Satina, 1944). The degree of union of carpels also varies from a rather loose one to a thorough interlocking of the epidermal cells, accompanied by divisions in these cells and a complete effacement of the suture (Baum, 1948*a, b, c*, 1950*b*). In the dicotyledons the carpels of syncarpous gynoecia are generally more firmly joined than in the monocotyledons (Baum, 1948*c*).

This review of histogenesis shows the value of developmental studies for clarifying the interrelation of various parts of the flower to one another and to the receptacle. Investigators have also attempted to draw conclusions regarding the morphologic nature of the flower and its parts on the basis of histogenesis (e.g., Boke, 1948, 1949; Brooks, 1940; Lawalrée, 1948; Satina, 1944; Satina and Blakeslee, 1943). Although the information on histogenesis is very important with regard to the solution of the problems of floral morphology, such information alone can hardly give a complete picture of morphologic relationships. The ontogenies of plant parts are known to undergo phylogenetic changes. Therefore, it would seem that developmental studies would contribute most to the understanding of the flower if they were combined with studies on the vascular anatomy. Furthermore, both kinds of studies should be carried out along broad comparative lines.

Vascular Development

The question regarding the direction of differentiation of procambium in the flower plays an important role in the speculations about the morphologic relation between the flower and the shoot. The assumption that there is an acropetal differentiation of procambium in the flower and a basipetal differentiation in the vegetative shoot has been used in support of the concept that the flower is a unique structure not comparable to the shoot (Grégoire, 1938). Later research has shown that there is no such simple and straightforward difference between the flower and the shoot. Acropetal differentiation of the procambium is common in the vegetative shoot in a wide variety of plants (see chapter 15). In the flowers, both acropetal and basipetal differentiation of procambium have been reported (Boke, 1949; Lawalrée, 1948).

The differentiation of the phloem and xylem elements in the floral procambium still awaits investigation with modern techniques. In the old literature xylem is reported to have a pattern of differentiation in the flower similar to that in the shoot, that is, appearing in one or more loci and then progressing bidirectionally toward the distal and the proximal parts of the flower (Trécul, 1881). The report that the phloem of the flowers has a bidirectional course (Grélot, 1897) needs reexamination.

Abscission of Floral Parts

The abscission of floral parts has been less thoroughly investigated than that of the leaves, but the basic phenomena appear to be similar in the separation of all these structures (Pfeiffer, 1928; see also chapter 16). Abscission of parts or of entire structures occurs at various stages in the reproductive process (Pfeiffer, 1928). The completion of flowering may be followed by the shedding of parts of flowers, of entire flowers, or of inflorescences. Particularly common is the shedding of petals. The petals may fall without previous wilting (*Canna, Aquilegia, Cydonia, Rosa, Geranium, Linum*). They also abscise in a wilted or dried state, either close to the level of their insertion (*Lilium, Tulipa*, most Cruciferae, *Cucurbita*), or a short distance above the insertion, with the basal part remaining attached to the flower (*Althaea, Datura, Nicotiana*). If the petals are not shed at the end of flowering, they remain temporarily or permanently attached to the fruit in the dry state (*Agapanthus, Hypericum, Convallaria*). In some monocotyledons the perianth becomes green and persists in the fruit (*Veratrum, Eucomis, Paris*).

Petals are often constricted in the abscission zone. Usually no cell division precedes abscission, and the separation layer is poorly differentiated. The cells in this layer remain small, little vacuolated, and closely packed. They may contain chloroplasts or chromoplasts, and also raphides. The cells are roundish or polygonal in outline, occasionally tabular, with their long diameters oriented transversely with reference to the long axis of the petal. If the petal is much constricted, collenchyma may be present beneath the epidermis. Apparently the separation results from a softening of the middle lamella. The protection of the scar seems to involve an impregnation of the walls with fatty substances without the deposition of a suberin lamella or formation of cork. Sepals, staminal filaments, and styles may abscise after flowering in essentially the same manner as the petals (Kendall, 1918; Pfeiffer, 1928).

The abscission of entire flowers is characteristic of plants with unisexual flowers. The staminal flowers are regularly abscised after the pollen is shed (Yampolsky, 1934). These flowers may fall singly (Cucurbitaceae) or as entire inflorescences (catkins of the Amentiferae). If fertilization does not take place, carpellate and bisexual flowers may drop also (*Solanum tuberosum, Nicotiana tabacum, Lycopersicon esculentum*). Floral abscission can be induced artificially by various treatments (Kendall, 1918; Laurie and Duffy, 1948). The separation layer in pedicels of flowers is, in some species, preformed during development (Kendall, 1918). Surface grooves are sometimes present in pedicels but do not necessarily coincide with the abscission zone.

REFERENCES

Agthe, C. *Über die physiologische Herkunft des Pflanzennektars.* Thesis. Zürich, Eidgenössische Technische Hochschule. 1951.

Arber, A. The interpretation of the flower: a study of some aspects of morphological thought. *Biol. Rev.* 12:157–184. 1937.

Arber, A. *The natural philosophy of plant form.* Cambridge, Cambridge University Press. 1950.

Baehni, C., and C. E. B. Bonner. La vascularisation des fleurs chez les Lopezieae (Onagracées). *Candollea* 11:305–322. 1947–48.

Bailey, I. W., and C. G. Nast. The comparative morphology of the Winteraceae. I. Pollen and stamens. *Arnold Arboretum Jour.* 24:340–346. 1943*a*.

Bailey, I. W., and C. G. Nast. The comparative morphology of the Winteraceae. II. Carpels. *Arnold Arboretum Jour.* 24:472–481. 1943*b*.

Bailey, I. W., and A. C. Smith. Degeneriaceae, a new family of flowering plants from Fiji. *Arnold Arboretum Jour.* 23:356–365. 1942.

Bailey, I. W., and B. G. L. Swamy. The morphology and relationships of *Austrobaileya*. *Arnold Arboretum Jour.* 30:211–226. 1949.

Bailey, I. W., and B. G. L. Swamy. The conduplicate carpel of dicotyledons and its initial trends of specialization. *Amer. Jour. Bot.* 38:373–379. 1951.

Bailey, I. W., C. G. Nast, and A. C. Smith. The family Himantandraceae. *Arnold Arboretum Jour.* 24:190–206. 1943.

Bancroft, H. A review of researches concerning floral morphology. *Bot. Rev.* 1:77–99. 1935.

Baum, H. Über die postgenitale Verwachsung in Karpellen. *Österr. Bot. Ztschr.* 95:86–94. 1948a.

Baum, H. Die Verbreitung der postgenitalen Verwachsung im Gynözeum und ihre Bedeutung für die typologische Betrachtung des coenokarpen Gynözeums. *Österr. Bot. Ztschr.* 95:124–128. 1948b.

Baum, H. Postgenitale Verwachsung in und zwischen Karpell- und Staubblattkreisen. *Akad. der Wiss. Wien, Math.-Nat. Kl. Sitzber.* Abt. 1. 157:17–38. 1948c.

Baum, H. Ontogenetische Beobachtungen an einkarpelligen Griffeln und Griffelenden. *Österr. Bot. Ztschr.* 95:362–372. 1948d.

Baum, H. Der einheitliche Bauplan der Angiospermengynözeen und die Homologie ihrer fertilen Abschnitte. *Österr. Bot. Ztschr.* 96:64–82. 1949a.

Baum, H. Zur Frage des schrittweisen Ueberganges vom apokarpen zum coenokarpen Gynözeum. *Österr. Bot. Ztschr.* 95:470–474. 1949b.

Baum, H. Beiträge zur Kenntnis der Schildform bei den Staubblättern. *Österr. Bot. Ztschr.* 96:453–466. 1949c.

Baum, H. Das Zustandekommen "offener" Angiospermengynözeen. *Österr. Bot. Ztschr.* 96:285–288. 1949d.

Baum, H. Unifaziale und subunifaziale Strukturen im Bereich der Blütenhülle und ihre Verwendbarkeit für die Homologisierung der Kelch- und Kronblätter. *Österr. Bot. Ztschr.* 97:1–43. 1950a.

Baum, H. Septalspalten im Gynözeum von *Koelreuteria paniculata*. *Österr. Bot. Ztschr.* 97:207–215. 1950b.

Baum, H. Lassen sich in der Ontogenese der Karpelle und Staubblätter noch Anklänge an ihre phylogenetische Entwicklung aus Telomen festellen? *Österr. Bot. Ztschr.* 97:333–341. 1950c.

Baum, H. Das Narbensekret von *Koelreuteria paniculata*. *Österr. Bot. Ztschr.* 97:517–519. 1950d.

Boke, N. H. Development of the adult shoot apex and floral initiation in *Vinca rosea* L. *Amer. Jour. Bot.* 34:433–439. 1947.

Boke, N. H. Development of the perianth in *Vinca rosea* L. *Amer. Jour. Bot.* 35:413–423. 1948.

Boke, N. H. Development of the stamens and carpels in *Vinca rosea* L. *Amer. Jour. Bot.* 36:535–547. 1949.

Bonne, G. *Recherches sur le pédicelle et la fleur des Rosacées.* Paris, Jouve et Cie. 1928.

Bonner, C. E. B. The floral vascular supply in *Epilobium* and related genera. *Candollea* 11:277–303. 1947–48.

Bonnett, O. T. The development of the barley spike. *Jour. Agr. Res.* 51:451–457. 1935.

Bonnett, O. T. The development of the wheat spike. *Jour. Agr. Res.* 53:445–451. 1936.

Bonnett, O. T. The development of the oat panicle. *Jour. Agr. Res.* 54:927–931. 1937.

Bonnett, O. T. Development of the staminate and pistillate inflorescences of sweet corn. *Jour. Agr. Res.* 60:25–37. 1940.

Bonnett, O. T. Ear and tassel development in maize. *Mo. Bot. Gard. Ann.* 35:269–287. 1948.

Borthwick, H. A. Development of the macrogametophyte and embryo of *Daucus carota*. *Bot. Gaz.* 92:23–44. 1931.

Brink, R. A. The physiology of pollen. *Amer. Jour. Bot.* 11:218–228, 283–294, 351–364, 417–436. 1924.

Brooks, R. M. Comparative histogenesis of vegetative and floral apices in *Amygdalus communis*, with special reference to the carpel. *Hilgardia* 13:249–306. 1940.

Brown, W. H. The bearing of nectaries on the phylogeny of flowering plants. *Amer. Phil. Soc. Proc.* 79:549–595. 1938.

Chadefaud, M. L'origine et l'évolution de l'ovule des Phanérogames. *Rev. Sci.* (*Paris*) 84:502–509. 1946.

Cooper, D. C. Nuclear divisions in the tapetal cells of certain angiosperms. *Amer. Jour. Bot.* 20:358–364. 1933.

Coulter, J. M., and C. J. Chamberlain. *Morphology of angiosperms.* New York, D. Appleton and Company. 1912.

Doak, C. C. The pistil anatomy of cotton as related to environmental control of fertilization under varied conditions of pollination. *Amer. Jour. Bot.* 24:187–194. 1937.

Douglas, G. E. The inferior ovary. *Bot. Rev.* 10:125–186. 1944.

Eames, A. J. The role of flower anatomy in the determination of angiosperm phylogeny. *Internatl. Cong. Plant Sci. Proc.* I:423–427. 1929.

Eames, A. J. The vascular anatomy of the flower with refutation of carpel polymorphism. *Ann. Bot.* 18:147–188. 1931.

Eames, A. J., and L. H. MacDaniels. *Introduction to plant anatomy.* 2nd ed. New York, McGraw-Hill Book Company. 1947.

Ehrenberg, L. Zur Kenntnis der Homologieverhältnisse in der angiospermen Blüte. *Bot. Notiser* 1945:438–444. 1945.

Engard, C. J. Organogenesis in *Rubus*. *University of Hawaii Research Publ.* 21. 1944.

Erickson, R. C. Cytological and growth correlations in the flower bud and anther of *Lilium longiflorum*. *Amer. Jour. Bot.* 35:729–739. 1948.

Evans, M. W., and F. O. Grover. Developmental morphology of the growing point of the shoot and the inflorescence in grasses. *Jour. Agr. Res.* 61:481–520. 1940.

Glück, H. *Blatt- und blütenmorphologische Studien.* Jena, Gustav Fischer. 1919.

Grainger, J. Studies upon the time of flowering of plants. Anatomical, floristic and phenological aspects of the problem. *Ann. Appl. Biol.* 26:684–704. 1939.

Grégoire, V. La morphogénèse et l'autonomie morphologique de l'appareil floral. I. Le carpelle. *Cellule* 17:287–452. 1938.

Grélot, P. Recherches sur le système libéroligneux floral des gamopétales bicar-pellés. *Ann. des Sci. Nat., Bot.* Ser. 8. 5:1–154. 1897.

Gumppenberg, O. von. Beiträge zur Entwicklungsgeschichte der Blumenblätter mit besonderer Berücksichtigung der Nervatur. *Bot. Arch.* 7:448–490. 1924.

Hiller, G. H. Untersuchungen über die Epidermis der Blühtenblätter. *Jahrb. f. Wiss. Bot.* 15:411–451. 1884.

Hunt, K. W. A study of the style and stigma, with reference to the nature of the carpel. *Amer. Jour. Bot.* 24:288–295. 1937.

Jackson, G. The morphology of flowers of *Rosa* and certain closely related genera. *Amer. Jour. Bot.* 21:453–466. 1934.

Johnson, A. M. *Taxonomy of the flowering plants.* New York, The Century Co. 1931.

Jones, H. A. Pollination and life history studies of lettuce (*Lactuca sativa* L.). *Hilgardia* 2:452–479. 1927.

Jones, H. A., and S. L. Emsweller. Development of the flower and macrogametophyte of *Allium cepa*. *Hilgardia* 10:415–428. 1936.

Joshi, A. C. Floral histogenesis and carpel morphology. *Indian Bot. Soc. Jour.* 28:64–74. 1947.

Juhnke, G., and H. Winkler. Der Balg als Grundelement des Angiospermengynaeceums. *Beitr. z. Biol. der Pflanz.* 25:290–324. 1938.

Kausmann, B. Vergleichende Untersuchungen über die Blattnatur der Kelch-, Blumen-, und Staubblätter. *Bot. Arch.* 42:503–572. 1941.

Kendall, J. N. Abscission of flowers and fruits in the Solanaceae, with special reference to *Nicotiana*. *Calif. Univ. Pubs. Bot.* 5:347–428. 1918.

Kiesselbach, T. A. The structure and reproduction of corn. *Nebr. Agr. Expt. Sta. Res. Bul.* 161. 1949.

Kirkwood, J. E. The pollen tube in some of the Cucurbitaceae. *Torrey Bot. Club Bul.* 33:327–341. 1906.

Kühn, G. Beiträge zur Kenntnis der intraseminalen Leitbündel bei den Angiospermen. *Bot. Jahrb.* 61:325–379. 1928.

Laurie, A., and J. Duffy. Anatomical studies of the abscission of *Gardenia* buds. *Amer. Soc. Hort. Sci. Proc.* 51:575–580. 1948.

Lawalrée, A. Histogénèse florale et végétative chez quelques Composées. *Cellule* 52:215–294. 1948.

Leinfellner, W. Der Bauplan des synkarpen Gynözeums. *Österr. Bot. Ztschr.* 97:403–436. 1950.

MacDaniels, L. H. The morphology of the apple and other pome fruits. *N. Y. (Cornell) Agr. Exp. Sta. Mem.* 230. 1940.

Maheshwari, P. *An introduction to the embryology of angiosperms.* New York, McGraw-Hill Book Company. 1950.

Martens, P. Recherches sur la cuticule. IV. Le relief cuticulaire et la différenciation épidermique des organes floraux. *Cellule* 43:289–320. 1934.

Martinet, J. Organes de sécrétion des végétaux. *Ann. des Sci. Nat., Bot.* Ser. 5. 14:91–232. 1872.

McCoy, R. W. Floral organogenesis in *Frasera carolinensis*. *Amer. Jour. Bot.* 27:600–609. 1940.

Murray, M. A. Carpellary and placental structure in the Solanaceae. *Bot. Gaz.* 107:243–260. 1945.

Nast, C. G. The comparative morphology of the Winteraceae. VI. Vascular anatomy of the flowering shoot. *Arnold Arboretum Jour.* 25:456–466. 1944.

Netolitzky, F. Anatomie der Angiospermen-Samen. In: K. Linsbauer. *Handbuch der Pflanzenanatomie.* Band 10. Lief. 14. 1926.

Okimoto, M. C. Anatomy and histology of the pineapple inflorescence and fruit. *Bot. Gaz.* 110:217–231. 1948.

Ozenda, P. La nature morphologique du carpelle. *Rev. Sci. (Paris)* 84:393–404. 1946.

Ozenda, P. *Recherches sur les Dicotylédones apocarpiques. Contribution a l'étude des Angiospermes dites primitives.* Thesis. Paris, École Normale Supérieure. Publ. Ser. Biol. Fasc. II. 1949.

Paton, J. V. Pollen and pollen enzymes. *Amer. Jour. Bot.* 8:471–501. 1921.

Payer, J. B. *Traité d'organogénie comparée de la fleur.* Texte, 748 pp. Atlas, 154 plates. Paris, Librarie de Victor Masson. 1857.

Pearson, O. H. Study of the life history of *Brassica oleracea. Bot. Gaz.* 94:534–550. 1933.

Pfeiffer, H. Die pflanzlichen Trennungsgewebe. In: K. Linsbauer. *Handbuch der Pflanzenanatomie.* Band 5. Lief. 22. 1928.

Philipson, W. R. The ontogeny of the shoot apex in dicotyledons. *Biol. Rev.* 24:21–50. 1949.

Plantefol, L. L'ontogénie de la fleur. *Ann. des Sci. Nat., Bot. et Biol. Vég.* Ser. 11. 9:35–186. 1948.

Pope, M. N. The course of the pollen tube in cultivated barley. *Amer. Soc. Agron. Jour.* 38:432–440. 1946.

Porsch, O. Die Abstammung der Monokotylen und die Blütennektarien. *Deut. Bot. Gesell. Ber.* 31:580–590. 1913.

Puri, V. Studies in floral anatomy. VI. Vascular anatomy of the flower of *Crataeva religiosa* Forst., with special reference to the nature of the carpels in the Capparidaceae. *Amer. Jour. Bot.* 37:363–370. 1950.

Puri, V. The role of floral anatomy in the solution of morphological problems. *Bot. Rev.* 17:471–553. 1951.

Reeves, R. G. Partition wall formation in the pollen mother cells of *Zea Mays. Amer. Jour. Bot.* 15:114–122. 1928.

Renner, O., and G. Preuss-Herzog. Der Weg der Pollenschläuche im Fruchtknoten der Oenotheren. *Flora* 36:215–222. 1943.

Rickett, H. W. The classification of inflorescences. *Bot. Rev.* 10:187–231. 1944.

Roberts, R. H. Blossom bud development and winter hardiness. *Amer. Jour. Bot.* 24:683–685. 1937.

Sass, J. E. The initiation and development of foliar and floral organs in the tulip. *Iowa State Col. Jour. Sci.* 18:447–456. 1944.

Satina, S. Periclinal chimeras in *Datura* in relation to development and structure (A) of the style and stigma (B) of calyx and corolla. *Amer. Jour. Bot.* 31:493–502. 1944.

Satina, S. Periclinal chimeras in *Datura* in relation to the development and structure of the ovule. *Amer. Jour. Bot.* 32:72–81. 1945.

Satina, S., and A. F. Blakeslee. Periclinal chimeras in *Datura stramonium* in relation to development of leaf and flower. *Amer. Jour. Bot.* 28:862–871. 1941.

Satina, S., and A. F. Blakeslee. Periclinal chimeras in *Datura* in relation to the development of the carpel. *Amer. Jour. Bot.* 30:453–462. 1943.

Saunders, E. R. *Floral morphology, a new outlook with special reference to the interpretation of the gynaeceum.* Vol. 1. Cambridge, W. Heffer and Sons. 1937.

Schaffner, J. H. The fundamental nature of the flower. *Torrey Bot. Club Bul.* 64:569–582. 1937.

Schnarf, K. Embryologie der Angiospermen. In: K. Linsbauer. *Handbuch der Pflanzenanatomie.* Band 10. Lief. 21. 1927; Lief. 23. 1928.

Schnarf, K. *Vergleichende Embryologie der Angiospermen.* Berlin, Gebrüder Borntraeger. 1931.

Schoch-Bodmer, H. Beiträge zur Kenntnis des Streckungswachstums der Gramineen-Filamente. *Planta* 30:168–204. 1939.

Schoch-Bodmer, H. Über das Spitzenwachstum der Pollenschläuche. *Schweiz. Bot. Gesell. Ber.* **55**:154–168. 1945.

Schoch-Bodmer, H., and P. Huber. Die Ernährung der Pollenschläuche durch das Leitgewebe. (Untersuchungen an *Lythrum Salicaria* L.) *Naturf. Gesell. in Zürich, Vrtljschr.* **92**:43–48. 1947.

Sharman, B. C. The biology and developmental morphology of the shoot in the Gramineae. *New Phytol.* **46**:20–34. 1947.

Sharp, L. W. *Introduction to cytology.* 3rd ed. New York, McGraw-Hill Book Company. 1934.

Smith, F. H., and E. C. Smith. Floral anatomy of the Santalaceae and some related forms. *Oreg. State Monographs, Stud. in Bot. 5.* 1942*a*.

Smith, F. H., and E. C. Smith. Anatomy of the inferior ovary of *Darbya. Amer. Jour. Bot.* **29**:464–471. 1942*b*.

Sosa-Bourdouil, C. Sur le développement comparé des organes floraux. *Soc. Bot. de France Bul.* **92**:154–158. 1945.

Sperlich, A. Das trophische Parenchym. B. Excretionsgewebe. In: K. Linsbauer. *Handbuch der Pflanzenanatomie.* Band 4. Lief. 38. 1939.

Sprotte, K. Untersuchungen über Wachstum und Nervatur der Fruchtblätter. *Bot. Arch.* **40**:463–506. 1940.

Swamy, B. G. L. On carpel. *Current Sci. (India)* **14**:258–259. 1945.

Swamy, B. G. L. Further contributions to the morphology of the Degeneriaceae. *Arnold Arboretum Jour.* **30**:10–38. 1949.

Trécul, A. Recherches sur l'ordre d'apparition des premiers vaisseaux dans les organes aériens. *Ann. des Sci. Nat., Bot.* Ser. 6. **12**:251–381. 1881.

Troll, W. Die morphologische Natur der Karpelle. *Chron. Bot.* **5**:38–41. 1939.

Unruh, M. Die morphologische Bedeutung des Karpells. *Beitr. z. Biol. der Pflanz.* **26**:90–124. 1939.

Unruh, M. Blattnervatur und Karpellennervatur. Kleiner Beitrag zur morphologischen Deutung des Karpells. *Beitr. z. Biol. der Pflanz.* **27**:232–241. 1941.

Verdoorn, F., Editor. *Vernalization and photoperiodism—a symposium. Lotsya.* Vol. 1. Waltham, Mass., Chronica Botanica Co. 1948.

Wilkinson, A. M. Floral anatomy and morphology of some species of the genus *Viburnum* of the Caprifoliaceae. *Amer. Jour. Bot.* **35**:455–465. 1948.

Wilkinson, A. M. Floral anatomy and morphology of *Triosetum* and of the Caprifoliaceae in general. *Amer. Jour. Bot.* **36**:481–489. 1949.

Wilson, C. L. The telome theory and the origin of the stamen. *Amer. Jour. Bot.* **29**:759–764. 1942.

Wilson, C. L. Vasculation of the stamen in the Melastomaceae, with some phyletic implications. *Amer. Jour. Bot.* **37**:431–444. 1950.

Wilson, C. L., and T. Just. The morphology of the flower. *Bot. Rev.* **5**:97–131. 1939.

Witkus, E. R. Endomitotic tapetal cell divisions in *Spinacia. Amer. Jour. Bot.* **32**:326–330. 1945.

Wodehouse, R. P. *Pollen grains.* New York, McGraw-Hill Book Company. 1935.

Wodehouse, R. P. Evolution of pollen grains. *Bot. Rev.* **2**:67–84. 1936.

Yampolsky, C. The cytology of the abscission zone in *Mercurialis annua. Torrey Bot. Club Bul.* **61**:279–289. 1934.

19

The Fruit

DEFINITION AND CLASSIFICATION

Fertilization of the egg commonly induces the development of a seed from the ovule and of a fruit from the ovary. (The style and stigma usually wither after pollination.) Formation of a fruit may occur also without seed development and without fertilization, a phenomenon known as parthenocarpy (from the Greek *parthenos*, virgin, and *carpos*, fruit).

Correlated with variation of the structure of flowers, the fruits are diversified in their morphology. Furthermore, changes leading to fruit development are not restricted to the ovary but often involve noncarpellary (accessory) parts of the flower, such as the receptacle in the strawberry, the calyx in the mulberry, the bracts in the pineapple, and the floral tube and the receptacle in epigynous flowers. Another complication in fruit development results from the various aggregations of separate carpels into unit structures. These carpels may be derived from one flower (aggregate fruit from an apocarpous gynoecium) or from several flowers (multiple fruit). A concomitant of the variation and complexity of fruit structure is the lack of common agreement on the definition and classification of fruits. The fruits derived from ovaries of hypogynous flowers, not associated with any noncarpellary parts, are commonly designated as true fruits, and those associated with accessory parts are called false or spurious (from the Latin for illegitimate). Spurious fruit is also sometimes called accessory fruit. It seems timely that these ambiguous designations be replaced by terms that reflect the basic structure of the flower from which the fruits are derived.

A definition and classification of fruits worthy of attention has been introduced by Winkler (1939). This author includes in the concept of the fruit the product of the entire gynoecium and any floral parts that may be associated with the gynoecium in the fruiting stage. His classification of the fruits is based primarily on four features: (1) choricarpelly (carpels free, Sammelfrucht or *aggregate fruit*); (2) syncarpelly (carpels united, Einheitsfrucht or *unit fruit*); (3) epichlamydy (hypogynous flower, Freifrucht or *free fruit*); (4) hypochlamydy (perigynous and epigynous flower, Becherfrucht or *cup fruit*). An individual carpel in an aggregate fruit forms the *fruitlet* (Winkler, 1940). Features 1 and 2 may be combined with either 3 or 4. Examples of some of the combinations are the choricarpellous epichlamydous fruit of *Ranunculus* (fig. 19.1, *A*); the syncarpellous epichlamydous fruit of *Solanum* (fig. 19.1, *B*); the choricarpellous hypochlamydous fruit of *Rosa* (fig. 19.1, *C*); and the syncarpellous hypochlamydous fruit of *Cornus* (fig. 19.1, *D*). In this scheme the choricarpous epichlamydous gynoecium is considered the most primitive, the syncarpellous hypochlamydous the most advanced; and the follicle is regarded as the most primitive type of gynoecial unit (Juhnke and Winkler, 1938; Winkler, 1939).

THE FRUIT WALL AND THE PERICARP

When an ovary develops into a fruit, the ovary wall (carpel wall) becomes the *pericarp* (in Greek *peri*, around, and *carpos*, fruit). In the unit cup fruits (fruits derived from syncarpous epigynous flowers) the pericarp merges more or less completely with the accessory parts of the fruit. No term is available to designate the compound structure consisting of pericarp and accessory parts. In this book Winkler's (1939) definition of the fruit (product of gynoecium together with any accessory parts that may be associated with it in fruit) is adopted, and the term *fruit wall* is applied to the pericarp of fruits derived from superior ovaries and to the combination of pericarp and noncarpellary parts found in fruits originating from inferior ovaries.

In the flower, the ovary wall consists of little-differentiated parenchyma cells, vascular tissues, and outer and inner epidermal layers. During maturation the pericarp frequently shows an increase in the number of cells. Its ground tissue either remains relatively homogeneous and parenchymatous or differentiates into parenchyma and sclerenchyma. The pericarp may become differentiated into three parts, more or less distinct morphologically: the exocarp or epicarp, the mesocarp, and the endocarp; that is, the outer, median, and inner layers, respectively. Sometimes only an exocarp and an endocarp may be distinguished, or the exocarp and the endocarp may be simply the outer and inner epidermal layers of the ovary wall. The terms applied to the different layers of the pericarp have little value for showing the origin of the various tissues of the fruit wall, but they are useful for the description of mature fruits.

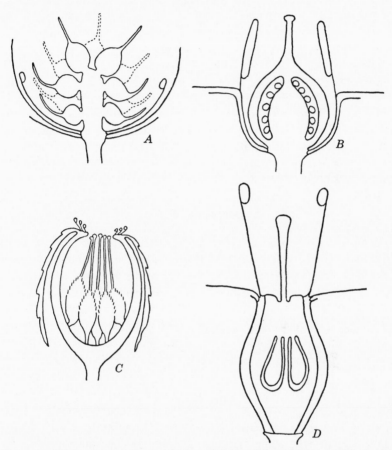

Fig. 19.1. Illustrations of flowers from which the following types of fruits, according to Winkler (1939), are derived: *A*, *Ranunculus*, aggregate free fruit, choricarpellous, epichlamydous; *B*, *Solanum*, unit free fruit, syncarpellous, epichlamydous; *C*, *Rosa*, aggregate cup fruit, choricarpellous, hypochlamydous; *D*, *Cornus*, unit cup fruit, syncarpellous, hypochlamydous.

The fruit wall encloses the ovarian locule in which the seed or seeds are borne (fig. 19.1, *B*). A vascular system, with characteristic variations in the different types of fruits, is present in the pericarp and the other parts of the fruit (fig. 18.1, *A*). The basic arrangement of the vascular system, as related to the manner of folding and of union of carpels, has been considered in connection with the description of the vascularization of the flower in chapter 18. During the development of large fruits the vascular tissues are increased in amount through a differentiation of additional vascular bundles within the ground parenchyma.

HISTOLOGY OF THE FRUIT WALL

Two structural types of fruit walls are recognized, the parenchymatous fleshy, often succulent fruit walls and the sclerenchymatous dry fruit walls. With reference to the structure of the fruit wall, fruits are referred to as fleshy or dry. The latter may be dry dehiscent fruits, if the fruit wall splits open at maturity, or dry indehiscent, if the fruit wall remains closed. Dry or fleshy, dehiscent or indehiscent fruit walls occur in fruits derived from both superior and inferior ovaries.

Dry Fruit Wall

Dehiscent Fruit Wall. If the ovary differentiating into a dry fruit contains several ovules, it commonly dehisces at maturity. Such a fruit may develop from a single carpel (follicle, legume) or from several united carpels (capsule). The pericarp of follicles usually has a relatively simple structure. There may be a narrow exocarp of thick-walled cells and a thin-walled parenchymatous mesocarp and endocarp. The three main longitudinal vascular bundles (one median and two lateral) and the transversely oriented branches from the main bundles may become enclosed in sclerenchymatous sheaths. As the fruit approaches maturity, the pericarp dries. Apparently the differential drying of the parenchymatous and sclerenchymatous parts of the pericarp creates tensions that cause the splitting of the follicle along the line where the margins of the carpel became fused during the ontogeny of the flower.

The legume commonly shows more complicated structure than the follicle. In the Leguminosae, for example, the ovary wall shows a considerable increase in the number of cells after fertilization and then matures into a pericarp with a thick-walled exocarp, a thin-walled parenchymatous mesocarp, and a highly sclerified endocarp (Monsi, 1943). The exocarp may be represented by the epidermis (*Pisum, Vicia*), or it may include a subepidermal layer of elongated cells (*Phaseolus, Glycine*). The endocarp is composed of several rows of thick-walled cells oriented at an angle to the long axis of the fruit and is covered, internally, by a thin-walled epidermis. The thick-walled part of the endocarp may be differentiated into two distinct layers (e.g., *Glycine*, Monsi, 1943). In one of these layers, located next to the mesocarp, the cellulose micelles (see chapter 3) in the cell walls are oriented in helices of low pitch; in the other the helices are steeply pitched. This cell-wall structure in the endocarp is interpreted as a mechanism facilitating the dehiscence of the fruit. As a result of the different orientation of the micelles in the cell walls of the two layers, these layers undergo their strongest contraction in different planes. The two lines of dehiscence, one following the line of union of carpel margins and the other located in the region of the median bundle, may consist of conspicuously thin-walled parenchyma cells.

An ovary wall maturing into the pericarp of a capsule may have but little increase in the number of cells, as in tobacco; or, as in certain lilies, numerous cell divisions may occur before the pericarp matures. The pericarps of capsules have both sclerenchymatous and parenchymatous tissues in variable distributions. The pericarp of *Linum usitatissimum*, for example, has an exocarp of highly lignified cells and a mesocarp and an endocarp of parenchymatous cells. That of *Nicotiana tabacum* shows, in contrast, a thick-walled endocarp, two or three cells in thickness, and parenchymatous lacunose exocarp and mesocarp. The dehiscence of capsules may be longitudinal and occurs either along the lines of juncture of the carpels (septicidal dehiscence, really separation into the individual carpels, Winkler, 1936; e.g., *Convolvulus*) or along the plane of the median bundle of each carpel (loculicidal dehiscence; e.g., *Allium*, fig. 18.12, *E*). In the two instances just cited, the longitudinal split extends the whole length of the pericarp. In some capsules, as in tobacco, dehiscence is confined to the terminal part of the fruit. A few plants have circumscissile dehiscence (from the Latin *circumscissus*, cut around), that is, dehiscence by a transverse lid (e.g., *Portulaca, Plantago*). Such dehiscence is made possible through the development of a zone of mechanical weakness between the lid and the base (Rethke, 1946). This zone may differ from the adjacent fruit parts in cell number, cell size, density of protoplasts, wall thickness, and various combinations of these features. Whereas in longitudinal dehiscence the differential shrinkage of the different tissues of the pericarp is assumed to be the primary force inducing the splitting, in circumscissile dehiscence the separation of the lid appears to result from a shrinkage of the pericarp and the lack of comparable shrinkage of the contents of the ovary (Rethke, 1946).

Indehiscent Fruit Wall. When the ovary contains a single ovule, it usually develops into an indehiscent fruit. The pericarp of many indehiscent one-seeded fruits resembles a seed coat in structure. In fact, commonly the seed coat of such fruits acquires no mechanical characteristics or is more or less obliterated during fruit development. If the pericarp and the testa (seed coat) are adherent in the fruit, the fruit is a grain or caryopsis (e.g., most Gramineae). If the seed is attached to the pericarp at one point only, the fruit is an achene. Examples of achenes derived from hypogynous flowers may be found among the Ranunculaceae. The term achene is also used with reference to the bicarpellate fruit of the Compositae in which the ovary is inferior and, therefore, the pericarp is confluent with the floral tube.

The caryopses of the Gramineae show certain conspicuous differences in the development of their fruit coats. Most commonly, as in *Triticum* and *Hordeum* (Krauss, 1933), the protective layer is developed in the pericarp. The two parts that compose the grain coats, the pericarp and the seed coat, are distinct in the ovary before fertilization. The ovary wall of wheat consists of the following cell layers, beginning from the outside: the outer epidermis, one cell layer in depth; many layers of colorless parenchyma cells; chlorophyll-containing parenchyma tissue consisting of one or two layers of cells over most of the grain and of several layers in the region where the grain is grooved; one layer of small cells of the inner epidermis. At this time both integuments are intact, each consisting of two layers of cells. The nucellus also is present and consists of several layers of thin-walled cells bounded by a distinct nucellar epidermis.

The changes in the ovary wall begin with the inner epidermis which partly disintegrates. The remaining cells elongate parallel with the long axis of the grain, and their walls lignify (fig. 19.2, tube cell). The chlorenchyma cells elongate transversely with respect to the long axis of the grain; their chlorophyll disappears and their walls thicken and lignify (fig. 19.2, cross cells). The parenchyma outside the chlorenchyma is partly resorbed, and the remaining spaces are filled with air (fig. 19.2, crushed parenchyma). One to four layers of this parenchyma persist in the mature grain but become compressed (fig. 19.2, subepidermal layer). The outer epidermis is compressed also and is covered with a cuticle.

The nucellus and the integuments in wheat undergo even more

profound changes than the ovary wall. The nucellar tissue, with the exception of the epidermis, is absorbed by the enlarging endosperm and embryo. The nucellar epidermis is eventually compressed into a hyaline layer covered with a cuticle (fig. 19.2, crushed nucellar cells). The inner layer of the inner integument becomes compressed (fig. 19.2, inner layer of i.i.). The outer layer of this integument

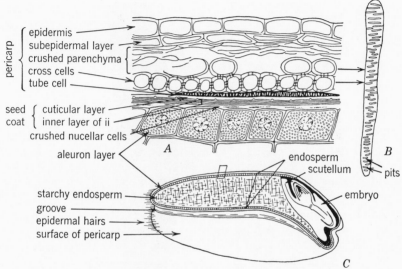

FIG. 19.2. The caryopsis (*C*) of *Triticum* (wheat) and its pericarp (*A, B*). The caryopsis was cut longitudinally through the groove. The small rectangle in *C*, above, indicates the approximate location of the section shown in *A*. The cross cells are elongated perpendicular to the long axis of the grain. *B* shows one such cell from a transection of the grain. The tube cell is part of the inner epidermis of pericarp. The letters ii signify inner integument. (*A, B,* ×300; *C,* ×7.)

is crushed into a hyaline membrane covered with a cuticle (fig. 19.2, cuticular layer). The outer integument disintegrates. In the grain of *Zea* the integuments disintegrate completely, but the nucellar epidermis is retained as a thick-walled layer showing a fatty reaction and covered with a cuticle (Randolph, 1936).

The bran of wheat includes all the grain coats derived from the pericarp, the integuments, and the nucellus. Within and adjacent to the grain coats lies the proteinaceous endosperm layer, the aleuron layer, which in turn encloses the starchy endosperm (fig. 19.2, *A, C*).

The achene type of fruit may be illustrated by reference to the fruit of lettuce, *Lactuca sativa*, a composite. The lettuce achene is derived from an inferior ovary (figs. 18.13 and 19.3). The adnation

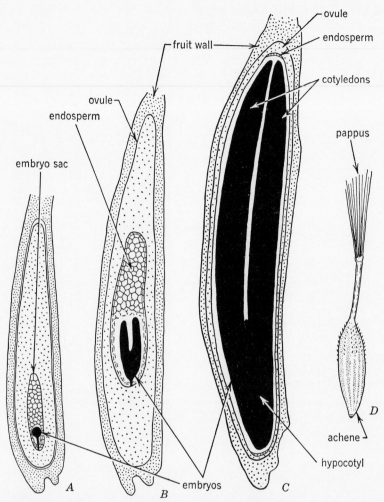

Fɪɢ. 19.3. Development of the embryo and the fruit (achene) enclosing it in *Lactuca sativa* (lettuce). *A–C*, longitudinal sections of achenes, showing embryos before (*A*) and after (*B*, *C*) the emergence of cotyledons. Note the increase in size of the embryo sac, its encroachment upon the ovule, the development of endosperm in the embryo sac, and the replacement of the endosperm by the embryo. *D*, sketch of a mature achene with pappus. (*A–C*, ✕33; *D*, ✕6. After Jones, 1927.)

between the carpels and the floral tube is so complete that through-out the development of the fruit wall no distinction can be made

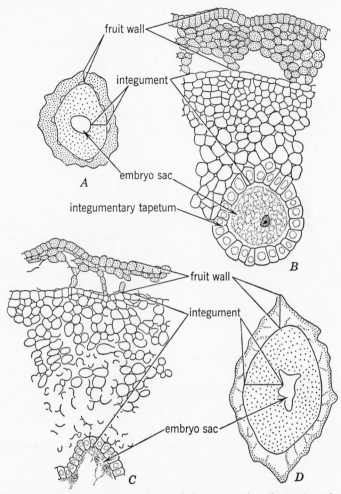

FIG. 19.4. Development of the achene of *Lactuca sativa* (lettuce). *A* and *D*, diagrams of entire transections of ovaries, *B* and *C*, details of parts of transections. *A* and *B*, sampled 2 hours before anthesis, *C* and *D*, 3 days after anthesis. Further details are in the text. (*A*, *D*, ×45; *B*, *C*, ×215. After Borthwick and Robbins, 1928.)

between the pericarp and the floral tube (Borthwick and Robbins, 1928).

In an ovule taken before anthesis the integument consists of many layers of cells. The innermost, next to the embryo sac, constitutes the integumentary tapetum. (The nucellus is largely absorbed during the development of the gametophyte.) The fruit wall, composed

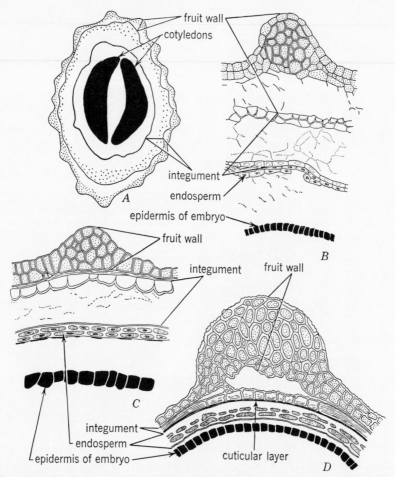

Fig. 19.5. Development of the achene of *Lactuca sativa* (lettuce). *A*, diagram of transection of achene 7 days after anthesis, *B–D*, details of parts of transections taken the following numbers of days after anthesis: 7 (*B*), 10 (*C*), and 19 (*D*). *D* is from a mature achene. Further details are in the text. (*A*, ×45; *B–D*, ×215. After Borthwick and Robbins, 1928.)

of rather small parenchyma cells, is in contact with the ovule. At this early stage some of the inner fruit-wall cells are already disorganized and have left cavities (fig. 19.4, *A*, *B*). After anthesis, while the achene enlarges in size, the integument is increasing in thickness but is also disorganizing next to the integumentary tapetum (fig. 19.4, *C*, *D*). Eventually this tapetum and all the parenchyma of the integument are destroyed (figs. 19.3, *A–C*, and 19.5, *B*, *C*). Only the outer epidermis of the integument persists and develops thick walls (fig. 19.5, *D*). The vascular bundle located in the integument is also identifiable in the mature fruit. The outer layer of the endosperm develops into a compact layer. This layer and another beneath it are retained in the mature fruit and develop thick walls (fig. 19.5). A cuticle becomes conspicuous between the endosperm and all that remains of the integument (fig. 19.5, *D*). In lettuce, the cuticle outside the endosperm has been interpreted as derived from the disorganized tapetum (Borthwick and Robbins, 1928); in guayule, another composite, as a secretion of the endosperm (Erickson and Benedict, 1947). In view of the information that cuticles occur on the surfaces of the nucellus and the integuments, the fatty membrane in question may be a combination of the nucellar and integumentary cuticles (Schnarf, 1927). The inner layers of the fruit wall become completely disorganized, but the outer layers persist. Certain parts of the remaining layers project in the form of ribs and develop into sclerenchyma (fig. 19.5). The fruit-wall cells between the ribs are large and have thin, slightly lignified walls. In the mature achene all the persisting layers are compressed close together and their identity becomes obscured (fig. 19.5, *D*).

Fleshy Fruit Wall

Many ovaries, monocarpellate or multicarpellate, develop into indehiscent fruits with fleshy fruit walls. As in the dry fruits, the fruit wall may consist either of the ovary wall (a pericarp), or of such a wall fused with the noncarpellary tissue in which it is imbedded (cup fruits of Winkler, 1939). According to the type of fleshy fruit, the entire ovary wall or the external part of it differentiates into a parenchymatous tissue whose cells retain their protoplasts in the mature fruit. An immature fleshy fruit wall has a firm texture, but it becomes softer as the fruit ripens. Chemical changes in the cell contents and in the structure of the walls are responsible for the softening. The cells may even become dissociated from each other.

The ripening of the fruit wall is generally accompanied by color changes. Immature fruits have numerous chloroplasts in the outermost cells and are consequently green. The disappearance of chlorophyll and the development of carotenoid pigments induces a change to a yellow, orange, or red color (e.g., tomato, *Pyracantha*). Ripening fruits may form anthocyanins which give the tissue a red, purple, or blue color. These pigments may be distributed in the entire fruit wall, as in some cherries, or, as in the plum or Concord grape, they may be restricted to peripheral parts of the fruit wall. The outer epidermis frequently accumulates tannins.

The fleshy tissue of fruits may develop by cell enlargement without any cell division (e.g., *Berberis, Rubus,* certain *Ribes*) or by cell division followed by cell enlargement (e.g., *Prunus, Cucurbita, Malus*) (Kraus, 1949; Sinnott, 1939, 1944; Smith, 1950).

If the entire ground tissue develops into a fleshy tissue, the fruit is a berry. All the fleshy tissue of the berry may originate from the ovary wall, as in the grape; or, as in the tomato, the main body of the mature fruit may consist of the placenta. In the development of the tomato berry there are but few cell divisions in the ovary wall and in the septa dividing the ovary into locules. In contrast, each placenta shows active multiplication of cells and an increase in volume, so that the locule is filled with the fleshy tissue and the seed is completely imbedded. The placental tissue constitutes the pulp of the mature fruit. The pericarp has a cutinized epidermis and subepidermal collenchyma. The inner tissue is parenchymatous, and the inner epidermis is thin walled. When berries have definite locules, the inner epidermis of the fruit wall may have thick walls and sometimes a cuticle (Kraus, 1949). In some berries the locules are filled by proliferations of pericarp wall as well as of placentae (*Physalis Alkekengi*); in others, by the growth of partition walls (*Bryonia dioica;* Kraus, 1949).

The citrus fruit, the hesperidium, is closely related to a berry. It develops from a multicarpellate ovary with axile placentation. As the fruit develops, cell multiplication occurs throughout the ovary, and eventually the pericarp becomes differentiated into three layers (Ford, 1942; Scott and Baker, 1947). The outer, the exocarp or flavedo, is compact, collenchymatous, and contains oil glands. The mesocarp, the albedo, is spongy because of the loose connection among cells. The endocarp is compact and gives rise to the juice sacs which at maturity fill the locules. The juice sacs develop as multicellular hairs. The distal part of each hair becomes enlarged, then the interior cells break down, and the cavity becomes filled with juice. The basal part of the hair develops into a stalk supporting the juice sac.

If the ovary wall matures into a pericarp with a conspicuous stony endocarp and a fleshy mesocarp, the fruit is called a drupe. During the development of a drupe, as exemplified by the peach, *Prunus persica* (Addoms et al., 1930; Dorsey and Porter, 1932; Ragland, 1934), most of the cell division in the pericarp occurs before or

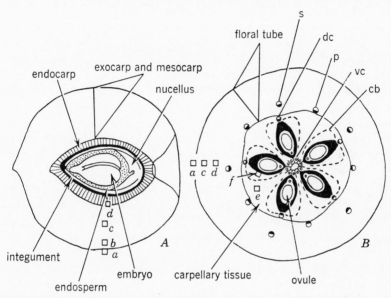

FIG. 19.6. Diagrammatic drawings of longitudinal section of peach fruit (*A*) and of transection of apple fruit (*B*). Details are: s, sepallary bundles; p, petallary bundles; dc, dorsal carpellary bundles; and vc, ventral carpellary bundles; cb are carpellary bundles connecting dorsal with ventral carpellary bundles. The rectangles accompanied by small letters indicate the positions of sections shown in figs. 19.7 and 19.8. (*A*, after Lee and Tuckey, 1942; *B*, after MacDaniels, 1939.)

shortly after fertilization. The later growth depends on cell enlargement (Ragland, 1934). During early growth the cells enlarge about equally along all diameters. Later, radial enlargement predominates, especially in the inner third of the flesh.

The pericarp of the mature peach fruit is composed of three distinct parts (fig. 19.6, *A*): the thin exocarp or skin, the thick fleshy mesocarp, and the stony endocarp. The exocarp includes the epidermis and several layers of collenchyma beneath it. The epidermis bears a cuticle and numerous unicellular hairs (fig. 19.7, *A*). The fleshy mesocarp consists of loosely packed parenchyma cells which increase in size from the periphery toward the interior (fig. 19.7, *B*,

C). In the same direction the cells change in shape from ovoid, with the longest diameter parallel to the surface of the fruit, to cylindrical, with the longest diameter in the radial direction. The smaller cells near the periphery contain most of the chloroplasts in the immature fruit (fig. 19.7, *B*). Chemical and histologic differences in the mesocarp differentiate the "melting-fleshed" types of peaches from the

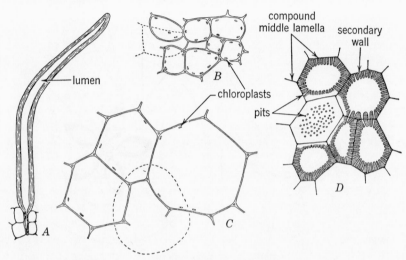

Fig. 19.7. Tissue elements of the fruit of *Prunus* (peach). *A*, epidermal hair. *B* and *C*, parenchyma of the mesocarp taken closer to (*B*) and farther from (*C*) the surface of the fruit. *D*, a group of sclereids from the endocarp. The drawings were made from a longitudinal section of a fruit about 3 cm in diameter. Compare with fig. 19.6, *A*. (All, ×300. Slide by R. M. Brooks.)

canning "cling" types. The former show a decrease of wall thickness and eventual disorganization of cells as the fruit ripens.

The endocarp is composed of tightly packed sclereids and forms the pit or stone of the fruit (fig. 19.7, *D*). The outer surface of the pit is very rough and pitted. Vascular bundles occur within channels in the endocarp. Branch bundles diverge from this system into the mesocarp. The endocarp is the first part of the fruit that reaches its maximum size.

A fleshy fruit derived from an inferior ovary is here illustrated by the apple fruit or pome (*Pyrus malus*), which has been investigated from the developmental standpoint (MacArthur and Wetmore, 1939, 1941; MacDaniels, 1940; Smith, 1940, 1950). Most workers accept the appendicular interpretation of the extracarpellary part of the pome fruit and describe the flesh of the fruit as composed of the floral tube and carpellary tissue. As seen in transections of the fruit, the floral tube region consists of fleshy parenchyma with a ring of vascular bundles (fig. 19.6, *B*). There are five petallary and five sepallary bundles alternating with one another. Branches from these bundles permeate the parenchyma as an anastomosing system. The subepidermal parenchyma of the floral tube region consists of several layers of tangentially elongated cells with thick walls (fig. 19.8, *A*, *B*). No intercellular spaces occur here until the late developmental stages. The ground parenchyma located somewhat deeper has abundant intercellular spaces (fig. 19.8, *C*). The still deeper-lying ground parenchyma consists of cells roughly elliptical in outline and showing an approximately radial orientation (fig. 19.8, *D*). This part of the fruit shows particularly intensive growth during development, first by cell division and cell enlargement, then by cell enlargement only.

The ovary region (the core) consists of five carpels (fig. 19.6, *B*). These are folded, but their margins are not fused. In some varieties the margins later spread and curve away from the center of the fruit (Bell, 1940). The vascular system of this region consists of five median (dorsal) carpellary bundles outside and opposite each locule and ten lateral (ventral) carpellary bundles forming a ring inside the locules (fig. 19.6, *B*). The median and lateral bundles anastomose with each other and form a network, chiefly following the outline of the locules. The boundary between the ovary and the floral tube may or may not be discernible, and it occurs between the median carpellary bundles and the ten main bundles of the floral tube (MacDaniels, 1940).

The ovary wall is considered to be differentiated into the fleshy parenchymatous exocarp and the cartilaginous endocarp lining the locules (MacDaniels, 1940). The exocarp consists of parenchyma cells (fig. 19.8, *E*). The cartilaginous endocarp consists of sclereids with such thick walls that the cell lumina are almost occluded (fig. 19.8, *G*). In the region of the median carpellary bundles, sclerenchymatous cells are absent so that the hard endocarp of each carpel forms two disconnected sheets of tissue, one on either side of the locule. The cartilaginous endocarp is the first tissue of the apple that attains its maximum development. The fleshy exocarp follows next, then the extracarpellary tissue. The latter continues growth up to the time of ripening of the fruit.

The epidermis of the apple fruit consists of radially elongated cells in young stages (fig. 19.8, *A*), but toward maturity the tangential

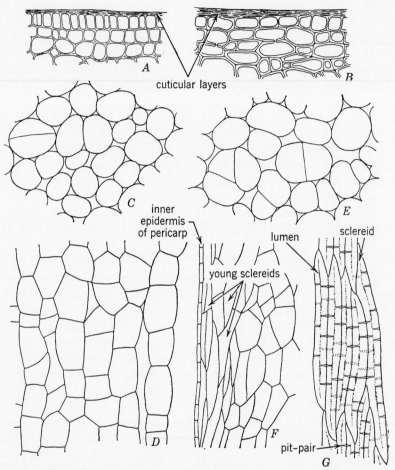

FIG. 19.8. Tissue elements of the fruit of *Malus* (apple). *A* and *B*, epidermis and subjacent collenchymatous tissue from young (*A*) and mature (*B*) fruits. *C* and *D*, parenchyma of the floral-tube part of the flesh. *C* was taken closer to the surface, *D* farther away. *E*, parenchyma from the exocarp. *F* and *G*, endocarp from young (*F*) and mature (*G*) fruits. *A*, *C–D*, from transections of a fruit 1 cm in diameter; *F* from radial longitudinal section of similar fruit. *B*, transverse and, *G*, tangential longitudinal sections from mature fruit. (*A–E*, ×178; *F* and *G*, ×310. Slide by R. M. Brooks.)

diameter surpasses the radial (fig. 19.8, *B*). Throughout the growth of the apple the cuticle on the external face of the epidermis increases in thickness (Tetley, 1930, 1931). Stomata are present in the young epidermis. Later they cease to function and are replaced by lenticels consisting mostly of patches of suberized cells (Clements, 1935). Unicellular epidermal hairs occur on young fruits but fall off later. Russeting of apples results from the replacement by cork of the outer layers of the fruit over parts of the fruit surface (Tetley, 1930).

ABSCISSION

In the abscission of fruits the separation layer may be prepared by cell division or differentiated without divisions. In fruit clusters there are often two to three separation layers. First the fruit abscises, then the axial parts (Fehér, 1925). Some fruits separate together with their stalks (*Carpinus, Ulmus, Salix, Populus, Pyrus, Tilia, Robinia*). In certain *Prunus* species the first abscission occurs at the base of the fruit, the second at the base of the pedicel, the third at the base of the spur. The scar left by the spur is healed over by a periderm soon after abscission. In *Castanea, Quercus*, and *Fagus* the fruit separates from the involucre without preceding cell division. The cells at the base of the fruit die after a sclerification of their walls and break away from the still living, relatively thin-walled cells of the involucre. The fruit of the Umbelliferae has special separation layers along which the two halves of the fruit (the two mericarps) break away at maturity. The separation layer consists of parenchyma tissue with many intercellular spaces. The tissue collapses at maturity. In many Compositae the abscission region of the achenes is constricted, and its ground tissue consists of small-celled parenchyma. At maturity the cells separate from one another or shrink and thus bring about the loosening of connection between the fruit and the receptacle (John, 1921). The abscission phenomena in grasses do not appear to have been investigated (Pfeiffer, 1928), except in *Aegilops triaristata* in which the fertile part of the spike abscises by a break through thin-walled dead cells (Markgraf, 1925).

In the apple the abscission phenomenon appears to vary, depending on the stage of development of the fruit (McCown, 1943). If a flower or an immature fruit becomes separated, abscission is preceded by cell enlargement and division. The separation of mature fruits, on the other hand, occurs without any cell division. In the abscission of some tropical fruits the process of fruit separation from the stalk is interpreted as a concomitant of the progressive softening and disintegration of tissues during the late stages of ripening (Barnell, 1939). The shedding of the fruit stalk occurs after the fruit falls and is associated with a development of a distinct separation layer. Abscission cork is formed in the fruit-stalk scar.

Fruits may abscise with the seeds still enclosed. The subsequent separation of seeds from fruits may be entirely passive without an abscission zone, or it may involve the development of a relatively poorly differentiated separation layer between the funiculus and the placenta (Pfeiffer, 1928). The cells of this layer are commonly thin-walled and give the cellulose reaction. In the Leguminosae, the separation layer between the seeds and the placenta shows a combination of thicker-walled sclerified and thinner-walled nonsclerified elements. Absence of a separation layer is exemplified by berries in which the seeds are severed from the placenta after the breakdown of the placenta.

REFERENCES

Addoms, R. M., G. T. Nightingale, and M. A. Blake. Development and ripening of peaches as correlated with physical characteristics, chemical composition, and histological structure of the fruit flesh: II. Histology and microchemistry. *N. Y. Agr. Exp. Sta. Bul.* 507. 1930.

Barnell, E. Studies in tropical fruits. V. Some anatomical aspects of fruit-fall in two tropical arboreal plants. *Ann. Bot.* 3:77–89. 1939.

Bell, H. P. Calyx end structure in Gravenstein apple. *Canad. Jour. Res. Sect. C, Bot. Sci.* 18:69–75. 1940.

Borthwick, H. A., and W. W. Robbins. Lettuce seed and its germination. *Hilgardia* 3:275–305. 1928.

Clements, H. Morphology and physiology of the pome lenticels of *Pyrus malus*. *Bot. Gaz.* 97:101–117. 1935.

Dorsey, M. J., and J. S. Porter. A study of the structure of the skin and pubescence of the peach in relation to brushing. *Ill. Agr. Exp. Sta. Bul.* 385: 407–424. 1932.

Erickson, L. C., and H. M. Benedict. Origin of the seed coats in guayule. *Jour. Agr. Res.* 74:329–334. 1947.

Fehér, D. Untersuchungen über den Abfall der Früchte einiger Holzpflanzen. *Deut. Bot. Gesell. Ber.* 43:52–61. 1925.

Ford, E. S. Anatomy and histology of the Eureka lemon. *Bot. Gaz.* 104:288–305. 1942.

John, A. Beiträge zur Kenntnis der Ablösungseinrichtungen der Kompositenfrüchte. *Bot. Centbl. Beihefte* 38:182–203. 1921.

Jones, H. A. Pollination and life history studies of lettuce (*Lactuca sativa* L.). *Hilgardia* 2:452–479. 1927.

Juhnke, G., and H. Winkler. Der Balg als Grundelement des Angiospermengynaeceums. *Beitr. z. Biol. der Pflanz.* 25:290–324. 1938.

Kraus, G. Morphologisch-anatomische Untersuchung der entwicklungsbedingten Veränderungen an Achse, Blatt und Fruchtknoten bei einigen Beerenfrüchten. *Österr. Bot. Ztschr.* **96**:325–360. 1949.

Krauss, L. Entwicklungsgeschichte der Früchte von *Hordeum, Triticum, Bromus* und *Poa* mit besonderer Berücksichtigung ihrer Samenschalen. *Jahrb. f. Wiss. Bot.* **77**:733–808. 1933.

Lee, F. A., and H. B. Tuckey. Chemical changes accompanying growth and development of seed and fruit of the Elberta peach. *Bot. Gaz.* **104**:348–355. 1942.

MacArthur, M., and R. H. Wetmore. Developmental studies in the apple fruit in the varieties McIntosh Red and Wagener. I. Vascular anatomy. *Jour. Pomol. and Hort. Sci.* **17**:218–232. 1939.

MacArthur, M., and R. H. Wetmore. Developmental studies of the apple fruit in the varieties McIntosh Red and Wagener. II. An analysis of development. *Canad. Jour. Res. Sect. C, Bot. Sci.* **19**:371–382. 1941.

MacDaniels, L. H. The morphology of the apple and other pome fruits. *N. Y. (Cornell) Agr. Exp. Sta. Mem.* 230. 1940.

Markgraf, F. Das Abbruchgewebe der Frucht von *Aegilops triaristata* Willd. *Deut. Bot. Gesell. Ber.* **43**:117–120. 1925.

McCown, M. Anatomical and chemical aspects of abscission of fruits of the apple. *Bot. Gaz.* **105**:212–220. 1943.

Monsi, M. Untersuchungen über den Mechanismus der Schleuderbewegung der Sojabohnen-Hülse. *Jap. Jour. Bot.* **12**:437–474. 1943.

Pfeiffer, H. Die pflanzlichen Trennungsgewebe. In: K. Linsbauer. *Handbuch der Pflanzenanatomie.* Band 5. Lief. 22. 1928.

Ragland, C. H. The development of the peach fruit, with special reference to split-pit and gumming. *Amer. Soc. Hort. Sci. Proc.* **31**:1–21. 1934.

Randolph, L. F. Developmental morphology of the caryopsis in maize. *Jour. Agr. Res.* **53**:881–916. 1936.

Rethke, R. V. The anatomy of circumscissile dehiscence. *Amer. Jour. Bot.* **33**: 677–683. 1946.

Schnarf, K. Embryologie der Angiospermen. In: K. Linsbauer. *Handbuch der Pflanzenanatomie.* Band 10. Lief. 21. 1927.

Scott, F. M., and K. C. Baker. Anatomy of Washington navel orange rind in relation to water spot. *Bot. Gaz.* **108**:459–475. 1947.

Sinnott, E. W. A developmental analysis of the relation between cell size and fruit size in cucurbits. *Amer. Jour. Bot.* **26**:179–189. 1939.

Sinnott, E. W. Cell polarity and the development of form in curcurbit fruits. *Amer. Jour. Bot.* **31**:388–391. 1944.

Smith, W. H. The histological structure of the flesh of the apple in relation to growth and senescence. *Jour. Pomol. and Hort. Sci.* **18**:249–260. 1940.

Smith, W. H. Cell-multiplication and cell-enlargement in the development of the flesh of the apple fruit. *Ann. Bot.* **14**:23–38. 1950.

Tetley, U. A study of the anatomical development of the apple and some observations on the "pectic constituents" of the cell walls. *Jour. Pomol. and Hort. Sci.* **8**:153–172. 1930.

Tetley, U. The morphology and cytology of the apple fruit with special reference to the Bramley's seedling variety. *Jour. Pomol. and Hort. Sci.* **9**:278–297. 1931.

Winkler, H.   Septizide Kapsel und Spaltfrucht.   *Beitr. z. Biol. der Pflanz.* 24:191–200.   1936.

Winkler, H.   Versuch eines "natürlichen" Systems der Früchte.   *Beitr. z. Biol. der Pflanz.* 26:201–220.   1939.

Winkler, H.   Zur Einigung und Weiterführung in der Frage des Fruchtsystems.   *Beitr. z. Biol. der Pflanz.* 27:92–130.   1940.

20

The Seed

SEED IN RELATION TO OVULE

This chapter deals with the seed of angiosperms. A seed develops from an ovule and, at maturity, consists of the following parts (figs. 20.3, *C*, and 20.5, *B*): the young, partially developed sporophyte called the *embryo;* variable amounts of *endosperm* (from the Greek words for within and seed), sometimes none; and the protective layers on the surface, the seed coat or *testa* (from the Latin, brick or tile), which is derived from the integument or integuments. Various external markings on the seed are traceable to certain structural details of the ovule. The micropyle may be completely obliterated, or it may remain in the form of an occluded pore. A scar, the *hilum* (from the Latin, a trifle), which is highly permeable to water, occurs where a seed abscises from the funiculus. In anatropous ovules the funiculus is adnate to the ovule, and the abscission of the seed occurs at the lower level of the funiculus, that is, near the placenta. The funiculus is recognizable in such a seed as a longitudinal ridge, the *raphe* (from the Greek, seam). A *caruncle* and an *aril* mentioned in connection with the ovule are present in some seeds.

EMBRYO

The embryo shows a variety of developmental patterns and attains different sizes and degrees of differentiation in the angiosperms. Commonly the future vegetative organs of the sporophyte plant are initiated during the development of the embryo, at least in the form of their apical meristems. As was reviewed in chapters 1 and 15, the embryo consists of an axis, the hypocotyl-root axis, bearing, at one end, the root meristem and, at the other, the cotyledon or cotyledons and the meristem of the first shoot. Sometimes a shoot bud, the epicotyl, and a primordial root, the radicle, are present in the embryo. Usually a rootcap develops on the root end of the embryo. A procambial system, continuous throughout the hypocotyl and the cotyledons, is commonly differentiated in the embryo. Some mature vascular elements may also be encountered in embryos.

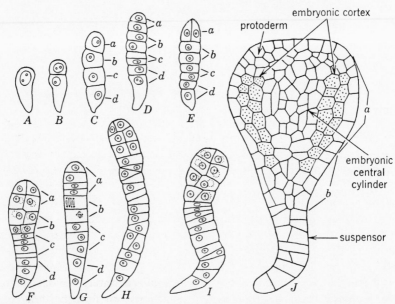

FIG. 20.1. Embryo development in *Daucus carota* (carrot) as seen in longitudinal sections. The lower end of the embryo in each drawing is the end directed toward the micropyle. *A–C*, stages in the development of a linear 4-celled embryo. *D* and *E* illustrate two common variations in 8-celled embryos: note the difference in the division of cell *a* of the 4-celled embryo. *F–I*, older embryos showing variations in cell arrangement. *J*, embryo differentiated into main body and suspensor. The initial organization of the tissue regions is also present in *J*. The relation of the parts of certain embryos to the cells of the 4-celled embryo is indicated by the letters *a–d*. (All, ×500. After Borthwick, 1931.)

When the embryo is initiated by the division of the zygote, most frequently a transverse division takes place (figs. 20.1, *B*, and 20.2, *B*). When each cell divides again, the orientation of the two new walls may vary. Commonly the cell oriented toward the micropyle, the proximal cell, divides transversely. The distal cell may divide transversely, vertically, or obliquely. As a result, the four-celled embryo appears either as a single file of cells (fig. 20.1, *C*) or as a three-tiered structure with the distal tier composed of two cells (fig. 20.2, *D*). The distribution of the subsequent divisions is usually unequal in the various tiers of the four-celled embryo. Furthermore, the divisions become specifically oriented in the different tiers so that the embryo differentiates into the main body or "embryo proper" and

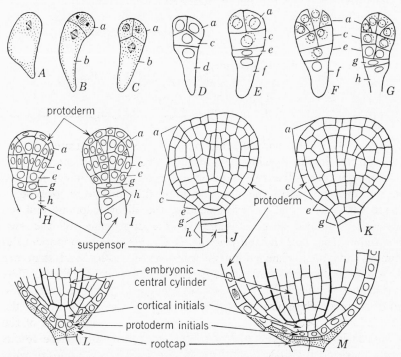

Fig. 20.2. Embryo development in *Lactuca sativa* (lettuce) as seen in longitudinal sections. The lower end of the embryo in each drawing is the end directed toward the micropyle. *A*, zygote in division. *B–G*, embryos in successive stages of development, showing the establishment of a number of horizontal tiers of cells. In *G*, cell *h* later gives rise to all of the suspensor cells, and the tiers above *h* develop into the main body of the embryo. *H–M* illustrate further developmental stages resulting in the initial organization of the tissue regions: protoderm, embryonic cortex, central cylinder, and rootcap. *L* and *M* show only the lower parts of the embryos. The embryo in *K* has a flattened apex characteristic of the stage preceding the emergence of the cotyledons. (All, ×400. After Jones, 1927.)

the suspensor (figs. 20.1, *J*, 20.2, *H*, and plate 85, *A–D*). The embryo proper is at this stage a relatively massive body, whereas the suspensor has the form of a stalk, variable in length, uniseriate, or more massive, and is attached to the wall of the embryo sac at the micropylar end. The young embryo before it differentiates into main body and suspensor is sometimes called the proembryo.

Students of embryo development treat the sequence of divisions and the fate of the resulting cells of the four-celled embryo as one of the main problems of embryology. The parts of the mature embryo derived from each tier of the four-celled embryo may differ from genus to genus, or from species to species, but they may also vary within the same species (Bhadurim, 1936; Borthwick, 1931). Despite the variations, however, the characteristics of embryos in their developmental stages are of major value for the delimitation of the large groups of plants (Johansen, 1950; Maheshwari, 1950). Furthermore, the morphology of the mature embryo and its position in the seed and relation to the endosperm are so distinctive in different groups of plants that they may be used in identifying seeds (Martin, 1946).

Figures 19.3, 20.1, and 20.2 and plates 84 and 85 illustrate some of the features in the development of dicotyledonous and monocotyledonous embryos. The two kinds of embryos may be similar in form up to the stage when the main body of the embryo is globose in shape (Johansen, 1950). Subsequently, the dicotyledonous embryo assumes a bilobed shape, because of the appearance of the two cotyledons (fig. 20.2, *K*, and plate 84, *B*, *C*), whereas the monocotyledonous embryo is changed into a more or less cylindrical structure by the direct extension of the single cotyledon (plate 85, *E*, *F*). The cotyledons of the dicotyledonous embryo arise as two meristematic protrusions on the apical end of the embryo. The emergence of the cotyledons is preceded by a lateral expansion of the apical end of the embryo (fig. 20.1, *J*, and plate 84, *B*). This change in shape results from localized divisions, mainly periclinal, in the two opposite parts of the embryo where the cotyledons later appear. The periclinal divisions occur in several superficial layers which may include the outermost layer (Miller and Wetmore, 1945; Nast, 1941). The widening of the apical end of the embryo in preparation for the emergence of the cotyledons is comparable to the formation of leaf buttresses in vegetative shoots. Subsequently, the cotyledons grow upward upon their buttresses (fig. 19.3 and plate 84) and expand laterally. As in foliage leaves apical and marginal growth may be recognized in the development of the cotyledons (Miller and Wetmore, 1945; Nast, 1941).

The part of the apex that is left in the notch between the two upwardly extending cotyledons constitutes the apical meristem of the epicotyl (plate 84, *D*). In monocotyledonous embryos the epicotylary meristem is organized in a depression which is formed at the base of the cotyledon early during the increase in thickness of the embryo. This depression is at first quite shallow (plate 85, *E*) but increases in depth as the tissue on its lower margin grows upward (plate 85, *G*). In the final stage of embryo development the apical meristem appears on one side of the cotyledon and is completely surrounded by a sheath-like lateral extension from the base of the cotyledon. Thus, the first epicotyl apex of the monocotyledon bears the same relation to the cotyledon as the vegetative shoot apex to a foliage leaf (see chapters 5 and 16). As was shown earlier, the relation between the cotyledons and the embryo apex on the one hand, and that between the foliage leaves and the vegetative shoot apex on the other are comparable in the dicotyledons also. Therefore, the suggestion that the embryo apex may be regarded as the first shoot apex of the plant (formulated with reference to the *Pinus* embryo by Spurr, 1950) deserves consideration.

The delimitation of the three meristems, the protoderm, the procambium, and the ground meristem, begins in the embryo long before it reaches its final size. The protoderm is initiated by periclinal divisions along the surface of the embryo, commonly starting in the distal tier and progressing toward the proximal end (figs. 20.2, *H–K*). The protoderm does not extend to the suspensor but merges with the apical meristem of the root that becomes organized in the proximal end of the embryo (fig. 20.2, *L*, *M*). The procambial system is first delimited by the vacuolation and decrease in stainability of the ground tissue (plate 84, *B*, *C*). Later the procambial cells assume their characteristic narrow elongated shape. The procambium may become discernible before the cotyledons emerge and, as the latter begin to grow, the procambium is organized in them in continuity with that in the embryo axis (plate 84). The procambial system in the hypocotyl-root axis varies in shape, depending on how much of the hypocotyl-root axis is organized as a root. In the Gramineae, for example, most of this axis is root-like in structure (Hayward, 1938); in *Juglans*, less than one-sixth of it (Nast, 1941).

The early embryogeny is treated comprehensively in the botanical literature (Johansen, 1950; Maheshwari, 1950; Schnarf, 1929, 1931; Souèges, see citations in Johansen, 1950). In contrast, studies on the later embryogeny, particularly those concerned with the organization of the system of primary meristems (protoderm, procambium, and ground meristem) and of the apical meristem are still scanty (Miller and Wetmore, 1945; Nast, 1941; Reeve, 1948; and for gymnosperms, Allen, 1947*a*, *b*; Spurr, 1949, 1950).

ENDOSPERM

The development of endosperm is treated here briefly. Further details must be sought in the pertinent literature (Brink and Cooper, 1947; Maheshwari, 1950; Schnarf, 1928, 1931). If fertilization occurs, the endosperm usually develops from the result of triple fusion, that is, the fusion of the two polar nuclei with one male gamete. The fusion nucleus is commonly termed the primary endosperm nucleus. As a rule, this nucleus begins dividing before the zygote. However, the timing of the initial divisions of the two structures is variable, and sometimes the endosperm does not develop at all. The lack of correlation between the development of embryo and endosperm has often been associated with apomictic phenomena (that is, development of embryo without gametic union; cf. Esau, 1946).

Two principal methods of endosperm formation are recognized: (1) a period of free nuclear division is followed by formation of walls after many nuclei have been formed in the embryo sac; (2) cell walls are formed immediately after the first nuclear division. If free nuclei are formed, these occur in the parietal layer of cytoplasm enclosing a central vacuole. The nuclear divisions are synchronized and occur nearly at the same time throughout the embryo sac. More exactly, at each division mitoses proceed across the embryo sac, beginning at the micropylar end. The formation of walls starts relatively late in the development of such endosperm. Two methods of wall formation have been reported: (1) by phragmoplasts and cell plates and (2) by furrowing (Schnarf, 1928; see also chapter 3). After the cell walls have been formed, cell division continues, with every mitosis followed by cytokinesis, until the embryo sac is filled with endosperm. Sometimes, however, a cavity filled with sap is retained (e.g., coconut). The divisions occurring after the free nuclear stage may show no particular orientation, or they may be as orderly as those in a vascular cambium.

If the endosperm is formed without a free nuclear stage, the first mitosis is followed by cytokinesis, and the formation of cell walls continues throughout the growth of the endosperm. Intermediate types of endosperm formation—partly with free nuclei, partly with cell walls—are also encountered and are sometimes treated as a separate type (helobial type, because it occurs in the Helobiae; cf. Maheshwari, 1950).

The structure of the fully developed endosperm varies considerably. It may be a thin-walled highly vacuolated tissue, storing no food. Such endosperm is usually used up, partly or completely, by the developing embryo (e.g., *Lactuca,* fig. 19.3). In many plants the endosperm is differentiated as a storage tissue (e.g., Gramineae, fig. 19.2). As such it may have thin or thick walls, sometimes very thick and horny in appearance (e.g., *Asparagus,* Robbins and Borthwick, 1925). As a rule endosperm lacks intercellular spaces.

The substances stored in the endosperm are varied. (Cf. also chapters 2 and 8.) The principal storage carbohydrate is starch in the form of starch grains. Hemicelluloses or related carbohydrates occurring in the thick walls are also interpreted as storage materials. Proteins found in seed occur in two principal forms: (1) the glutens, amorphous in structure; (2) the aleuron grains, composed of a proteinaceous substrate with a crystalloid body (protein crystal) and a globoid body (double phosphate of calcium and magnesium with an organic radical). Glutens are common in the starch-containing cells of cereal grains. Aleuron grains occur in all endosperm cells of *Ricinus* (castor bean) and in the peripheral endosperm layer (aleuron layer) of the Polygonaceae and Gramineae. Starchless endosperm may contain oil and fats as storage materials.

Seeds lacking endosperm in the mature state are called *exalbuminous* (from the Latin *albumen,* the white of an egg). In such seeds the embryo is large in relation to the seed as a whole. It fills the seed almost completely, and its body parts, particularly the cotyledons, store the food reserves (e.g., Leguminosae, Cucurbitaceae, Compositae; fig. 19.3, *C*). Seeds with endosperm are called *albuminous.* In such seeds the embryo varies in size in relation to the amount of endosperm left at maturity. The monocotyledons commonly have albuminous seeds (fig. 19.2 and plate 85, *G*). In addition to the two kinds of seeds just listed, there is a third one, in which part of the nucellus is retained and becomes a storage tissue, the *perisperm* (Chenopodiaceae and other Centrospermae; fig. 20.4, *A*).

SEED COAT

The young testa or seed coat developing from the integument or integuments consists of more or less vacuolate thin-walled cells. During the maturation of the seed, the testa undergoes varied degrees of structural alteration. There may be a change in contents and wall structure as well as destruction of some or all of the original integumentary layers (Netolitzky, 1926).

Some seed-coat differences among plants may be traced to differences in the structure of the ovule, such as the number and thickness of the integuments and the arrangement of the vascular tissues. Similar ovules, however, may become highly dissimilar during development. There may be variations in the intensity of cellular destruction; in the degree of sclerification and the distribution of mechanical cells; in the deposition of coloring and other organic substances; and in the differentiation of specialized trichomes, such as hairs, papillae, and hooks. The epidermis of the seed frequently develops very thick walls and is filled with coloring matter (plate 85, *F, G*). In the Leguminosae the protodermal cells elongate at right angles to the surface and differentiate into macrosclereids (fig. 10.6; Corner, 1951; Reeve, 1946*a, b*; Schmidt, 1902). In *Gossypium* the epidermal cells elongate into hairs, the commercially used cotton fibers. In certain seeds (e.g., *Linum, Plantago psyllium*) the epidermal walls are highly hygroscopic and become mucilaginous on contact with moisture.

The mechanically protective tissue may differentiate in the outer or the inner integument. In *Asparagus* such tissue is represented by the outer epidermis of the outer integument, in *Capsella* by the second layer of the outer integument, in *Reseda* by the first layer of the inner integument. The seeds are also protected by cuticles that originate in the ovule (see p. 554). The seed cuticles usually combine into a continuous membrane (probably interrupted in the hilar region, however) which encloses the embryo and the associated endosperm (if the latter is present).

The development of seed coats is here described by reference to specific examples of the following kinds of seed: (1) seed derived from an ovule with two integuments and having a mechanically strong seed coat (*Asparagus officinalis*); (2) seed derived from an ovule with two integuments and having a mechanically weak seed coat (*Beta vulgaris*); (3) seed derived from an ovule with a single integument and having a mechanically weak seed coat (*Lycopersicon esculentum*).

Asparagus Seed (Robbins and Borthwick, 1925). The anatropous ovule of asparagus has two integuments and a relatively large nucellus (fig. 20.3, *A, B*). In the mature seed the integuments are transformed into a black, finely rugose, somewhat brittle seed coat. The nucellus is completely absorbed during the enlargement of the embryo sac. The mature embryo is a slender cylindrical structure (fig. 20.3, *C*), completely imbedded in a massive horny endosperm with walls of hemicellulose. At the time of pollination the outer integument consists of from five to ten layers of cells, the inner of only

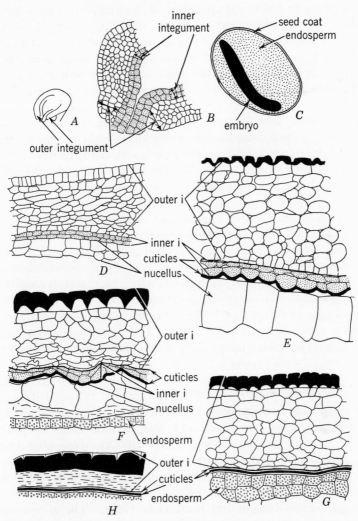

Fig. 20.3. Development of seed coat in *Asparagus officinalis*. *A*, diagram of ovule. *B*, integuments at the time of pollination. *C*, diagram of entire seed sampled 44 days after pollination. *D–H*, sections of seed coat in different stages of development. These sections were made the following numbers of days after pollination: 8 (*D*), 16 (*E*), 20 (*F*), and 29 (*G*). *H* is from mature seed. (*B*, *D–H*, ×140; *C*, ×7. After Robbins and Borthwick, 1925.)

two (fig. 20.3, *B*). The cells are small and closely packed. During the first 16 days after pollination the seed coat reaches its maximum thickness as a result of cell enlargement (fig. 20.3, *D, E*). In addition, the outer wall in the outer integument develops a pronounced thickening, and some yellowish granular substance is deposited in the inner layer of the inner integument. When the seed coat is of maximum thickness, two cuticles are discernible, one located between the two integuments, the other, a thicker one, between the inner integument and the nucellus (fig. 20.3, *E*).

In subsequent developmental stages the seed coat progressively desiccates and shrinks and is gradually compressed by the enlarging endosperm (fig. 20.3, *F, G*). About 30 days after pollination the cells of the inner integument are disintegrated and compressed so that the two fatty membranes closely approach each other (fig. 20.3, *G*). In the mature seed they become indistinguishable from one another, though they can be separated by treatment with alkali (fig. 20.3, *H*). The walls of the outer epidermal cells continue to thicken until, at maturity, the cell lumina are completely filled with dark-brown wall material (fig. 20.3, *H*). The outer surface is covered with a thin transparent membrane which appears to be pectic in nature and is hydrophilous. Thus, the principal structural features of the mature seed coat are: (1) the thick-walled epidermis offering mechanical protection and bearing a surface membrane which readily absorbs water and (2) a thick cuticular membrane enclosing the endosperm and embryo.

Beta Seed (Artschwager, 1927; Bennett and Esau, 1936). The campylotropous ovule (curved, but not grown fast to the funiculus as an anatropous ovule) has two integuments, each two cells in thickness (plate 80, *B*). The nucellus is relatively large. During the development of the seed, a curved sac (the caecum) is formed through breakdown of nucellar cells in continuity with the embryo sac at its chalazal end. The embryo, which eventually fills the embryo sac and the caecum, curves around the remaining part of the nucellus which becomes a storage tissue, the perisperm (fig. 20.4, *A*). The endosperm is reduced to a single layer at the micropylar end of the embryo sac. The mature seed is a shiny lenticular structure with a thin seed coat.

The seed coat develops from the two integuments (fig. 20.4, *B*). The protoplasts of the outer layer of the outer integument die, and the cells become filled with brown resinous material (fig. 20.4, *C, D*). The inner layer of the outer integument may increase in thickness by cell division, but it remains thin walled and parenchymatous. The outer layer of the inner integument disintegrates. The inner layer of the inner integument develops somewhat thickened, delicately sculptured walls (fig. 20.4, *D*). The outer surface of the seed is covered with a cuticle. No cuticle has been identified between the

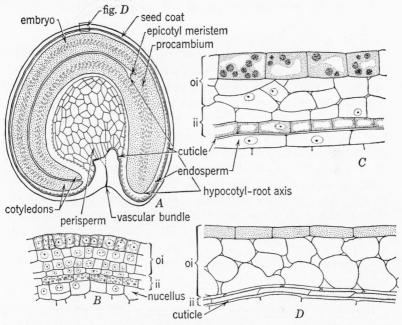

FIG. 20.4. The seed of *Beta vulgaris* (sugar beet) shown in longitudinal section (*A*), and its seed coat in 3 developmental stages (*B–D*). The letters ii signify inner integument, oi, outer integument. The rootcap is not visible because the root end of the hypocotyl lies in a different plane than does the rest of the hypocotyl. Further details are in the text. (*A*, ×20; *B–D*, ×310; *A* adapted from Bennett and Esau, 1936.)

two integuments, but there is a conspicuous cuticle on the inner side of the inner integument (fig. 20.4). This cuticle stops abruptly in the chalazal region where the vascular tissue approaches the perisperm. A tightly packed layer of cells, rich in tannin, intervenes between the vascular tissues and the perisperm. When the seed is mature, the walls of these tannin cells give a positive fat reaction. Although the mature beet seed coat is mechanically weak, the seed is well protected because it is retained within the fruit, which develops an extremely hard wall. Usually several such fruits remain united in a structure known as the seed ball which, if planted, permits the emergence of the seedlings after the effect of moisture loosens the upper lid-like parts of the fruits along a predetermined line of dehiscence.

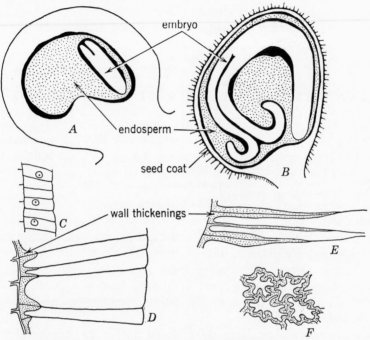

FIG. 20.5. Development of seed coat in *Lycopersicon esculentum* (tomato). Diagrams of longitudinal sections of ovules sampled 25 (*A*) and 40 (*B*) days after pollination. The ovule in *B* shows hair-like extensions on the surface. These are wall thickenings of epidermal cells exposed after a partial breakdown of the cells. *C–E* show developmental stages of the epidermis in longitudinal section. *F*, transverse section of the epidermis through the wall thickenings. (*C–F*, ×170. Adapted from Smith, 1935.)

Lycopersicon Seed (Netolitzky, 1926; Smith, 1935). The seed is derived from an anatropous ovule, and the seed coat from a thick single integument. The small nucellus and the large integument are largely digested during the development of the seed. The integumentary tapetum investing the embryo sac after the nucellar epidermis breaks down is conspicuously differentiated. All the tissue outside it, except the outer epidermis of the integument, is digested (fig. 20.5, *A*, *B*). The epidermis develops thickenings on the inner tangential walls and the innermost parts of the anticlinal walls (fig. 20.5, *C, D*). The outer walls break down, while the thickened radial walls remain and appear like hairs (fig. 20.5, *E, F*). In the mature seed the testa includes the integumentary tapetum, remains of the epidermis, and remains of the digested integumentary parenchyma. This seed coat encloses a curved filiform embryo and an endosperm which practically fills the part of the seed not occupied by the embryo (fig. 20.5, *B*). A cuticle occurs between the seed coat and the endosperm.

NUTRITIONAL ASPECTS IN SEED DEVELOPMENT

The characteristic feature of the development of female reproductive structures in seed plants is that not only does the gametophyte develop in the tissues of the sporophyte but the new sporophyte arising from the gametophyte is also supported by the old sporophyte during its early growth. The development of these gametophytic and sporophytic bodies obviously involves an active transfer of food from the old sporophyte to the new structures. This transfer occurs not merely by translocation of food through the vascular tissues to a close proximity of reproductive structures but also by an extensive digestion of tissues. Microsporogenesis and microgametogenesis, too, are associated with destruction of tissues, but on a much smaller scale than in the formation of the female reproductive structures and of the new sporophyte.

The digestive phenomena encountered during the development of the seed occur in the following chronological order. In normal sporogenesis the early growth of one of the megaspores (the functioning megaspore) into an embryo sac involves the destruction of the three nonfunctioning megaspores. Subsequently, the embryo sac increases in size by encroaching upon the nucellus, which is digested either partially or entirely. In the latter instance, there is frequently a differentiation of the integumentary tapetum next to the embryo sac. During the development of the embryo several phenomena may occur: formation of endosperm; partial or complete digestion of the endosperm by the embryo; digestion of the parenchyma of the nucellus (if the nucellus is still present at this stage) and of the integuments.

A simple enumeration of phenomena fails to bring out the complexity of the relationship between the tissues being digested and those that apparently utilize the products of breakdown. The endosperm itself, for example, utilizes such products and is, at the same time, absorbed by the embryo. The relation between the embryo and the endosperm is not entirely clear. Commonly embryo development depends on the presence of the endosperm, but under certain conditions the embryo appears to be able to draw directly upon the food supply in the integument (Cooper and Brink, 1949). The role of the integumentary tapetum is not known definitely either. The breakdown of the parenchyma outside the tapetum suggests that the latter might be the source of digestive enzymes. With reference to the transfer of food from the tapetum to the embryo sac, it is of interest that a cuticle is originally present between the nucellus and the inner integumentary epidermis. There is, however, a cuticle-free avenue to the embryo sac in the chalazal region. Some plants develop highly specialized mechanisms of food absorption. Various cells of the embryo sac, and also the endosperm and the suspensor, may develop haustoria that penetrate into the adjacent tissues (Maheshwari, 1950).

The embryo is not known to have any vascular connection with the old sporophyte. In fact, its cellular connection with the next-lying tissues is usually ephemeral. In the early stages of its development the embryo is attached to the embryo-sac wall by means of the suspensor, but the suspensor frequently appears shrivelled before the embryo is full grown. The exact nature of the connection between the suspensor and the embryo-sac wall, particularly whether there are any plasmodesmata in this connection, has not been determined. Probably the suspensor is mainly an anchoring structure. In the transfer of food from the endosperm to the embryo during the germination of albuminous seeds parts of the embryo may be differentiated as absorbing organs. In the Gramineae, for example, the cotyledon (the scutellum) has a glandular epidermis which is in contact with the endosperm, and, in the onion, the tip of the cotyledon is a digestive structure (plate 85, *G*). In many seeds, however, the embryo has no specialized digestive tissues and appears to depend on transfer of materials through its epidermis when, during germination, it takes up food from the endosperm.

REFERENCES

Allen, G. S. Embryogeny and the development of the apical meristems of *Pseudotsuga*. II. Late embryogeny. *Amer. Jour. Bot.* 34:73–80. 1947a.

Allen, G. S. Embryogeny and the development of the apical meristems of Pseudotsuga. III. Development of the apical meristems. *Amer. Jour. Bot.* 34: 204–211. 1947b.

Artschwager, E. Development of flowers and seed in the sugar beet. *Jour. Agr. Res.* 34:1–25. 1927.

Bennett, C. W., and K. Esau. Further studies on the relation of the curly-top virus to plant tissues. *Jour. Agr. Res.* 53:595–620. 1936.

Bhadurim, P. N. Studies on the embryogeny of the Solanaceae. I. *Bot. Gaz.* 98: 283–295. 1936.

Borthwick, H. A. Development of the macrogametophyte and embryo of Daucus carota. *Bot. Gaz.* 92:23–44. 1931.

Brink, R. A., and D. C. Cooper. The endosperm in seed development. *Bot. Rev.* 13:423–477, 479–541. 1947.

Cooper, D. C., and R. A. Brink. The endosperm-embryo relationship in an autonomous apomict, Taraxacum officinale. *Bot. Gaz.* 111:139–153. 1949.

Corner, E. J. H. The leguminous seed. *Phytomorph.* 1:117–150. 1951.

Esau, K. Morphology and reproduction in guayule and certain other species of Parthenium. *Hilgardia* 17:61–120. 1946.

Hayward, H. E. *The structure of economic plants.* New York, The Macmillan Company. 1938.

Johansen, D. A. *Plant embryology.* Waltham, Mass., Chronica Botanica Company. 1950.

Jones, H. A. Pollination and life history studies of lettuce (Lactuca sativa L.). *Hilgardia* 2:425–479. 1927.

Maheshwari, P. *An introduction to the embryology of angiosperms.* New York, McGraw-Hill Book Company. 1950.

Martin, A. C. The comparative internal morphology of seeds. *Amer. Midland Nat.* 36:513–660. 1946.

Miller, H. A., and R. H. Wetmore. Studies in the developmental anatomy of Phlox drummondii Hook. I. The embryo. *Amer. Jour. Bot.* 32:588–599. 1945.

Nast, C. G. The embryogeny and seedling morphology of Juglans regia L. *Lilloa* 6:163–205. 1941.

Netolitzky, F. Anatomie der Angiospermen-Samen. In: K. Linsbauer. *Handbuch der Pflanzenanatomie.* Band 10. Lief. 14. 1926.

Reeve, R. M. Structural composition of the sclereids in the integument of Pisum sativum L. *Amer. Jour. Bot.* 33:191–204. 1946a.

Reeve, R. M. Ontogeny of the sclereids in the integument of Pisum sativum L. *Amer. Jour. Bot.* 33:806–816. 1946b.

Reeve, R. M. Late embryogeny and histogenesis in Pisum. *Amer. Jour. Bot.* 35:591–602. 1948.

Robbins, W. W., and H. A. Borthwick. Development of the seed of Asparagus officinalis. *Bot. Gaz.* 80:426–438. 1925.

Schmidt, W. Untersuchungen über die Blatt- und Samenstruktur bei den Loteen. *Bot. Centbl. Beihefte.* 12:425–428. 1902.

Schnarf, K. Embryologie der Angiospermen. In: K. Linsbauer. *Handbuch der Pflanzenanatomie.* Band 10. Lief. 21. 1927; Lief. 23. 1928; Lief. 24. 1929.

Schnarf, K. *Vergleichende Embryologie der Angiospermen.* Berlin, Gebrüder
  Borntraeger. 1931.
Smith, O. Pollination and life-history studies of the tomato (*Lycopersicon escu-
  lentum* Mill.). *N. Y. (Cornell) Agr. Exp. Sta. Mem.* 184. 1935.
Spurr, A. R. Histogenesis and organization of the embryo in *Pinus Strobus* L.
  Amer. Jour. Bot. 36:629–641. 1949.
Spurr, A. R. Organization of the procambium and development of the secretory
  cells in the embryo of *Pinus Strobus* L. *Amer. Jour. Bot.* 37:185–197. 1950.

Plates

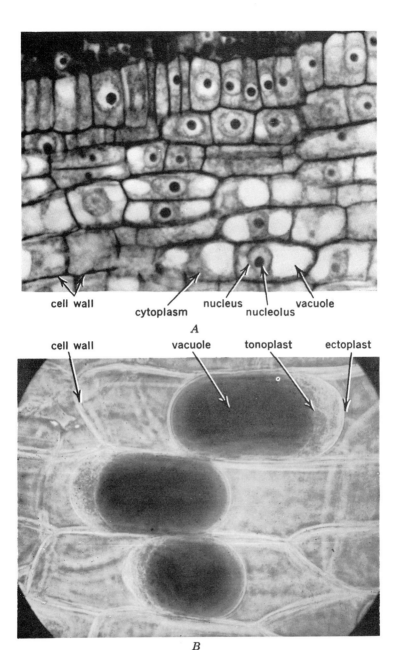

cell wall   nucleus   vacuole

cytoplasm   nucleolus

A

cell wall   vacuole   tonoplast   ectoplast

B

PLATE 1. Cytoplasm and vacuoles. *A*, differentiating cells of root of *Drimys* illustrating different degrees of vacuolation of protoplasts. *B*, abaxial epidermis of red onion bulb scale with cells that were in living state but plasmolyzed by a KNO_3 solution. The vacuoles contain anthocyanin and therefore appear dark. (*A*, ×280, *B*, ×288. *A*, slide by E. M. Gifford; *B*, photomicrograph by H. B. Currier.)

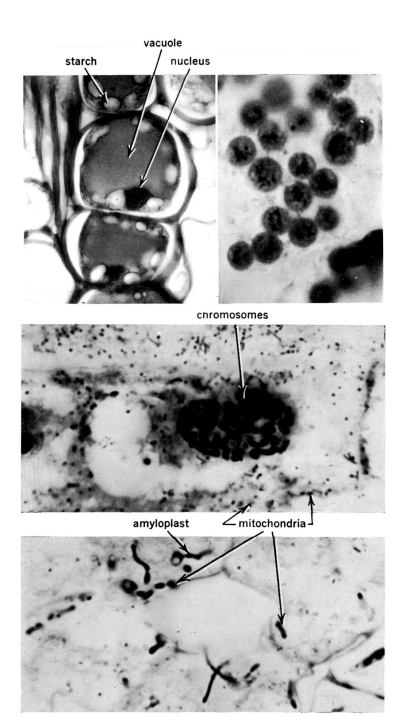

PLATE 2. Components of plant cells. *A*, starch grains in parietal cytoplasm and tannins in vacuoles of *Abies* root parenchyma cells. *B*, chloroplasts from *Nicotiana* leaf cell. *C*, mitochondria and prophase chromosomes from *Narcissus* root. *D*, mitochondria and amyloplasts from scutellum of germinated *Zea* grain. (*A*, ×500; *B*, ×1,200; *C*, *D*, ×1,800. *C*, *D*, from Newcomer, *Amer. Jour. Bot.* 33:684, 1946.)

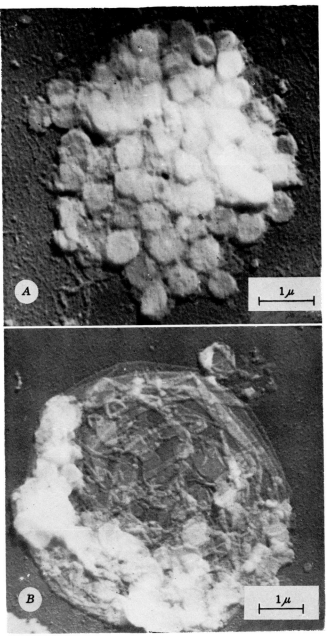

PLATE 3. Chloroplasts of tobacco (*Nicotiana tabacum* L.) photographed by means of an electron microscope. *A*, illustration of chloroplast grana. *B*, grana enclosed in the chloroplast membrane. (Both from Frey-Wyssling and Mühlethaler, *Naturf. Gesell. Zürich, Vrtljschr.* **94**:181, 1949.)

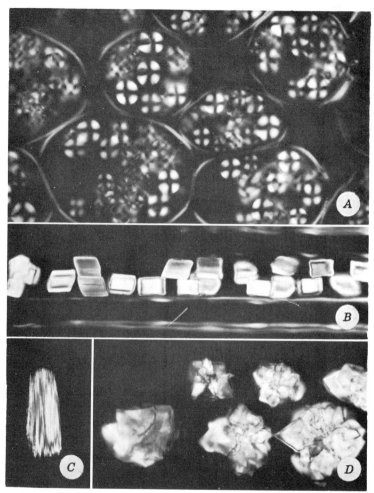

PLATE 4. Doubly refractive ergastic bodies seen in polarized light. *A*, starch grains in cells of *Convolvulus* root showing the characteristic dark cross traversing the body. *B*, prismatic crystals in phloem parenchyma of root of *Abies*. *C*, raphides in leaf of *Vitis*. *D*, druses in cortex of stem of *Tilia*. The double refraction of cell walls is also shown in *A* and *B*. (*A, C, D*, ×750; *B*, ×500.)

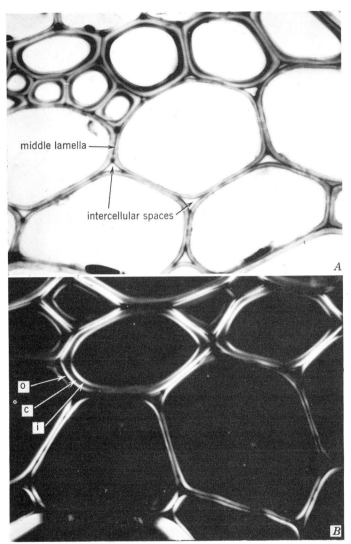

middle lamella ⎯

intercellular spaces

A

O

C

i

B

PLATE 5. Cell walls seen in ordinary (*A*) and polarized (*B*) light. Sections from the inner edge of xylem in petioles of *Nicotiana*. The larger cells, below, are parenchyma cells; the smaller, above, tracheary elements and fibers. All these cells have secondary walls. The primary and secondary wall layers in the parenchyma cells are so closely united that they are indistinguishable. In the other cells the primary wall is merged with the outermost secondary layer. The middle lamella or intercellular substance is visible, in *A*, as a darkly stained line between the walls of contiguous cells. The intercellular spaces are lined with intercellular material. *B* reveals the double refraction of primary and secondary walls. The middle lamella appears dark because it is isotropic. The central layer of the secondary wall in the tracheary cells exhibits the phenomenon of extinction. It would show double refraction in another orientation with respect to the light. Details are: c, central and, i, inner layers of secondary wall; o, outer layer of secondary wall united with primary wall. (Both, ×800.)

619

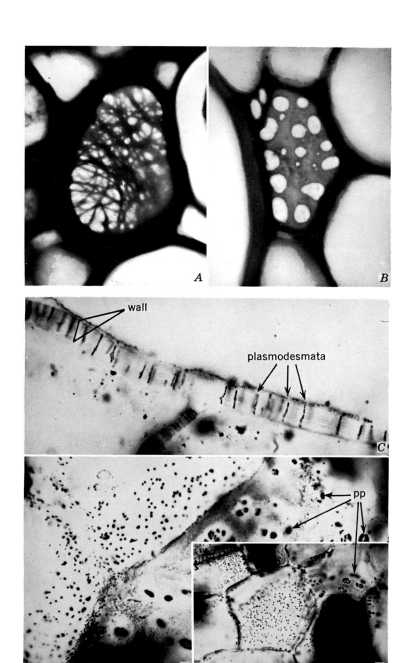

PLATE 6. Primary pit fields, pits, and plasmodesmata. *A*, face view of wall of a parenchyma cell from a root of *Abies*. The coarse reticulum reflects the manner of orientation of the microfibrils of cellulose in the primary wall. The unstained meshes in the darkly stained reticulum represent thin places in the wall. They are primary pit fields. *B*, face view of wall of a parenchyma cell from the primary xylem of *Nicotiana*. The light areas are simple pits in the secondary wall. Their pit membranes appear unstained. *C–E*, structures interpreted as plasmodesmata in parenchyma cells of *Solanum* (potato): *C*, from section of stem; *D* and *E*, from sections of tuber. Plasmodesmata appear as individual strands in sectional views of walls in *C*. In *D* and *E*, to the left, there are mostly individual strands in face view of wall; to the right, the plasmodesmata are aggregated in primary pit fields (pp). (*A*, ×750; *B*, ×1,034; *C*, ×750; *D*, ×950; *E*, ×325. *A*, slide by H. E. Wilcox. *C–D*, photomicrographs by A. S. Crafts. *C*, *E*, from Crafts, *Plant Physiol.* **8**:81, 1933.)

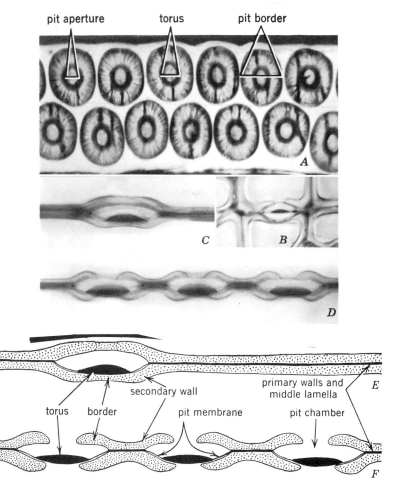

PLATE 7. Bordered pits of conifers. *A*, bordered pits of *Tsuga* in face view. They are in alternate arrangement, and their pit membranes show thickenings in the form of radial and tangential bands. The torus appears especially dark where it extends beyond the limits of the pit aperture. *B*, bordered pit-pair from transection of xylem of *Abies* with torus in central position. *C–F*, bordered pit-pairs of *Pinus* as they appear in tangential sections of xylem. The tori are lying against one of the borders. In *D* and *F*, the section passed through the apertures; in *C* and *E*, somewhat above or below the aperture. (*A*, $\times$731; *B–D*, $\times$960; *A*, from Bannan, *Torrey Bot. Club Bul.* **68**:173, 1941.)

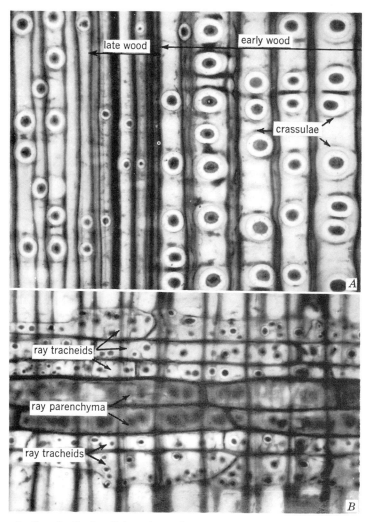

PLATE 8. Longitudinal radial sections of wood of *Pinus* showing distribution of pits. The section in *A* shows only the tracheids and related elements of the longitudinal system, all with bordered pits. *B* shows part of a ray with two rows of ray parenchyma cells and five rows of ray tracheids. In *A* the pits in the late wood are considerably smaller than those in the early wood. The crassulae (or bars of Sanio) are thicker portions of the intercellular layer and primary walls. In *B* small bordered pits occur in the ray tracheids. The large simple pits of the ray parenchyma cells appear only as dark spots in the background. (Both, ×255.)

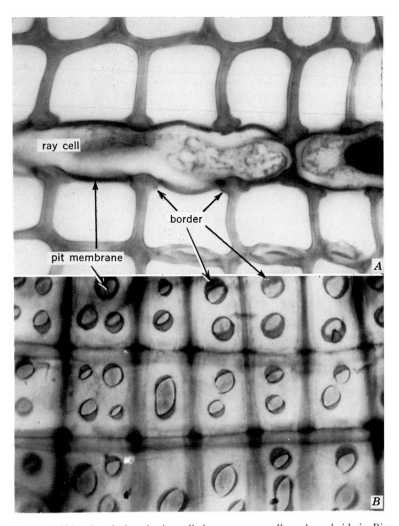

PLATE 9. Half-bordered pit-pairs in walls between ray cells and tracheids in *Pinus* wood, seen in sectional view (transection of the wood) in *A*, and in face view (radial longitudinal section of the wood) in *B*. The border occurs on the side of the tracheid and is relatively narrow and uneven in width. (*A*, ×1,500; *B*, ×750)

624

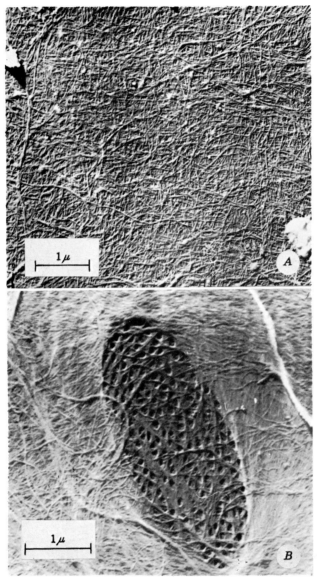

PLATE 10. Electron micrographs of primary walls of *Linum* fiber (*A*) and of *Zea* coleoptile (*B*). The scattered reticulate arrangement of the microfibrils is clearly shown in *A*. The oval area in the center of *B* is a primary pit field in which the largest meshes might be the canals that contained plasmodesmata in the living state. (*A*, from Frey-Wyssling et al., *Experientia* **4**:475, 1948; *B*, from Mühlethaler, *Biochim. Biophys. Acta* **5**:1, 1950.)

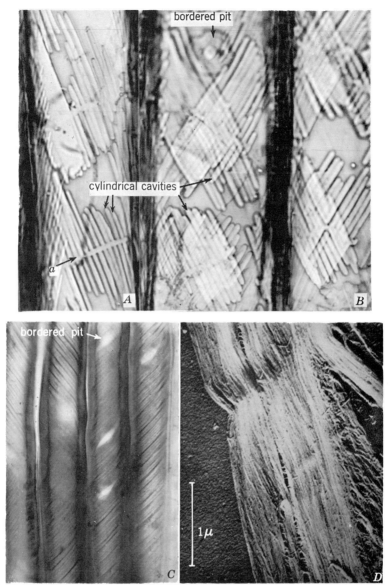

PLATE 11. Fine structure of cell walls, longitudinal sections. *A* and *B*, sections from *Sequoia sempervirens* rotted heartwood showing elongated cylindrical cavities produced by dissolving action of fungal enzymes. Cavities are oriented helically in conformity with orientation of microfibrils in central layer of secondary wall of tracheids. Parallel series of cavities in two opposing walls cross each other. Cavity at *a* is probably in the outer layer of secondary wall. *C*, compression wood of pine showing closely packed helical bands in inner layer of secondary wall. *D*, electron micrograph of secondary wall of cotton fiber showing parallel arrangement of microfibrils. (*A, B*, ×630, courtesy of Lee Bonar; *C*, ×600; *D*, from Frey-Wyssling, et al., *Experientia* **4**:475, 1948.)

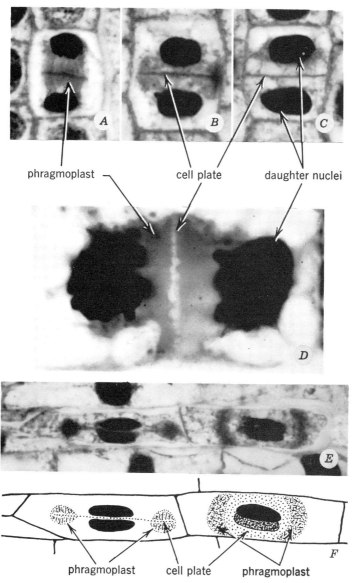

phragmoplast   cell plate   daughter nuclei

phragmoplast   cell plate   phragmoplast

PLATE 12. Origin of wall during cytokinesis. *A–C*, successive stages in the division of a cell in the root tip of *Allium.* Note gradual extension of the cell plate until it transects the mother-cell wall. *D*, cytokinesis in *Narcissus* root shows the cell plate as though it were formed of a series of vacuoles. *E* and *F*, division of two cells in procambium of *Nicotiana.* The cell to the left shows the phragmoplast in sectional view; the cell to the right, in surface view. (*A–C*, ×1,220; *D*, × about 4,000; *E, F*, ×930; *A–C*, from *Encyclopaedia Britannica*, copyright 1945; *D*, photomicrograph by E. H. Newcomer.)

627

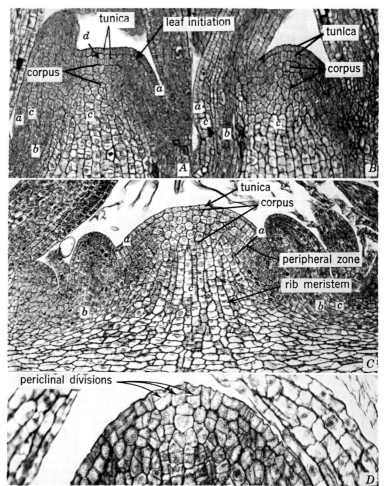

PLATE 13. Structure of apical meristems. *A* and *B*, median longitudinal sections of shoot apices, with associated leaf primordia and subjacent stem parts, of *Salix laevigata*. The apex has a two-layered tunica and a corpus. A differentiation into protoderm (*a*), procambium (*b*), and ground meristem (*c*) has occurred beneath the apical meristem. The shoot apex in *A* appears wide and flat because of the development of a leaf buttress to the right; the shoot apex in *B* is narrow and conical. A periclinal division (*d*) has occurred in the second tunica layer in *A*. *C*, *Opuntia cylindrica* shoot apex with a uniseriate tunica and a massive corpus. Derivatives of the corpus are the densely staining peripheral zone and the rib meristem. Protoderm at *a*, procambium at *b*, ground meristem at *c*. *D*, shoot apex of *Torreya californica* illustrating the apical initials that have divided periclinally, the central group of vacuolated mother cells beneath the apical initials, and the rather densely staining cells on the flanks and beneath the mother cells. (*A*, *B*, ×180; *C*, ×126; *D*, ×216. From: *A*, *B*, Reeve, *Amer. Jour. Bot.* 35:65, 1948; *C*, Boke, *Amer. Jour. Bot.* 31:299, 1944; *D*, Kemp, *Amer. Jour. Bot.* 30:504, 1943.)

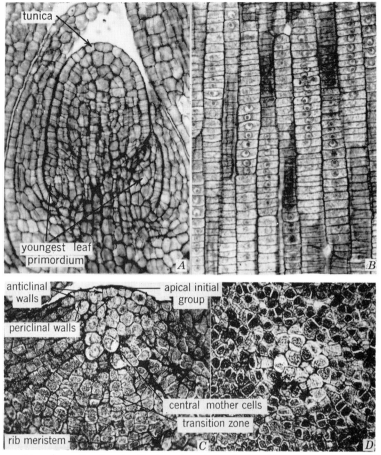

PLATE 14. *A*, median longitudinal section through the shoot apex and associated leaf primordia of *Zea mays*. A one-layered tunica covers a relatively massive corpus. The youngest leaf primordium shows periclinal divisions in the protoderm at the left. *B*, cortical rib meristem from a root tip of *Zea mays*. *C*, longitudinal and, *D*, transverse sections of the shoot apex of *Ginkgo biloba*. (Compare with fig. 5.3.) The transection was taken 63 microns below the apical initial group. Note the conspicuous vacuolation of cells in the initial and the mother-cell zones, and the thickened walls in the latter. (*A*, *B*, ×225; *C*, *D*, ×190. Slides by: *A*, G. I. Patel; *B*, E. M. Gifford. *C*, *D*, from Foster, *Torrey Bot. Club Bul.* **65**:531, 1938.)

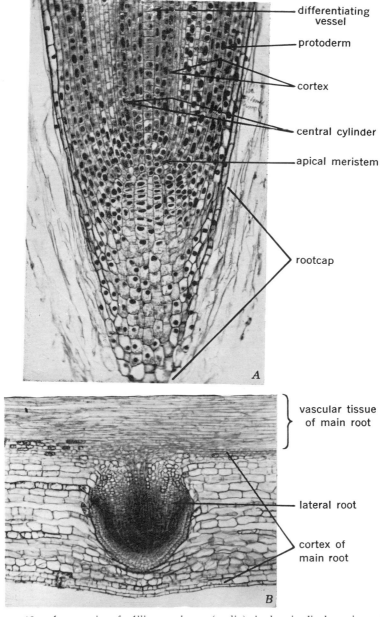

differentiating
vessel

protoderm

cortex

central cylinder

apical meristem

rootcap

A

vascular tissue
of main root

lateral root

cortex of
main root

B

PLATE 15. *A*, root tip of *Allium sativum* (garlic) in longitudinal section. *B*, longitudinal section through a root of *Salix* showing a young lateral root in connection with the vascular cylinder of the main root. Note the compression of cortical cells in front of the lateral root. (*A*, ×158; *B*, ×75. *A*, photomicrograph by L. K. Mann.)

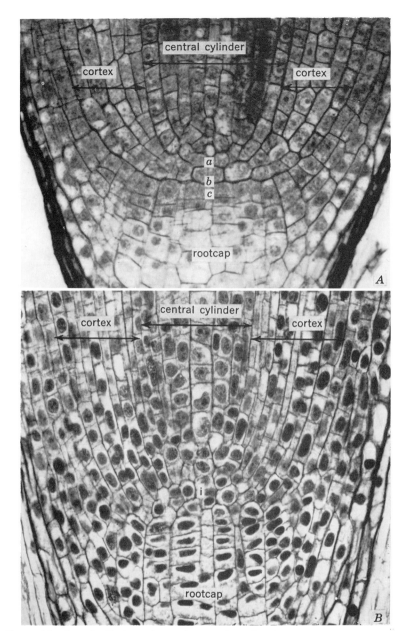

PLATE 16. Longitudinal sections of root tips of *Nicotiana tabacum* (*A*) and *Allium sativum* (*B*), showing contrasting organizations of the apical meristem. In *A* there are separate initials of, *a*, central cylinder, *b*, cortex, and, *c*, rootcap. The epidermis has common origin with the rootcap (see fig. 5.13, *A*). In *B* the initial region (i) shows a less precise arrangement of cells than in *A*, and, if there are two tiers of initials, as suggested in fig. 5.11, the initials in one tier are probably displaced from time to time by cells derived from the other tier. (*A*, ×455; *B*, ×600. B, from Mann, *Hilgardia* 21:195, 1952.)

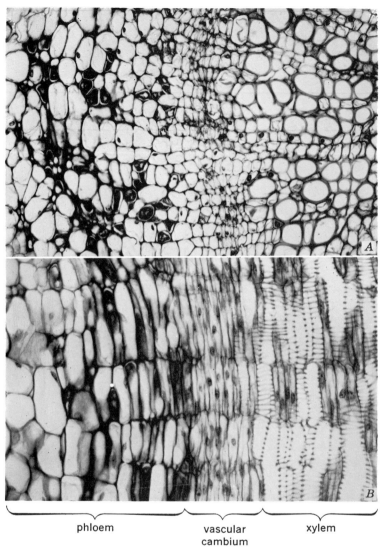

phloem   vascular   xylem
cambium

PLATE 17. Transverse (*A*) and radial longitudinal (*B*) sections through the secondary vascular region in the hypocotyl of *Spinacea oleracea*, showing the vascular cambium in relation to the secondary phloem and the secondary xylem derived from it. The widest cells in the xylem are vessel elements. In the phloem
the companion cells associated with the sieve elements have densely stained protoplasts. In the oldest part of the phloem, to the left in the photographs, the sieve
tubes and the companion cells are partly crushed. (Cf. chapter 12.) Radial rows
of cells may be followed from the cambium into the xylem and the phloem in
both sections. This orderly arrangement of cells is a result of repeated tangential
divisions in the cambium. (Both, ×250.)

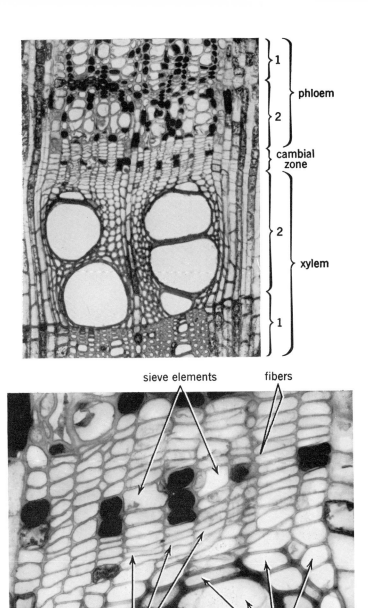

PLATE 18. Transections of vascular cambium and adjacent secondary xylem and phloem of *Vitis vinifera*. Xylem and phloem in *A* show structural differences between the latest part of one seasonal increment (1) and the earliest part of another (2). Enlarged vessels have disturbed radial seriation of cells in xylem. *B*, cambial zone from *A*, enlarged. Note recently formed tangential walls in some of the cambial initials. (*A*, ×112; *B*, ×400. From Esau, *Hilgardia* **18**:217, 1948a.)

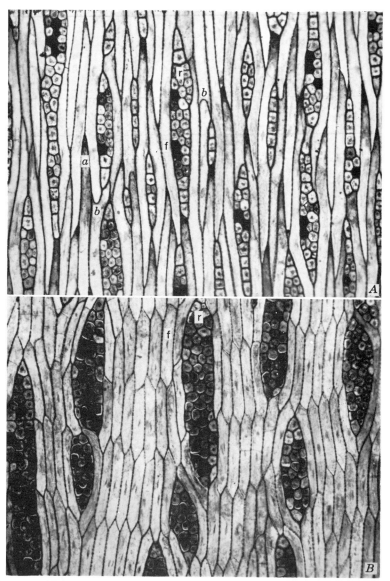

PLATE 19. Tangential longitudinal sections of vascular cambium of *Juglans hindsii* (*A*) and *Robinia pseudoacacia* (*B*). *A* exemplifies a nonstoried cambium; *B*, a storied cambium. In *A* the long fusiform initials (f) overlap each other. In *B* the short fusiform initials (f) are in horizontal tiers. In both cambia the ray initials (r) are arranged in groups, lenticular in outline in these sections. There is evidence of apical intrusive growth in fusiform cells in *A*: dense cytoplasm in the ends of some cells (*a*) and forking in others (*b*). (Both, ×155. Slides by V. I. Cheadle.)

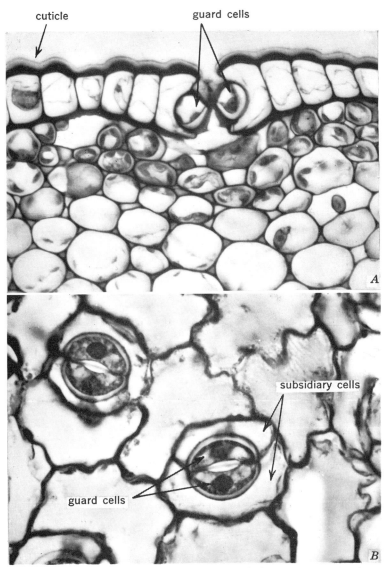

PLATE 20. Structure of epidermis. *A*, transection of *Asparagus* stem showing epidermis with guard cells, ordinary epidermal cells, and cuticle. The subepidermal cortical layers are differentiated as chlorenchyma. Beneath the guard cells is an air space, the substomatal chamber. *B*, surface view of epidermis of *Convolvulus* (morning-glory) leaf showing wavy walls and stomata with subsidiary cells. (Both, ×760. From *Encyclopaedia Britannica*, copyright 1945.)

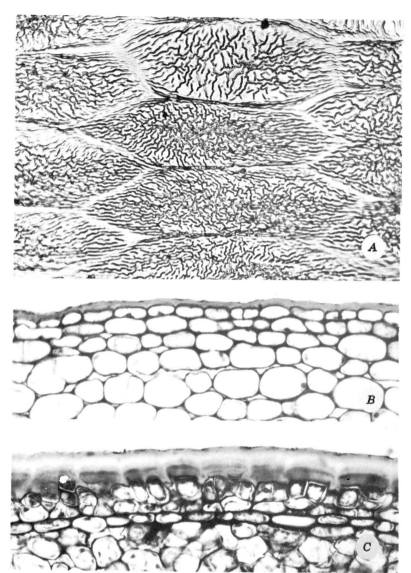

PLATE 21. Cuticle. *A*, surface view of cuticle over the veins stripped from lower surface of petals of *Pelargonium*. Hexagonal areas indicate limits of individual cells. *B* and *C*, cuticular layers in transections of *Menispermum* underground stems. *B* shows cuticle on cutinized outer epidermal walls. In *C* (older stem) cutin has occluded some cells. (*A*, ×400; by G. Girolami; *B*, *C*, ×700.)

PLATE 22 (p. 637). *A*, parenchyma tissue from pith of tomato stem. Some cell walls are visible in surface view (long arrows). Short arrows point to schizogenous intercellular spaces. Collenchyma of *Vitis* stem in longitudinal section (*B*) and of *Beta* petiole in transection (*C*). (*A*, ×49; *B*, *C*, ×285. *C*, from *Encyclopaedia Britannica*, copyright 1945.)

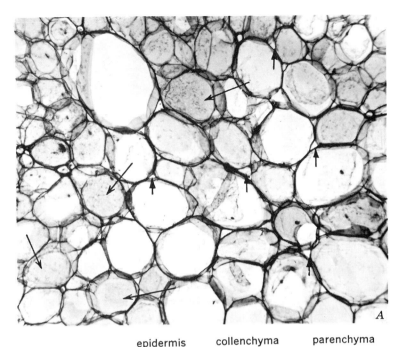

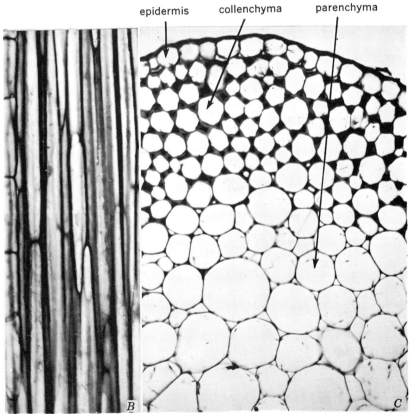

epidermis   collenchyma   parenchyma

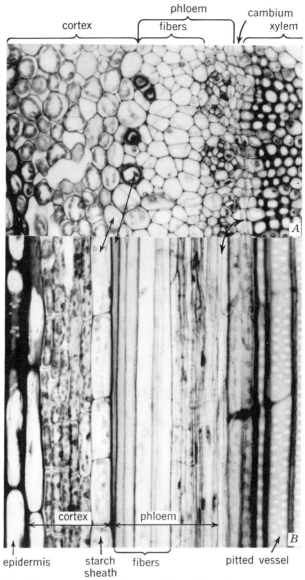

PLATE 23. Development of the primary phloem fibers in *Linum perenne* L. *A*, transverse and, *B*, radial longitudinal sections of young stems showing arrangement of tissues and the characteristic appearance of differentiating fibers: wide lumina, scanty contents, first layers of secondary walls in the fibers nearest the cortex, and, in *B*, great length as compared with that of the adjacent cortical cells. (Both, ×385. *A*, from Esau, *Amer. Jour. Bot.* **30**:579, 1943c.)

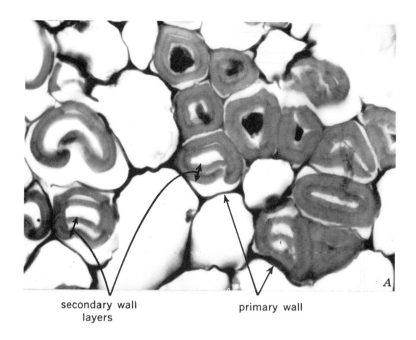

secondary wall
layers   primary wall

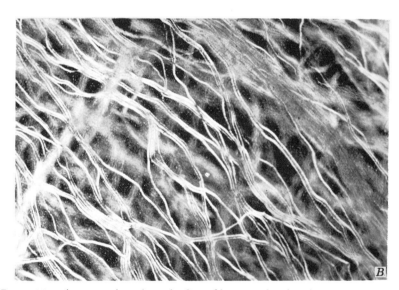

PLATE 24. *A*, transection through *Cannabis* stem showing immature primary phloem fibers. The young secondary wall is layered and, through the handling of the material in preparation of the slide, has become partly infolded. *B*, piece of a cleared olive leaf photographed with polarized light and showing the doubly refractive fiber-like sclereids permeating the mesophyll. (*A*, ×750; *B*, ×57.)

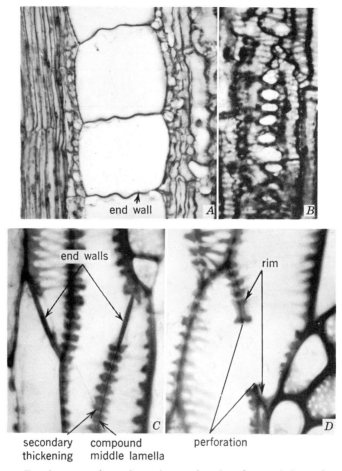

labels in image:
end wall — A — B
end walls — rim — C — D
secondary thickening — compound middle lamella — perforation

PLATE 25. Development of vessel members. *A*, series of expanded vessel members of *Cucurbita* with the end walls still intact and no secondary thickenings on the side walls. Note the crowding of cells along the sides of the vessel members. *B*, longitudinal section through cells occurring in contact with vessel members in *Cucurbita*. Some of these cells were partly pulled apart because of the lateral expansion of the vessel members. *C* and *D*, development of perforation plates in vessel members of *Asimina triloba*. Thickened but entirely primary end walls are present in *C*, absent in *D*. Secondary thickening is present on side walls and rim in *C* and *D*, except in the lower element at left in *C*. (*A*, ×200; *B*, ×320; *C*, *D*, ×680. *B*, from Esau and Hewitt, *Hilgardia* 13:229, 1940; *C*, *D*, slide by V. I. Cheadle.)

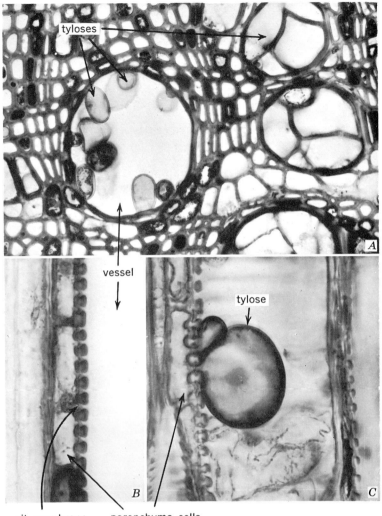

PLATE 26. Tylose development in the vessels of *Vitis vinifera* as seen in transverse (*A*) and longitudinal (*B* and *C*) sections. *A*, left, young tyloses protruding into the vessel lumen; right, vessels filled with tyloses. *B*, xylem parenchyma cell located next to a vessel. Note the thin pit membranes in the pit-pairs between the parenchyma cell and the vessel member. *C*, tyloses, one large and one small, developing through the pit-pairs between a parenchyma cell and a vessel member. The central shadow in the large tylose is that of a nucleus. (*A*, ×290; *B*, *C*, ×750. From Esau, *Hilgardia* **18**:423, 1948*b*.)

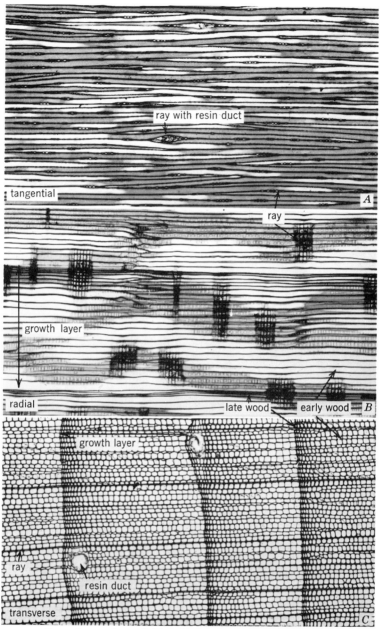

PLATE 27. Secondary xylem of *Pinus strobus* (White Pine) in tangential (*A*), radial (*B*), and transverse (*C*) sections. An example of gymnosperm (conifer) wood. (All, ×35.)

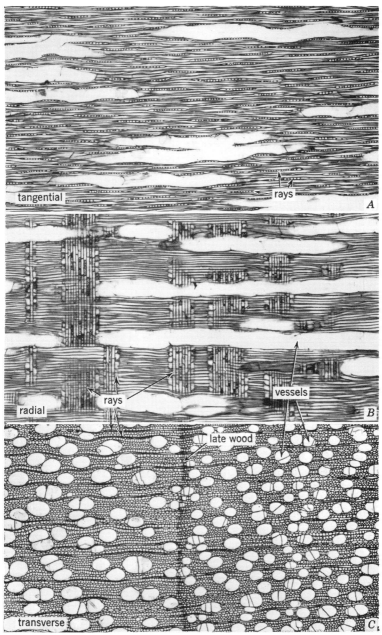

PLATE 28. Secondary xylem of *Salix nigra* (Black Willow) in tangential, (*A*), radial (*B*), and transverse (*C*) sections. An example of a diffuse-porous non-storied angiosperm (dicotyledon) wood with uniseriate heterogeneous rays. (All, ×35.)

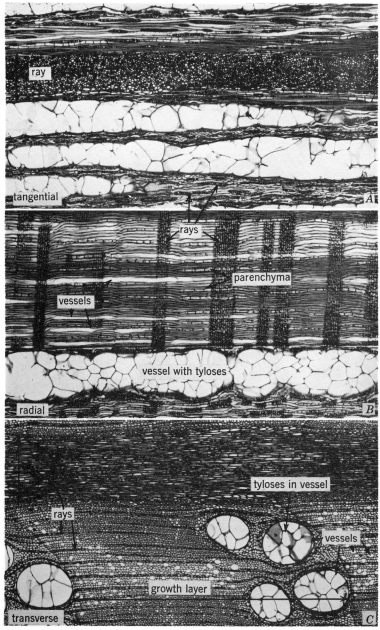

PLATE 29. Secondary xylem of *Quercus alba* (White Oak) in tangential (*A*), radial (*B*), and transverse (*C*) sections. An example of a ring-porous nonstoried angiosperm (dicotyledon) wood with high multiseriate and low uniseriate rays. Large vessels occluded by tyloses. (All, ×35.)

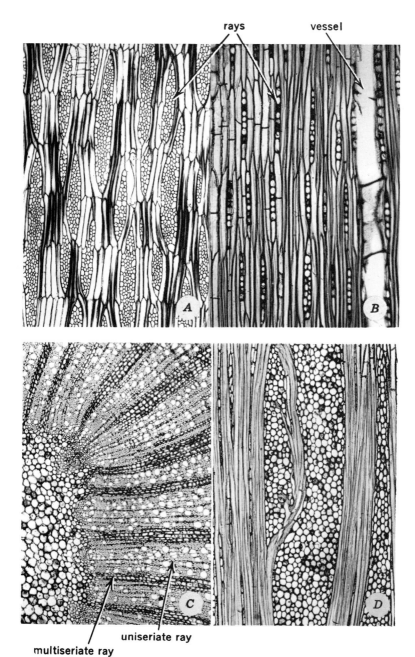

rays   vessel

multiseriate ray

uniseriate ray

PLATE 30. *A* and *B*, tangential sections of secondary xylem of storied structure. *A*, high multiseriate rays extending through more than one horizontal tier (*Triplochiton*). *B*, low uniseriate rays, each limited to one horizontal tier (*Canavalia*). *C*, transection of xylem and pith (lower left) of *Villaresia* showing multiseriate (continuous with pith) and uniseriate rays. *C*, primitive dicotyledonous ray structure. *D*, tangential section of *Crossostyles* xylem. Multiseriate ray dissected by change of ray initials into fusiform initials. (*A*, *C*, *D*, ×50; *B*, ×100. From Barghoorn, *Amer. Jour. Bot.* **27**:918, 1940; **28**:273, 1941.)

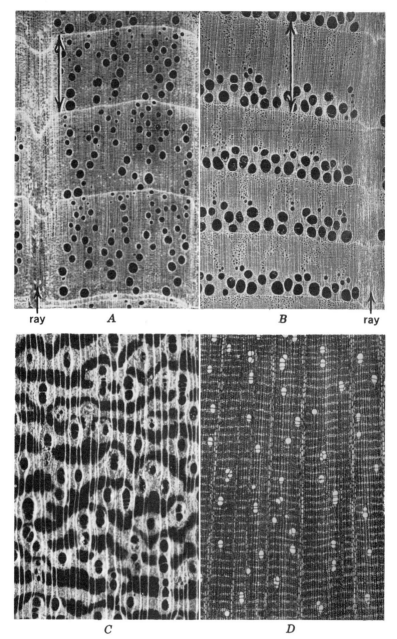

PLATE 31. Distribution of vessels ("pores") and xylem parenchyma in secondary xylem as seen in transections. *A*, semiporous wood of *Quercus virginiana*. *B*, porous wood of *Quercus bicolor*. Arrows delimit single growth layers. Distribution of parenchyma is paratracheal in *Andira* (*C*) and apotracheal in *Cymbopetalum* (*D*). (*A*, *B*, courtesy of H. P. Brown, N. Y. S. Coll. Forestry. *B*, from Williams, *Torrey Bot. Club Bul.* 66:353, 1939. *C*, *D*, from Record and Hess, *Timbers of the New World*, Yale University Press, 1943.)

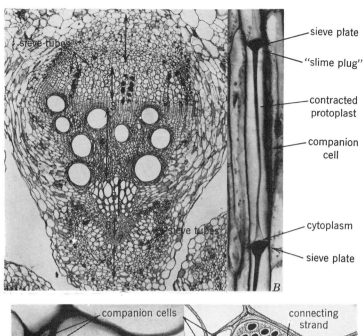

sieve plate

"slime plug"

contracted protoplast

companion cell

cytoplasm

sieve plate

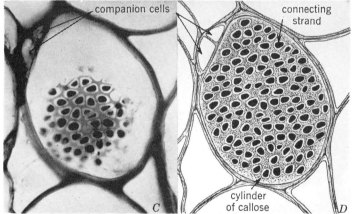

companion cells

connecting strand

cylinder of callose

PLATE 32. Phloem of *Cucurbita.* *A*, transection of a vascular bundle. Details are: 1, external primary phloem; 2, secondary phloem; 3, vascular cambium; 4, secondary xylem; 5, metaxylem; 6, protoxylem (5 and 6, together, constitute the primary xylem); 7, incompletely developed vascular cambium; 8, internal phloem, mostly primary. *B*, part of a sieve tube, in longitudinal section, with one complete member. The darkly stained material in the protoplasts in *A* and *B* is slime. *C*, transection of a sieve tube showing part of a sieve plate. *D*, reconstruction, from two successive sections, of the same sieve plate as in *C*. (Compare with fig. 12.2.) (*A*, ×18; *B*, ×185; *C*, *D*, ×540.)

647

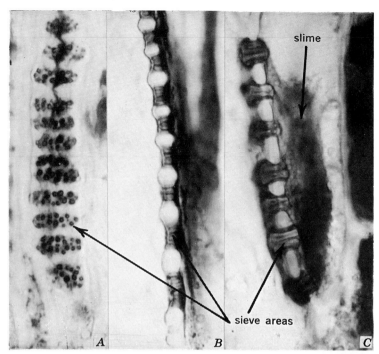

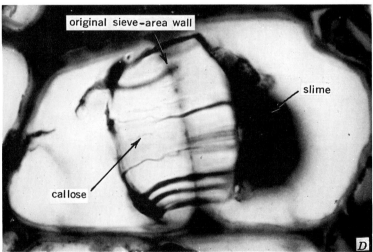

PLATE 33. Sieve plates of *Vitis* in surface (radial) view (*A*), in tangential longitudinal sections (*B* and *C*), and in transection (*D*). *A–C* show that each sieve plate consists of several sieve areas. The connecting strands traversing the sieve areas are darkly stained (dots in *A*, lines in *B–D*). *A* and *B* from newly differentiated phloem; *C* and *D* from a year-old phloem. In *C* and *D* the relatively large masses of dormancy callose on the sieve areas were in the process of dissolution because the phloem was undergoing reactivation. (*A–C*, ×750; *D*, ×1,200. *A–C*, from Esau, *Hilgardia* 18:217, 1948*a*.)

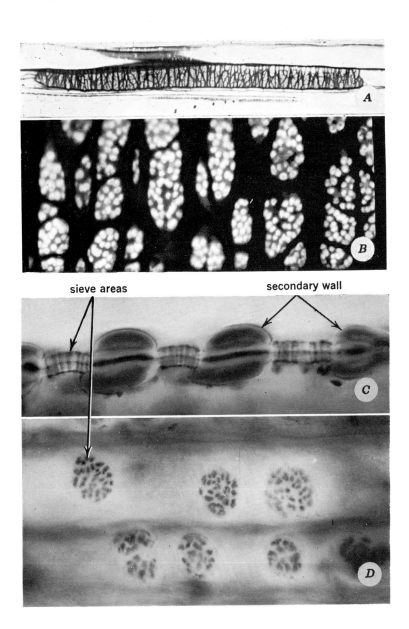

sieve areas   secondary wall

PLATE 34. *A*, face view of an oblique end wall from a sieve-tube member of *Cocos plumosa* (Palmae) bearing a compound sieve plate with sieve areas in a reticulate arrangement. *B*, part of a compound sieve plate from *Cocos romanzoffiana*, much enlarged. The sieve areas in *B* are shown to be composed of small units, the callose cylinders enclosing barely discernible connecting strands. *C*, sectional and, *D*, surface views of sieve areas from sieve cells of *Pinus strobus* (White Pine). Connecting strands traverse the sieve-area wall. In *D* each of the small units recognizable in a sieve area represents one or more connecting strands enclosed within callose. (*A*, ×128; *B*, ×1,085; *C*, *D*, ×1,000. *A*, *B*, from Cheadle and Whitford, *Amer. Jour. Bot.* 28:623, 1941; *C*, *D*, from Abbe and Crafts, *Bot. Gaz.* 100:695, 1939.)

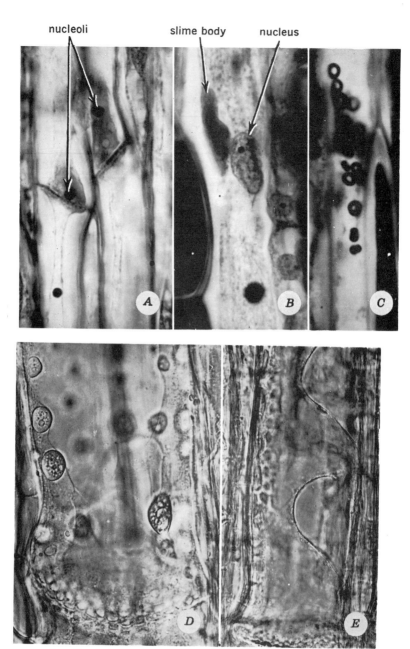

PLATE 35. Details of sieve-element protoplasts. *A* (*Gossypium*), slime accumulations on sieve plates and extruded nucleoli. *B* (*Eucalyptus*), slime body, nucleus with one nucleolus, and extruded nucleolus (below). *C* (*Beta*), sieve-tube plastids. *D* (*Cucurbita*), sieve plate below and slime bodies in parietal cytoplasm. *E* (*Cucurbita*), sieve plate below and plasmolyzed protoplast above. (*A, B,* ×1,200; *C,* ×2,200; *D,* ×800; *E,* ×500; *A, B,* from Esau, *Amer. Jour. Bot.* **34**:224, 1947; *D, E,* from Huber and Rouschal, *Deut. Bot. Gesell. Ber.* **56**:380, 1938.)

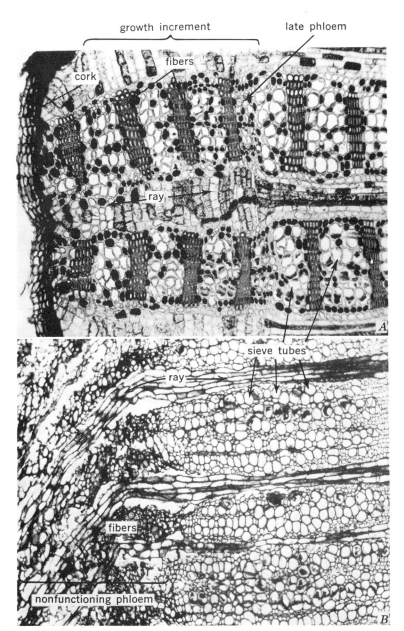

PLATE 36. Transections of secondary phloem of *A*, *Vitis vinifera* (grapevine) and, *B*, *Prunus avium* (sweet cherry). The vascular cambium was to the right in both sections. In the phloem of *Vitis* tangential bands of fibers alternate with tangential bands containing the sieve tubes with companion cells and phloem parenchyma cells. The rays are somewhat dilated in the older phloem (left). In *Prunus* the fibers occur, not in the functioning phloem, but in the nonfunctioning phloem (left) where the sieve tubes are collapsed. Note the bending of the rays in the nonfunctioning phloem. (*A*, ×90; *B*, ×88; *A*, from Esau, *Hilgardia* **18**:217, 1948a; *B*, from Schneider, *Torrey Bot. Club Bul.* **72**:137, 1945.)

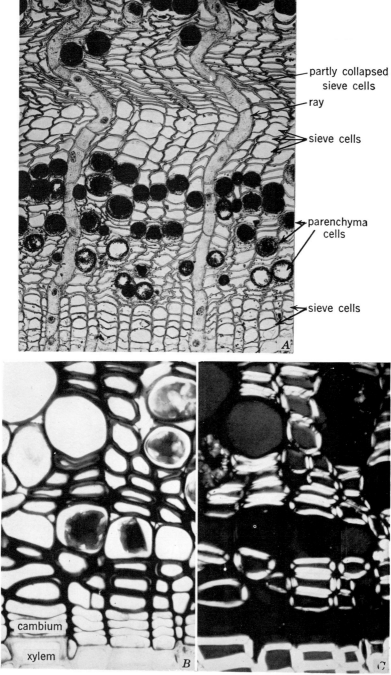

Partly collapsed sieve cells

ray

sieve cells

parenchyma cells

sieve cells

cambium

xylem

B

C

PLATE 37. Transections of secondary phloem of *Pinus strobus* (*A*) and *Abies procera* (*B, C*). In *A*, nonfunctioning phloem above; tanniferous compounds (darkly stained) in phloem parenchyma. Ordinary light in *A* and *B*, polarized in *C*. Cells with doubly refractive (probably secondary) walls in phloem in *C* are sieve cells. Weak double refraction of cell walls of parenchyma and cambium does not show. (*A*, ×240; *B, C*, ×400; *A*, from Abbe and Crafts, *Bot. Gaz.* **100**:695, 1939; *B, C*, slide by H. E. Wilcox.)

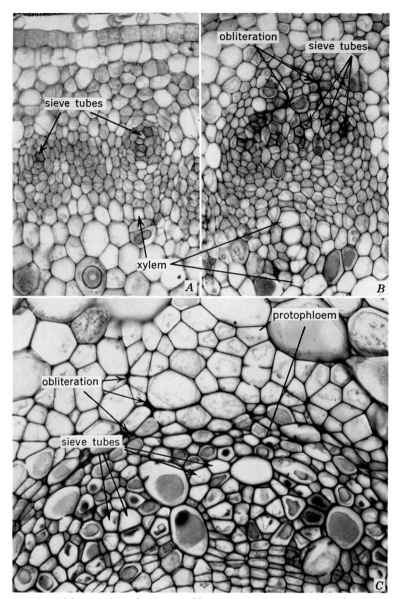

PLATE 38. Differentiation of primary phloem as seen in transection of a shoot of *Vitis vinifera*. *A* shows two procambial bundles, one with one sieve tube, the other with several. The vascular bundle in *B* has many protophloem elements. Some of the first of these elements are obliterated. Some protoxylem is also present in *A* and *B*. In *C* the protophloem sieve tubes are all obliterated and the metaphloem has differentiated (lower half of the figure). The protophloem is now represented by the enlarged primordia of the fibers. The metaphloem contains sieve tubes, with companion cells, and phloem parenchyma. The much enlarged cells are tannin-containing parenchyma cells. (All, ×500. From Esau, *Hilgardia* **18**:217, 1948a.)

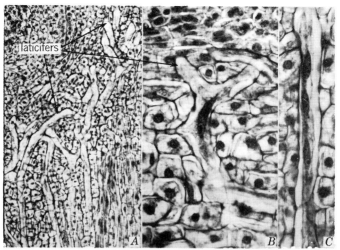

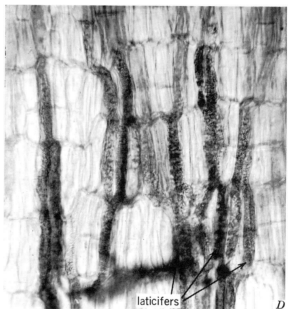

PLATE 39. *A–C*, nonarticulated laticifers of *Nerium oleander*. *A*, longitudinal section of stem near shoot apex showing branches of laticifers among parenchyma cells. *B*, high-power view of the end of a branching laticifer illustrating the result of intrusive growth among parenchyma cells. *C*, part of a laticifer with several nuclei. *D*, articulated anastomosing laticifers of *Taraxacum kok-saghyz* in a longitudinal section of secondary phloem from the fleshy taproot. The laticifers are recognizable by their dense granular contents (latex). (*A*, ×200; *B*, *C*, ×530; *D*, ×305. *D*, from Artschwager and McGuire, *U. S. Dept. Agric. Tech. Bul.* 843, 1943.)

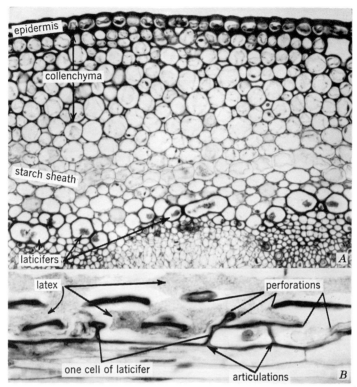

PLATE 40. Articulated laticifers of *Lactuca scariola*. *A*, transection of part of stem showing the following tissues from the top downward: epidermis; outer part of cortex differentiated as lacunate collenchyma; cortical parenchyma; innermost cortical layer differentiated as a thin-walled starch sheath; outer part of vascular region consisting of parenchyma cells and containing laticifers (elements with thickened walls and dense contracted contents); outer part of phloem. *B*, longitudinal section of stem showing a part of a laticifer consisting of two longitudinal series of cells (and part of a third, above) with portions of the cell walls resorbed so that the latex is completely continuous from one cell to another. (*A*, ×195; *B* ×525.)

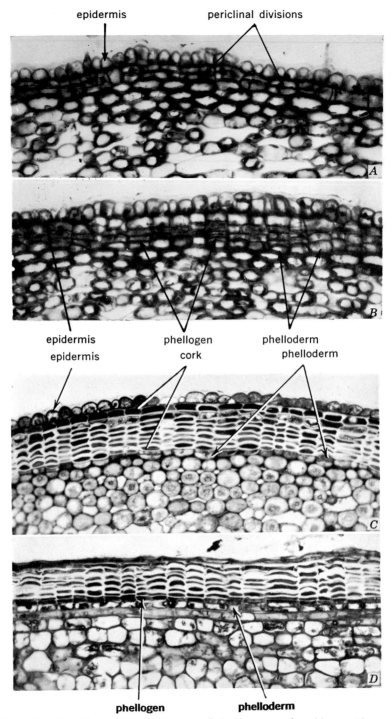

epidermis   periclinal divisions

A

B

epidermis   phellogen   phelloderm

epidermis   cork   phelloderm

C

D

phellogen   **phelloderm**

PLATE 41. *A*, earlier, and *B*, later stages of development of periderm. Transections of *Prunus* stem. First divisions beneath epidermis in *A* have formed phellogen cells outward and phelloderm cells inward. One to three rows of cork cells in *B*. Periderm in transverse (*C*) and radial (*D*) sections in a dormant *Betula* twig. All cork cells are mature. Epidermis is collapsed in *D*. (All, ×280.)

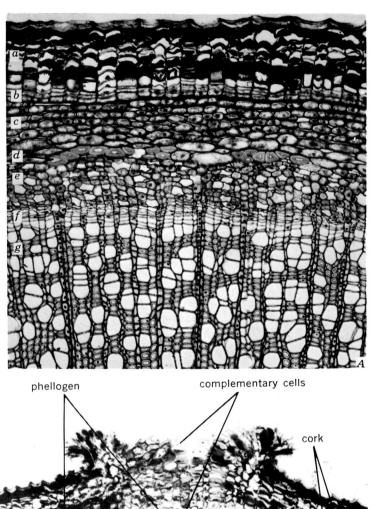

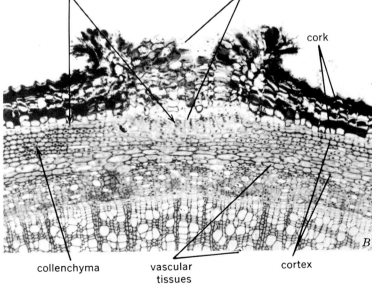

PLATE 42. Periderm in transections of *Sambucus* stem. *a*, cork; *b*, phellogen and phelloderm beneath it (one layer); *c*, cortex with collenchyma in outer part; *d*, primary phloem fibers; *e*, secondary phloem (sieve tubes have wide, clear lumina); *f*, vascular cambium; *g*, secondary xylem. *B*, lenticel. (*A*, ×127; *B*, ×75.)

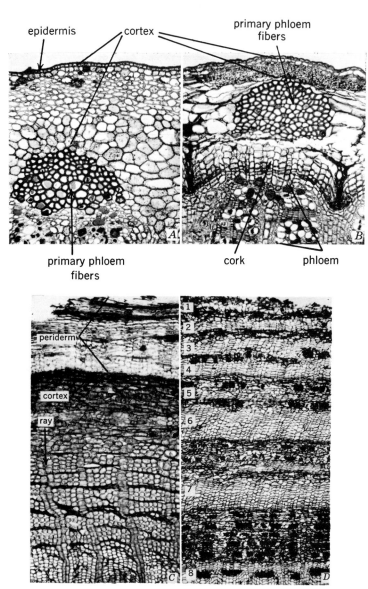

PLATE 43. *A* and *B*, transections of formation of first periderm in stem of *Vitis vinifera*. *A*, periderm absent. *B*, periderm which arose internally from primary phloem fibers; tissues outside periderm have died and nonsclerified cells have collapsed. *C* and *D*, transections of *Robinia pseudoacacia* stem with first periderm (*C*) and rhytidome (*D*). Within secondary phloem in *C* (lower half of section) are dark, tangentially oriented layers of crushed cells, mainly sieve-tube elements. Intact sieve tubes occur below. Nonfunctioning primary phloem between cortex and ends of rays. In rhytidome in *D*, periderm layers are numbered. Tissue layers alternating with periderm layers are dead portions of secondary phloem, the dark patches within which are fibers. (*A*, *B*, ×72; *C*, ×73; *D*, ×35. *A*, *B*, from Esau, *Hilgardia* 18:423, 1948*b*.)

658

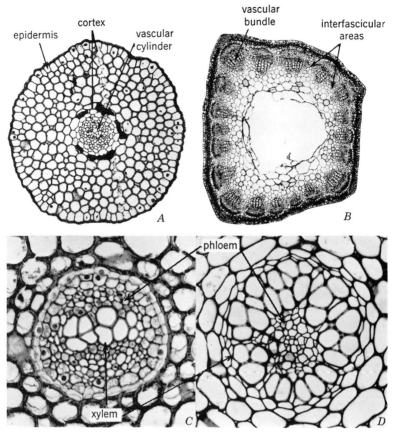

PLATE 44. Stems and vascular bundles in transections. *A, Tmesipteris,* a primitive type of stem with a rather clear separation between the fundamental and the vas-` cular systems. The cortex has collenchymatously thickened walls and its inner-most layer contains some darkly stained material. The solid vascular cylinder is surrounded by one to two layers of parenchyma cells, usually interpreted as constituting a pericycle. *B, Medicago* (alfalfa), a specialized type of stem (her-baceous dicotyledon), with the vascular system in the form of discrete strands imbedded in ground tissue and surrounding a pith. (The central part of the pith is broken down.) *C* and *D,* concentric vascular bundles. In *C* the phloem surrounds the xylem almost completely (amphicribral bundle of *Polypodium*). In *D* the xylem surrounds the phloem (amphivasal bundle of *Cordyline*). (*A*, ×50; *B*, ×33; *C*, ×187; *D*, ×180. *A, B,* from *Encyclopaedia Britannica,* copyright 1945; *D*, slide by V. I. Cheadle.)

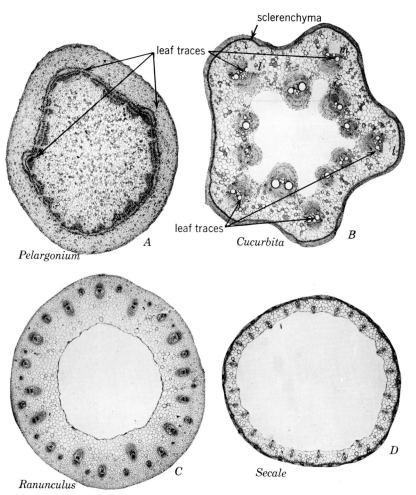

sclerenchyma

leaf traces

leaf traces   *Cucurbita*   B

A

Pelargonium

C   *Secale*   *D*

Ranunculus

PLATE 45. Transections of herbaceous stems. *A*, *Pelargonium*, dicotyledon at the beginning of secondary growth. *B*, *Cucurbita*, dicotyledonous vine with secondary growth localized within the individual vascular bundles (see also plate 32, *A*). *C*, *Ranunculus*, extreme dicotyledonous herb lacking secondary growth. *D*, *Secale* (rye), monocotyledon, grass, lacking secondary growth. Details are: *l*, lateral, and *m*, median, leaf traces. (*A*, ×6; *B*, ×7; *C*, ×11; *D*, ×13.)

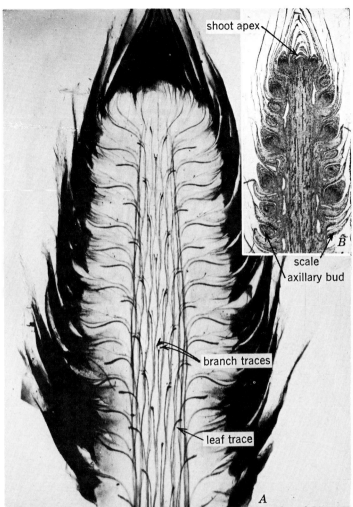

PLATE 46. Structure of young shoot with unexpanded internodes of *Pinus strobus*. *A*, thick cleared section showing the primary vascular system. It is composed of leaf traces in sympodial linkages and of branch traces. *B*, median section through a similar shoot as in *A* showing scales (the leaf traces in *A* constitute the vascular supply of these scales) and axillary buds (the branch traces in *A* diverge into such buds) subtended by the scales. The branch traces occur in pairs. Each branch trace is connected to a different leaf-trace sympodium. (*A*, ×14; *B*, ×9.5. Slides by A. R. Spurr.)

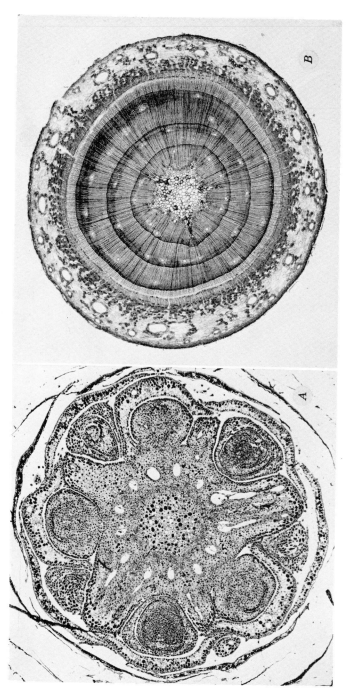

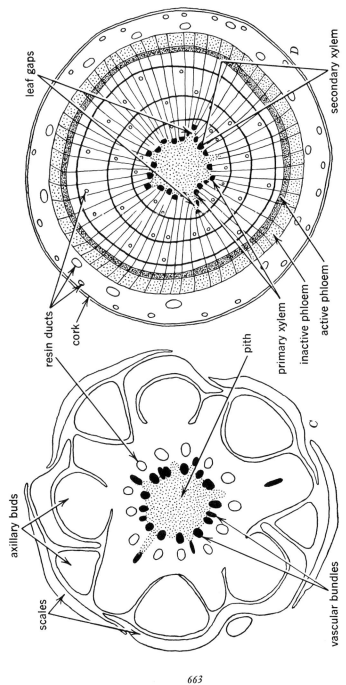

leaf gaps

secondary xylem

resin ducts

cork

primary xylem

inactive phloem

active phloem

axillary buds

pith

scales

vascular bundles

PLATE 47. Conifer stem: *Pinus*. Transections of stem in primary state, with scales and axillary buds (*A* and *C*), and in the fourth year of secondary growth (*B* and *D*). *C* and *D*, drawings interpreting details of *A* and *B*. (*A, C,* ×37; *B, D,* ×17. *A,* slide by A. R. Spurr.)

663

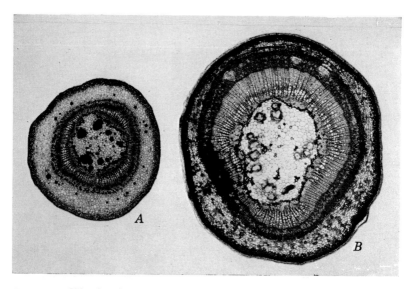

PLATE 48. Woody dicotyledon stem: *Tilia*. Transections of stems taken at the end of primary growth (*A*) and after completion of the first year's secondary growth (*B*). For further details see p. 665. (Both, ×22.)

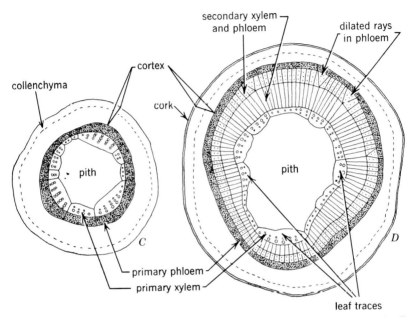

collenchyma

cortex

cork

secondary xylem and phloem

dilated rays in phloem

pith

pith

C

D

primary phloem

primary xylem

leaf traces

PLATE 48 (*Continued*). Transections of *Tilia* stem. Drawings interpreting details of *A* and *B* on p. 664. Compare *C* with *A*, and *D* with *B*. (Both, ×23.)

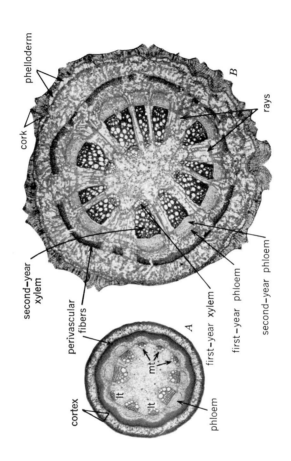

phelloderm

cork

rays

second–year xylem

perivascular fibers

first–year xylem

first–year phloem

second–year phloem

cortex

lt

lt

mt

phloem

A

B

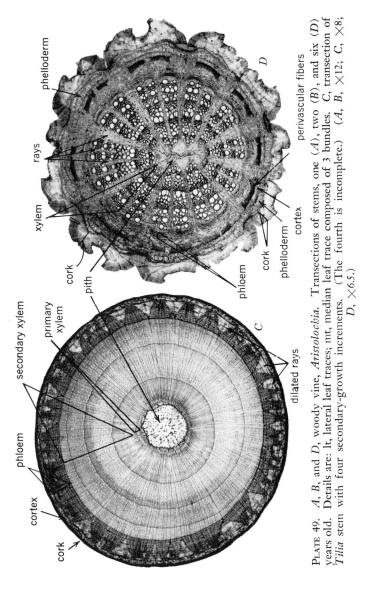

phelloderm

rays

xylem

cork

pith

phloem

cork

phelloderm

cortex

perivascular fibers

D

C

secondary xylem

primary xylem

phloem

cortex

cork

dilated rays

PLATE 49. *A, B,* and *D,* woody vine, *Aristolochia.* Transections of stems, one *(A),* two *(B),* and six *(D)* years old. Details are: lt, lateral leaf traces; mt, median leaf trace composed of 3 bundles. *C,* transection of *Tilia* stem with four secondary-growth increments. (The fourth is incomplete.) *(A, B,* ×12; *C,* ×8; *D,* ×6.5.)

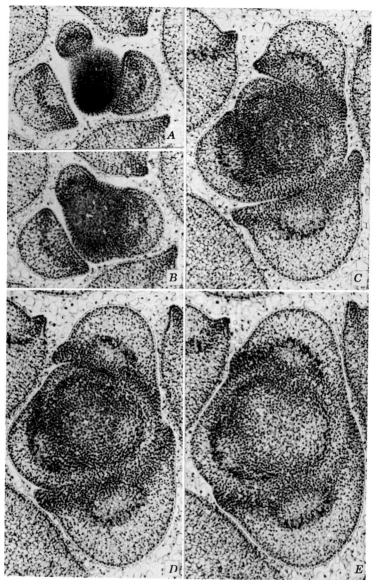

PLATE 50. Initial stages in differentiation of the vascular system in a *Nicotiana tabacum* shoot (including stem and associated leaf primordia) as seen in transections. The section in *A* was cut at the level of the shoot apex, and the other sections the following numbers of microns below the apex: *B*, 20; *C*, 50; *D*, 70; *E*, 90. At the successive levels the prospective vascular region is delimited because of the gradual increase in the difference in stainability of the cells in the prospective vascular tissue (stains deeply) and those of the ground parenchyma (stainability decreases). Compare with plate 51. (All, ×75.)

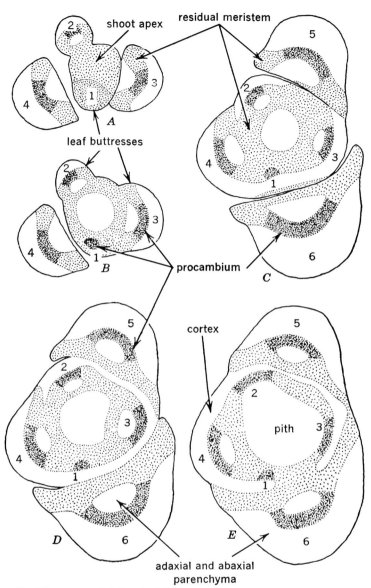

PLATE 51. Diagrams explaining the initial vascularization depicted in plate 50. The leaf primordia and their traces are numbered 1–6, beginning with the youngest. Parenchymatous differentiation in the cortex, the pith, and the adaxial and abaxial parts of the leaf primordia (all left blank in the drawings) delimits as a unit the prospective vascular system of stem and leaves. At the early stage of differentiation here depicted the constituent tissues of the vascular system are (1) procambium (densely stippled) with a few mature vascular elements (not indicated) and (2) some less differentiated meristem, residual meristem (lightly stippled), which is the source of additional procambium and of the interfascicular and leaf-gap parenchyma. (All, ×75.)

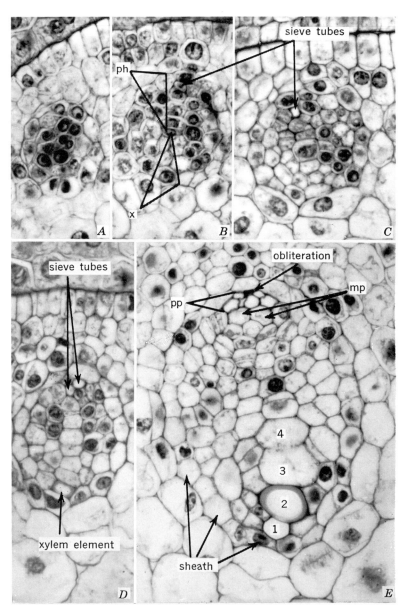

PLATE 52. Differentiation of a vascular bundle of *Zea mays* as seen in transections of young leaves. *A–E*, successively older bundles. (See also plate 53, *A, B*.) *A*, the strand consists of procambium only. *B*, phloic (ph) and xylary (x) parts of procambium are discernible. First sieve element, still immature, at the phloem pole of the bundle. *C*, the first sieve element is mature. *D*, two sieve elements and one xylem element (at the xylem pole). *E*, the protophloem (pp) is completely developed. It consists of sieve tubes only. The earliest of these are undergoing obliteration. The first metaphloem cells (mp) are in evidence. In the 1–4 series of protoxylem elements, 1 has annular secondary thickenings, 2 has annular or helical thickenings, 3 and 4 are still without secondary walls. (All, ×750. From Esau, *Hilgardia* **15**:327, 1943*b*.)

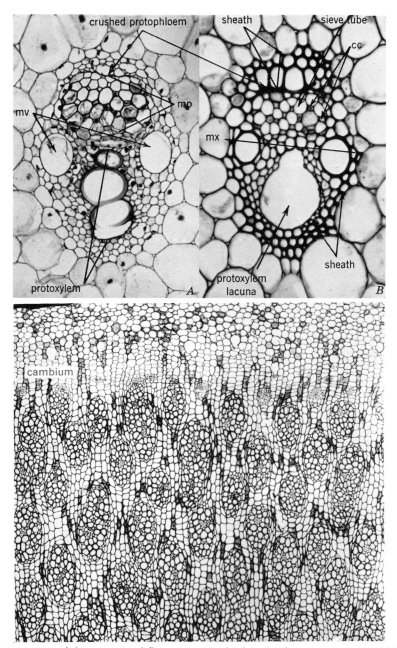

PLATE 53. *A*, immature, and *B*, mature vascular bundles from transections of *Zea* stem. Tracheary elements of protoxylem partly destroyed in *A* and replaced by a lacuna in *B*. Metaxylem (mx) contains two wide vessels (mv), tracheids, and parenchyma cells. Vessels without secondary walls in *A*. Companion cells at cc in metaphloem (mp). Bundle sheath cells in *B* (enlarged above) have lignified secondary walls. *C*, transection of *Cordyline* stem illustrating secondary growth in a monocotyledon. In secondary tissue below cambium are amphivasal vascular bundles and parenchyma. Outwardly cambium has formed some parenchyma (radially seriated). Cortex in uppermost position. (*A*, ×191; *B*, ×312; *C*, ×50; *C*, from Cheadle, *Amer. Jour. Bot.* 30:484, 1943.)

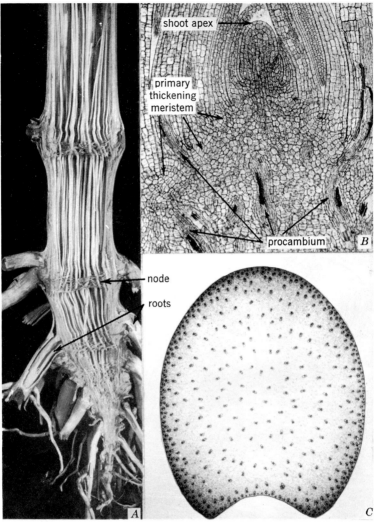

The labels in the figure read:
- shoot apex
- primary thickening meristem
- procambium — *B*
- node
- roots
- *A*
- *C*

PLATE 54. Structure of stem in *Zea mays*. *A*, mature stem split longitudinally, then partially retted to expose the vascular system. Note the increase in the width of the stem from the base upward. *B*, shoot apex, part of subjacent axis, and bases of the youngest leaf primordia. (Compare with fig. 15.21.) *C*, transection of an immature internode showing vascular bundles scattered within the ground parenchyma. The indentation in the stem at the base of the figure indicates the former location of an axillary bud. (*B*, ×90; *C*, ×4.5; *A*, from Sharman, *Ann. Bot.* 6:245, 1942; *B*, slide by G. I. Patel.)

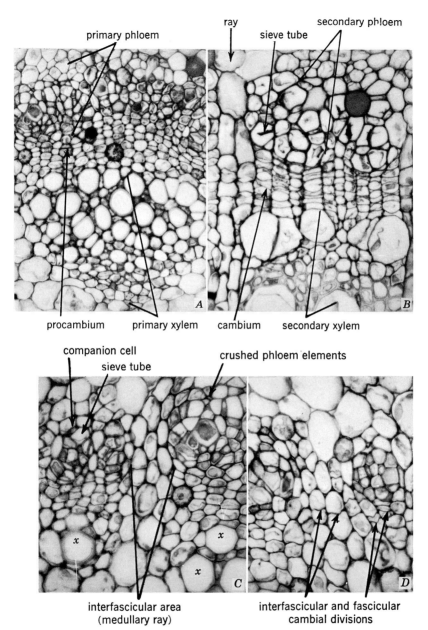

primary phloem   ray   sieve tube   secondary phloem

A   *B*

procambium   primary xylem   cambium   secondary xylem

companion cell   crushed phloem elements
sieve tube

x   *x*

x   *C*   *D*

interfascicular area   interfascicular and fascicular
(medullary ray)   cambial divisions

PLATE 55. Vascular tissues from transections of *Sambucus* stem, at end of primary growth (*A*, *C*, *D*, all from same section) and during secondary growth (*B*). In *A*, protoxylem below, with partly obliterated tracheary elements. Metaxylem above protoxylem. Radial seriation of cells in procambial zone. In *B*, fascicular cambial zone with expanding vessels below it. To the left is a ray with interfascicular cambium in line with the fascicular to the right. In *C*, primary phloem and metaxylem elements (x); in *D*, only phloem. First cambial divisions in *D*. (*A*, *B*, ×280; *C*, *D*, ×430; *A*, *C*, *D*, from Esau, *Amer. Jour. Bot.* **32**:18, 1945. *B*, from *Encyclopaedia Britannica*, copyright 1945.)

stock

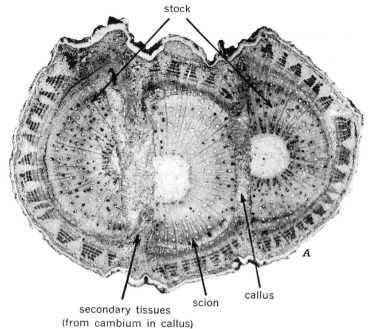

A

secondary tissues
(from cambium in callus)

scion

callus

callus

xylem

ray

B

PLATE 56. Callus in grafting and wound-healing. Transections of *Hibiscus* stems. *A*, cleft-graft union. Cambial activity and resulting secondary tissues in callus have joined the vascular tissues of stock and scion. *B*, xylem, exposed by excision

(*continued on page* 675)

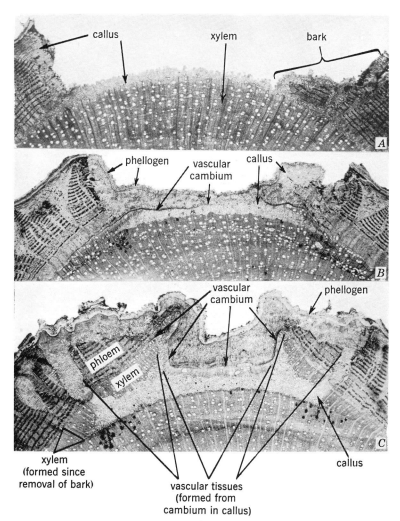

callus   xylem   bark

A

phellogen   vascular   callus
              cambium

B

vascular   phellogen
cambium

phloem

xylem

xylem
(formed since
removal of bark)   vascular tissues   callus
                          (formed from
                          cambium in callus)

C

PLATE 57. Callus in the healing of a surface wound produced by an excision of a strip of bark from a stem of *Hibiscus Rosa-sinensis*. Three successive stages in the process as seen in transections. *A*, callus formed on the exposed surfaces of the wood and bark (compare with plate 56, *B*). *B*, callus cushion covers the entire exposed surface. Phellogen producing cork cells has appeared beneath the surface of the callus cushion. Some vascular cambium has differentiated in the callus in continuity with the cambium of the uninjured part of the stem and has produced some vascular tissues at the edges of the wound. *C*, completion of regeneration of the missing part of the stem. The vascular cambium is continuous across the callus and has formed secondary xylem and phloem. Some callus tissue has been imbedded beneath the new xylem. (All, ✕9.5. Slides courtesy of H. Gunnery; see also Sharples and Gunnery, *Ann. Bot.* **47**:827, 1933.)

of a strip of bark, has produced callus from incompletely differentiated cells, mainly ray cells. These cells enlarged outwardly and divided by periclinal walls. (*A*, ✕10; *B*, ✕120. Slides courtesy of H. Gunnery; see also Sharples and Gunnery, *Ann. Bot.* **47**:827, 1933.)

675

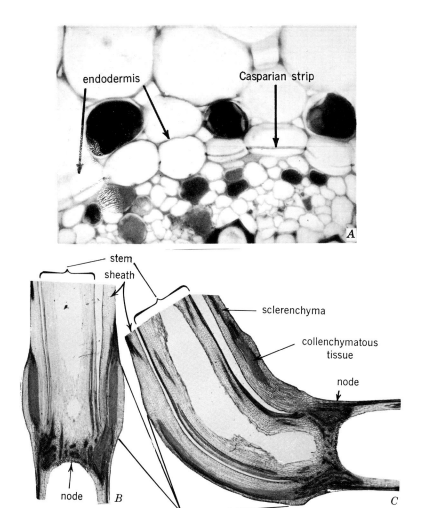

PLATE 58. *A*, transection from *Myriophyllum* rhizome showing some cortical parenchyma (above), endodermis with Casparian strips, and phloem (beneath the endodermis). *B* and *C*, longitudinal sections of intercalary growth regions (joints) of barley stems. *B* was obtained from an upright stem, *C* from one that was in the process of rising after it had lodged. In *C* the thickened part of the sheath (intercalary growth region) and the internode became extended on the side next to the ground and thus induced the curving of the stem away from the ground. Collenchymatous strands appear in association with the vascular bundles in the joint in place of sclerenchyma present elsewhere in the sheath and the stem. (*A*, ×390; *B*, *C*, ×6. *A*, from *Encyclopaedia Britannica*, copyright 1945.)

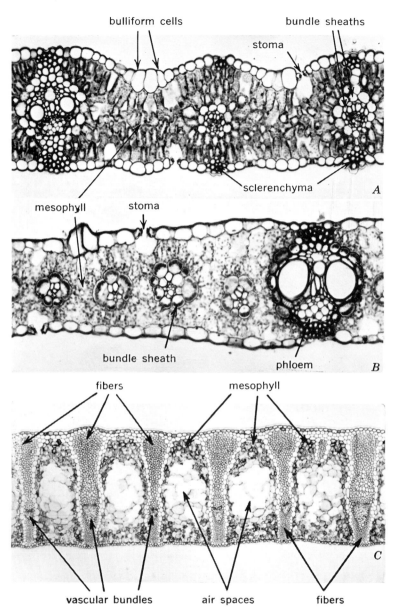

bulliform cells · bundle sheaths

stoma

sclerenchyma · A

mesophyll · stoma

bundle sheath · phloem · B

fibers · mesophyll

C

vascular bundles · air spaces · fibers

PLATE 59. Transections of monocotyledonous leaves. In *A, Triticum*, the adaxial (upper) epidermis bears bulliform cells in the grooved parts of the blade. The subepidermal cells are elongated like palisade cells. The cells in the median layers are not so elongated. There is an inner thick-walled and an outer thin-walled bundle sheath. (Compare with fig. 16.8.) Sclerenchyma occurs in the ribs associated with the bundles. In *B, Zea*, the mesophyll is relatively undifferentiated. Single-layered thin-walled sheaths enclose the vascular bundles. In *C, Phormium tenax*, the vascular bundles are accompanied, above and below, by massive strands of fibers. Through breakdown of mesophyll large air spaces are formed. (*A, B*, ×140; *C*, ×55. *A* and *B*, from *Encyclopaedia Britannica*, copyright 1945.)

677

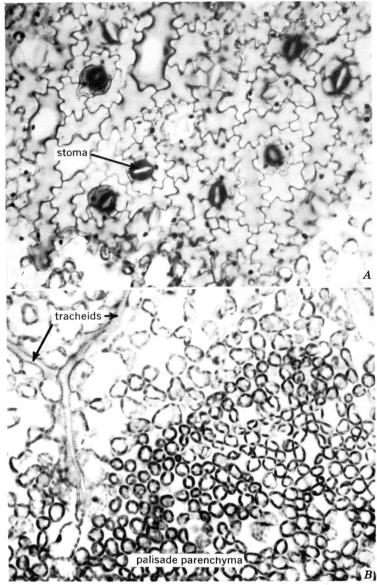

PLATE 60. Structure of leaf of *Nicotiana tabacum.* Tangential sections showing abaxial epidermis (*A*) and mesophyll (*B*). In *B* the palisade parenchyma appears to the right, some spongy parenchyma and tracheids of a small vein to the left. The tracheids are isolated from the intercellular spaces by a continuous layer of parenchyma, the bundle sheath or border parenchyma. The chloroplasts in all the mesophyll cells in *B* line the walls. (Both, ×280.)

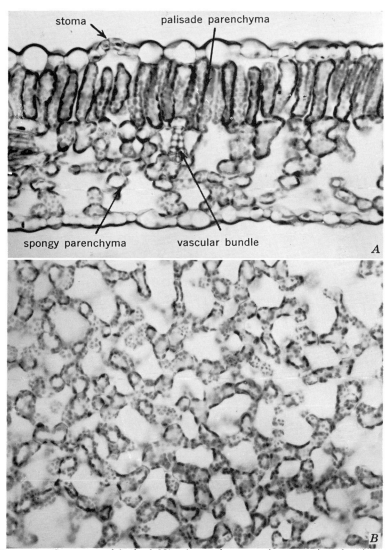

stoma   palisade parenchyma

spongy parenchyma   vascular bundle   *A*

B

PLATE 61. Structure of leaf of *Nicotiana tabacum*. *A*, transection showing the bifacial structure of mesophyll with the palisade occupying the adaxial (upper) and the spongy parenchyma the abaxial (lower) side of the leaf. *B*, tangential section through the spongy parenchyma. Note the large intercellular spaces and lateral contacts among the cells. The tissue has the appearance of a reticulum. The chloroplasts in the mesophyll occur in single layers along the walls. (Both, $\times 280$.)

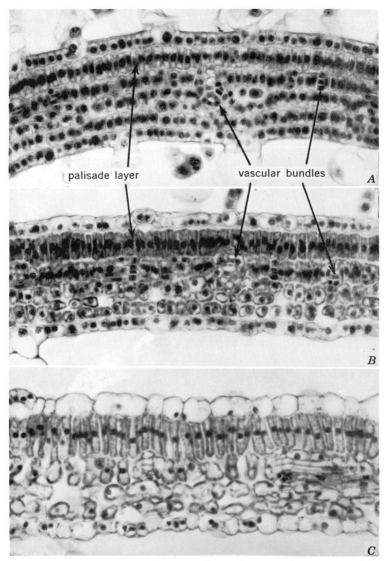

palisade layer   vascular bundles   A

B

C

PLATE 62. Development of leaf of *Nicotiana tabacum*. Transections of leaves showing three stages of development of mesophyll and epidermis. (The fourth and final stage is depicted in plate 61, *A*.) The palisade is just becoming distinct in *A* because of repeated anticlinal divisions and slight elongation of cells at right angles to the surface. A comparison of *A–C* with plate 61, *A*, shows that the elongation of palisade cells continues until the final stage of leaf development. The extension of cells in the spongy parenchyma is mainly parallel with the leaf surface. Note the increasing difference between epidermal and palisade cells in tangential dimension. (All, ×280.)

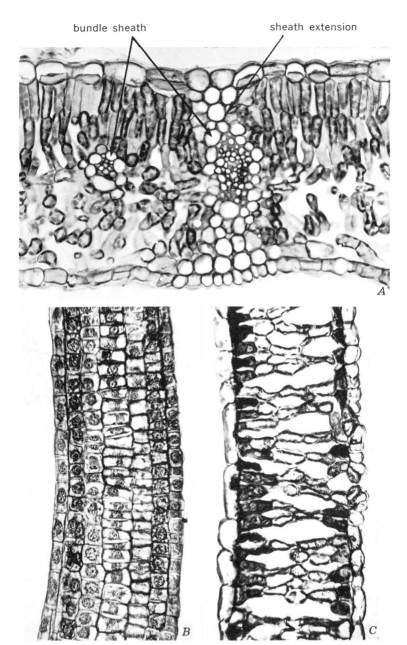

bundle sheath   sheath extension

A

B   *C*

PLATE 63. *A*, transection of *Pyrus* (pear) leaf. Bundle sheaths consist of parenchyma cells. Bundle-sheath extensions connect the sheath of the large vascular
bundle with both epidermal layers. (Compare with fig. 16.1.) *B*, younger, and
C, older leaves of *Taxodium* in longitudinal sections. In *B* cells occur in longitudinal columns. *C* shows horizontal orientation of intercellular spaces. (*A*,
      ×280; *B*, *C*, ×386. *C*, *D*, from Cross, *Amer. Jour. Bot.* 27:471, 1940.)

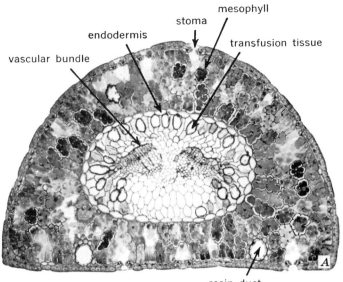

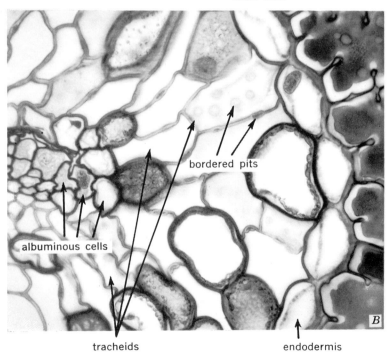

PLATE 64. Structure of conifer leaf, *Pinus resinosa*. *A*, entire section. *B*, transection through parts of vascular bundle (left), transfusion tissue (middle), and endodermis (right). Further details are in the text. (*A*, ×78; *B*, ×490.)

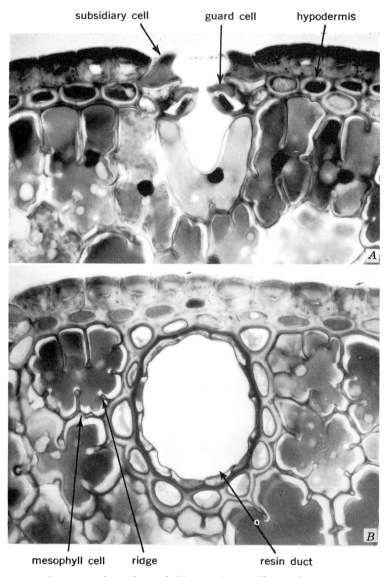

subsidiary cell   guard cell   hypodermis

A

B

mesophyll cell   ridge   resin duct

PLATE 65. Structure of conifer leaf, *Pinus resinosa*. Transections through outer parts of a needle showing stoma (*A*) and resin duct (*B*), both with associated mesophyll and some epidermis and hypodermis. Further details are in the text. (Both, ×490.)

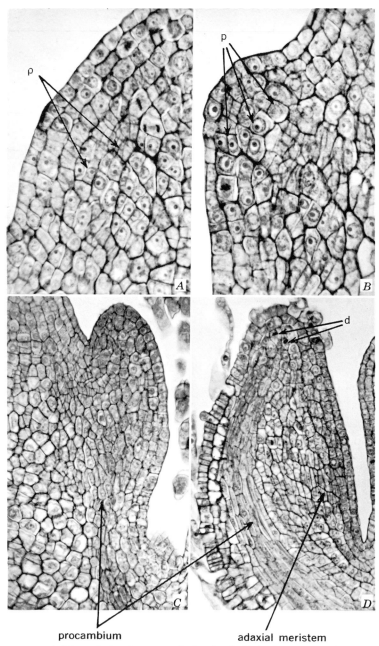

procambium   adaxial meristem

PLATE 66. Origin and development of *Acacia* phyllode (foliar organ) as seen in longitudinal sections. The apical meristem has a three-layered tunica (see fig. 16.11). *A*, periclinal divisions occur in corpus at p, and then, *B*, also in second and third layers of tunica. Leaf buttress appears on the side of the shoot apex (*B*). *C*, phyllode primordium (45 microns high) has grown upward from buttress. *D*, primordium 234 microns high, with procambial strand and conspicuous vacuolation on the abaxial side. Adaxial meristem increases the thickness of the primordium. Primordia in *C* and *D* were still growing at their apices (division figures at d). (All, ✕300. From Boke, *Amer. Jour. Bot.* **27**:73, 1940.)

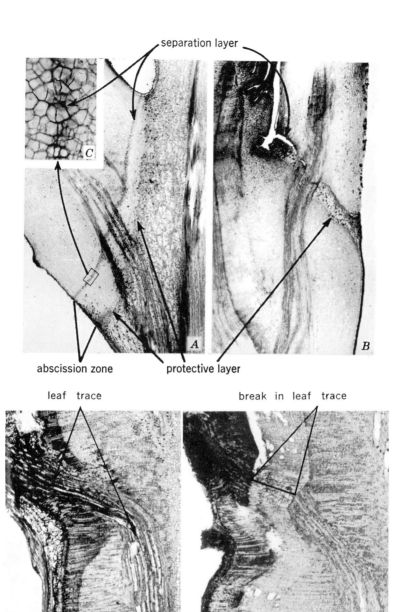

PLATE 67. *A–C*, leaf abscission zones of, *A* and *C*, *Juglans* (walnut) and, *B*, *Prunus* (cherry) in longitudinal sections through leaf bases. In each the abscission zone has a separation layer and a protective layer of suberised cells. Cell division occurs in the development of both layers. *C*, enlarged view of part of the separation layer from *A*. *D* and *E*, rupture of leaf trace during secondary growth in *Prunus* (apricot). Leaf trace intact in *D*, broken in *E*. (*A*, ×10; *B*, ×13.5; *C*, ×78; *D*, ×17; *E*, ×17. *D*, *E*, slides by K. E. Nelson.)

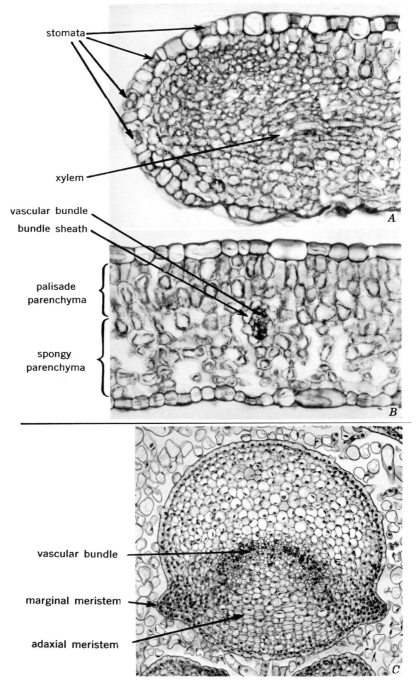

stomata

xylem

vascular bundle
bundle sheath

palisade
parenchyma

spongy
parenchyma

A

B

vascular bundle

marginal meristem

adaxial meristem

C

PLATE 68. Hydathode (*A*) and adjacent mesophyll (*B*) from transection of cabbage leaf. In *A* xylem terminates in a small-celled lacunate tissue (epithem). Several stomata in epidermis of hydathode. *C*, transection of *Nicotiana* leaf showing initial development of lamina (marginal meristem) and growth of midvein in thickness (adaxial meristem). (*A*, *B*, ×190; *C*, ×100.)

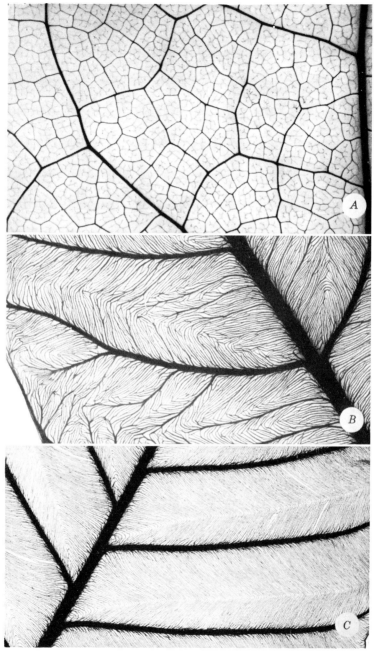

PLATE 69. Cleared leaf sections showing venation. *A, Liriodendron tulipifera*, reticulate venation with ultimate branchings ending freely in the mesophyll. *B, Quiina acutangula*, anastomosing plumose venation. *C, Touroulia guianensis*, anastomosing arcuate venation. (*A, B,* ×8; *C,* ×9. Courtesy of A. S. Foster. *B, C,* from Foster, *Amer. Jour. Bot.* **37**:159, 1950*a*; **37**:848, 1950*b*.)

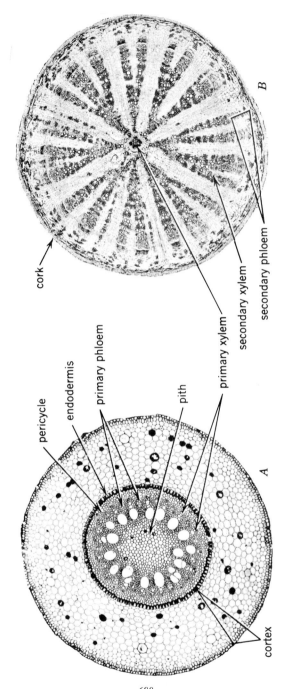

cork

pericycle

endodermis

primary phloem

pith

primary xylem

secondary xylem

secondary phloem

B

A

cortex

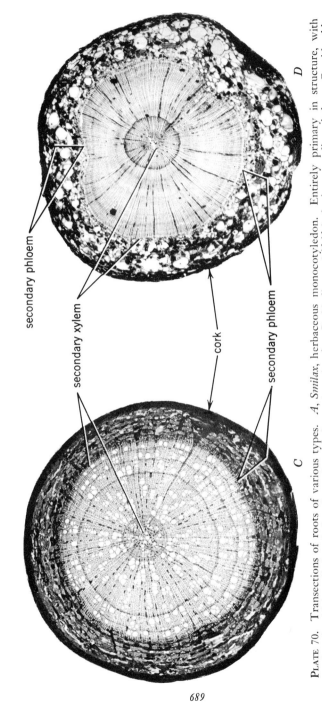

PLATE 70. Transections of roots of various types. *A, Smilax,* herbaceous monocotyledon. Entirely primary in structure, with exodermis, thick-walled endodermis, and many-layered pericycle. *B, Medicago* (alfalfa), herbaceous dicotyledon. Considerable secondary growth, the secondary xylem with much parenchyma in the form of wide rays. *C, Tilia,* arborescent dicotyledon. Several increments of secondary tissues, with the xylem showing narrow layers of late wood and numerous large vessels. *D, Abies,* conifer, with two increments of secondary tissues. (*A,* ×23; *B,* ×10; *C,* ×15; *D,* ×11. *D,* slide by H. E. Wilcox.)

689

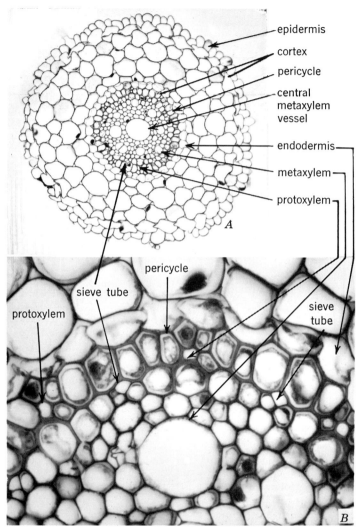

epidermis
cortex
pericycle
central
metaxylem
vessel
endodermis
metaxylem
protoxylem

A

pericycle
sieve tube
protoxylem
sieve
tube

B

PLATE 71. Transections of a young *Triticum* root. *A*, entire section. *B*, inner
part of root. The metaxylem (still without secondary walls) includes a circle of
relatively small vessels and one large one in the center. There is no pith. The
protoxylem elements were derived from sister cells of the pericyclic cells. At each
phloem pole only one sieve tube is mature. It is flanked by parenchyma cells.
Contrast the thin-walled endodermis (still only with Casparian strips) with that
shown in figs. 17.3 and 17.4. (*A*, ×130; *B*, ×600.)

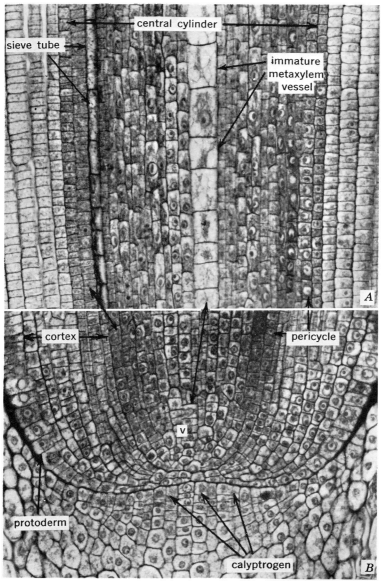

PLATE 72. Longitudinal sections from a root tip of *Zea*. *A*, central part of root with partly differentiated first sieve tube and a series of much enlarged metaxylem vessel-member primordia. *B*, section through the apical meristem and recently formed parts of the root. The apical meristem includes (1) the initials of the central cylinder, (2) the initials of cortex and epidermis, and (3) the rootcap meristem or calyptrogen. The primordia of the late-metaxylem vessel members (v) may be discerned close to the apical initials. The series at v is not continued upward because of oblique cut. (Both, ×280. Slides by E. M. Gifford.)

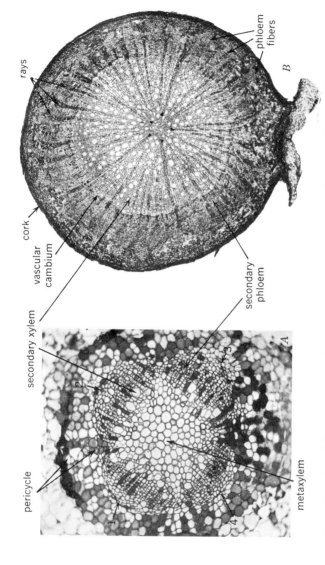

PLATE 75. *A* and *B*, development of pear root. Two stages succeeding those illustrated in plate 74. *A*, vascular cylinder in early stages of secondary growth and with proliferated pericycle. Numbered arrows indicate the protophloem poles. *B*, complete transection of root after considerable secondary growth has been added and the cortex sloughed off. The protoxylem poles are indicated by arrowheads. Conspicuous rays extend from the protoxylem poles. The flared part below occurred at the base of a lateral root. (*A*, ×120; *B*, ×33. From Esau, *Hilgardia* 15:299, 1943*a*.)

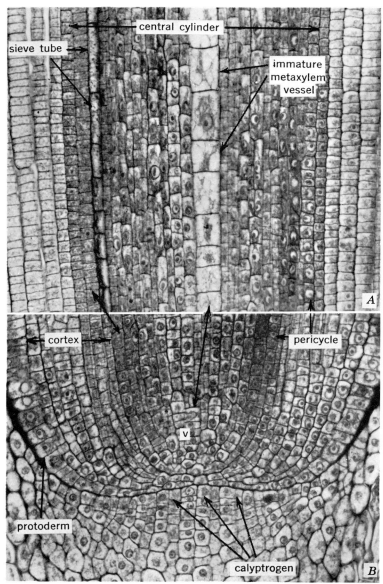

PLATE 72. Longitudinal sections from a root tip of *Zea*. *A*, central part of root with partly differentiated first sieve tube and a series of much enlarged metaxylem vessel-member primordia. *B*, section through the apical meristem and recently formed parts of the root. The apical meristem includes (1) the initials of the central cylinder, (2) the initials of cortex and epidermis, and (3) the rootcap meristem or calyptrogen. The primordia of the late-metaxylem vessel members (v) may be discerned close to the apical initials. The series at v is not continued upward because of oblique cut. (Both, ×280. Slides by E. M. Gifford.)

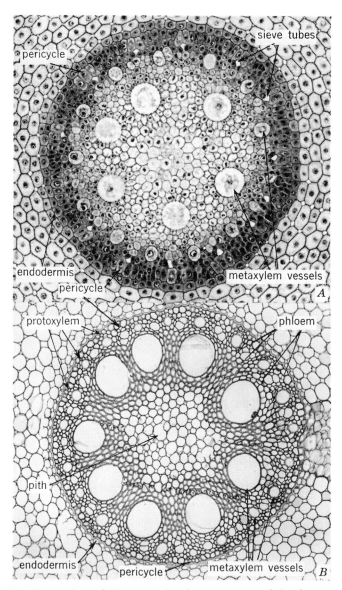

PLATE 73. Transections of *Zea* roots showing two stages of development of the central cylinder. In *A* only the first sieve tubes are mature. All cells are differentiated in *B*, the vascular parenchyma is sclerified, and the endodermis is in tertiary state. (Compare with fig. 17.3.) The late metaxylem vessels are numerous and encircle a pith. (Contrast with the wheat root in plate 71.) (*A*, ×170; *B*, ×102.)

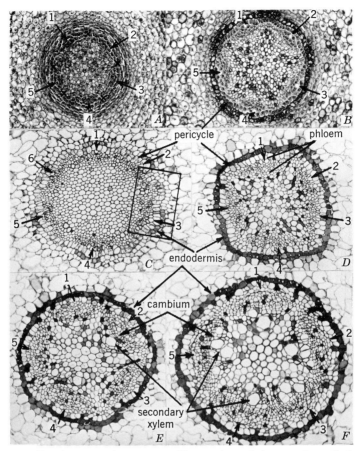

PLATE 74. Development of pear root. Transections of the vascular cylinder and adjacent layers of cortex in successive stages of differentiation. Numbered arrows indicate the phloem poles; crosses indicate the protoxylem poles (in *A*). The root is pentarch. *A*, vascular cylinder in procambial state. The prospective metaxylem (center) is visibly vacuolated. The inner cortex shows radial seriation of cells. *B*, first sieve tubes are mature. *C*, some protoxylem has differentiated in alternate positions with the protophloem. (Part in rectangle appears, enlarged, in fig. 17.10.) *D*, primary growth is completed, although the metaxylem is not yet mature. *E*, vascular cambium has formed the first secondary elements, and the metaxylem is mature. Note tannin accumulation in the endodermis. (All, ×120. From Esau, *Hilgardia* **15**:299, 1943*a*.)

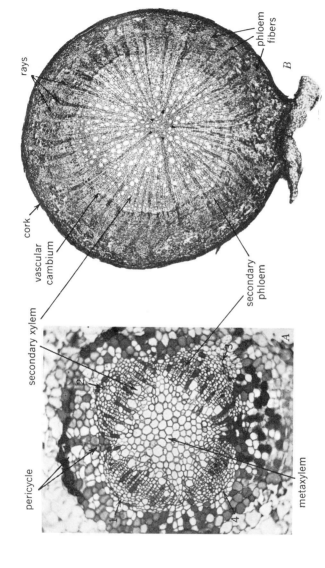

PLATE 75. *A* and *B*, development of pear root. Two stages succeeding those illustrated in plate 74. *A*, vascular cylinder in early stages of secondary growth and with proliferated pericycle. Numbered arrows indicate the protophloem poles. *B*, complete transection of root after considerable secondary growth has been added and the cortex sloughed off. The protoxylem poles are indicated by arrowheads. Conspicuous rays extend from the protoxylem poles. The flared part below occurred at the base of a lateral root. (*A*, ×120; *B*, ×33. From Esau, *Hilgardia* 15:299, 1943*a*.)

694

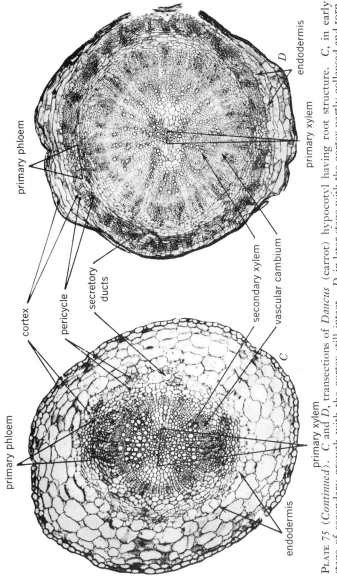

PLATE 75 (*Continued*). *C* and *D*, transections of *Daucus* (carrot) hypocotyl having root structure. *C*, in early stage of secondary growth with the cortex still intact. *D*, in later stage with the cortex partly collapsed and torn. Only one of two primary phloem strands (partly obliterated) is indicated in each photograph. Outside the protoxylem poles some parenchyma developed before secondary xylem was formed here. The pericycle is several cells wide in *A* and contains secretory ducts. In *B*, the pericycle has undergone tangential divisions in preparation for periderm formation. (*D*, ×33; *C*, ×61. From Esau, *Hilgardia* 13:175, 1940.)

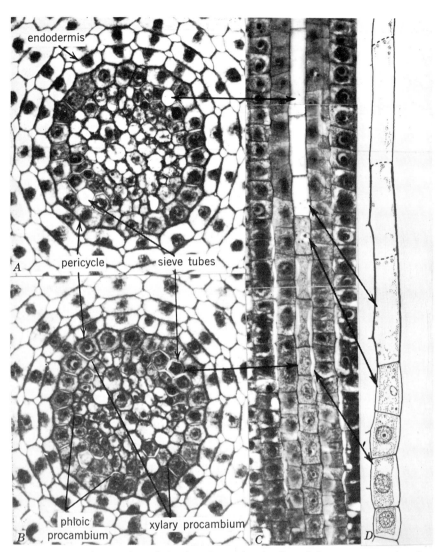

PLATE 76. Differentiation of the first sieve tubes in dicotyledonous roots. *A* and *B*, transections of young tobacco roots showing vascular cylinder differentiated into phloic and xylary procambium. The first sieve-tube elements are immature in *B*, mature in *A*. *C*, tangential longitudinal section through a vertical series of sieve-tube elements and associated procambial cells. The elements in the lower part of the series are immature, as shown by their dense protoplasts; those above are fully differentiated. *D*, drawing of a series of sieve-tube elements from a carrot root illustrating similar developmental details as *C*. The fourth element from below shows a disintegrating nucleus. Above this element the first two mature elements have relatively thick walls and contain plastids. The transverse end walls bear sieve plates (drawn as broken lines). (*A*, *B*, ×410; *C*, ×515; *D*, ×1,020. *A*–*C*, from Esau, *Hilgardia* **13**:437, 1941; *D*, from Esau, *Hilgardia*, **13**:175, 1940.)

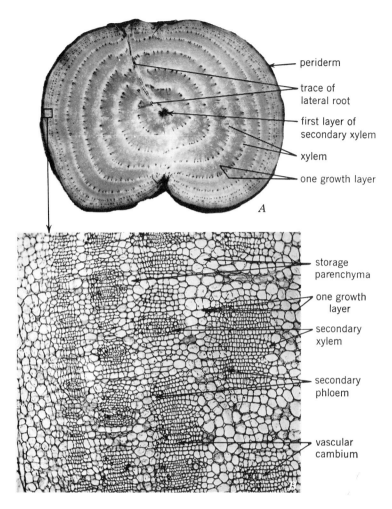

periderm

trace of
lateral root

first layer of
secondary xylem

xylem

one growth layer

A

storage
parenchyma

one growth
layer

secondary
xylem

secondary
phloem

vascular
cambium

B

PLATE 77. Sugar-beet (*Beta*) root, an example of a fleshy storage root involving anomalous growth in its development. *A*, entire fresh section treated with phloroglucinol and HCl. The xylem appears black in the photograph. The central core contains the primary xylem and the first layer of secondary xylem. Most of the root consists of anomalous layers, each including storage parenchyma, xylem, cambium, and phloem. *B* shows at high magnification four anomalous growth increments taken from the peripheral part of a mature root. From processed material imbedded in paraffin. (*A*, ×0.66; *B*, ×60. From Artschwager, *Jour. Agr. Res.* **33**:143, 1926.)

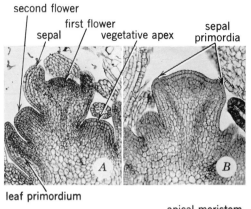

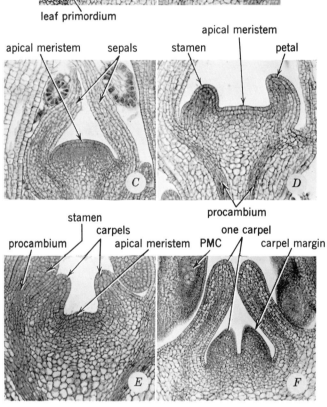

PLATE 78. Development of *Vinca* flower as seen in longitudinal sections. *A*, young inflorescence with vegetative apex at right and a floral apex (second flower) at left. Both have a two-layered tunica. The first flower has sepals. *B*, flower with sepal primordia. *C*, flower with somewhat larger sepals than in *B*. *D*, median section of a flower showing the apical meristem with a two-layered tunica and primordia of a petal and a stamen. *E* and *F*, sections showing two stages in the development of carpels. In *F* the apices of the carpels are touching each other and their ventral margins appear below in the center (compare with plate 79, *A*). (*A*, *F*, ×106; *B*, *C*, ×112; *D*, *E*, ×126. From Boke, *Amer. Jour. Bot.* 34:433, 1947; 35:413, 1948; 36:535, 1949.)

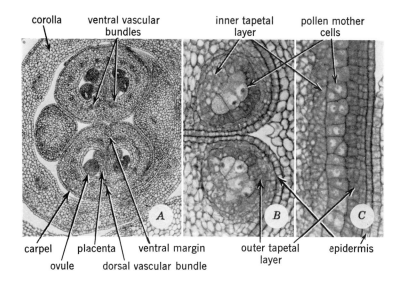

corolla   ventral vascular bundles   inner tapetal layer   pollen mother cells

carpel   placenta   ventral margin   outer tapetal layer   epidermis

ovule   dorsal vascular bundle

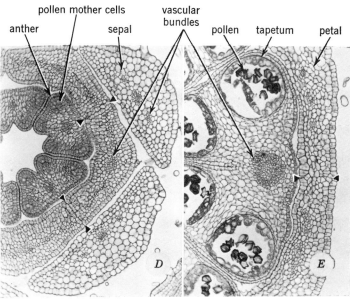

pollen mother cells   vascular bundles

anther   sepal   pollen   tapetum   petal

PLATE 79. Details of developing *Vinca* flowers. *A*, carpels in transection with ventral margins fused. Inwardly projecting placental ridges bear ovules. *B*, transverse and, *C*, longitudinal sections of young anthers of *Vinca* showing pollen mother cells and the wall layers. The outer tapetal layer and the wall layers between it and the epidermis are derived from the same archesporial cells as the pollen mother cells. The inner tapetal layer originates in the ground tissue located next to the sporogenous. *D* and *E*, transections of flowers showing earlier (*D*) and later (*E*) stages in the ontogenetic fusion of petal margins during formation of the corolla tube. Arrowheads indicate the line of union of petal margins. (*A*, ✕60; *B*, ✕247; *C*, ✕275; *D*, *E*, ✕110. From Boke, *Amer. Jour. Bot.* 35:413, 1948; 36:535, 1949.)

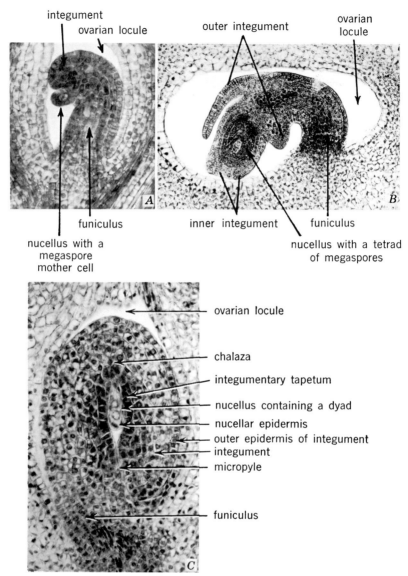

PLATE 80. Longitudinal sections through ovaries of *Parthenium* (*A* and *C*) and *Beta* (*B*) showing young ovules. The ovules are still only partly inverted in *A* and *B*, completely so in *C*. The ovule in *Parthenium* has one integument (*A* and *C*); that in *Beta* has two (*B*). (*A*, ×230; *B*, ×150; *C*, ×230. *A*, *C*, from Esau, *Hilgardia* 17:61, 1946.)

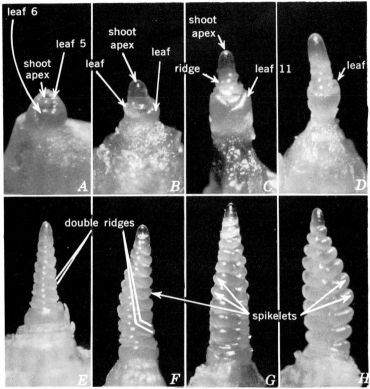

PLATE 81. Developmental changes in the shoot apex of *Triticum* during the shift from vegetative growth to inflorescence development. *A–C*, shoot apex and associated leaf primordia during vegetative growth. *D*, elongated shoot tip just before spikelet initiation. *E–H*, spike during early stages of spikelet differentiation. The vegetative apex forms leaf primordia. The fifth and sixth primordia are visible in *A*, the eleventh in *C*. The leaf primordia are initiated as single alternate ridges (*C*). A young spike shows double ridges (*E* and *F*), but the lower of a pair of ridges is small and is soon obscured by the growth of the upper ridge (*H*). The spikelet primordia develop from the upper members of the pairs of ridges (*F–H*). (*A*, ✕35; the others somewhat smaller. Courtesy of O. T. Bonnett. *A, C, D, H*, from Bonnett, *Jour. Agr. Res.* **53**:445, 1936.)

PLATE 82. Development of a *Triticum* (wheat) spike. *A*, spikes of wheat showing spikelets in front view (left) and in side view (right). Some of the spikelets
were removed from the spike to the right to expose the rachis. Each spikelet
consists of several florets. *B* and *C*, spikes in two stages of development. *D*,
single spikelet, partly differentiated. The spikelet in *D* was derived from an
awned variety of wheat. (*A*, slightly enlarged; *B–D*, ×20. Courtesy of O. T.
Bonnett.)

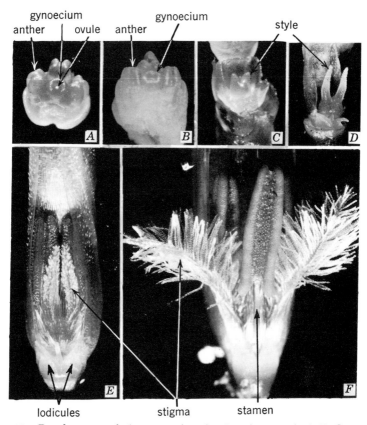

gynoecium
anther · ovule · anther · gynoecium · style

A · *B* · *C* · *D*

lodicules · stigma · stamen · *E* · *F*

PLATE 83. Development of the gynoecium in Gramineae. *A, C–F,* florets of *Avena* (oat); *B,* floret of *Triticum.* The gynoecium appears as a semicircular ridge in *A,* not enclosing the ovule. In *B* the ovule is completely surrounded by the ridge. *C–F* illustrates stages in the development of the styles. (*A,* ×40; *B,* ×36; *C,* ×28; *D* and *E,* ×16; *F,* ×12. Courtesy of O. T. Bonnett. *A, D, F,* from Bonnett, *Jour. Agr. Res.* **54**:927, 1937.)

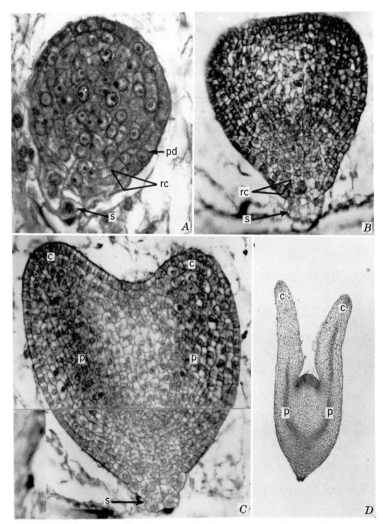

PLATE 84. Development of embryo in *Juglans regia* (walnut). The embryo is spheroidal in *A*, has a flattened apex in *B*, and shows the initiation of cotyledons (c) in *C*. The oldest embryo in *D* shows the epicotylary meristem between the two cotyledons. Details are: c, cotyledon; p, procambium; pd, protoderm; rc, rootcap; s, suspensor. (*A*, ×540; *B*, *C*, ×240; *D*, ×48. From Nast, *Lilloa* **6**:163, 1941.)

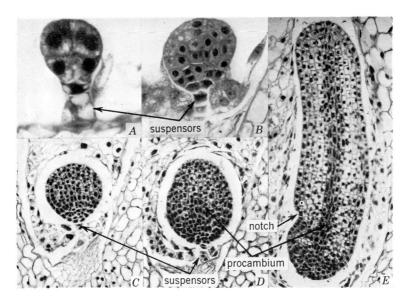

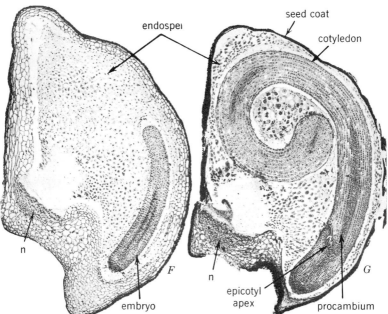

PLATE 85. Embryo development in *Allium cepa* (onion) as seen in longitudinal sections. Parts of ovules with embryos in *A–E*, entire seeds in *F* and *G*. The suspensor is present in the embryos in *A–D*. The embryo in *E* shows a notch below the cotyledon. The epicotyl meristem is organized in the notch region in older embryos (*G*). Procambium is present in embryos in *D–G*. The enlarged apex of the cotyledon in *C* is a digestive structure. At n in *F* is partly digested nucellar tissue. The endosperm next to n has no cell walls. The ages of the embryos in days after anthesis are: *A*, 12; *B*, 14; *C*, 16; *D*, 18; *E*, 20; *F*, 20; *G*, 30. The seed in *G* is fully developed. (*A*, ×320; *B*, ×195; *C–E*, ×94; *F*, *G*, ×22.)

REFERENCES FOR LEGENDS TO PLATES

Abbe, L. B., and A. S. Crafts. Phloem of white pine and other coniferous species. *Bot. Gaz.* **100**:695–722. 1939.

Artschwager, Ernst. Anatomy of the vegetative organs of the sugar beet. *Jour. Agr. Res.* **33**:143–176. 1926.

Artschwager, Ernst, and R. C. McGuire. Contribution to the morphology and anatomy of the Russian dandelion (*Taraxacum kok-saghyz*). *U. S. Dept. Agric. Tech. Bul.* 843. 1943.

Bannan, M. W. Variability in wood structure in roots of native Ontario conifers. *Torrey Bot. Club Bul.* **68**:173–194. 1941.

Barghoorn, E. S., Jr. The ontogenetic development and phylogenetic specialization of rays in the xylem of dicotyledons. I. The primitive ray structure. *Amer. Jour. Bot.* **27**:918–928. 1940.

Barghoorn, E. S., Jr. The ontogenetic development and phylogenetic specialization of rays in the xylem of dicotyledons. II. Modification of the multiseriate and uniseriate rays. *Amer. Jour. Bot.* **28**:273–282. 1941.

Boke, N. H. Histogenesis and morphology of the phyllode in certain species of *Acacia. Amer. Jour. Bot.* **27**:73–90. 1940.

Boke, N. H. Histogenesis of the leaf and areole in *Opuntia cylindrica. Amer. Jour. Bot.* **31**:299–316. 1944.

Boke, N. H. Development of the adult shoot apex and floral initiation in *Vinca rosea* L. *Amer. Jour. Bot.* **34**:433–439. 1947.

Boke, N. H. Development of the perianth in *Vinca rosea* L. *Amer. Jour. Bot.* **35**:413–423. 1948.

Boke, N. H. Development of the stamens and carpels in *Vinca rosea* L. *Amer. Jour. Bot.* **36**:535–547. 1949.

Bonnett, O. T. The development of the wheat spike. *Jour. Agr. Res.* **53**:445–451. 1936.

Bonnett, O. T. The development of the oat panicle. *Jour. Agr. Res.* **54**:927–931. 1937.

Cheadle, V. I. Vessel specialization in the late metaxylem of the various organs in the Monocotyledoneae. *Amer. Jour. Bot.* **30**:484–490. 1943.

Cheadle, V. I., and N. B. Whitford. Observations on the phloem in the Monocotyledoneae. I. The occurrence and phylogenetic specialization in structure of the sieve tubes in the metaphloem. *Amer. Jour. Bot.* **28**:623–627. 1941.

Crafts, A. S. Sieve-tube structure and translocation in the potato. *Plant Physiol.* **8**:81–104. 1933.

Cross, G. L. Development of the foliage leaves of *Taxodium distichum. Amer. Jour. Bot.* **27**:471–482. 1940.

Encyclopaedia Britannica. Chicago, copyright 1945.

Esau, Katherine. Developmental anatomy of the fleshy storage organ of *Daucus carota. Hilgardia* **13**:175–226. 1940.

Esau, Katherine. Phloem anatomy of tobacco affected with curly top and mosaic. *Hilgardia* 13:437–490. 1941.

Esau, Katherine. Vascular differentiation in the pear root. *Hilgardia* 15:299–324. 1943*a*.

Esau, Katherine. Ontogeny of the vascular bundle in *Zea Mays*. *Hilgardia* 15:327–368. 1943*b*.

Esau, Katherine. Vascular differentiation in the vegetative shoot of *Linum*. III. The origin of the bast fibers. *Amer. Jour. Bot.* 30:579–586. 1943*c*.

Esau, Katherine. Vascularization of the vegetative shoots of *Helianthus* and *Sambucus*. *Amer. Jour. Bot.* 32:18–29. 1945.

Esau, Katherine. Morphology and reproduction in guayule and certain other species of *Parthenium*. *Hilgardia* 17:61–120. 1946.

Esau, Katherine. A study of some sieve-tube inclusions. *Amer. Jour. Bot.* 34, 224–233. 1947.

Esau, Katherine. Phloem structure in the grapevine, and its seasonal changes. *Hilgardia* 18:217–296. 1948*a*.

Esau, Katherine. Anatomic effects of the viruses of Pierce's disease and phony peach. *Hilgardia* 18:423–482. 1948*b*.

Esau, K., and W. B. Hewitt. Structure of end walls in differentiating vessels. *Hilgardia* 13:229–244. 1940.

Foster, A. S. Structure and growth of the shoot apex in *Ginkgo biloba*. *Torrey Bot. Club Bul.* 65:531–556. 1938.

Foster, A. S. Morphology and venation of the leaf in *Quiina acutangula* Ducke. *Amer. Jour. Bot.* 37:159–171. 1950*a*.

Foster, A. S. Venation and histology of the leaflets in *Touroulia guianensis* Aubl. and *Froesia tricarpa* Pires. *Amer. Jour. Bot.* 37:848–862. 1950*b*.

Frey-Wyssling, A., and K. Mühlethaler. Ueber den Feinbau der Chlorophyll-körner. *Naturf. Gesell. Zürich. Vrtljschr.* 94:181–183. 1949.

Frey-Wyssling, A., K. Mühlethaler, and R. W. G. Wyckoff. Mikrofibrillen der pflanzlichen Zellwände. *Experientia* 4:475–476. 1948.

Huber, B., and E. Rouschal. Anatomische und zellphysiologische Beobachtungen am Siebröhrensystem der Bäume. *Deut. Bot. Gesell. Ber.* 56:380–391. 1938.

Kemp, Margaret. Morphological and ontogenetic studies on *Torreya californica* Torr. I. The vegetative apex of the megasporangiate tree. *Amer. Jour. Bot.* 30:504–517. 1943.

Mann, L. K. Anatomy of the garlic bulb and factors affecting bulb development. *Hilgardia* 21:195–251. 1952.

Mühlethaler, K. Electron microscopy of developing walls. *Biochim. Biophys. Acta* 5:1–9. 1950.

Nast, C. G. The embryogeny and seedling morphology of *Juglans regia* L. *Lilloa* 6:163–205. 1941.

Newcomer, E. H. Concerning the duality of the mitochondria and the validity of the osmiophilic platelets in plants. *Amer. Jour. Bot.* 33:684–697. 1946.

Record, S. J., and R. W. Hess. *Timbers of the New World*. New Haven, Yale University Press. 1943.

Reeve, R. M. The "tunica-corpus" concept and development of shoot apices in certain dicotyledons. *Amer. Jour. Bot.* 35:65–75. 1948.

Esau, Katherine. Phloem anatomy of tobacco affected with curly top and mosaic. *Hilgardia* 13:437–490. 1941.

Esau, Katherine. Vascular differentiation in the pear root. *Hilgardia* 15:299–324. 1943*a*.

Esau, Katherine. Ontogeny of the vascular bundle in *Zea Mays*. *Hilgardia* 15:327–368. 1943*b*.

Esau, Katherine. Vascular differentiation in the vegetative shoot of *Linum*. III. The origin of the bast fibers. *Amer. Jour. Bot.* 30:579–586. 1943*c*.

Esau, Katherine. Vascularization of the vegetative shoots of *Helianthus* and *Sambucus*. *Amer. Jour. Bot.* 32:18–29. 1945.

Esau, Katherine. Morphology and reproduction in guayule and certain other species of *Parthenium*. *Hilgardia* 17:61–120. 1946.

Esau, Katherine. A study of some sieve-tube inclusions. *Amer. Jour. Bot.* 34, 224–233. 1947.

Esau, Katherine. Phloem structure in the grapevine, and its seasonal changes. *Hilgardia* 18:217–296. 1948*a*.

Esau, Katherine. Anatomic effects of the viruses of Pierce's disease and phony peach. *Hilgardia* 18:423–482. 1948*b*.

Esau, K., and W. B. Hewitt. Structure of end walls in differentiating vessels. *Hilgardia* 13:229–244. 1940.

Foster, A. S. Structure and growth of the shoot apex in *Ginkgo biloba*. *Torrey Bot. Club Bul.* 65:531–556. 1938.

Foster, A. S. Morphology and venation of the leaf in *Quiina acutangula* Ducke. *Amer. Jour. Bot.* 37:159–171. 1950*a*.

Foster, A. S. Venation and histology of the leaflets in *Touroulia guianensis* Aubl. and *Froesia tricarpa* Pires. *Amer. Jour. Bot.* 37:848–862. 1950*b*.

Frey-Wyssling, A., and K. Mühlethaler. Ueber den Feinbau der Chlorophyll-körner. *Naturf. Gesell. Zürich. Vrtljschr.* 94:181–183. 1949.

Frey-Wyssling, A., K. Mühlethaler, and R. W. G. Wyckoff. Mikrofibrillen der pflanzlichen Zellwände. *Experientia* 4:475–476. 1948.

Huber, B., and E. Rouschal. Anatomische und zellphysiologische Beobachtungen am Siebröhrensystem der Bäume. *Deut. Bot. Gesell. Ber.* 56:380–391. 1938.

Kemp, Margaret. Morphological and ontogenetic studies on *Torreya californica* Torr. I. The vegetative apex of the megasporangiate tree. *Amer. Jour. Bot.* 30:504–517. 1943.

Mann, L. K. Anatomy of the garlic bulb and factors affecting bulb development. *Hilgardia* 21:195–251. 1952.

Mühlethaler, K. Electron microscopy of developing walls. *Biochim. Biophys. Acta* 5:1–9. 1950.

Nast, C. G. The embryogeny and seedling morphology of *Juglans regia* L. *Lilloa* 6:163–205. 1941.

Newcomer, E. H. Concerning the duality of the mitochondria and the validity of the osmiophilic platelets in plants. *Amer. Jour. Bot.* 33:684–697. 1946.

Record, S. J., and R. W. Hess. *Timbers of the New World*. New Haven, Yale University Press. 1943.

Reeve, R. M. The "tunica-corpus" concept and development of shoot apices in certain dicotyledons. *Amer. Jour. Bot.* 35:65–75. 1948.

Schneider, Henry. The anatomy of peach and cherry phloem. *Torrey Bot. Club Bul.* **72**:137–156. 1945.

Sharman, B. C. Developmental anatomy of the shoot of *Zea mays* L. *Ann. Bot.* **6**:245–282. 1942.

Sharples, A., and H. Gunnery. Callus formation in *Hibiscus Rosa-sinensis* L. and *Hevea brasiliensis* Möll. Arg. *Ann. Bot.* **47**:827–840. 1933.

Williams, Simon. Secondary vascular tissues of the oaks indigenous to the United States—I. The importance of secondary xylem in delimiting *Erythrobalanus* and *Leucobalanus*. *Torrey Bot. Club Bul.* **66**:353–365. 1939.

Author Index

(Bold-face type indicates bibliographic references.)

Abagon, M. A., 148, **165**, 437, **462**
Abbe, E. C., 449, **462**
Abbe, L. B., 276, 291, 292, 300, **300**, 649, 652, **706**
Addicott, F. T., 461, **462**
Addoms, R. M., 589, **594**
Aggelen-Bot, G. M. van, 321, **322**
Agthe, C., 434, **462**, 557, 558, **571**
Ajello, L., 162, **165**
Aldaba, V. C., 202, 208, 209, 210, **218**
Alexandrov, W. G., 377, **402**, 431, **462**
Alexandrova, O. G., 377, **402**
Allen, G. S., 98, 114, 116, 118, **119**, 136, 165, 470, 472, **522**, 601, **610**, **611**
Ambronn, H., 189–**193**
Anderson, D., 187, 188, **193**
Anderson, D. B., 37, 49–51, 58, 60, 61, **69**, 72, 146, 157, 158, **165**, **168**, 202, 208–210, 212, **218**
Anderson, L. E., 23, **31**
Andrews, H. N., Jr., 231, 232, **259**, **262**
Arber, A., 1, **10**, 338, 353, **402**, 412, 453, **462**, 470, 509, 518, 519, **522**, 531, 548, **571**
Armacost, R. R., 429, 430, 432, **462**
Arnold, C. A., 1, **10**, 232, **259**, 347, **402**
Artschwager, E. F., 79, 81, **89**, 139, 140, 161, **165**, 289, 293, 298, **300**, 314, 315, 317, 318, **321**, 331, 336, 398, 399, **402**, 507, **522**, 606, **611**, 654, 697, **706**
Ash, A. L., 209, 211, **218**
Ashby, E., 455–457, **462**, **463**
Askenasy, E., 104, **119**
Avery, A. G., **123**
Avery, G. S., Jr., 134, **134**, 139, **165**, 422, 423, 443, 444–446, 455–458, **462**, **463**, 465, 519, 520, **522**, **523**

Baehni, C., 534, **571**
Bailey, I. W., 25, 31, 35–39, 41, 42, 45–47, 50, 51, 53, 54, 56–58, 60–63, 65, **69**–72, 81, 88, **89**, 127–129, 131, 133, **134**, 150, **165**, 175, **180**, 188, **193**, **194**, 196, 201, 202, 204, 205, 207, 216, **218**, 225, 229, 231–233, 235, 237, 241, 245–250, 252, 256, **259**, 263, 283, **300**, 350, 351, 383, 393, 394, **402**, **403**, **408**, **409**, 413, 430, 432, 433, **463**, 467, 531, 539, 544–548, **571**
Bain, H. F., 92–94, **120**, **121**
Baker, K. C., 588, **595**
Baker, R. E., 93, **120**
Ball, E., 97–99, 103, 105, **120**, 371, 380, 386, **403**
Bancroft, H., 531, 532, **571**
Bannan, M. W., 45, 70, 88, **89**, **89**, 128, 129, 132, **135**, 245, 247, 249, 250, 254, **259**, 260, 503, 513, **522**, 622, **706**
Baranova, E. A., 315, **322**
Barghoorn, E. S., Jr., 132, **135**, 245, 247, 249, 252–254, **260**, 285, 290, **300**, 513, **522**, 645, **706**
Barkley, G., 240, **260**
Barnell, E., 594, **594**
Barthelmess, A., 347, 350, **403**
Bartley, M., **123**
Bartoo, D. R., 361, **403**
Bath, J. D., 15, 16, **33**
Baum, H., 531, 532, 546–548, 560, 561, 569, **572**
Beadle, G. M., 85, **89**
Beakbane, A. B., 512, 513, **522**
Becker, W. A., 62, 63, **70**
Behrisch, P., 479, **523**
Bell, H. P., 591, **594**
Benedict, H. M., 321, **322**, 587, **594**

709

Subject Index

(Numbers in bold face indicate illustrations located apart from the description of the subject in the illustration.)

721